MERRILL
LIFE SCIENCE

GLENCOE

Macmillan/McGraw-Hill

Lake Forest, Illinois   Columbus, Ohio   Mission Hills, California   Peoria, Illinois

A GLENCOE PROGRAM

MERRILL LIFE SCIENCE

Student Edition
Teacher Wraparound Edition
Teacher Resource Package
Study Guide, Student Edition
Reinforcement, Student Edition
Enrichment, Student Edition
Transparency Package

Laboratory Manual
Laboratory Manual,
    Teacher Annotated Edition
Spanish Resources
Chapter Review Software
Computer Test Bank
Videodisc Correlation

REVIEWERS

Agnes B. Adamson
Rosarian Academy
West Palm Beach, Florida

Janice E. Barry
C.A. Gray Middle School
Moultrie, Georgia

James Chin
Day Junior High School
Newtonville, Massachusetts

Gary E. Downes
Vista Verde Middle School
Irvine, California

Angeline Eliakopoulos
Chappell School
Chicago, Illinois

Donald E. Goldstein
Greenfield School
Phoenix, Arizona

Pilar Gonzalez de Killough
Silver Consolidated Schools
Silver City, New Mexico

Jeanne Lynn Helen Hatok
St. Charles Borromeo School
Albequerque, New Mexico

George E. Judd
Elk Grove United School District
Elk Grove, California

Amy L. Messinger
Guyan Valley High School
Branchland, West Virginia

Joe A. Starcher
Brooke County Schools
Follarsbee, West Virginia

Catherine R. Sullivan
Bellview Middle School
Pensacola, Florida

Cover Photograph: Bobcat *Felis rufa* by Tom and Pat Leeson

Send all inquiries to:
GLENCOE DIVISION
Macmillan/McGraw-Hill
936 Eastwind Drive
Westerville, OH 43081

ISBN 0-675-16760-4

Printed in the United States of America.

2 3 4 5 6 7 8 9-VH-99 98 97 96 95 94 93 92

Lucy Daniel is a Science-helping Teacher for Rutherford County Schools, Spindale, North Carolina. She has thirty-five years of teaching experience in biology. Ms. Daniel holds a B.S. degree from the University of North Carolina at Greensboro and an M.A.S.E. from Western Carolina University at Cullowhee. She received the Presidential Award for Excellence in Science and Mathematics Teaching in 1984. She is a co-author of Merrill Publishing Company's *Biology: An Everyday Experience.*

Edward Paul Ortleb is the Science Supervisor for the St. Louis, Missouri Board of Education. He holds an A.B. in Education from Harris Teachers College, an M.A. in Education, and an Advanced Graduate Certificate in Science Education from Washington University, St. Louis. Mr. Ortleb is a lifetime member of NSTA, having served as its president in 1978-79. He is a contributing author for the Teacher Resource Books for Merrill Publishing Company's *Accent on Science* and *General Science* and is co-author of Merrill Publishing Company's *Science Connections.*

Alton Biggs is Biology Instructor and Science Department Chairperson at Allen High School, Allen, Texas. Mr. Biggs received his B.S. in Natural Sciences and an M.S. in Biology from East Texas State University. He was a Resident in Science and Technology at Oak Ridge National Laboratory in 1986. Among the teaching awards he has received are Texas Outstanding Biology Teacher in 1982, Presidential Science Teacher Award Finalist in 1986, Teacher of the Year Award, Allen Independent School District, in 1987, and Texas Teacher of the Year Finalist in 1988. Mr. Biggs is currently the President of NABT. He is co-author of Merrill Publishing Company's *Biology: The Dynamics of Life.* Mr. Biggs has led several naturalist excursions abroad and is the founding president of TABT.

CONSULTANTS

Zoology:
Jerry Downhower, Ph.D.
Professor of Zoology
Department of Zoology
The Ohio State University
Columbus, Ohio

Genetics and Evolution:
Kathleen A. Fleiszar, Ph.D.
Professor of Biology
Department of Biology
Kennesaw State College
Marietta, Georgia

Human Body Systems:
Chris Teruo Hasegewa, Ph.D.
Associate Professor of Science
Education
California State University,
Sacramento
Sacramento, California

Cell Biology and Plants:
Eloy Rodriguez, Ph.D.
Professor of Biological Sciences
Department of Developmental and
Cell Biology
University of California, Irvine
Irvine, California

Viruses, Immunity, and Drugs:
Melissa Sue Millam Stanley, Ph.D.
Professor of Biology
George Mason University
Fairfax, Virginia

Life Science and Ecology:
Richard D. Storey, Ph.D.
Associate Professor of Biology
Department of Biology
Colorado College
Colorado Springs, Colorado

Reading:
Barbara Pettegrew, Ph.D.
Director of Reading/Study Center
Assistant Professor of Education
Otterbein College
Westerville, Ohio

Gifted and Mainstreamed:
Barbara Murdock
Elementary Consultant For
Instructions
Gahanna-Jefferson Public Schools
Gahanna, Ohio

Judy Ratzenberger
Middle School Science Instructor
Gahanna Middle School West
Gahanna, Ohio

Safety:
Robert Tatz, Ph.D.
Instructional Lab Supervisor
Department of Chemistry
The Ohio State University
Columbus, Ohio

Special Features:
Stephen C. Blume
Presidential Award for Excellence
in Science and Mathematics, 1990
Elementary Science Specialist
St. Tammany Public School System
Slidell, Louisiana

Karen Muir, Ph.D.
Adjunct Professor
Social and Behavioral Sciences
Columbus State Community
College
Columbus, Ohio

Mary Garvin
Managing Director, J.H. Barrow
Biological Field Station
Hiram College
Hiram, Ohio

CONTENTS

UNIT 1 LIFE 2

CHAPTER 1 Exploring Life 4

1-1 Living Things 6
1-2 Where Does Life Come From? 10
1-3 What is Science? 13
Problem Solving: Susan's Experiment 16
Flex Your Brain 18
Technology: Cockleburs and Space Shuttles 19
1-4 Science and Society—The Impact of Science on Your Life 22
Activity 1-1: Using a Scientific Method 24

CHAPTER 2 The Cell 28

2-1 Cells: The Units of Life 30
Technology: A Touch of Diamonds 33
2-2 Cell Structure 36
Problem Solving: A Tale of a Tail 40
Activity 2-1: Comparing Plant and Animal Cells 43
2-3 Cell Organization 44
2-4 Science and Society—Organ Transplants 46
Activity 2-2: Comparing Plant and Animal Tissues 48

CHAPTER 3 Cell Processes 52

3-1 Chemistry of Living Things 54
3-2 Cell Transport 58
Problem Solving: What Happened to the Salad? 61
Activity 3-1: Observing Osmosis 62
3-3 Energy in Cells 63
Technology: Biodegradable Plastics 64
3-4 Science and Society—Nonbiodegradable Materials in Your Environment 66
Activity 3-2: Photosynthesis and Respiration 68

CHAPTER 4   Cell Reproduction   **72**

4-1   Cell Growth and Division   74
      Problem Solving: Divide and Repair!   78
      Activity 4-1: Mitosis in Plant and Animal Cells   79
4-2   Sexual Reproduction and Meiosis   82
4-3   DNA   86
      Technology: The Bacteria Factory   89
4-4   Science and Society—Inventing Organisms   92
      Activity 4-2: Making a Model   94

      Global Connections   98
      Careers   100
      Science and Literature   101

UNIT 2   HEREDITY AND EVOLUTION   102

CHAPTER 5   Heredity   **104**

5-1   What Is Genetics?   106
      Activity 5-1: Expected and Observed Results   113
5-2   Genetics Since Mendel   114
5-3   Human Genetics   117
      Problem Solving: Boy or Girl?   118
      Technology: Karyotyping   120
5-4   Science and Society—The Human Genome   122
      Activity 5-2: Comparing Polygenic Inheritance   124

CHAPTER 6   Evolution   **128**

6-1   Mechanisms of Evolution   130
      Problem Solving: Why Isn't Earth Covered with
        Pumpkins and Pike?   133
6-2   Evidence for Evolution   136
      Technology: An Ostrich Egg Timer   140
      Activity 6-1: A Radioactive Dating Model   143
6-3   Science and Society—Plant and Animal
        Extinction   144
6-4   Human Evolution   146
      Activity 6-2: Making a Time Line   150

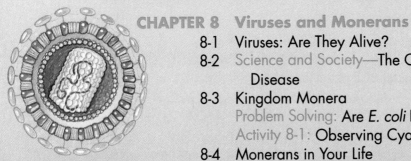

CHAPTER 7 Classification of Living Things   154
    7-1   What Is Classification?   156
          Problem Solving: Whose Shoe?   158
          Activity 7-1: Classifying Seeds   159
    7-2   Modern Classification   160
          Technology: Beyond Appearances   161
    7-3   Science and Society—The Rain Forest Crisis   164
    7-4   Identifying Organisms   166
          Activity 7-2: Using a Dichotomous Key   170

          Global Connections   174
          Careers   176
          Science and Literature   177

UNIT 3 SIMPLE LIVING THINGS   178

CHAPTER 8 Viruses and Monerans   180
    8-1   Viruses: Are They Alive?   182
    8-2   Science and Society—The Cost of Curing a
          Disease   186
    8-3   Kingdom Monera   188
          Problem Solving: Are *E. coli* Bacteria Helpful?   190
          Activity 8-1: Observing Cyanobacteria   192
    8-4   Monerans in Your Life   193
          Technology: Hungry Bacteria   195
          Activity 8-2: Observing and Culturing Bacteria   196

CHAPTER 9 Protists and Fungi   200
    9-1   Kingdom Protista   202
          Problem Solving: Puzzled about Slime   208
          Activity 9-1: Comparing Algae and Protozoa   210
    9-2   Kingdom Fungi   211
          Technology: A Yeast Library   213
    9-3   Science and Society—Fungus—Can't Live
          Without It   216
          Activity 9-2: Observing Bread Mold   218

          Global Connections   222
          Careers   224
          Science and Literature   225

UNIT 4 PLANTS 226

CHAPTER 10 **Introduction to Plants** 228
- 10-1 Characteristics of Plants 230
  - Technology: Oil from Desert Plants 235
- 10-2 Seedless Plants 236
  - Activity 10-1: Comparing Mosses and Liverworts 240
  - Problem Solving: What Are the Brown Spots on the Leaves? 245
- 10-3 Science and Society—Peat Moss as Fuel 246
  - Activity 10-2: The Life Cycle of a Fern 248

CHAPTER 11 **The Seed Plants** 252
- 11-1 Seed Plants 254
- 11-2 Parts of Complex Plants 259
  - Technology: Plants in Space? 260
- 11-3 Seed Plant Reproduction 262
  - Problem Solving: How Can You Tell If Seeds Are Living? 265
  - Activity 11-1: Inside a Seed 267
- 11-4 Science and Society—Effects of Acid Rain 268
  - Activity 11-2: Parts of a Flower 270

CHAPTER 12 **Plant Processes** 274
- 12-1 Photosynthesis and Respiration 276
  - Technology: Designer Plants 278
  - Activity 12-1: Stomata in Leaves 281
- 12-2 Plant Responses 282
  - Problem Solving: How Do Plants Climb Fences? 283
- 12-3 Plant Relationships 285
- 12-4 Science and Society—The Treasure of Tropical Plants 288
  - Activity 12-2: Plant Tropisms 290

  - Global Connections 294
  - Careers 296
  - Science and Literature 297

UNIT 5 ANIMALS   298

CHAPTER 13   Introduction to Animals   300
13-1   What Is an Animal?   302
        Activity 13-1: Determining Symmetry   305
13-2   Science and Society—Experiments Using Animals   306
13-3   The Simplest Invertebrates   308
        Technology: Sea Pharmacy   310
        Activity 13-2: Observing a Cnidarian   314
13-4   The Simple Worms   315
        Problem Solving: Barbara's New Puppy   317

CHAPTER 14   Complex Invertebrates   322
14-1   Mollusks   324
14-2   Segmented Worms   327
        Technology: Leeches to the Rescue   329
        Activity 14-1: Observing a Segmented Worm   331
14-3   Arthropods   332
        Problem Solving: Spinning Spiders   334
        Activity 14-2: Observing a Crayfish   339
14-4   Science and Society—Pesticides   340
14-5   Echinoderms   342

CHAPTER 15   Cold-Blooded Vertebrates   348
15-1   Fish   350
        Activity 15-1: Effects of Water Temperature
            on Fish   355
15-2   Amphibians   356
        Problem Solving: Marsupial Frogs   359
15-3   Science and Society—Amphibian Population
            Decline   360
        Activity 15-2: Metamorphosis in Frogs   362
15-4   Reptiles   363
        Technology: Snake Oil Medicines   366

CHAPTER 16   Warm-Blooded Animals   370
16-1   Birds   372
        Technology: Healthier Eggs   376
        Activity 16-1: Observing Contour and Down
            Feathers   378

16-2   Mammals   379
        Problem Solving: What Colors Can Spot See?   384
16-3   Science and Society—Saving the Manatee   386
        Activity 16-2: Classifying Vertebrates   388

CHAPTER 17   Animal Behavior   392
17-1   Types of Behavior   394
        Problem Solving: The Disappearing Lizards   398
        Activity 17-1: Conditioning   400
17-2   Behavioral Adaptations   401
        Technology: Looking for a Sign   404
17-3   Science and Society—Rehabilitation of Wild
        Animals   406
        Activity 17-2: Observing Social Behavior in Ants   408

        Global Connections   412
        Careers   414
        Science and Art   415

UNIT 6 THE HUMAN BODY   416

CHAPTER 18   Bones, Muscles, and Skin   418
18-1   The Skeletal System   420
        Activity 18-1: Observing Bones   425
18-2   The Muscular System   426
        Problem Solving: The Case of the Skinny Arm   429
18-3   Science and Society—Drugs for Fitness?   430
18-4   Skin   432
        Technology: Robot Skin   434
        Activity 18-2: Observing Muscle   436

CHAPTER 19   Nutrients and Digestion   440
19-1   Nutrition   442
        Technology: Fake Fat   445
        Problem Solving: The Big Race   449
        Activity 19-1: Identifying Vitamin C Content   450
19-2   Your Digestive System   451
19-3   Science and Society—Eating Disorders   456
        Activity 19-2: Protein Digestion   458

CHAPTER 20 **Your Circulatory System** **462**
20-1 Circulation 464
Technology: An Assist for the Heart 469
Activity 20-1: Blood Pressure 470
20-2 Blood 471
Problem Solving: The Blood Type Mystery 475
Activity 20-2: Comparing Blood Cells 477
20-3 Science and Society—Autologous Blood
Transfusions 478
20-4 Your Lymphatic System 480

CHAPTER 21 **Respiration and Excretion** **486**
21-1 Your Respiratory System 488
Activity 21-1: The Effects of Respiration 495
21-2 Science and Society—Dangerous Breathing 496
21-3 Your Urinary System 498
Problem Solving: Frederick's First Baseball
Game 499
Technology: Kidney Transplants 501
Activity 21-2: Sweat Glands in the Skin 502

CHAPTER 22 **Body Regulation** **506**
22-1 Your Nervous System 508
Technology: Watching the Brain at Work 511
Activity 22-1: Reaction Time 514
22-2 The Senses 515
Activity 22-2: Predicting and Experimenting 519
22-3 Science and Society—Alzheimer's Disease 520
22-4 Your Endocrine System 522
Problem Solving: Why Am I So Tired? 524

CHAPTER 23 **Reproduction and Growth** **528**
23-1 Human Reproduction 530
Activity 23-1: Interpreting Diagrams 534
23-2 Fertilization to Birth 535
Problem Solving: When Is the Baby Due? 536
Technology: Operating in the Womb 538
23-3 Development after Birth 540
23-4 Science and Society—Aging 544
Activity 23-2: Average Growth Rate in Humans 546

Global Connections   550
Careers   552
Science and Literature   553

UNIT 7 STAYING HEALTHY   554

CHAPTER 24   Immunity   556
24-1   The Nature of Disease   558
24-2   Your Immune System   563
        Technology: Super Sleuth!   565
        Activity 24-1: Microbes and Disease   567
24-3   Science and Society—Preventing Disease   568
24-4   Noncommunicable Disease   570
        Problem Solving: Allergic to What?   573
        Activity 24-2: Preventing Microorganism Growth   574

CHAPTER 25   Facts about Drugs   578
25-1   Drugs and Health   580
        Technology: Taking Your Medicine   581
        Activity 25-1: Interpreting Drug Label Information   582
        Problem Solving: Passive Smoke   583
25-2   Science and Society—Drugs in Society   586
25-3   Problems with Illegal Drugs   588
        Activity 25-2: The Effect of Drugs on
           Heartbeat Rate   594

        Global Connections   598
        Careers   600
        Science and Literature   601

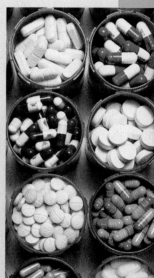

UNIT 8 ECOLOGY   602

CHAPTER 26   Organisms and Their Environments   604
26-1   Organisms and Their Environments   606
        Problem Solving: The Milk Carton Garden   607
        Activity 26-1: Counting Populations   609
26-2   Biotic Relationships   612
26-3   Abiotic Factors in the Biosphere   617
        Technology: Monitoring Mayflies   618

| 26-4 | Science and Society—Friendly Fires | 620 |
| | Activity 26-2: Studying an Ecosystem | 622 |

CHAPTER 27   Biomes   **626**
27-1	Factors That Affect Biomes	628
	Activity 27-1: Interpreting a Map	630
27-2	Land Biomes	632
	Technology: Life in a Glass World	636
27-3	Water Ecosystems	637
	Problem Solving: What Caused the Fish to Die?	639
27-4	Science and Society—Coastal Wetlands	640
	Activity 27-2: Investigating a Limiting Factor	642

CHAPTER 28   Resources and the Environment   **646**
28-1	Natural Resources	648
	Problem Solving: The Mystery of the Dirty Shirt	650
	Activity 28-1: Managing the Environment	652
28-2	Conserving Resources	654
	Technology: Test Tube Tigers	657
28-3	Future Responsibility	658
28-4	Science and Society—Earth in 2030	660
	Activity 28-2: Identifying Air Pollution Sites	662

	Global Connections	666
	Careers	668
	Science and Art	669

APPENDICES
Appendix A	The Microscope	670
Appendix B	SI/Metric to English Conversions	671
Appendix C	Safety	672
Appendix D	Classification	674

| **SKILL HANDBOOK** | **680** |

| **GLOSSARY** | **694** |

| **INDEX** | **705** |

ACTIVITIES

	Flex Your Brain	18
1-1	Using a Scientific Method	24
2-1	Comparing Plant and Animal Cells	43
2-2	Comparing Plant and Animal Tissues	48
3-1	Observing Osmosis	62
3-2	Photosynthesis and Respiration	68
4-1	Mitosis in Plant and Animal Cells	79
4-2	Making a Model	94
5-1	Expected and Observed Results	113
5-2	Comparing Polygenic Inheritance	124
6-1	A Radioactive Dating Model	143
6-2	Making a Time Line	150
7-1	Classifying Seeds	159
7-2	Using a Dichotomous Key	170
8-1	Observing Cyanobacteria	192
8-2	Observing and Culturing Bacteria	196
9-1	Comparing Algae and Protozoa	210
9-2	Observing Bread Mold	218
10-1	Comparing Mosses and Liverworts	240
10-2	The Life Cycle of a Fern	248
11-1	Inside a Seed	267
11-2	Parts of a Flower	270
12-1	Stomata in Leaves	281
12-2	Plant Tropisms	290
13-1	Determining Symmetry	305
13-2	Observing a Cnidarian	314
14-1	Observing a Segmented Worm	331
14-2	Observing a Crayfish	339
15-1	Effects of Water Temperature on Fish	355
15-2	Metamorphosis in Frogs	362
16-1	Observing Contour and Down Feathers	378
16-2	Classifying Vertebrates	388
17-1	Conditioning	400
17-2	Observing Social Behavior in Ants	408
18-1	Observing Bones	425
18-2	Observing Muscle	436
19-1	Identifying Vitamin C Content	450
19-2	Protein Digestion	458
20-1	Blood Pressure	470
20-2	Comparing Blood Cells	477
21-1	The Effects of Respiration	495
21-2	Sweat Glands in the Skin	502
22-1	Reaction Time	514
22-2	Predicting and Experimenting	519
23-1	Interpreting Diagrams	534
23-2	Average Growth Rate in Humans	546
24-1	Microbes and Disease	567
24-2	Preventing Microorganism Growth	574
25-1	Interpreting Drug Label Information	582
25-2	The Effect of Drugs on Heartbeat Rate	594
26-1	Counting Populations	609
26-2	Studying an Ecosystem	622
27-1	Interpreting a Map	630
27-2	Investigating a Limiting Factor	642
28-1	Managing the Environment	652
28-2	Identifying Air Pollution Sites	662

MINI-Labs

1-1 What is an experiment? 15
1-2 How are things measured? 21

2-1 How are objects magnified? 31
2-2 What is cytoplasm like? 38

3-1 How do enzymes work? 57
3-2 How does temperature affect the rate of diffusion of molecules? 59

4-1 How does one cell become two? 78
4-2 How can you make a protein? 90

5-1 What are some common traits? 106
5-2 What are fingerprints? 115

6-1 How does evolution occur? 134
6-2 How are fossils made? 137

7-1 How can leaves be classified? 156
7-2 How are organisms named? 166

8-1 Is your cat vaccinated? 184
8-2 How do you make yogurt? 193

9-1 What do slime molds look like? 209
9-2 How are spore prints made? 214

10-1 Where do the seedless vascular plants live? 241
10-2 How much water do simple plants hold? 246

11-1 How does water travel in a plant? 259
11-2 How do plants disperse seeds? 265

12-1 How do plants use carbon dioxide? 278
12-2 How do yeast respire? 280

13-1 How do planarians move? 315
13-2 How do planarians respond to light? 316

14-1 What type of metamorphosis do fruit flies undergo? 337
14-2 How do tube feet open clam shells? 344

15-1 How does a fish adjust to depths? 353
15-2 How many types of amphibians are there? 358

16-1 What are the parts of a bird's egg? 375
16-2 What are the characteristics of hair? 382

17-1 How does insight help you solve problems? 399
17-2 How does an animal enter into hibernation? 405

18-1 How do muscle pairs work? 428
18-2 Is there water in sweat? 435

19-1 How much water? 447
19-2 What is the advantage of a rough inner lining? 452

20-1 What are the parts of the heart? 468
20-2 How does a stethoscope work? 474

21-1 What is percussing? 494
21-2 What do kidneys look like? 500

22-1 Who has a better sense of smell? 508
22-2 How is balance maintained? 516

23-1 How long is an embryo? 537
23-2 What is the immunization schedule for babies and young children? 541

24-1 Are bacteria present in food? 560
24-2 How fast do bacteria reproduce? 562

25-1 Can you make a childproof package? 584
25-2 How are drugs classified? 593

26-1 What organisms are found in an ecosystem? 611
26-2 What are the requirements of ecosystems? 615

27-1 How do communities change? 631
27-2 Is there tundra in Africa? 633

28-1 How much garbage do you produce? 650
28-2 Does your family recycle? 659

PROBLEM SOLVING

Susan's Experiment	16
A Tale of a Tail	40
What Happened to the Salad?	61
Divide and Repair!	78
Boy or Girl?	118
Why Isn't Earth Covered with Pumpkins and Pike?	133
Whose Shoe?	158
Are *E. coli* Bacteria Helpful?	190
Puzzled about Slime	208
What Are the Brown Spots on the Leaves?	245
How Can You Tell If Seeds Are Living?	265
How Do Plants Climb Fences?	283
Barbara's New Puppy	317
Spinning Spiders	334
Marsupial Frogs	359

What Colors Can Spot See?	384
The Disappearing Lizards	398
The Case of the Skinny Arm	429
The Big Race	449
The Blood Type Mystery	475
Frederick's First Baseball Game	499
Why Am I So Tired?	524
When Is the Baby Due?	536
Allergic to What?	573
Passive Smoke	583
The Milk Carton Garden	607
What Caused the Fish to Die?	639
The Mystery of the Dirty Shirt	650

TECHNOLOGY

Cockleburs and Space Shuttles	19
A Touch of Diamonds	33
Biodegradable Plastics	64
The Bacteria Factory	89
Karyotyping	120
An Ostrich Egg Timer	140
Beyond Appearances	161
Hungry Bacteria	195
A Yeast Library	213
Oil from Desert Plants	235
Plants in Space?	260
Designer Plants	278
Sea Pharmacy	310
Leeches to the Rescue	329
Snake Oil Medicines	366
Healthier Eggs	376
Looking for a Sign	404

Robot Skin	434
Fake Fat	445
An Assist for the Heart	469
Kidney Transplants	501
Watching the Brain at Work	511
Operating in the Womb	538
Super Sleuth!	565
Taking Your Medicine	581
Monitoring Mayflies	618
Life in a Glass World	636
Test Tube Tigers	657

SKILL BUILDERS

ORGANIZING INFORMATION

Classifying: 27, 51, 71, 127, 135, 169, 173, 221, 251, 261, 293, 338, 347, 385, 391, 411, 527, 549, 577, 593, 625, 665

Sequencing: 51, 71, 97, 149, 153, 163, 199, 251, 321, 359, 369, 391, 429, 461, 469, 485, 494, 527, 533, 549, 619, 665

Outlining: 81, 153, 245, 318, 354, 424, 543, 585, 593

THINKING CRITICALLY

Observing and Inferring: 9, 12, 51, 112, 153, 158, 173, 199, 221, 266, 273, 293, 321, 344, 347, 391, 405, 411, 439, 455, 527, 611

Comparing and Contrasting: 42, 65, 97, 116, 153, 173, 191, 199, 221, 258, 273, 280, 284, 293, 313, 326, 347, 369, 377, 391, 411, 461, 482, 485, 505, 524, 527, 566, 577, 597, 645

Recognizing Cause and Effect: 61, 127, 505, 562, 577, 659

EXPERIMENTATION SKILLS

Measuring in SI: 21, 195

Hypothesizing: 71, 97, 153, 185, 235, 287, 293, 321, 411, 439, 485, 505, 549, 597, 631, 639, 653, 665

Using Variables, Constants, and Controls: 27, 215, 321, 405, 411

Interpreting Data: 51, 71, 153, 199, 273, 461, 476, 485, 505, 549, 597, 645

Designing an Experiment: 27, 127, 293, 369, 411, 439, 485, 665

GRAPHICS

Concept Mapping: 35, 51, 61, 71, 85, 91, 127, 149, 163, 173, 191, 199, 221, 245, 251, 273, 304, 321, 338, 347, 366, 369, 391, 411, 435, 439, 469, 501, 505, 513, 549, 577, 585, 597, 625, 636, 645, 657, 665

Making and Using Tables: 51, 57, 97, 142, 209, 399, 449, 476, 518, 573

Making and Using Graphs: 71, 173, 199, 251, 304, 347, 369, 461, 505, 539, 549, 577, 597, 625, 645

Interpreting Scientific Illustrations: 45, 51, 330, 527, 597, 616

GLOBAL CONNECTIONS

UNIT 1: Life 98
Oceanography, Biology, Astronomy, History, Meteorology

UNIT 2: Heredity and Evolution 174
History, Biology, Geology, Astronomy, Paleontology

UNIT 3: Simple Living Things 222
Health, History, Chemistry, Geology, Biology, Geography

UNIT 4: Plants 294
Geology, Meteorology, Geography, Chemistry, Health

UNIT 5: Animals 412
Oceanography, History, Geography, Social Studies, Meteorology

UNIT 6: The Human Body 550
Astronomy, History, Physics, Social Studies, Oceanography

UNIT 7: Staying Healthy 598
History, Geography, Health, Social Studies, Chemistry

UNIT 8: Ecology 666
Social Studies, Chemistry, Oceanography, Meteorology, History

CAREERS

UNIT 1:   Research Biologist, Laboratory Technician 100
UNIT 2:   Genetic Counselor, Farmer 176
UNIT 3:   Epidemiologist, Mushroom Farmer 224
UNIT 4:   Plant Pathologist, Professional Gardener 296
UNIT 5:   Zoologist, Veterinarian's Assistant 414
UNIT 6:   Physical Therapist, Home Healthcare Aide 552
UNIT 7:   Microbiologist, Licensed Practical Nurse 600
UNIT 8:   Environmental Engineer, Marine Animal Trainer 668

SCIENCE AND LITERATURE/ART

UNIT 1:   *An Essay* by Sir Francis Bacon 101
UNIT 2:   *The Voyage of the Beagle* by Charles Darwin 177
UNIT 3:   *The Sea around Us* by Rachel Carson 225
UNIT 4:   *Where the Sky Began* by John Madson 297
UNIT 5:   *The American Bison* by John James Audubon 415
UNIT 6:   *Sula* by Toni Morrison 553
UNIT 7:   The Hippocratic Oath 601
UNIT 8:   *Abuelitos Piscando Napolitos* by Carmen Lomas Garza 669

USING MERRILL LIFE SCIENCE

Life Science is an everyday experience. It's a subject you're familiar with because every part of your day is based upon principles of life science… the simple act of walking involves your muscles to move your body, your nervous system to tell your muscles what to do and where you want to go, and your circulatory system to transport nutrients, energy, and oxygen to all parts of your body. Depending on where you walk, you may encounter a variety of insects, plants, and animals that are living their lives also based upon principles of life science. **Merrill Life Science** will help you understand life science principles and recognize how they affect you and the life around you everyday.

a quick tour of your textbook

What's happening here? Have you ever seen a raft setting on the tops of trees? Each unit begins with thought-provoking photographs that will make you wonder. The unit introduction then explains what is happening in the photographs and how the two relate to each other and to the content of the unit. What is a raft doing on the tops of trees? Read the opener to Unit 4 to find out.

It's clearly organized to get you started and keep you going.

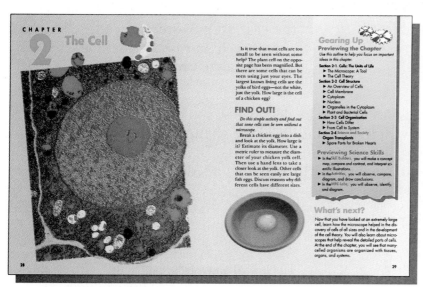

As you begin each new chapter, use the **Gearing Up** to preview what topics are covered and how they are organized. You will also preview the skills you will use in this chapter.

After you've performed the **FIND OUT** activity and previewed the chapter, you're ready to further explore the topics ahead. Read **What's next** to see what's ahead.

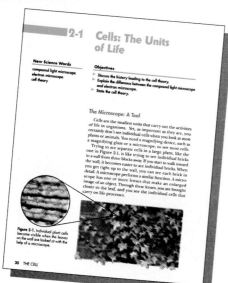

Chapters are organized into three to five numbered sections. The **Objectives** at the beginning of the numbered section tell you what major topics you'll be covering and what you should expect to learn about them. The **New Science Words** are also listed in the order in which they appear in the section.

Experience science by observing, experimenting, and asking questions.

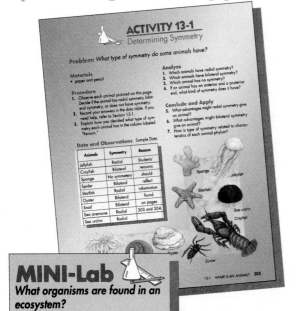

Science is more than words in a book. The two Activities and the MINI-Labs in each chapter give you the chance to further explore and investigate the science topics covered in your textbook.

In the **Activities,** you'll use household items and laboratory equipment as you follow the easy, step-by-step procedure. At the end of each Activity are questions that ask you to analyze what you've done.

MINI-Lab

What organisms are found in an ecosystem?

Choose an ecosystem you are familiar with, such as a stream, garden plot, or pond, and identify the organisms found there. Make a list of all the populations you can see in the ecosystem. What is the niche of each species in the community?

Most **MINI-Labs** are designed so you can do them on your own or with friends outside of the science classroom using materials you find around the house. Doing a MINI-Lab is an easy and fun way to further your knowledge about the topics you're studying.

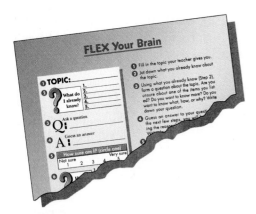

Each **Problem Solving** feature gives you a chance to solve a real life problem.

PROBLEM SOLVING

Why Isn't Earth Covered with Pumpkins and Pike?

Assume that there are 70 seeds in one pumpkin and that this is the typical number for the species. The 70 seeds are planted and each seed grows into a plant that produces two pumpkins. The first year 70 seeds are planted. The number of seeds produced in three years can be calculated by multiplying the number of seeds times two pumpkins for each plant times 70 seeds in each pumpkin:

Year 1: 70 x 2 x 70 = 9800
Year 2: 9800 x 2 x 70 = 1 372 000
Year 3: 1 372 000 x 2 x 70
= 192 080 000 seeds

The largest possible number of offspring produced by one individual is known as the biotic potential of a species.

If the ovaries of a pike contain 42 000 eggs, all the eggs are fertilized and hatched, all the young survive to reproduce, and one-half of the young are females, how many pike would there be after two more generations?

Think Critically: Why is the maximum rate of biotic potential never reached?

Flex Your Brain is a unique activity you can use to sharpen your critical thinking skills. Starting from what you already know about a science topic, you will apply a simple ten-step procedure to extend your knowledge about the topic from a perspective that interests you.

Explore news-making issues, concerns about the environment, and how science shapes your world through technology.

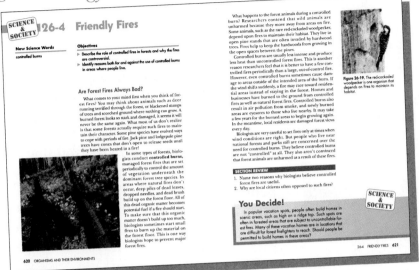

The impact of science on society directly affects you. In the **Science and Society** section in each chapter, you'll learn about an issue that's affecting the world around you. The topics you'll read about are controversial, and you'll explore them from several sides. Then, you'll have a chance to express your opinion in the You Decide feature that follows.

In the **Technology** feature in each chapter, you'll read about recent discoveries, newly developed instruments, and applications of technology that have shaped our world and furthered our knowledge.

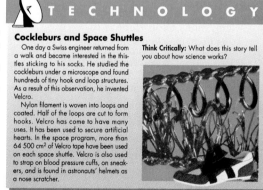

TECHNOLOGY

Cockleburs and Space Shuttles

One day a Swiss engineer returned from a walk and became interested in the thistles sticking to his socks. He studied the cockleburs under a microscope and found hundreds of tiny hook and loop structures. As a result of this observation, he invented Velcro.

Nylon filament is woven into loops and coated. Half of the loops are cut to form hooks. Velcro has come to have many uses. It has been used to secure artificial hearts. In the space program, more than 64 500 cm² of Velcro tape have been used on each space shuttle. Velcro is also used to strap on blood pressure cuffs, on sneakers, and is found in astronauts' helmets as a nose scratcher.

Think Critically: What does this story tell you about how science works?

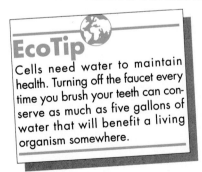

EcoTip

Cells need water to maintain health. Turning off the faucet every time you brush your teeth can conserve as much as five gallons of water that will benefit a living organism somewhere.

Each **EcoTip** suggests a simple step you can take to help improve the environment. EcoTips explain how you can get involved in making Earth a better place to live.

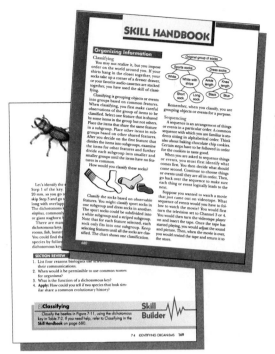

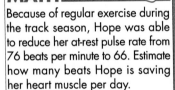

Discover that you can apply what you've learned as you answer questions and practice your science skills.

At the end of each section are several Section Review questions that help you test your knowledge. The last question challenges you to think critically and **Apply** what you've learned.

The **Skill Builder** feature lets you sharpen your science skills using only paper and pencil. If you need help with these skills, refer to the **Skill Handbook** at the back of the book. Here, you can find complete information about each type of skill covered in the Skill Builders.

Science is related to every other subject you study. The **Science And** features challenge you to solve math problems, read literature excerpts, and to write about topics you're studying as you make the connections between science and other disciplines.

Science and MATH

Because of regular exercise during the track season, Hope was able to reduce her at-rest pulse rate from 76 beats per minute to 66. Estimate how many beats Hope is saving her heart muscle per day.

The **Chapter Review** starts with a summary so you can review the major concepts from each section. Then, you'll apply your knowledge and practice thinking skills as you answer the questions that follow.

Discover how life science topics relate to people and places all over the world.

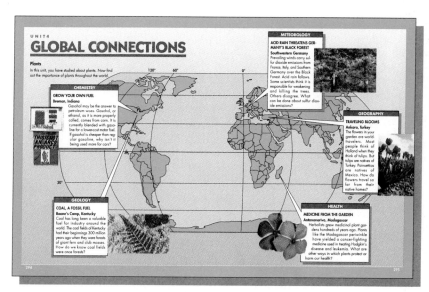

Global Connections help you to see how life science is related to other sciences as well as social studies, history and health.

Also at the end of each unit you will find two **Careers** that describe jobs that relate to the material in the unit you just read. What kind of jobs may be related to maintaining health and what do the people that have these jobs do? Read the careers at the end of Unit 7 to find out.

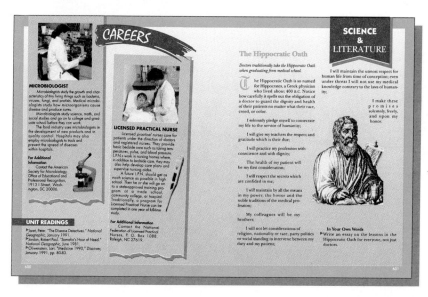

What do life science and literature have in common? A lot, as you'll discover when you read the unit close to Unit 7. Each unit is closed with a reading from literature or an example of art that makes a connection with life science.

UNIT 1 LIFE

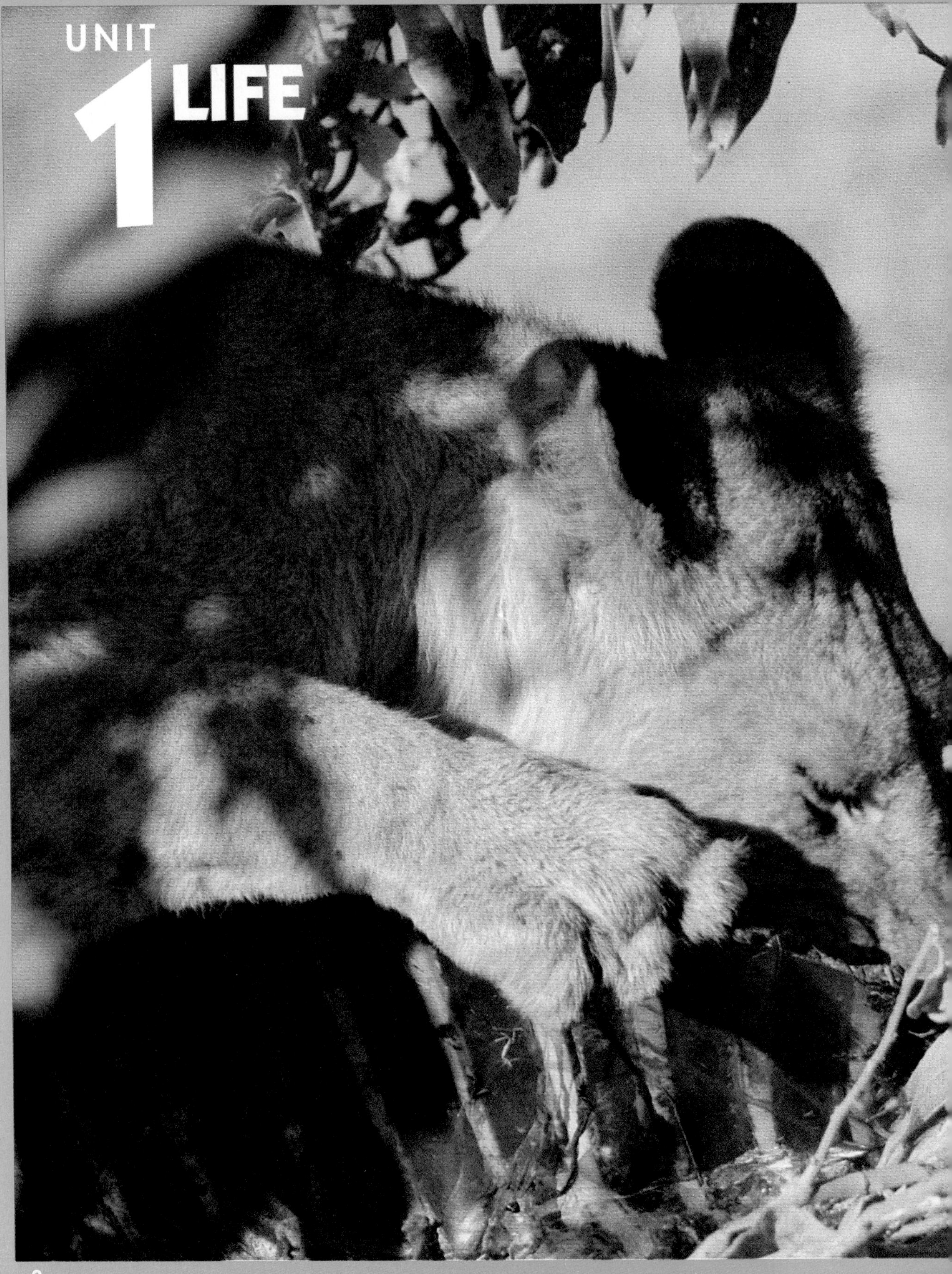

What's Happening Here?

A lion cub looks up from the feast he shares with a lioness. In his contented state, he is unaware that he is consuming energy, which will build muscle and bone and eventually bring him to the stage of development where he will reproduce. Living things require energy to grow, develop, and reproduce. The amoeba, the one-celled organism in the small photograph, is less dramatic than a lion, but it too, requires energy, which it derives from other organisms. In this unit, you will learn about the characteristics that all living things share.

UNIT CONTENTS

Chapter 1   Exploring Life
Chapter 2   The Cell
Chapter 3   Cell Processes
Chapter 4   Cell Reproduction

1 Exploring Life

Many people think that science is the work of people in white coats who spend hours in a laboratory. But laboratory research is only part of the story. Often, the first work of science is to observe, observe, observe, then think, and ask questions. What observations would you make in the following situation?

FIND OUT!

Do this activity to find out about the first steps in scientific research.

Cut a strip of coffee filter paper 3 cm by 12 cm. Using a black felt tip pen, draw a line across the strip of paper towel about 2 cm from one end. Describe the color of the line. Put 1 cm of water in a small beaker or glass. Hang the paper strip over the beaker so that one end is in the water and the black line is above the water. Observe what happens to the black line. Will you change your original description? If so, how?

Gearing Up
Previewing the Chapter
Use this outline to help you focus on important ideas in this chapter.

Section 1-1   Living Things
 ▶ Features of Life
 ▶ Needs of Living Things
Section 1-2   Where Does Life Come From?
 ▶ Life Comes from Life
 ▶ Origins
Section 1-3   What Is Science?
 ▶ The Work of Science
 ▶ Solving Problems
 ▶ Theories and Laws
 ▶ Critical Thinking
 ▶ Measuring in Science
 ▶ Safety First
Section 1-4   Science and Society
The Impact of Science on Your Life
 ▶ Times Have Changed
 ▶ Living with Technology

Previewing Science Skills

▶ In the **Skill Builders**, you will observe and infer, and measure in SI.
▶ In the **Activities**, you will Flex Your Brain and observe.
▶ In the **MINI-Labs**, you will use variables, constants and controls, and measure in SI.

What's next?

In the Find Out activity, you have had a chance to use scientific methods to test an idea. Now find out about the features of living things and the methods that are used in science to study organisms.

1-1 Living Things

New Science Words

organisms
cells
stimulus
response
homeostasis
development
adaptation
life span

Objectives

▶ **Identify the features of living things.**
▶ **Recognize the needs of living things and explain how they are provided.**
▶ **Determine that living things and nonliving things interact in the environment.**

Features of Life

This book is about life—what it is and how it is maintained. Life is something we may take for granted. Have you ever tried to explain what it means to be alive? Think about life characteristics as you read the following.

Imagine that it's a hot summer day and you can't wait to get out of your house or apartment. With your dog, you head off to a nearby stream, collecting a pocketful of flat stones as you go. At first, you practice skipping stones across the water, while the dog runs along the bank barking. Then you sit down on some sand on the bank under a large tree. Dragonflies skim over the water, and the noise of the insects and birds is all you can hear. The dog settles down on the bank under a tree and appears to fall asleep. It sure is great to be alive. But what does this mean? Living things are **organisms.** Organisms have certain features that rocks and water don't have. What makes you and your dog different from water and rocks?

Organisms are made of one or more cells. You have some things in common with water and rocks in the stream because you are made up of chemicals as they are. However, if someone were to look at you or your dog or the tree under a microscope, it would be clear that each of you is made of units called cells. Water and rocks are not. **Cells** are the smallest units of organisms that carry on the functions of life.

Figure 1-1. An organism is made of cells, uses energy, and responds to its environment.

Figure 1-2. Organisms use energy that is supplied by food. For many animals, food is in the form of other animals.

Organisms use energy. Plants produce food, which both plants and animals then use for energy. Food you eat is converted to energy in a process called respiration. Energy powers an organism every second of every day through all the phases of its life.

Organisms move. "Do you see any signs of life?" If you've ever watched a sleeping dog, it often looks completely still. Then an ear may twitch, or the dog may snore. Movement tells you that the dog is alive.

Organisms respond to changes in their environment. What happens when you feed your dog? Does he come running as soon as he hears the can opener? Anything that an organism responds to, such as the sound of the can opener, is a **stimulus.** The reaction of an organism to a stimulus, in this case probably tail wagging and barking, is a **response.**

What is a stimulus?

Organisms adjust to changes in their environment. Think about driving a car. The driver constantly makes small adjustments with the steering wheel and gas pedal to keep the car on the road at a steady rate of speed. The body systems of an organism do something similar. The ability to maintain steady conditions no matter what is going on inside or outside the organism is called **homeostasis.** Controls in an organism work constantly to bring it back to "normal" after it has been stimulated.

Organisms reproduce. Your dog came from a litter of puppies. You might have looked at his parents to see what he would be like when full grown. Organisms produce new individuals that are usually very like the parent organisms. Oak trees produce acorns that become oak trees. Bluejays lay eggs that hatch into young bluejays.

Figure 1-3. Organisms reproduce their own kind.

Figure 1-4. As organisms grow and develop, they usually change in appearance.

Science and READING

Go to a library and use references to find the life span of horses, cows, dogs, cats, shrews, and cockroaches. Organize this information in a table.

Organisms grow and develop. When a dog is born, it is very small. With care and feeding, it grows larger. All living things increase in size. They grow. All the changes organisms undergo as they grow are called **development.** Dogs can't see or walk when they are first born. But in eight or nine days, their eyes open, and their legs become strong enough to hold them up. A dog develops into an adult in about two years.

Organisms adapt. Any characteristic an organism has that makes it better able to survive in its environment is an **adaptation.** Your dog's coat is an adaptation. In summer, the dog sheds hair and his body is cooled. Dogs also pant a great deal to release excess body heat. If dogs couldn't shed hair or pant, they would be uncomfortable in the summer heat. It would be obvious to you that the dog wasn't well adapted. Adaptations are inherited. They are not merely responses the organism makes to an immediate need.

Organisms have life spans. The length of time an organism is expected to live is its **life span.** For some, the life span is very short. Millions of mayflies live only one day. But some bristlecone pine trees have been alive more than 4500 years. Your life span is about 80 years. What is the life span of your dog? How are the needs of living things met during this life span?

Needs of Living Things

Sitting on the bank of the stream, you and your dog are probably not aware that you interact with everything else in the environment. However, all organisms take part in many interacting cycles with each other and with all the nonliving things around them. When an organism is part of these relationships, its needs are met.

What are these needs? All organisms need energy and raw materials. The energy that you use comes from food. The main source of this energy for most organisms is the sun. Green plants use the sun's energy, along with carbon dioxide, water, and minerals from the soil, to make glucose. Chlorophyll in leaves converts these materials to food. This process also releases oxygen, which all organisms need. Oxygen is used by all organisms to release energy from food.

Raw materials that organisms use are the water, oxygen, and minerals that have been used since life began. Oxygen, water, carbon dioxide, and other chemicals are used, returned to the environment, and used over again.

Water is especially important. Your dog might live two or three weeks without food, but he would die in a few days without water. Living things are made up of about 70 percent water, and they need to maintain that level. Many substances in nature dissolve in water. Blood and the sap of trees are mostly water. Many organisms are born in and live in water all their lives.

Are you and your dog different from the water and rocks? To be considered alive, an organism must have all the features of life. It must be made of cells, use energy, move, respond, adjust, reproduce, grow and develop, and adapt. Organisms need to have energy, water, and oxygen. Rocks and water do not have these properties.

Figure 1-5. In the living world, energy is transferred from one organism to another. Grasshoppers feed on plants and an owl obtains energy when it feeds on a rabbit.

What do organisms need for life?

SECTION REVIEW

1. What is an organism?
2. What are the features of organisms?
3. What is the main source of energy used by most organisms?
4. What are the needs of organisms and how are these needs supplied?
5. **Apply:** Explain how a tree shows each of the features of living things.

☑ Observing and Inferring

Virus crystals can remain in a jar on a shelf for years. Then once they are put into living cells, they reproduce. Are viruses alive? If you need help, refer to Observing and Inferring in the **Skill Handbook** on page 682.

Skill Builder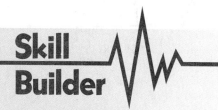

1-2 Where Does Life Come From?

New Science Words

spontaneous generation
biogenesis

Objectives

▶ Summarize the results of Redi's and Spallanzani's experiments.
▶ Explain how Pasteur's experiments disproved the theory of spontaneous generation.
▶ Summarize Oparin's hypothesis and how it was tested.

Life Comes from Life

Have you ever walked out after a thunderstorm and found earthworms all over the sidewalk? Earthworms have been found in large numbers after rainstorms for hundreds of years. It's no wonder that people used to think the earthworms had fallen from the sky when it rained. It was a logical conclusion based on repeated experience. But was it true? For much of history, people believed that living things came from nonliving matter, an idea called the theory of **spontaneous generation.**

Jan Baptist van Helmont wrote a recipe for making mice by placing grain in a corner and covering it with rags.

People also believed that maggots came from decaying meat. In 1668, Francesco Redi, an Italian doctor, conducted one of the first controlled experiments in science. He showed that maggots hatch from eggs that flies had laid on meat, and not from the meat itself.

In the late 1700s, Lazzaro Spallanzani designed an experiment to show that tiny organisms came from other tiny organisms in the air. He boiled broth in two flasks, sealed one, and left the other one open to the air. The open flask became cloudy with organisms. The sealed flask developed no organisms. People believed Spallanzani had destroyed a "vital force" when he boiled the broth.

Figure 1-6. In Redi's experiment, maggots developed on snake meat that flies could reach, but not on meat that was protected from the flies.

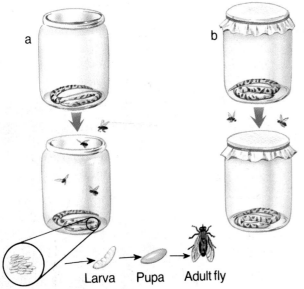

a

b

Eggs   Larva   Pupa   Adult fly

It was not until the mid-1800s that Louis Pasteur, a French chemist, showed that living things do not come from non-living materials. In the experiment shown in Figure 1-7, Pasteur boiled broth in flasks with long, curved necks. The broth became contaminated only when dust that had collected in the curved neck of one flask was allowed to mix with the broth. The work of Redi, Spallanzani, Pasteur, and others provided enough evidence finally to disprove the theory of spontaneous generation. It was replaced with **biogenesis,** the theory that living things come only from other living things.

Broth is boiled.
Air and microbes driven out.

Microbes are trapped in the neck.

One year or more: broth remains without growth.

Shortly, microbes develop in broth.

Flask is tilted.

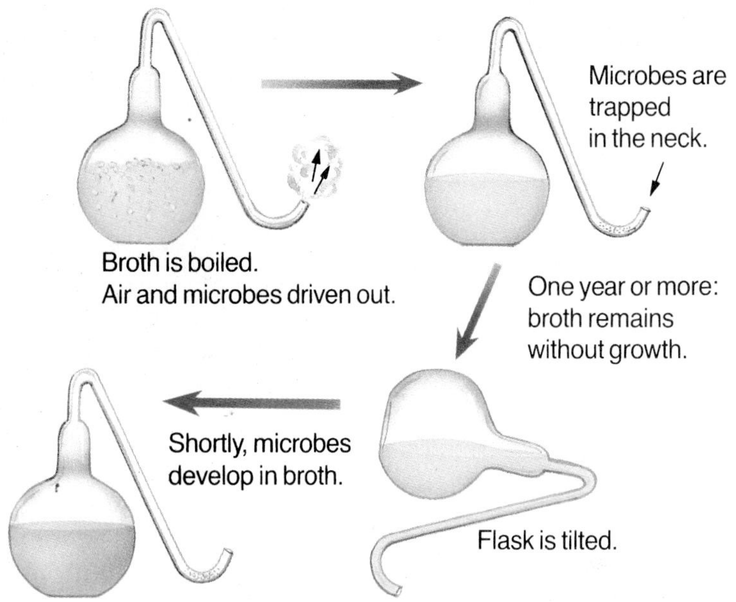

Figure 1-7. Pasteur's experiment disproved the theory of spontaneous generation.

Origins

If living things can come only from other living things, how then did life on Earth begin? Scientists hypothesize that about 5 billion years ago, the solar system was a whirling mass of gas and dust. The sun and planets formed from this mass. Our planet is thought to be about 4.6 billion years old. Rocks found in Australia that are more than 3.5 billion years old contain fossils of once-living organisms.

One hypothesis on the origin of life was proposed by Alexander I. Oparin, a Russian scientist. Oparin suggested that the atmosphere of early Earth was made up of gases similar to ammonia, hydrogen, methane, and water vapor. No free oxygen was present as it is today. Energy from lightning, and ultraviolet rays from the sun, helped these early gases to combine. The gases formed the chemical compounds of which living things are made. Oparin suggested that as the compounds were formed, they fell into hot seas. Over a period of time, the chemical compounds in the seas formed new and more complex compounds. Eventually, the complex compounds were able to copy themselves and make use of other chemicals for energy and food.

Figure 1-8. Lightning is powerful enough to cause chemicals to combine in nature.

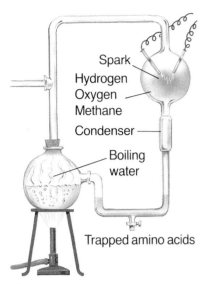

Figure 1-9. Miller's experiment was a model of what many scientists think Earth's early atmosphere was like. Volcanic eruptions like the one to the right remind us of what Earth was probably like while it was in its formative stages.

In the figure: Spark, Hydrogen, Oxygen, Methane, Condenser, Boiling water, Trapped amino acids

Ever since Oparin formed his hypothesis, other scientists have been testing it. In 1953, an American scientist, Stanley L. Miller, set up an experiment using the chemicals suggested in Oparin's hypothesis. Electrical sparks were sent through the mixture of chemicals. At the end of a week, new substances, similar to amino acids that are found in all living things, had formed. This showed that substances present in living things *could* come from non-living materials in the environment. It did not prove that life was formed in this way.

Evidence suggests that life was formed from nonliving matter sometime between 4.6 billion and 3.5 billion years ago. However, scientists are still investigating where the first life came from.

SECTION REVIEW

1. What is the theory of spontaneous generation?
2. What was most important about Redi's experiment?
3. What is the theory of biogenesis?
4. What was Oparin's hypothesis?
5. **Apply:** Explain how it could be possible for some of Pasteur's flasks to be uncontaminated still after 100 years.

Skill Builder

☑ Observing and Inferring

People believed that Spallanzani had destroyed some "vital force" in the broth. Did he? Based on the experiment, what could they have inferred about where organisms come from? If you need help, refer to Observing and Inferring in the **Skill Handbook** on page 682.

What Is Science?

Objectives

▶ Describe what science is and how scientists solve problems.
▶ Identify and use the SI units of length, volume, mass, and temperature.

New Science Words

scientific methods
hypothesis
variable
control
theory
law

The Work of Science

Where do the fleas on your dog come from? Have you ever tried to figure out how to get rid of them? Why do some trees lose their leaves in the fall and others in spring? If you ever have questions about the world in which you live, you are thinking like a scientist. Scientists observe what goes on around them. They ask questions about their observations and may try to find answers to their questions by using tests called experiments.

Life scientists study living things. In this textbook, you'll be exposed to many branches of science as they touch on life science. For instance, you'll learn some basic chemistry, which is the study of the matter of which things are made. In the study of physics, you will learn that matter and energy are related. Earth science, the study of planet Earth, and life science use both chemistry and physics.

With more than 5 million kinds of organisms on Earth, it would be difficult to study every one. Many life scientists work with only one group of living organisms. Some life scientists are botanists who study plants. Others are zoologists who work with animals. More and more, scientists are seeing that none of these organisms exists alone. Ecologists are scientists who study how living things interact with each other and their environment on Earth. Genetics explains how traits of organisms are passed from generation to generation.

Figure 1-10. In life science, you will study plants and animals, what they are made of, and how they interact with each other.

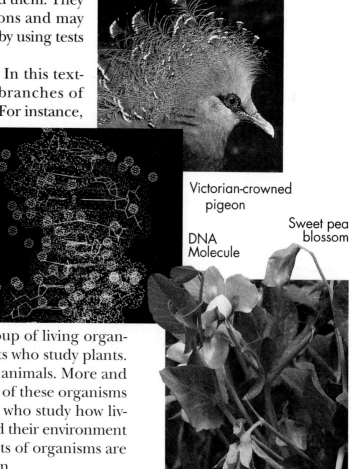

Victorian-crowned pigeon

DNA Molecule

Sweet pea blossom

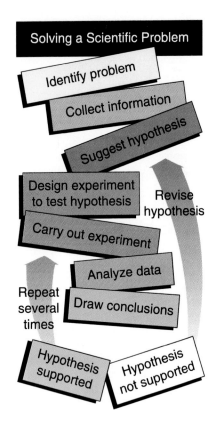

Solving a Scientific Problem

Identify problem

Collect information

Suggest hypothesis

Design experiment to test hypothesis

Revise hypothesis

Carry out experiment

Analyze data

Repeat several times

Draw conclusions

Hypothesis supported

Hypothesis not supported

What is a hypothesis?

Solving Problems

Do scientists always find answers to their questions? No. Do they always do experiments in laboratories? Not always. There is no set method that all scientists use to solve problems. Each problem is different. Yet, solving any problem requires organization, doesn't it? In science, this organization often takes the form of a series of procedures or **scientific methods.**

The diagram to the left shows an order in which scientific methods might be used. You begin by observing something that you cannot explain. Suppose you awake one morning with a sore throat. It hurts all day, so you go to the doctor after school. The first step in a scientific method is to *state the problem.* A scientist can't begin to solve a problem until it's clearly stated. You tell the doctor that you have a sore throat.

The second step is to *gather information* about the problem. Tell the doctor everything you've observed about your sore throat—when it began hurting and how it feels now. The doctor makes her own observations. She takes your temperature and examines your throat.

The next step is to *form a hypothesis.* A **hypothesis** is a prediction that can be tested. Based on her experience, the doctor hypothesizes that you have strep throat. She knows she can test her hypothesis right there in her laboratory. A hypothesis always has to be something you can test.

To test her hypothesis the doctor will *perform an experiment.* In an experiment, a series of steps is followed that tests a hypothesis using controlled conditions. The doctor

Figure 1-11. Gathering information is an important step in solving any problem, including whether or not your throat infection is caused by the streptococcus bacterium. The larger photograph shows some streptococcus cells.

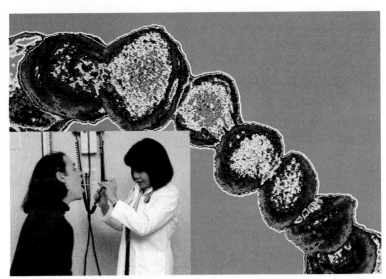

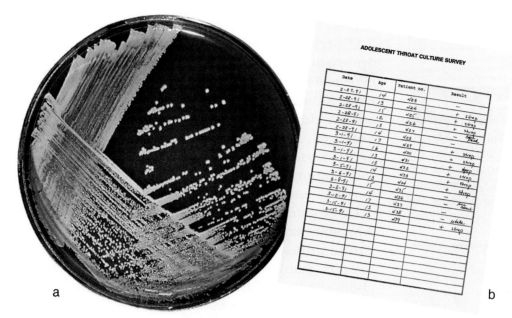

ADOLESCENT THROAT CULTURE SURVEY

Date	Age	Patient no.	Result
2-27-91	14	423	−
2-28-91	13	424	−
2-28-91	15	425	+ strep
2-28-91	12	426	+ strep
2-28-91	13	427	+ strep
3-1-91	14	428	−
3-1-91	17	429	−
3-1-91	16	430	+ strep
3-1-91	13	431	+ strep
3-5-91	14	432	+ strep
3-6-91	13	433	+ strep
3-8-91	15	434	+ strep
3-8-91	14	435	+ strep
3-12-91	14	436	−
3-12-91	17	437	−
3-15-91	13	438	−
3-15-91	13	439	+ strep

a   b

takes a throat culture from you. She has a petri dish with a growth medium, which she marks "experimental." She gently rubs the surface of the medium in the experimental dish with your throat culture. The dish marked experimental is the variable. A **variable** is the factor tested in an experiment. The doctor also has a sample of the organism that is known to cause strep throat. She will use this sample as a control to compare with your culture. A **control** is the standard used to compare with the outcome of a test.

The doctor may give you a prescription for some capsules that will relieve your symptoms. She tells you that she will call you in 24 hours with the test results. The next day, a lab technician identifies the growth in the experimental petri dish. This *data is recorded* in your chart. The doctor uses the data to draw her conclusions. A *conclusion* is a logical answer to a problem based on data and observations of the test materials.

The next step in the search for an answer is to *accept or reject the hypothesis.* When you return, the doctor tells you that the growth in the experimental dish shows that your sore throat was caused by another kind of bacterium. You don't have strep throat. She has had to reject her original hypothesis.

The last step in solving a problem scientifically is to *do something with the results.* Your doctor may use the data in a paper she is preparing on different kinds of sore throats found in adolescents. She may have begun to notice some common factors in her data.

Figure 1-12. Research in life science may involve equipment such as a petri dish (a). Data is a record of observations (b).

MINI-Lab

What is an experiment?

Heat 50 mL of water to 98°C and 50 mL of water to 65°C. Cool 50 mL of water to 10°C. Measure the amount of sugar that dissolves in each of the three containers of water. Make a data table that could be used to record the results of this experiment. What are the variables in the experiment? Refer to Using Variables, Constants, and Controls in the **Skill Handbook** on page 683.

Theories and Laws

Observations and conclusions in science either develop or support existing information. A **theory** is an explanation of things or events based on many observations. A theory is not someone's opinion, nor is a theory a vague idea. Hypotheses that have been tested over and over again and cannot be shown to be false support theories. You have already read about the theory of spontaneous generation. Theories can be changed as new data uncover new information.

Large amounts of data in science often show a trend. A scientific **law** based on these repeating data tells us how nature works. A law is a reliable description of nature based on many observations. In life science, you will learn about the laws of heredity. Laws may change as more information becomes known.

Scientific methods help answer questions. Your questions may be as simple as "Where did I leave my house key?" or as complex as "What can we do about air pollution?" Will these methods guarantee that you will get an answer? Not always. Often they just lead you to more questions, but that is the work of science.

PROBLEM SOLVING

Susan's Experiment

When a bottle of acne medication was almost empty, Susan went to the drugstore to purchase some more. She thought she would try a different brand to see if it was more effective. The brand she selected was more expensive, so Susan decided to try an experiment to determine if it really was better than the one she had been using.

Susan followed her morning routine except she used the old brand on the left side of her face and the new brand on the right side of her face. She recorded every inflammation on her face and how long the inflammation lasted. After two weeks, she compared the data of the two medications. What was Susan's hypothesis about the new medication?

Think Critically: What scientific methods did Susan use to solve the problem?

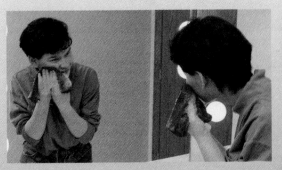

Critical Thinking

Whether you become a scientist or not, you are going to solve problems all your life. Most of the problems you encounter will be solved in your head by a process of sorting through ideas to see what will or will not work. Suppose you make a batch of chili and it turns out badly. What went wrong with the chili? Even though you followed the usual recipe, it just didn't seem to have a zippy taste. After thinking for a bit, you realize that you left out one very important ingredient—chili powder! How did you figure out that lack of chili powder was the problem? Without being aware of it, you probably used a form of problem solving called critical thinking.

Critical thinking is a process that uses certain skills to solve problems. For example, you identified the problem by mentally comparing the not-so-great batch of chili with other batches of chili you've eaten. First you separated important information from unimportant information. For instance, you may have realized that temperature had little to do with the flavor of the chili. You may have examined your assumption that you followed the recipe correctly. After looking at the recipe again, you concluded that it was chili powder that was missing.

Finally, you probably went one step further and analyzed your conclusion. Would lack of chili powder have made the chili taste blah? If your answer was "yes," then you may have solved the problem.

"Flex Your Brain" is an activity that will help you think about and examine your way of thinking. "Flex Your Brain" is a way to keep your thinking on track when you are investigating a topic or problem. It takes you through steps of exploration from what you already know and believe, to new conclusions and awareness. Then, it encourages you to review and talk about the steps you took.

"Flex Your Brain" will help you improve your critical thinking skills. You'll become a better problem solver, and your next batch of chili will taste great. "Flex Your Brain" is found on the next page.

FLEX Your Brain

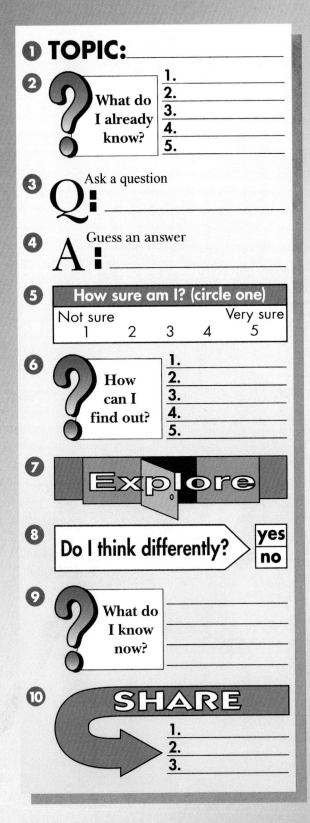

1 TOPIC:_____

2 **?** What do I already know?
1._____
2._____
3._____
4._____
5._____

3 Ask a question
Q:_____

4 Guess an answer
A:_____

5 How sure am I? (circle one)

Not sure				Very sure
1	2	3	4	5

6 **?** How can I find out?
1._____
2._____
3._____
4._____
5._____

7 Explore

8 Do I think differently? → yes / no

9 **?** What do I know now?
_____
_____
_____

10 SHARE
1._____
2._____
3._____

1. Fill in the topic your teacher gives you.

2. Jot down what you already know about the topic.

3. Using what you already know (Step 2), form a question about the topic. Are you unsure about one of the items you listed? Do you want to know more? Do you want to know what, how, or why? Write down your question.

4. Guess an answer to your question. In the next few steps, you will be exploring the reasonableness of your answer. Write down your guess.

5. Circle the number in the box that matches how sure you are of your answer in Step 4. This is your chance to rate your confidence in what you've done so far and, later, to see how your level of sureness affects your thinking.

6. How can you find out more about your topic? You might want to read a book, ask an expert, or do an experiment. Write down ways you can find out more.

7. Make a plan to explore your answer. Use the resources you listed in Step 6. Then, carry out your plan.

8. Now that you've explored, go back to your answer in Step 4. Would you answer differently? Mark one of the boxes.

9. Considering what you learned in your exploration, answer your question again, adding new things you've learned. You may completely change your answer.

10. It's important to be able to talk about thinking. Choose three people to tell about how you arrived at your response in every step. For example, don't just read what you wrote down in Step 2. Try to share how you thought of those things.

Cockleburs and Space Shuttles

One day a Swiss engineer returned from a walk and became interested in the thistles sticking to his socks. He studied the cockleburs under a microscope and found hundreds of tiny hook and loop structures. As a result of this observation, he invented Velcro.

Nylon filament is woven into loops and coated. Half of the loops are cut to form hooks. Velcro has come to have many uses. It has been used to secure artificial hearts. In the space program, more than 64 500 cm² of Velcro tape have been used on each space shuttle. Velcro is also used to strap on blood pressure cuffs, on sneakers, and is found in astronauts' helmets as a nose scratcher.

Think Critically: What does this story tell you about how science works?

Measuring in Science

Think about how many things you use every day that measure or are measured. The thermostat keeps the air in your home at a certain temperature. Meters outside your house measure water, electricity, and gas usage. Your food comes in pounds, ounces, and liters, and you step on a scale to check your weight.

Scientists use a system of measurement to make observations. Scientists around the world have agreed to use the International System of Units, or SI. SI is based on certain metric units. Using the same system gives scientists a common language. They can understand each other's research and compare results. Most of the units you will use in this textbook are shown in Table 1-2 on page 20. Because you are used to using the English system of pounds, ounces, and inches, a chart has been included in Appendix B on page 671 to help you convert these units to SI.

Science and READING

What do doctors, dentists, veterinarians, hairdressers, and school nurses have to learn about life science before they are allowed to do their jobs? Look up these careers in the United States Government Guide to Careers.

Table 1-1

COMMON METRIC UNITS AND PREFIXES						
Length	Mass	Volume	Prefix	Symbol	Meaning	
kilometer	kilogram	cubic meter	kilo-	k	1000.0	
meter	gram	liter	centi-	c	0.01 (1/100)	
centimeter		cubic centimeter	milli-	m	0.001 (1/1000)	
millimeter	milligram	milliliter				

Figure 1-13. A graduated cylinder (a) is used to measure volumes. Metric rulers (b) are used to measure lengths. A pan balance (c) is used to measure mass.

SI is based on units of ten. It is easy to use because the calculations are made by multiplying or dividing by ten. Prefixes are used with units to change them to larger or smaller units.

The SI unit of length is the *meter.* A metric ruler or a meterstick is used to measure length. If you look at the table, you see that 1000 meters equal one kilometer. Large distances are measured in kilometers.

Mass is the amount of matter in an object. Mass is measured with a balance. The SI unit of mass is the *kilogram.* Smaller masses are measured in grams and milligrams.

The amount of space occupied by an object is its volume. Units of volume are based on units of length. Volume is found by multiplying the length times the width times the height. The SI unit of volume is the *cubic meter.* Cubic meters are too large to be of any use in the laboratory. Because of this, the cubic centimeter (cm^3) is used to measure volume. Liquid volumes are measured in liters (L). One liter has the same volume as 1000 cm^3. Millimeters are used to measure smaller volumes.

The *degree* is the unit for measuring temperature. The kelvin scale is the SI standard for measuring temperature. Scientists also often use the Celsius scale. On the Celsius scale, water freezes at 0°C and boils at 100°C at sea level.

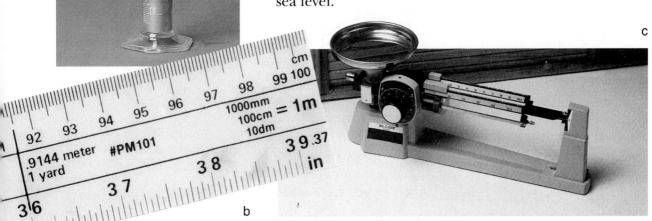

You will use these measurements to work in the laboratory this year. Working in the laboratory will help you understand the life science concepts in your textbook. You will observe and conduct experiments. Some of the observations you will make will be the same ones made by students and researchers for years and years. The important thing is that *you* will have seen these things yourself.

Safety First

Having the chance to do science is much more interesting than merely reading about it. Some of the scientific equipment that you will use is the same that scientists use in the field or in their laboratories. Of course, safety is of great importance in a laboratory. Most injuries are due to burns from heated objects or splatters and broken glass. The symbols shown below are used throughout your text to alert you to situations that require your special attention. A description of each symbol can be found on page 673 in the Safety Appendix. Following safety rules will protect you and others from injury and help you get more from your lab experiences.

SECTION REVIEW

1. What is life science?
2. What is a hypothesis?
3. How does a control differ from a variable?
4. How are theories different from laws?
5. **Apply:** Read the Find Out activity on page 5 again and identify the scientific methods that were used in performing the experiment.

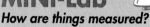

MINI-Lab

How are things measured?

Working in Paired Partners, measure the mass of the following items: a small paper clip, a sealed sugar packet, a pack of sugarless gum, a metal spoon, and a rock. Use a pan balance. Record your data in a table. Are these items best measured in kilograms, milligrams, or grams?

☑ Measuring in SI

Measure the volume of space in your classroom in cubic meters. Then figure out how much of this volume each student occupies. If you need help, refer to Measuring in SI in the **Skill Handbook** on page 684.

Skill Builder

1-4 The Impact of Science on Your Life

New Science Words

technology
ecology

Objectives

▶ State two ways in which life on Earth has been affected by technology in the life sciences.

Times Have Changed

Did you know that if you were born 100 years ago, you would probably not have lived past your first birthday? What a thought! When your parents were born, there were some places in the United States in which about one half of all infants died in their first year of life due to contaminated water and milk. This could still happen if your communities didn't have sanitation plants. Have you ever had a shot of penicillin to fight infection? Before the discovery of penicillin in 1940, infection was difficult to control, and many people died. Did you brush your teeth this morning? Before studies on why and how teeth decay, many people did not brush. Decayed teeth were pulled at an early age. Now most water systems are fluoridated, and tooth decay has decreased. Before modern techniques in food processing, such as irradiation of packaged foods, many diseases were acquired from contaminated foods. Sanitation, penicillin, fluoridated water, and irradiated food are examples of technologies that have extended lives. **Technology** is applied science, or the use of scientific knowledge to solve everyday problems or improve the quality of life.

Figure 1-14. Optical fibers are used to transmit voices and data. They are also used in new forms of surgery.

Living with Technology

Years of research in the life sciences have enabled people to benefit directly from science economically, nutritionally, medically, and environmentally. Advances in agriculture allow you to have fish, meat, bread, and milk regularly. Because of agricultural research, farmers produce great quantities of healthful food at reasonable prices in many countries of the world.

Have all of the advances in the life sciences been beneficial? With the many great advances have also come many problems due to unforseen side effects. For example, you probably run a much greater chance of developing cancer than your ancestors of 100 years ago. The technology involved in the development of pesticides, food preservatives, and artificial sweeteners has contributed to increased incidence of cancer. Are the technologies the problem? Or is it how they are used that creates problems?

Now scientists are turning their energy to the environment. Many technologies seem to have a strong impact on the environment. **Ecology** is the study of how organisms interact with each other and the environment. Ecological problems such as global warming, the warming of Earth due to the buildup of carbon dioxide in the atmosphere, and deforestation, the destruction of forests that help take carbon dioxide out of the atmosphere, are sources of concern. Have these problems been caused by our own technology? Can we make use of all the knowledge we've gained through research to prevent these problems? Do we really know that technology is to blame for the problems of the environment? What is there in the framework of science that can help answer these questions?

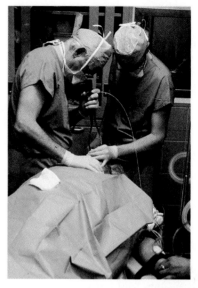

Figure 1-15. Laser surgery has reduced the time it takes to recover and has reduced infection.

SECTION REVIEW

1. Describe two ways in which Earth has benefitted from technology.
2. Describe two ways in which Earth may have been damaged as a result of technology.

You Decide!

How easy is it for a company to do what's best for the environment? Many fast-food companies are being urged to stop using styrofoam containers because the use of these products is thought to contribute to the destruction of the ozone layer. If companies go back to using paper products, however, where will these paper materials come from? If you were the company president, what would you have to do to make an informed decision?

SCIENCE & SOCIETY

ACTIVITY 1-1
Using a Scientific Method

Problem: *How does vinegar affect milk?*

Materials
- whole milk (300 mL)
- water (15 mL)
- vinegar (15 mL)
- 250-mL beakers (2)
- 50-mL graduated cylinder

Procedure
1. Use a reference book to find out what kind of substances milk and vinegar are.
2. Based on what you have read about milk and vinegar, make a hypothesis about how vinegar affects milk. Write your hypothesis in a data table like the one shown.
3. Use the following experiment to test your hypothesis:
   a. Label two beakers A and B. Pour 150 mL of milk into each beaker.
   b. Add 15 mL of water to beaker A and 15 mL of vinegar to beaker B.
   c. Allow the beakers to remain undisturbed for three or four minutes.
4. Record what you observe about each beaker in the data table.
5. Using your observations, write a conclusion in the data table.

Data and Observations

Effect of vinegar on Milk		
Test	Observation	Conclusion
A		
B		
Hypothesis		

Analyze
1. Which beaker was the control?
2. Which beaker was the variable?
3. Why did you use the same amount of milk in both beakers?
4. Why did you use the same amount of water and vinegar?

Conclude and Apply
5. Why didn't water have an effect on the milk?
6. How did vinegar affect the milk?

CHAPTER
REVIEW

SUMMARY

1-1: Living Things
1. Organisms are made up of cells, use energy, move, respond, adjust, reproduce, grow and develop, and adapt to their environment.
2. Organisms need energy and materials.
3. Organisms interact with other organisms and nonliving things in their environment.

1-2: Where Does Life Come From?
1. Early experiments of Redi and Spallanzani tried to disprove the idea that living things come from nonliving matter.
2. Pasteur's experiment proved the theory that life comes from life, biogenesis.
3. Scientists try to explain how life began on Earth. Oparin's hypothesis, which says that energy combined early gases to form the chemical compounds of life, has been tested.

1-3: What is Science?
1. Scientists investigate observations that are made about living and nonliving things with the help of problem-solving techniques.
2. Scientists use SI measurements to gather measurable data.
3. Safe laboratory practices help you to learn more about science.

1-4: Science and Society: The Impact of Science on Your Life
1. Technology has improved health but also produced some harmful side effects.

KEY SCIENCE WORDS

a. adaptation
b. biogenesis
c. cells
d. control
e. development
f. ecology
g. homeostasis
h. hypothesis
i. law
j. life span
k. organism
l. response
m. scientific methods
n. spontaneous generation
o. stimulus
p. technology
q. theory
r. variable

UNDERSTANDING VOCABULARY

Match each phrase with the correct term from the list of Key Science Words.

1. the length of time an organism is expected to live
2. changes undergone during growth
3. a change in the environment that brings about a response
4. a living thing
5. the use of science for solving problems or improving life
6. theory that nonliving things produce living things
7. organized steps used to solve a problem
8. a prediction that can be tested
9. the units of life
10. a standard for comparing the result of an experiment

CHAPTER
REVIEW

CHECKING CONCEPTS

Choose the word or phrase that completes the sentence.

1. An infant cutting teeth is an example of _____.
   a. growth   c. respiration
   b. development   d. none of these

2. A bright light causing you to shut your eyes is a _____.
   a. need   c. stimulus
   b. response   d. all of these

3. The _____ is the main source of energy for all organisms.
   a. sun   c. carbon dioxide
   b. oxygen   d. none of these

4. Water is important to organisms for _____.
   a. making food   c. part of blood
   b. dissolving substances d. all of these

5. _____ disproved the theory of spontaneous generation.
   a. Oparin   c. Pasteur
   b. Spallanzani   d. Redi

6. Scientists think that _____ was missing from Earth's early atmosphere.
   a. ammonia   c. methane
   b. hydrogen   d. oxygen

7. _____ are inherited characteristics that help an organism to survive.
   a. Adaptations   c. Raw materials
   b. Stimuli   d. Theories

8. A _____ is the part of the experiment that is being tested.
   a. conclusion   c. control
   b. variable   d. data

9. A(n) _____ is a prediction that has to be testable.
   a. experiment   c. theory
   b. hypothesis   d. law

10. The SI unit used to measure liquids is _____.
    a. meter   c. gram
    b. liter   d. degree

UNDERSTANDING CONCEPTS

Complete each sentence.

11. The theory that only living things produce living things is _____.

12. Recorded measurements in an experiment are called _____.

13. The variable of an experiment is compared to the _____.

14. A rule of nature is called a scientific _____.

15. Scientists use _____ units of scientific measurement.

THINK AND WRITE CRITICALLY

16. How might technology have an effect on the environment?

17. Distinguish between growth and development using humans as an example.

18. How does technology help science?

19. What is the difference between a response and an adaptation?

20. Explain why living things need energy.

21. How does SI benefit scientists from different parts of the world?
22. Using a bird as an example, explain how it has all the characteristics of living things.
23. If a plant had no carbon dioxide available, would this affect animal life?
24. Show how Pasteur correctly used scientific methods to disprove the theory of spontaneous generation.
25. How are stimulus and response related to homeostasis?

MORE SKILL BUILDERS

If you need help, refer to the Skill Handbook.

1. **Designing an Experiment:** Devise an experiment to test the use of a plant food on growing plants. Be sure to include scientific methods in your experiments.
2. **Concept Mapping:** Use the following terms to complete a chain-of-events concept map showing the order in which you might use scientific methods: *collect data, perform an experiment, state your hypothesis.*

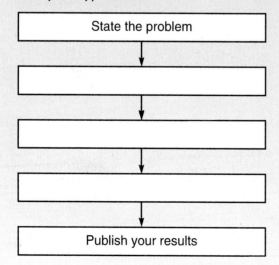

```
┌─────────────────────────────┐
│     State the problem        │
└─────────────────────────────┘
              ↓
┌─────────────────────────────┐
│                             │
└─────────────────────────────┘
              ↓
┌─────────────────────────────┐
│                             │
└─────────────────────────────┘
              ↓
┌─────────────────────────────┐
│                             │
└─────────────────────────────┘
              ↓
┌─────────────────────────────┐
│    Publish your results      │
└─────────────────────────────┘
```

3. **Designing an Experiment:** You place one lima bean plant under a green light, another under a red light, and a third under a blue light. You measure their growth for 4 weeks to determine which color is most favorable to plant growth. What are the variables in this experiment? What is the hypothesis in this experiment? How could the experiment be improved?
4. **Observing and Inferring:** What evidence must scientists have to prove that cancer can be caused by cigarette smoking?
5. **Classifying:** Which type of measurement would you use for each of the following? Classify as meter, gram, cubic meter, degree, or liter.
   a. distance run
   b. how hot a pan of water is
   c. how much juice is in a glass
   d. your mass

PROJECTS

1. Interview people in your community whose jobs require a knowledge of life science. Make a Life Science Careers bulletin board. Summarize each person's job and what they had to study to prepare for that job.
2. Try to recreate Pasteur's experiment.

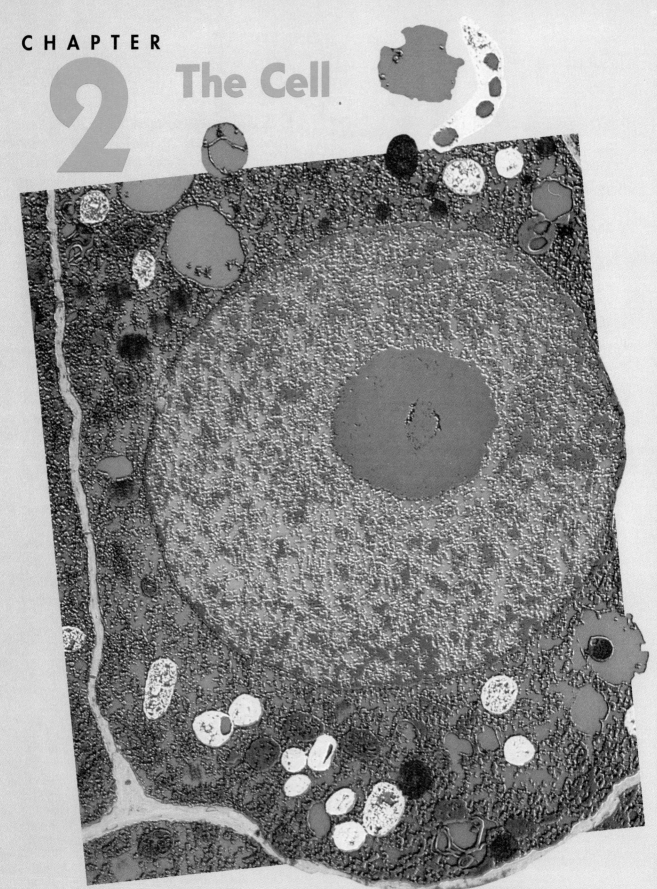

Is it true that most cells are too small to be seen without some help? The plant cell on the opposite page has been magnified. But there are some cells that can be seen using just your eyes. The largest known living cells are the yolks of bird eggs—not the white, just the yolk. How large is the cell of a chicken egg?

FIND OUT!

Do this simple activity and find out that some cells can be seen without a microscope.

Break a chicken egg into a dish and look at the yolk. How large is it? Estimate its diameter. Use a metric ruler to measure the diameter of your chicken yolk cell. Then use a hand lens to take a closer look at the yolk. Other cells that can be seen easily are large fish eggs. Discuss reasons why different cells have different sizes.

Gearing Up

Previewing the Chapter

Use this outline to help you focus on important ideas in this chapter.

Section 2-1 Cells: The Units of Life
▶ The Microscope: A Tool
▶ The Cell Theory

Section 2-2 Cell Structure
▶ An Overview of Cells
▶ Cell Membrane
▶ Cytoplasm
▶ Nucleus
▶ Organelles in the Cytoplasm
▶ Plant and Bacterial Cells

Section 2-3 Cell Organization
▶ How Cells Differ
▶ From Cell to System

Section 2-4 Science and Society
Organ Transplants
▶ Spare Parts for Broken Hearts

Previewing Science Skills

▶ In the **Skill Builders**, you will make a concept map, compare and contrast, and interpret scientific illustrations.
▶ In the **Activities,** you will observe, infer, compare, diagram, and draw conclusions.
▶ In the **MINI-Labs,** you will observe, identify, compare and infer.

What's next?

Now that you have looked at an extremely large cell, learn how the microscope helped in the discovery of cells of all sizes and in the development of the cell theory. You will also learn about microscopes that help reveal the detailed parts of cells. At the end of the chapter, you will see that many-celled organisms are organized with tissues, organs, and systems.

Cells: The Units of Life

New Science Words

compound light microscope
electron microscope
cell theory

Objectives

▶ Discuss the history leading to the cell theory.
▶ Explain the difference between the compound light microscope and electron microscope.
▶ State the cell theory.

The Microscope: A Tool

Cells are the smallest units that carry out the activities of life in organisms. Yet, as important as they are, you certainly don't see individual cells when you look at most plants or animals. You need a magnifying device, such as a magnifying glass or a microscope, to see most cells.

Trying to see separate cells in a large plant, like the one in Figure 2-1, is like trying to see individual bricks in a wall from three blocks away. If you start to walk toward the wall, it becomes easier to see individual bricks. When you get right up to the wall, you can see each brick in detail. A microscope performs a similar function. A microscope has one or more lenses that make an enlarged image of an object. Through these lenses, you are brought closer to the leaf, and you see the individual cells that carry on life processes.

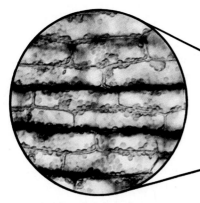

Figure 2-1. Individual plant cells become visible when the leaves on the wall are looked at with the help of a microscope.

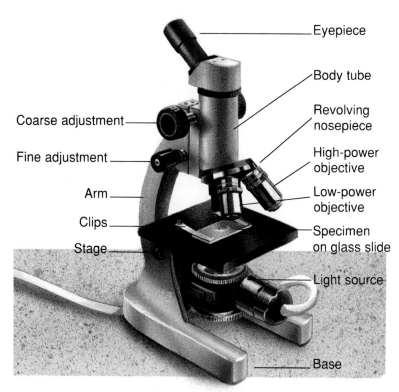

Eyepiece

Body tube

Revolving nosepiece

High-power objective

Low-power objective

Specimen on glass slide

Light source

Coarse adjustment

Fine adjustment

Arm

Clips

Stage

Base

Figure 2-2. The Parts of a Compound Light Microscope

Microscopes are simple or compound, depending on how many lenses they contain. A simple microscope is similar to a magnifying glass. It has only one lens. In 1590, a Dutch maker of reading glasses, Zacharias Janssen, put two magnifying glasses together in a tube. The result was the first crude compound microscope. By combining two lenses he got an image that was larger than an image made by only one lens. These early compound microscopes weren't satisfactory, however. The lenses would make a large image, but it wasn't always clear.

In the mid 1600s, Anton Van Leeuwenhoek, another Dutch scientist, made a simple microscope with a tiny glass bead for a lens. With it, he reported seeing things in pond water that no one had ever imagined before. His microscope could magnify up to 270 times. Another way to say this is that his microscope could make an image of an object 270 times larger than its actual size. Today we would say his lens had a power of 270X.

The microscope you will use in studying life science is a compound light microscope like the one in Figure 2-2. A **compound light microscope** lets light pass through an object and then through two or more lenses. The lenses enlarge the image and bend the light toward your eye. It has an eyepiece lens and an objective lens. An eyepiece

MINI-Lab

How are objects magnified?
Early scientists used various tools to help view objects. Try looking at a newspaper through the curved side of an empty glass, the flat bottom of an empty glass, a bowl filled with water, and a magnifying glass. Compare what you can see through each. What did early scientists learn by using such tools?

lens usually has a power of 10X. An objective lens may have a power of 43X. Together, they have a total magnification of 430X (10X times 43X). Some compound microscopes have more powerful lenses that magnify an object up to 2000 times (2000X) its original size.

Your classroom may have a stereoscopic (stereo) light microscope that gives you a three-dimensional view of an object. Stereo microscopes are used to look at thick structures that light can't pass through, such as whole insects or leaves, or your fingerprints.

Things that are too small to be seen with a light microscope can be seen with an electron microscope. Instead of using lenses to bend beams of light, an **electron microscope** uses a magnetic field to bend beams of electrons. Electron microscopes can magnify images more than 300 000 times. Figure 2-3 shows the kind of detail that can be seen with an electron microscope.

There are several kinds of electron microscopes. One is the transmission electron microscope (TEM), which is used to study parts inside a cell. The object has to be sliced very thin and placed in a vacuum. There is no air in a vacuum. As a result, only dead cells can be observed this way. A scanning electron microscope (SEM) is used to see the surfaces of whole objects. With an SEM, you can view and photograph living cells. From the time of Van Leeuwenhoek until the present, the microscope has been a valuable tool for studying cells. You will see how it was used to develop the cell theory.

Science and MATH

What is the total magnification of your microscope if the eyepiece is 10X and the high power objective is 40X?

Figure 2-3. The electron microscope shows details on these insects that can't be seen with a compound microscope.

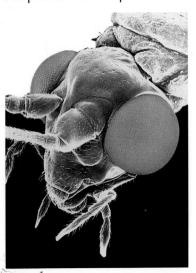

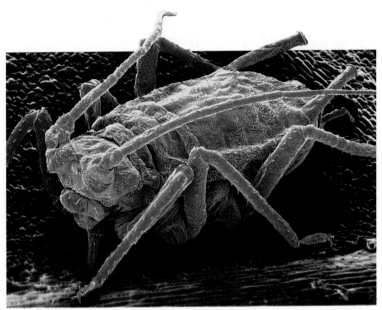

A Touch of Diamonds

One of the newest members of the microscope family is the atomic-force microscope. It makes use of a diamond-tipped probe that moves across the surface of a specimen. The tip moves up and down as it probes the hills and valleys of tissues. Just as a phonograph needle traces the grooves in a record, the diamond tip is moved up and down by the force of electrons on the surface of the atoms making up the tissue. As it does, it traces the shape of the surface of a cell. This tracing is then projected as a visual image on a screen. The diamond used is so small that human eyebrow hairs are used to move it when the probe is being assembled.

The atomic-force microscope "sees" individual living cells without damaging them. The first video made with an atomic-force microscope shows the clotting of blood. With this microscope, such events can now be watched as they take place.

Think Critically: How might an atomic-force microscope help medical research?

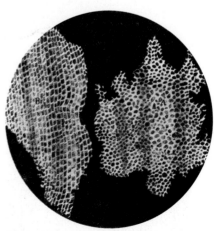

The Cell Theory

During the centuries when explorers like Columbus and Magellan set out to find new lands, scientists were busy observing everything they could about the small world around them. Curiosity made them look through their microscopes and lenses at mud from ponds and drops of rainwater. They examined blood and scrapings from their own teeth.

Cells weren't discovered until the microscope was improved. In 1665, Robert Hooke, an English scientist, made a very thin slice of cork and looked at it under his microscope. To Hooke, the cork seemed to be made up of little empty boxes, which he called *cells*. The drawing of cork cells in Figure 2-4 was made by Robert Hooke more than 300 years ago. Actually, Hooke was not aware of the importance of what he was seeing.

In 1838, Matthias Schleiden, a German scientist, used a microscope to study plant parts. He concluded that all plants were made of cells. Just a year later, another

What did Robert Hooke see when he looked at cork?

Figure 2-4.
Hooke's Cork Cells

Science and WRITING

Put yourself in the shoes of a Schleiden, Schwann, or Van Leeuwenhoek. Consider the times in which they lived. Write a dialogue between the scientist and his son or daughter, as he tries to explain his discovery.

German scientist, Theodor Schwann, after observing many different animal cells, concluded that all animals were made up of cells. Together, they became convinced that all living things were made of cells.

About 15 years later, a German doctor, Rudolph Virchow, hypothesized that new cells don't form on their own. Instead, cells divide to form new cells. This was a startling idea. Remember that at that time, people thought earthworms fell from the sky when it rained. They thought that life came about spontaneously. What Virchow said was that every cell that is or has ever been came from a cell that already existed. The observations and conclusions of Schleiden, Schwann, Virchow, and other scientists became known as the cell theory. The major ideas of the **cell theory** are:

1. All organisms are made up of one or more cells.
2. Cells are the basic units of structure and function in all organisms.
3. All cells come from cells that already exist.

Figure 2-5. Cells divide to produce new cells. Pictured below are four early stages in the development of a frog.

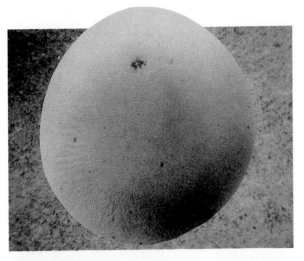

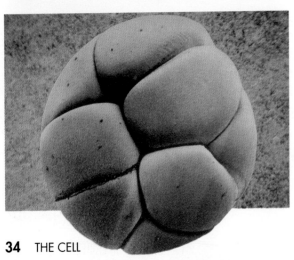

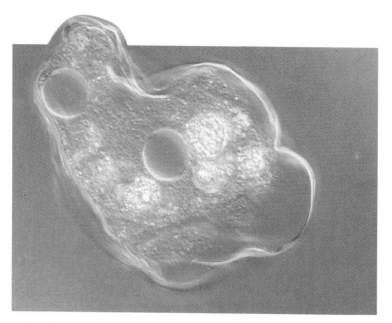

Figure 2-6. One-celled organisms like this amoeba may look simple, but they carry on many complex life processes.

The cell theory is one of the major theories in life science. It is not based on the hypothesis and observations of only one person, but is result of the discoveries of many scientists. Today it serves as the basis for scientists who study the parts of cells, how they are organized, and how they reproduce and change through time.

What are the three parts of the cell theory?

SECTION REVIEW

1. Explain why the invention of the microscope was important in the study of cells.
2. How is a compound light microscope different from an electron microscope?
3. Why is the cell theory important?
4. Name three scientists whose work led to the cell theory. Tell what each one contributed.
5. **Apply:** Why would it be better to be able to see the details of living cells than dead cells?

☑ Concept Mapping

Using a network tree concept map, show the differences between compound light microscopes and electron microscopes. If you need help, refer to Concept Mapping in the **Skill Handbook** on pages 688 and 689.

Skill Builder

2-2 Cell Structure

New Science Words

cell membrane
cytoplasm
organelles
nucleus
chromatin
endoplasmic reticulum
ribosomes
Golgi bodies
mitochondria
lysosomes
vacuoles
cell wall
chloroplasts

How does a prokaryotic cell differ from a eukaryotic cell?

Objectives

▶ Diagram a plant cell and an animal cell; identify the parts and the function of each part.
▶ Describe the importance of the nucleus in the cell.
▶ Compare and contrast prokaryotic and eukaryotic cells.

An Overview of Cells

In contrast to the dry cork boxes that Hooke saw, living cells have several things in common. They all have a membrane and a gel-like material called cytoplasm inside the membrane. In addition, they all have something that controls the life of the cell. This control center is either a nucleus or nuclear material.

Scientists have found that there are two basic types of cells. Cells that have no membrane around their nuclear material are prokaryotic cells. Bacteria and cells that form pond scum are prokaryotic cells. A eukaryotic cell has a nucleus with a membrane around it. The animal and plant cells in this chapter are all eukaryotic cells.

Figure 2-7. Pond scum is made up of prokaryotic cells.

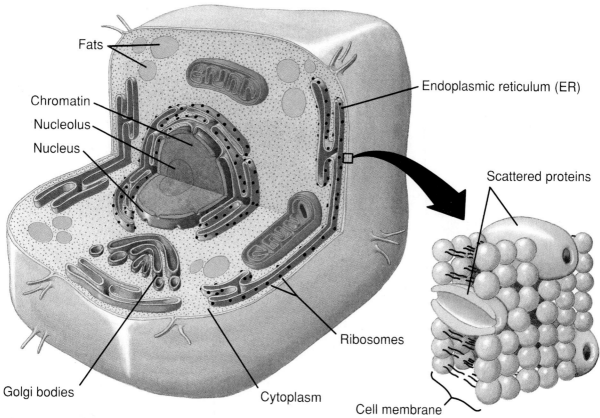

Figure 2-8. The Parts of a Typical Animal Cell

Labels: Fats, Chromatin, Nucleolus, Nucleus, Golgi bodies, Endoplasmic reticulum (ER), Scattered proteins, Ribosomes, Cytoplasm, Cell membrane

Cell Membrane

Each cell in your body is constantly active and has a specific job to do. The activities in your cells might be compared to a business that operates 24 hours a day making dozens of different products. It operates inside a building. Only materials that are needed to make specific products are brought into the building. Finished products are then moved out. A cell is similar. It functions within a structure called the cell membrane.

The **cell membrane** is a structure that forms the outer boundary of the cell and allows only certain materials to move into and out of the cell. The membrane is flexible. It is made up of a double layer of fats with some proteins scattered throughout. The cell membrane helps to maintain a chemical balance between materials inside and outside the cell. Food and oxygen move into the cell through the membrane. Waste products also leave through the membrane. In Chapter 3, you will learn that different types of substances enter and leave the cell in different ways.

What is the cell membrane made of?

Cytoplasm

Cytoplasm is the gel-like material inside the cell membrane. Cytoplasm contains a large amount of water and many chemicals and structures that carry out the life processes in the cell. Unlike a gelatin dessert however, cytoplasm constantly moves or streams.

The structures within the cytoplasm of eukaryotic cells are **organelles.** Each one has a specific job. Some organelles break down food. Others move wastes to be expelled from the cell. Still others store materials. Most organelles are surrounded by membranes.

Nucleus

The largest organelle in the cytoplasm of a eukaryotic cell is the **nucleus,** a structure that directs all the activities of the cell. The nucleus is like a manager who directs everyday business for a company. The nucleus contains genetic blueprints for the operations of the cell in the form of long strands called **chromatin.** Chromatin is made up of proteins and DNA, the chemical that controls the activities of the cell. When a cell begins to divide, the strands of chromatin become thick and take on the form of chromosomes, which are easier to see. A structure called a nucleolus is also found in the nucleus.

A nucleus is separated from the cytoplasm by a nuclear envelope. Materials enter and leave through openings in the envelope.

Figure 2-9. A nucleus is surrounded by a membrane, or envelope. DNA in the nucleus controls the activities in the cell.

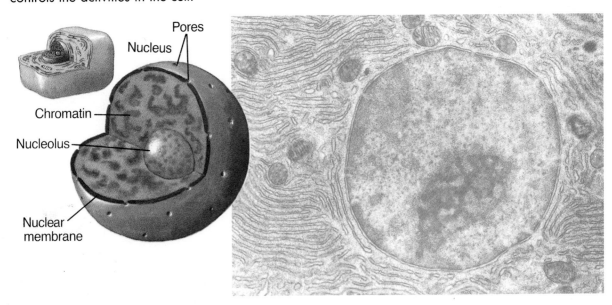

Pores
Nucleus
Chromatin
Nucleolus
Nuclear membrane

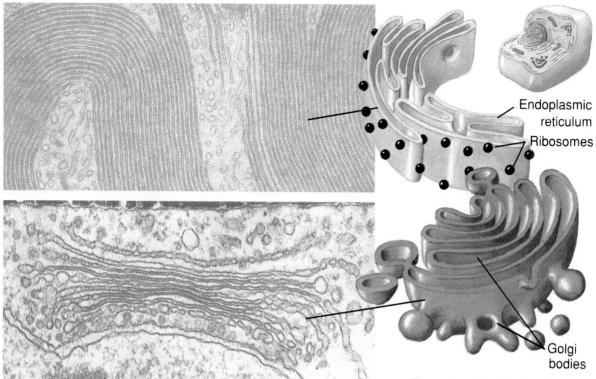

Figure 2-10. Endoplasmic reticulum is smooth or rough. Proteins are made on ribosomes. Golgi bodies may move materials to the outside of the cell.

Endoplasmic reticulum

Ribosomes

Golgi bodies

Organelles in the Cytoplasm

The **endoplasmic reticulum** (**ER**) is a folded membrane that moves materials around in the cell. The ER extends from the nucleus to the cell membrane and takes up quite a lot of space in some cells. The ER is like a system of conveyor belts in a business that moves material from one place to another.

One chemical that takes part in nearly every cell activity is protein. Proteins are found in cell membranes. Other proteins are needed for chemical reactions that take place in the cytoplasm. Cells make their own proteins on small structures in the cytoplasm called **ribosomes.** Ribosomes receive directions from the nucleus on how to make specific proteins. Some ribosomes are scattered in the cytoplasm. Others are attached to the ER. Ribosome parts are made in the nucleolus.

In a business, products are made, packaged, and moved to loading docks to be carried away. Structures called Golgi bodies are stacks of membrane-covered sacs that move proteins to the outside of the cell. **Golgi bodies** are the packaging and secreting organelles of the cell. When something is secreted, it is given off by the cell.

Where are ribosomes found?

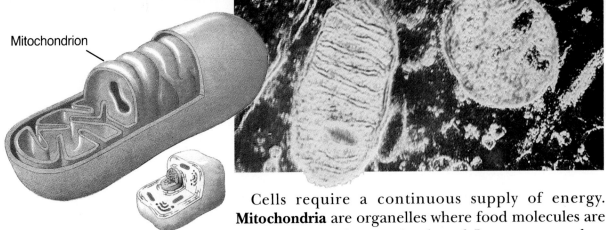

Mitochondrion

Figure 2-11. Energy is released in mitochondria.

Cells require a continuous supply of energy. **Mitochondria** are organelles where food molecules are broken down and energy is released. Just as a power plant supplies energy to a business, mitochondria generate energy for the cell. Some types of cells are more active than others. Muscle cells, which are always undergoing some type of movement, have large numbers of mitochondria. Why would active cells have more mitochondria?

An active cell also constantly produces waste products. In the cytoplasm, organelles called **lysosomes** contain chemicals that digest wastes and worn-out cell parts. When a cell dies, chemicals in the lysosomes act to quickly break down the cell. In a healthy cell, the membrane around the lysosome keeps it from breaking down the cell itself.

PROBLEM SOLVING

A Tale of a Tail

In September, Mrs. Tallman's class studied the parts of plant and animal cells.

In the spring, while on a field trip, the class captured tiny tadpoles in a local stream. Mrs. Tallman showed the students how to care for the tadpoles in the classroom. Gradually, as the animals grew, it was obvious that their bodies were changing shape. Back and front legs grew out, and the mouth expanded from a small hole to a large opening capable of swallowing large insects. In addition, the tails started to disappear. Mrs. Tallman told the whole class that there would be a bonus question about the tadpoles on the test on animals. For a study hint, she told them to look back at their notes on cells. What do changes in the body parts of the tadpoles have to do with cells?

Think Critically: Answer the bonus question: What cell part is making the tadpole tails disappear and why?

Many businesses have warehouses for storing products until they are sold. **Vacuoles** are storage areas in cells. They may store water, food, or waste products. Figure 2-12 shows that a vacuole may take up most of the space in a plant cell. In animal cells, vacuoles are small.

Plant and Bacterial Cells

The major difference between an animal cell and a plant cell is that plant cells have cell walls. The **cell wall** is a rigid structure outside the cell membrane that supports and protects the plant cell. It is made of bundles of tough cellulose fibers and other materials made by the cell.

Plant cells also differ from animal cells because they can make energy in the form of food. **Chloroplasts** are organelles in plant cells in which light energy is changed into chemical energy in the form of a sugar called glucose. The chemical in chloroplasts that traps light energy is chlorophyll, the pigment that makes plants green.

How do plant and animal cells differ?

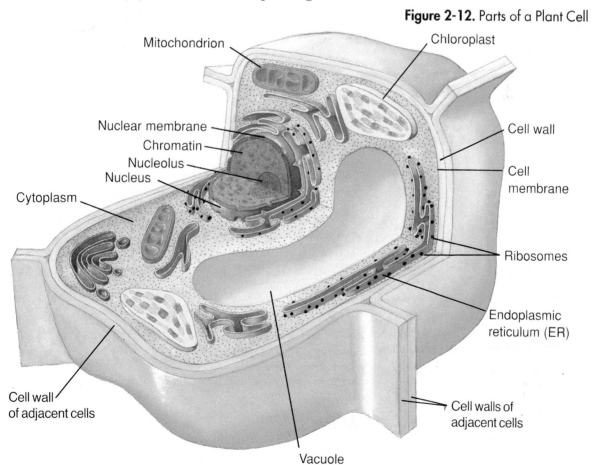

Figure 2-12. Parts of a Plant Cell

Mitochondrion
Chloroplast
Nuclear membrane
Chromatin
Nucleolus
Nucleus
Cytoplasm
Cell wall
Cell membrane
Ribosomes
Endoplasmic reticulum (ER)
Cell wall of adjacent cells
Cell walls of adjacent cells
Vacuole

Figure 2-13. A bacterial cell is a one-celled prokaryotic organism. It has no membrane around its nuclear material. This type of bacterial cell lives in human intestines.

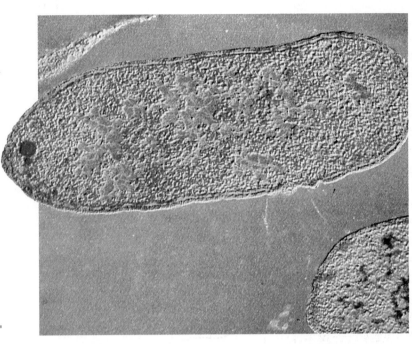

In contrast to plant and animal cells, bacterial cells are prokaryotic cells. Bacteria don't have membrane-covered organelles. In Figure 2-13, you can see the parts of a bacterial cell. It has a cell wall and cytoplasm, but it has only a single chromosome. There are no nuclei in bacteria, but they do contain ribosomes.

All cells have similar parts. However, animal and plant cells have organelles. Bacterial cells have no membrane-covered structures.

SECTION REVIEW

1. Diagram an animal cell and label its organelles.
2. Explain the importance of the cell nucleus in the life of a cell.
3. How are bacterial cells different from other cells?
4. **Apply:** Explain why you could be called a eukaryotic organism.

Skill Builder

☑ Comparing and Contrasting

Organize information about cell organelles in a table. Use this information to compare and contrast animal cells, plant cells, and bacterial cells. If you need help, refer to Comparing and Contrasting in the **Skill Handbook** on page 683.

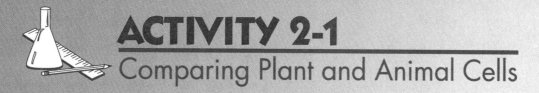

ACTIVITY 2-1
Comparing Plant and Animal Cells

Problem: *How do plant and animal cells differ?*

Materials

- microscope
- 1 microscope slide
- 1 coverslip
- forceps
- dropper
- *Elodea* plant
- prepared slide of human cheek cells

Procedure

1. Follow the directions in Appendix A for use of low and high power objectives on your microscope.
2. With forceps, remove a young leaf from the tip of an *Elodea* plant. Place it on a microscope slide. Add a drop of water and a coverslip.
3. Place the slide on the microscope stage and observe the leaf on low power. Focus on the top layer of cells. Make a drawing of what you see.
4. Carefully focus down through the top layer of cells to observe the layers of cells.
5. Focus on one cell. Observe the movement of chloroplasts along the cell membrane.
6. Observe the cell nucleus. It looks like a clear ball. Look at the nucleus on high power.
7. Make a drawing of the *Elodea* cell. Label the cell wall, cytoplasm, chloroplasts, and nucleus. Return to low power and remove the slide.
8. Place a prepared slide of cheek cells on the microscope stage. Locate the cells under low power.
9. Switch to high power and observe the cell nucleus. Draw and label the cell membrane, cytoplasm, and nucleus.

Analyze

1. What parts of the *Elodea* cell were you able to identify?

2. How many cell layers could you see in the *Elodea* leaf?
3. Describe any movement you observed in the *Elodea* leaf.
4. What parts of the cheek cell were easy to identify?

Data and Observations

Cell Part	Elodea	Cheek
cytoplasm		
nucleus		
chloroplasts		
cell wall		
cell membrane		

Conclude and Apply

5. How is the shape of the cheek cell different from the *Elodea* cell?
6. What part determines the shape of a plant cell? An animal cell?
7. What conclusions can you make about the differences in plant and animal cells?

2-3 Cell Organization

New Science Words

tissues
organ
organ system

Objectives

▶ Recognize that cells differ in size, shape, and function.
▶ Explain how cells of one-celled organisms differ from cells of many-celled organisms.
▶ Explain the differences among tissues, organs, and organ systems.

How Cells Differ

Cells come in a variety of sizes. A single nerve cell in your leg may be a meter in length. A human egg cell, on the other hand, is no bigger than a dot on this *i*. Going a step further, a human red blood cell is about one-tenth of the size of a human egg cell.

The shape of a cell can also tell you something about the job the cell does. The nerve cell in Figure 2-14 with its fine extensions sends impulses through your body. Look at its shape in contrast to the white blood cell, which can change shape. Some cells in its plant stems are long and hollow with holes. They transport food and water throughout the plant. Human blood cells, on the other hand, are disk-shaped and have to be small and flexible enough to move through tiny blood vessels.

From Cell to System

A one-celled organism has to perform all its life functions by itself. Cells in a many-celled organism, however, do not work alone. Instead, each cell depends on other cells to carry out its functions. This interaction helps the whole organism stay alive.

In Figure 2-15 you can see a single plant cell. In Figure 2-15 you also see a group of the same type of plant cells that together form a tissue on the outside of a plant leaf.

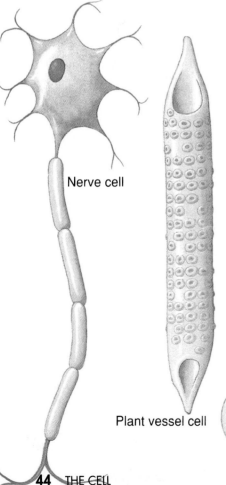

Figure 2-14. Often the shape of a cell tells you something about the job it performs.

Nerve cell

Plant vessel cell

Human egg

Red blood cell

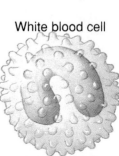

White blood cell

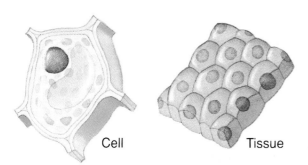

Cell   Tissue   Organ

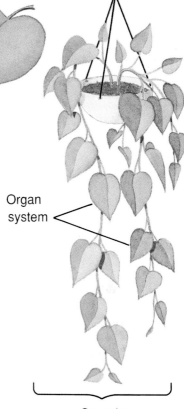

Organ
system

In many-celled organisms, cells are organized into **tissues,** which are groups of similar cells that do the same sort of work. Each tissue cell carries on all the functions needed to keep it alive. The cells in a tissue look alike.

Different tissues are further organized into organs. An **organ** is a structure made up of different types of tissues that work together to do a particular job. Your heart is an organ made up of muscle, nerve, and blood tissues. In Figure 2-15, different tissues make up a plant leaf, an organ of the plant in which food is made.

A group of organs working together to do a certain job is an **organ system**. Your heart is part of your circulatory system. All the leaves on the plant in Figure 2-15 make up an organ system.

Systems working together make up an organism. The roots, stems, and leaves of a plant work together to keep the plant alive. The whole plant with all these systems is an organism.

Each cell in a many-celled organism carries on its own life functions. Although cells in an organism may differ in appearance and function, all the cells work together to keep the organism alive.

Organism

Figure 2-15. In a many-celled organism, different types of cells are organized into tissues, organs, and systems.

SECTION REVIEW

1. How is a tissue different from an organ system?
2. Give an example of an organ system in an animal and name the parts that make up the organ system.
3. **Apply:** How are cells of one-celled organisms different from those in many-celled organisms?

☑ **Interpreting Scientific Illustrations**

Use the diagram above to explain the levels of organization in living things. If you need help, refer to Interpreting Scientific Illustrations in the **Skill Handbook** on page 693.

Skill Builder

2-4 Organ Transplants

New Science Words

rejection

Objectives

▶ Relate the importance of science in your life.
▶ Discuss problems in organ transplants.

Spare Parts for Broken Hearts

Have you ever considered the thousands of things that take place in your body? Think of your body as an auto mobile. Mechanics are always busy replacing this belt, or that valve. The brakes, tires, battery, and spark plugs are all parts that often need to be changed. When an accident occurs, fenders, doors, or a hood may need to be replaced. Auto mechanics run to the local junkyard where usable parts can be recycled from cars that are no longer driveable. Who would have thought that a similar idea could someday be used to save lives?

Organ transplants have become quite common in today's medical world. You may have heard of the kidney transplant. This surgery is fairly common. Hearts and lungs have also been transplanted.

Unfortunately, organ transplants are not always successful. Just as patients who receive blood transfusions must be matched with the donor's blood type, organs also must match. The human immune system, the network in our body that fights infections, is an eternal watchdog that attacks foreign invaders. This is to your advantage when the invader is a virus or bacteria. However, **rejection** is a process whereby the immune system attacks the transplanted organ because it is foreign to the body. Care must be taken to match the donor organs with the tissues of the person receiving the organ.

Drugs are given to turn down the body's immune system and keep rejection from happening. These drugs have greatly increased the success of transplant surgeries by keeping the immune system from attacking the new organ, but the patient has to take the drug every day of his or her life.

Today, hearts, kidneys, livers, and other organs are transplanted. Doctors believe that someday, with more research, certain animals could be raised specifically to supply organs for human transplants. Yet other exciting ideas are being considered. For example, can one part of the body be used to replace another? Scientists have already constructed a heart for a dog using the muscle taken from the dog's back.

Where will technology end? Someday scientists may be able to grow new organs in the laboratory using organ tissue. We may each have our own spare organs on the shelf ready to fix our broken parts!

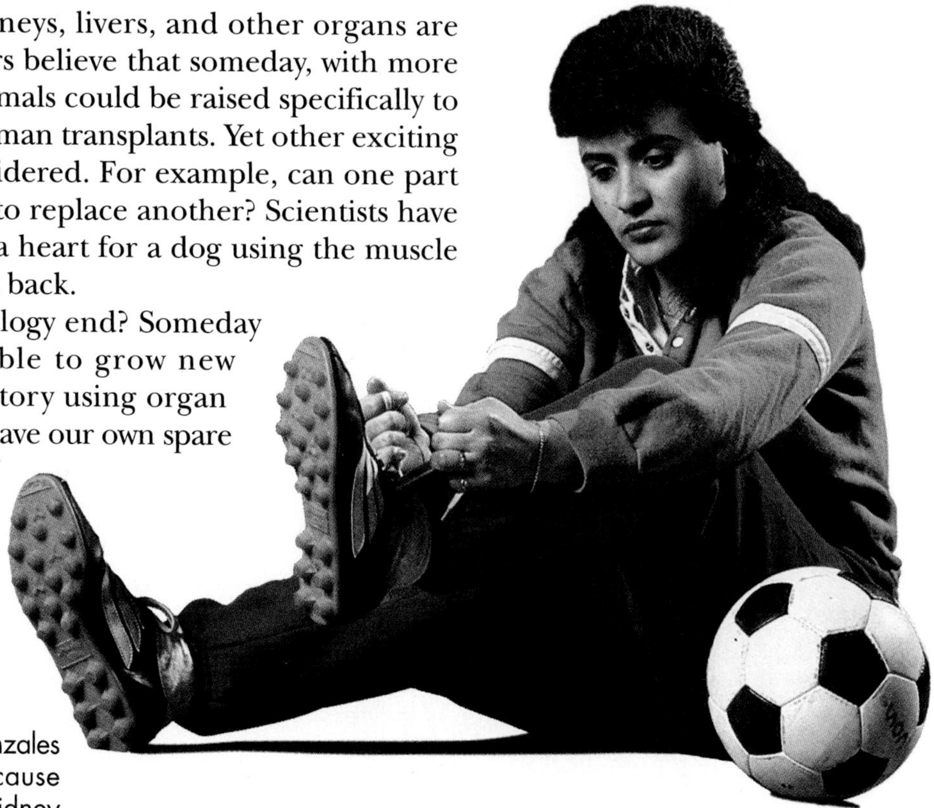

Figure 2-16. Cynthia Gonzales is able to run today because she received a healthy kidney from a donor.

SECTION REVIEW

1. Why have organ transplants become more successful?
2. Describe one problem with transplanting organs into humans.

You Decide!

Do you think that organs should be donated? Because there is such great demand for organs, but so few donors, some doctors are suggesting that donors be paid for their organs. Such an idea would make more organs available, but is it right to sell human body organs?

ACTIVITY 2-2
Comparing Plant and Animal Tissues

Problem: *How do tissues differ?*

Materials

- hamburger
- microscope slides (2)
- coverslips (2)
- dropper
- water
- microscope
- onion sections
- forceps
- iodine stain
- apron

Procedure

1. Make a data table like the one shown.
2. Make a wet mount slide of a very thin piece of hamburger.
3. Place the slide on the microscope stage and focus on the cells using the low power objective. Turn to high power. Make a drawing of what you observe. Return to low power and remove your slide.
4. Use forceps to remove the thin membrane from inside a layer of onion. Make a wet mount slide of this membrane. Add a drop of iodine stain to the onion before adding the coverslip. **CAUTION:** *Iodine is poisonous and may burn your skin.*
5. Set the microscope on low power. Place the slide on the microscope stage and focus on the cells in the onion membrane using low power first.

6. Turn to high power. Make a drawing of what you observe. Return to low power and remove your slide.

Analyze

1. What is the shape of the cells in the hamburger tissue?
2. What is the shape of the cells in the onion membrane?
3. How many cell layers make up the tissue of the onion membrane?
4. What cell parts can you see in the onion cells?

Conclude and Apply

5. How is the onion tissue different from the hamburger tissue?
6. What evidence do you have that each kind of cell makes up a tissue?

Data and Observations

Tissue	Observation	Description
hamburger		
onion		

CHAPTER
REVIEW

2-1: Cells: The Units of Life

1. Janssen made the first compound microscope in 1590. Leeuwenhoek used fine lenses to make accurate observations. Hooke, Schleiden, and Schwann all drew their conclusions about cells with the help of the microscope.

2. Compound light microscopes use light and lenses to make images. Electron microscopes bend beams of electrons in a magnetic field.

3. According to the cell theory, the cell is the basic unit of life. Organisms are made of cells and cells come from other cells.

2-2: Cell Structure

1. There are differences among animal, plant, and bacterial cells. Plant cells have a cell wall and chloroplasts.

2. Cell functions are performed by organelles under control of DNA in the nucleus.

3. Prokaryotic cells do not have membrane-covered organelles; eukaryotic cells have membrane-bound organelles and a formed nucleus.

2-3: Cell Organization

1. Cells differ in size and shape. Shape is related to a cell's function.

2. One-celled organisms carry on all life activities within the single cell. Many-celled organisms may have tissues that perform separate functions.

3. Most many-celled organisms are organized into tissues, organs, and organ systems that perform specific jobs to keep an organism alive.

2-4: Science and Society: Organ Transplants

1. Through organ transplants, science works to provide ways to save lives.

2. Rejection and availability of matching organs are problems connected with organ transplants.

KEY SCIENCE WORDS

a. **cell membrane**
b. **cell theory**
c. **cell wall**
d. **chloroplasts**
e. **chromatin**
f. **compound light microscope**
g. **cytoplasm**
h. **electron microscope**
i. **endoplasmic reticulum**
j. **Golgi bodies**
k. **lysosomes**
l. **mitochondria**
m. **nucleus**
n. **organ**
o. **organelles**
p. **organ system**
q. **rejection**
r. **ribosomes**
s. **tissues**
t. **vacuoles**

UNDERSTANDING VOCABULARY

Match each phrase with the correct term from the list of Key Science Words.

1. hereditary material in the nucleus
2. directs cell activities
3. where energy is generated for the cell
4. store food, water, or waste products
5. supports the plant cell
6. contain all the same kind of cell
7. where proteins are made
8. gel-like substance inside cell membrane
9. trap light energy in plant cells
10. package and secrete substances

CHAPTER
REVIEW

Choose the word or phrase that completes the sentence.

1. A microscope that uses lenses and objectives to magnify is the _____.
   a. compound light microscope
   b. scanning electron microscope
   c. transmission electron microscope
   d. all of the above

2. A microscope that magnifies parts inside a cell 300 000 times or more is the _____.
   a. compound light microscope
   b. stereoscopic microscope
   c. transmission electron microscope
   d. all of the above

3. The scientist who gave the name *cells* to structures he viewed was _____.
   a. Hooke   c. Schleiden
   b. Schwann   d. Virchow

4. A _____ is an organelle that can destroy old cell parts.
   a. chloroplast   c. lysosome
   b. vacuole   d. cell wall

5. According to the cell theory, cells are _____.
   a. basic units of function
   b. basic units of structure
   c. made by cells
   d. all of the above

6. A structure that allows only certain things to pass in and out of the cell is the _____.
   a. cytoplasm   c. cell wall
   b. cell membrane   d. nuclear envelope

7. Structures in the cytoplasm of the eukaryotic cell are called _____.
   a. organs   c. organ system
   b. organelles   d. tissues

8. Materials can move around inside the cell through the folded membranes of _____.
   a. chromatin   c. endoplasmic reticulum
   b. cytoplasm   d. Golgi bodies

9. A bacterial cell contains _____.
   a. a cell wall   c. mitochondria
   b. lysosomes   d. a nucleus

10. Groups of different tissues work together in an _____.
    a. organ   c. organ system
    b. organelle   d. organism

Complete each sentence.

11. A magnifying device used to see living cells is a(n) _____.

12. Microscopes work by bending rays or beams of _____.

13. Inside a(n) _____, food breaks down and energy is released.

14. The _____ is made of a double layer of fats with scattered proteins.

15. _____ of most plant cells are made of cellulose.

16. How has the development of different microscopes helped scientists study cells?

17. Suggest a reason why a lysosome can exist inside a living cell without destroying it.

18. Explain why the cell theory is important.

19. Compare the structures and functions of the cell membrane and the cell wall.

20. What are some things to consider when an organ becomes available and a doctor has to decide between two patients?

21. What type of microscope would be best to use to look at a piece of moldy bread? Give reasons to support your choice.

22. What would happen to a plant cell that suddenly lost its chloroplasts?

23. What would happen to an animal cell if it was missing ribosomes?

24. Choose two organelles of a plant cell and explain how they work together to help perform a life function.

25. How would you decide whether an unknown cell was an animal cell, a plant cell, or a bacterial cell?

MORE SKILL BUILDERS

If you need help, refer to the Skill Handbook.

1. Interpreting Scientific Illustrations: Use the illustrations of cells on page 44 to describe how the shape of each cell is related to its function.

2. Sequencing: Sequence the major events and the scientists involved in the formation of the cell theory.

3. Observing and Inferring: Infer the effects of a damaged cell membrane on a cell.

4. Making and Using Tables: Make a table that lists the names of the cell structure(s) that are involved in each of the functions below. Structures may be listed in more than one column.

Function	Structures
Protection	
Movement of materials	
Breaking down substances	
Making substances	
Storing substances	

5. Concept Mapping: Use the list of events below to make a series of events concept map to show, in correct order, the cell structures involved in each step of making a protein.
- packages proteins for movement outside of the cell
- gives instructions to make proteins
- allows packaged proteins to leave the cell
- receives instructions and is the place where proteins are made

PROJECTS

1. Using the directions for Activity 2-1 (page 43), observe cells in a flower petal. Write a report based on your observations. Illustrate your report.

2. Build a three-dimensional animal cell and use common objects for various cell parts.

Cell Processes

You may have washed dishes in soapy water or stayed in a pool long enough for your fingers to become wrinkled. What is there about water that causes your fingers to wrinkle? How long does it take your fingers to return to normal? Why does this happen?

FIND OUT!

Do this simple activity to find out why your fingers wrinkle.

Pour 250 mL of water into each of two small bowls. Stir 15 g of salt into one of the bowls of water. Label it salt water. Place slices of raw potato into each bowl. After 20 minutes, pick up the slices and examine them. What happened to the slices? How does this compare with your wrinkled fingers?

Gearing Up

Previewing the Chapter

Use this outline to help you focus on important ideas in this chapter.

Section 3-1   Chemistry of Living Things
▶ The Nature of Matter
▶ The Chemistry of Life
Section 3-2   Cell Transport
▶ Diffusion and Osmosis
▶ Other Kinds of Transport
Section 3-3   Energy in Cells
▶ Energy for Life
▶ Respiration
▶ Fermentation
**Section 3-4   Science and Society
Nonbiodegradable Materials in Your Environment**
▶ Recycling and the Environment

Previewing Science Skills

▶ In the Skill Builders, you will make and use tables, make a concept map, and compare and contrast.
▶ In the Activities, you will measure, use tables, and infer.
▶ In the MINI-Labs, you will observe and experiment.

What's next?

What you've just seen is the effect of water moving into and out of the potato cells. You will learn how atoms, molecules, and compounds relate to the movement of materials into and out of cells. You will also study how organisms produce and use food as a source of energy.

3-1 Chemistry of Living Things

New Science Words

carbohydrates
lipids
proteins
enzymes
nucleic acids

Objectives

▶ Distinguish the differences among atoms, elements, molecules, and compounds.
▶ Recognize the relationship between chemistry and life science.
▶ Compare inorganic and organic compounds.

The Nature of Matter

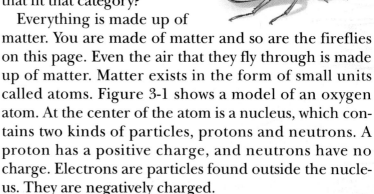

Do you know what makes up the universe? If you ask a scientist, he or she will probably say "matter and energy." Matter is anything that has mass and takes up space. How many things can you think of that fit that category?

Everything is made up of matter. You are made of matter and so are the fireflies on this page. Even the air that they fly through is made up of matter. Matter exists in the form of small units called atoms. Figure 3-1 shows a model of an oxygen atom. At the center of the atom is a nucleus, which contains two kinds of particles, protons and neutrons. A proton has a positive charge, and neutrons have no charge. Electrons are particles found outside the nucleus. They are negatively charged.

What about the energy that the scientist mentioned? Energy in the universe is wrapped up in bonds that hold atoms together. When fireflies blink and shine in the dark, they release some of that energy in the form of light. To release this energy, the atoms that were bound together had to be broken apart. A chemical reaction took place.

When something is made up of only one kind of atom, it is called an element. An element can't be broken down into any simpler form. The element oxygen (O_2) is made

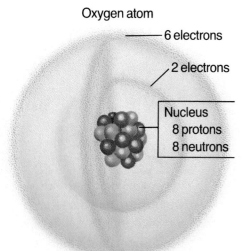

Oxygen atom

6 electrons

2 electrons

Nucleus
8 protons
8 neutrons

Figure 3-1. An Oxygen Atom Model

Table 3-1

ELEMENTS THAT COMPOSE THE HUMAN BODY

Symbol	Element	Percent
O	Oxygen	65.0
C	Carbon	18.5
H	Hydrogen	9.5
N	Nitrogen	3.3
Ca	Calcium	1.5
P	Phosphorus	1.0
K	Potassium	0.4
S	Sulfur	0.3
Na	Sodium	0.2
Cl	Chlorine	0.2
Mg	Magnesium	0.1

up of only oxygen atoms, and hydrogen (H_2) is made up of only hydrogen atoms. Each element has its own symbol. More than 92 elements occur naturally on Earth. Everything, including you, is made of one or a combination of these elements. Table 3-1 lists elements as they occur in the human body. What are the two most common elements in your body?

When atoms of two or more elements are joined, or bonded together, a compound is formed. For example, water is made of the elements hydrogen and oxygen, as shown in Figure 3-2. In water, there are two atoms of hydrogen for every atom of oxygen. The chemical formula for water is H_2O. A chemical formula shows the kind and number of atoms that form a compound. The formula represents a single molecule of a compound. A molecule is the smallest part of a compound with all the properties of that compound. Glucose, the major form of sugar used by cells for energy, is a compound. It is made of the elements carbon, hydrogen, and oxygen, and its formula is $C_6H_{12}O_6$.

What is so important about molecules? In living organisms, cell membranes, cytoplasm, and other substances are all in the form of molecules. During its lifetime, a

Figure 3-2. The chemical formula for water is H_2O.

Hydrogen

Hydrogen

Oxygen

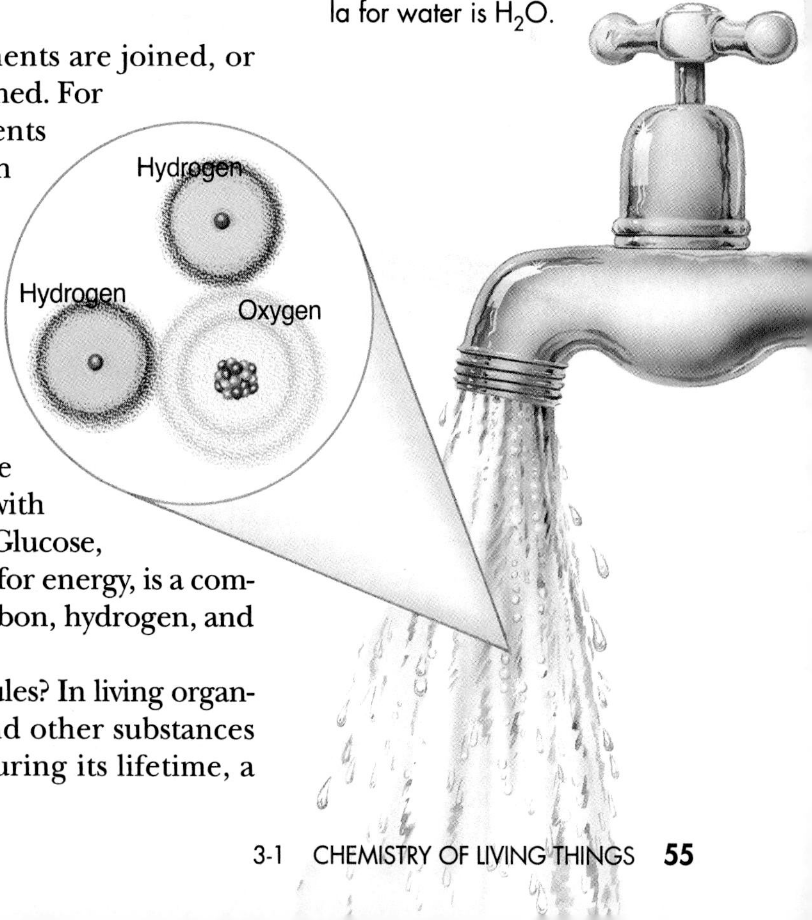

Figure 3-3. All organisms are dependent on water for life.

Figure 3-4. Some salad dressings are suspensions. Large pieces separate and fall to the bottom after the dressing stands a while.

cell will put together and break apart many molecules to build new cell parts and supply itself with energy. Many of these molecules are found in solution in cytoplasm. A solution is a mixture in which one or more substances mix evenly with other substances. When you dissolve salt in water, you get a salt solution. You've probably noticed the taste of salt when you perspire. That's because your cells are bathed in a salt solution. Living organisms also have suspensions. A suspension is a mixture in which substances spread through a liquid or gas, then settle out over time. Your blood is a suspension. If a test tube of blood is left undisturbed, the red blood cells and white blood cells will gradually settle to the bottom. Of course, blood in your body is moved constantly by the pumping action of your heart. Therefore, the cells don't settle out.

The Chemistry of Life

Compounds in living organisms are classified into two groups, organic and inorganic. Organic compounds contain carbon. Organic compounds make up some foods and membranes in cells. Inorganic compounds are made from elements other than carbon.

Water, an inorganic compound, makes up a large part of living matter. It is, therefore, one of the most important compounds in living things. In order for substances to be used in cells, they have to be dissolved in water. Nutrients and waste materials are carried throughout your body in solution form.

Four groups of organic compounds make up all living things. These are carbohydrates, lipids, proteins, and nucleic acids. **Carbohydrates** are organic compounds made up of carbon, hydrogen, and oxygen. Sugars, starch, and cellulose are carbohydrates. By breaking down

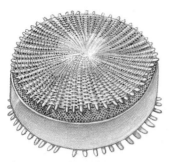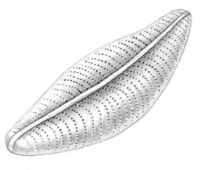

Figure 3-5. Some organisms, such as diatoms, store oils instead of carbohydrates as sources of energy.

these molecules, organisms release energy. The energy is then used to power cell processes.

Carbohydrates supply energy, but **lipids** are organic compounds that store and release even larger amounts of energy. In Chapter 2 you learned that cell membranes are made up of two layers of lipids. Fats, oils, and waxes are types of lipids found in different organisms.

Proteins, the third group of organic compounds, are used for building cell parts. Protein molecules are scattered throughout cell membranes. Proteins are made up of smaller molecules called amino acids. Certain proteins called **enzymes** (EN zimez) speed up chemical reactions in cells without being changed. In cells, enzymes break down the food into a usable form.

Nucleic acids are large organic molecules that store important information in the cell. Deoxyribonucleic acid (DNA) is found in chromosomes, mitochondria, and chloroplasts. It carries information that directs each cell's activities. Ribonucleic acid (RNA) uses information for making proteins and enzymes.

MINI-Lab
How do enzymes work?
Fill a test tube with milk. Crush a rennin tablet on a plate with the back of a spoon. Add the crushed tablet to the milk. Let the milk stand during your class period. Watch what happens to the milk and try to explain.

SECTION REVIEW

1. How are atoms different from molecules?
2. What does a chemical formula represent?
3. Why is water important to living organisms?
4. How are all organic compounds alike?
5. **Apply:** Diatoms are one-celled organisms that store oils instead of carbohydrates. How do they benefit from these oils?

Science and WRITING
Chart the food you eat in a day as being either carbohydrates, lipids, or proteins.

☑ Making and Using Tables

Use Table 3-1 on page 55 to determine what elements make up more than 98 percent of the human body. If you need help, refer to Making and Using Tables in the **Skill Handbook** on page 690.

Skill Builder

Cell Transport

New Science Words

passive transport
active transport
diffusion
equilibrium
osmosis
endocytosis
exocytosis

Objectives

▶ Explain the function of a selectively permeable membrane.
▶ Describe the processes of diffusion and osmosis.
▶ Compare and contrast passive transport and active transport and give examples of each.

Diffusion and Osmosis

Cells obtain food, oxygen, and other substances from their environment. They also release waste materials. If a cell has a membrane around it, how do these things move into and out of the cell? How does the cell control what enters and leaves?

Have you ever seen marbles in a mesh bag? Although the mesh bag has holes in it, the marbles stay inside because they are larger than the holes. If you put sand in with the marbles, the sand will fall right through the holes because sand grains are smaller than the holes. The mesh bag is said to be selectively permeable because it allows some things to pass through it but not others. The marbles and sand are models for molecules. The cell membrane is selectively permeable. It allows some molecules to pass through but not others.

If materials move through a cell membrane without the help of energy, **passive transport** takes place. If materials require energy to move through a cell membrane, **active transport** takes place.

Passive transport depends on the fact that molecules in liquids and gases move about. Molecules move constantly. As they move, they tend to move from places where they are crowded together into areas where there are fewer of them. One type of passive transport is **diffusion,** the movement of molecules from an area where there are many to an area where there are few.

Molecules diffuse in air and in liquid. You experience diffusion when someone opens a bottle of perfume in a closed room.

Figure 3-6. A cell membrane, like a mesh bag, will let some things through more easily than others.

Drop a sugar cube into a glass of water and taste the water. Then taste it again in three or four hours. At first, the water doesn't taste sweet. The sugar molecules are concentrated near the sugar cube in the bottom of the glass. Slowly, the sugar molecules diffuse throughout the water until they are evenly distributed. When the number of molecules of a substance is the same throughout a space, a state called **equilibrium** occurs. Molecules don't stop moving when equilibrium is reached. They continue to move, and equilibrium is maintained. Many substances diffuse through cell membranes. Diffusion is a type of passive transport, because energy is not used to move these substances.

The passive transport of *water* through a membrane by diffusion is called **osmosis.** Water molecules move from where they are in large numbers to where they are in small numbers. Osmosis is important to cells because cells are surrounded by water molecules and they contain water molecules. You remember that water makes up a large part of living matter. The number of water molecules inside and outside the cell is the same when a state of equilibrium is reached.

If cells don't have the water that they need, they dehydrate, or lose water. If you forget to water a plant, it will soon wilt. There is less water in the soil around the roots. Therefore, water tends to move out of the root cells. The cells in the rest of the plant don't get supplied with water from the roots. Cell membranes shrink away from cell walls in a condition called *plasmolysis*. When the plant is watered, the water moves into the root cells and on up into the other parts of the plant. The cell membranes expand, and the plant becomes upright again.

What is equilibrium?

Figure 3-7. Lack of water eventually causes a plant to wilt because its cells lose water.

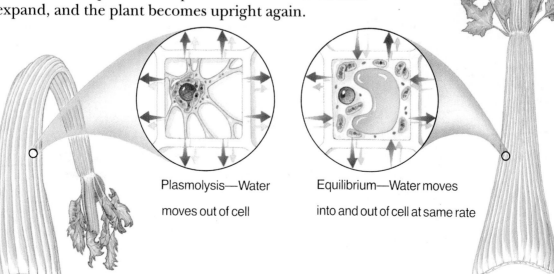

Plasmolysis—Water moves out of cell

Equilibrium—Water moves into and out of cell at same rate

Other Kinds of Transport

Cells take in a variety of substances. Some, like glucose molecules, are so large that they enter the cell only with the help of protein carrier molecules in the cell membrane. Each carrier molecule helps to move only one type of molecule through the cell membrane. Glucose molecules are too large to move quickly across the cell membrane, so carrier molecules help speed up their movement. Carrier proteins use energy when moving molecules into and out of a cell. Therefore, carrier molecules are involved in active transport.

Sometimes cells have to move substances from where there are small amounts to where there are larger amounts. This process is the opposite of diffusion. It requires energy and is a type of active transport. An example of this type of active transport can be seen when plant root cells take in minerals. These cells need minerals from the soil, and there are already more minerals in the root cells than in the water around the roots. The cells use energy to move additional minerals into the root cells. In your body, wastes are moved by active transport out of some kidney cells.

Some substances are too large to pass through the cell membrane by passive or active transport. Large protein molecules and bacteria enter the cell by becoming enclosed in a part of the membrane that folds in to form a sac. The sac pinches off and goes into the cytoplasm in a process called **endocytosis.** In the opposite way, wastes in vacuoles or proteins packaged by Golgi bodies move to the cell membrane. The package fuses with the cell membrane, and its contents are released from the cell in a process called **exocytosis.**

Figure 3-8. A white blood cell uses endocytosis to engulf a bacterial cell (a). In exocytosis, substances in small sacs are released at the cell membrane (b).

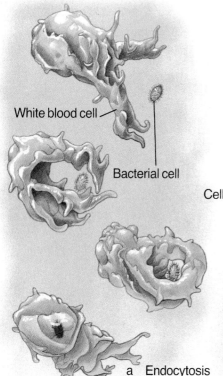

White blood cell

Bacterial cell

a Endocytosis

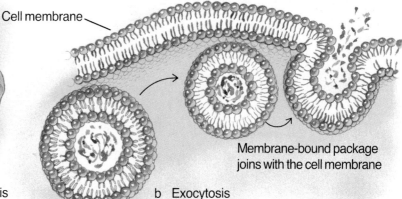

Cell membrane

Membrane-bound package joins with the cell membrane

b Exocytosis

PROBLEM SOLVING

What Happened to the Salad?

Carla made a salad of lettuce, tomatoes, carrots, and cucumbers. She seasoned the damp salad with herbs, salt, and pepper. Then she placed it in the refrigerator for a couple of hours.

When Carla returned, she took the salad from the refrigerator. The lettuce had wilted, and the other vegetables were limp. She noticed that there was liquid in the bottom of the bowl. Where did the liquid come from?

Think Critically: Why had the lettuce wilted?

Cells have to stay in balance with their environment. Cells keep this balance, called homeostasis, by controlling what enters and leaves the cells through passive and active transport. You can see how important the selectively permeable cell membrane and its transport systems are in keeping cells, tissues, organs, and organisms alive and healthy.

SECTION REVIEW

1. What is there about a cell membrane that makes it selectively permeable?
2. Compare and contrast osmosis and diffusion.
3. What is active transport?
4. How does a cell take in large bacterial cells?
5. **Apply:** Why are fresh fruits and vegetables sprinkled with water in produce markets?

☑ Concept Mapping

Skill Builder

Make a network tree concept map to use as a study guide to help you tell the difference between passive transport and active transport. Begin with the phrase *Transport through membranes*. If you need help, refer to Concept Mapping in the **Skill Handbook** on pages 688 and 689.

ACTIVITY 3-1
Observing Osmosis

Problem: *How does osmosis occur in an egg?*

Materials

- raw eggs in shells (2)
- 600-mL beakers with lids (4)
- white vinegar (600 mL)
- distilled water (900 mL)
- 20% salt solution (900 mL)
- graduated cylinder

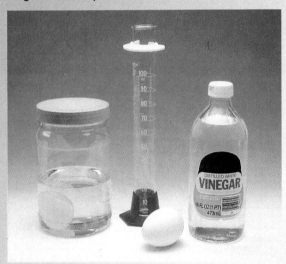

Procedure

1. Place one egg in each of two beakers labeled A and B. Cover each egg with white vinegar. Observe the eggs after 30 minutes.
2. After 24 hours observe the eggs and record your observations. Pour the vinegar off each egg and rinse with plain water.
3. Place one egg in beaker A. Add 300 mL of distilled water to the beaker.
4. Place the second egg in beaker B. Add 300 mL of 20% salt solution to the beaker.
5. On the third day, carefully remove the egg from beaker A. Measure the volume of distilled water in the beaker. Record the amount in the data table. Discard the distilled water in the beaker and add 300 mL of fresh distilled water. Return the egg to the beaker.

6. Remove the egg from beaker B. Measure the salt water remaining. Record the amount in the data table. Discard the salt water, and add 300 mL of fresh salt water to the beaker. Return the egg to the beaker.
7. On the fourth day, repeat Steps 5 and 6.
8. On the fifth day, repeat Steps 5 and 6. Then give the eggs to your teacher for disposal.

Analyze

1. What did you observe after 30 minutes?
2. After 24 hours, what did you observe?
3. What happened to the size of the egg in distilled water? In salt water?

Conclude and Apply

4. Is the egg membrane selectively permeable? Explain your answer.
5. Explain why water was able to move into the egg in beaker A.
6. Why did water move out of the egg in beaker B?
7. How does osmosis occur in an egg?

Data and Observations

Day	1	2	2	4	5
Salt water volume					
Observations					
Distilled water volume					
Observations					

Energy in Cells

Objectives

▶ Distinguish between producers and consumers.
▶ Compare and contrast the processes of photosynthesis and respiration.
▶ Describe how cells get energy from glucose through the process of fermentation.

New Science Words

metabolism
producers
photosynthesis
consumers
respiration
fermentation

Energy for Life

Think of all the energy used in a basketball game. Where do the players get all that energy? The simplest answer is, "from the food they eat". Cells take energy stored in food and change it into energy that can be used in metabolism (muh TAB uh lihz um). **Metabolism** is the total of all the activities of an organism that enable it to stay alive, grow, and reproduce.

All living things are divided into two groups based on how they obtain their food. These two groups are producers and consumers. Organisms that make their own food, such as plants, are called **producers.** Producers change light energy into chemical energy by a process called **photosynthesis** (foht oh SIHN thuh sus). During photosynthesis, the energy from sunlight is used to make glucose from carbon dioxide (CO_2) and water. During this process oxygen is also given off. Plants and other producers use a green pigment called chlorophyll found in chloroplasts. Therefore, photosynthesis in green plants takes place in the chloroplasts. Producers use some of the glucose they make during photosynthesis for energy. The glucose is stored in roots.

Do you eat many vegetables? Have you ever seen a sheep graze? Organisms that can't make their own food are **consumers.** Consumers eat producers such as vegetables and take in the stored energy. Consumers also eat other consumers in order to get energy. These relationships form a food chain. A producer is at the beginning of every food chain.

Figure 3-9. Green plants are producers because they use sunlight, carbon dioxide, and water to produce chemical energy in the form of glucose.

What is the difference between a producer and a consumer?

EcoTip

Promote photosynthesis! Save a tree. The next time you buy something small, tell the clerk that you don't need a paper bag.

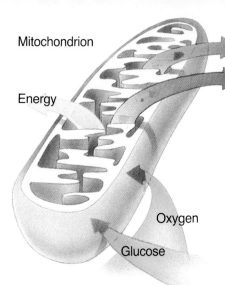

Mitochondrion

Water

Carbon dioxide

Energy

Oxygen

Glucose

$$C_6 H_{12} O_6 + 6 O_2 \rightarrow 6 CO_2 + 6 H_2O + Energy$$

Figure 3-10. Respiration produces carbon dioxide, water, and energy. In what way do these products remind you of photosynthesis?

Respiration

Whether an organism is a producer or a consumer, it has to have some way to release energy from food. To do this, both producers and consumers break down food in their cells in a process called respiration. Inside most cells, glucose is the food that is broken down. Respiration takes place within mitochondria.

During **respiration,** oxygen combines with glucose to release stored energy. The energy is released in a series of steps. Carbon dioxide and water are given off as waste products. Some of the energy produced in respiration is stored, and some of the energy is lost as heat.

TECHNOLOGY

Biodegradable Plastics

Discarded plastics make up 32 percent of the garbage produced in the United States. Most of this plastic lasts forever. To reduce waste, scientists are working on plastics that can be broken down naturally.

One current method of breaking down plastic is to build molecules of cornstarch into the plastic. Cornstarch breaks down in nature, so the plastic is at least broken into smaller pieces. However, most of these plastic products are only 6 to 8 percent cornstarch, so the remaining plastic pieces are still large. Some scientists predict they will soon be able to produce plastics with a 50 percent cornstarch content.

A second method to help solve the plastic garbage problem involves the use of plastics produced by bacteria. Some soil bacteria are known to produce natural plas-

tics and store them to use as energy sources. By changing factors such as temperature and food sources for the bacteria, scientists can adjust the characteristics of the plastic produced.

Think Critically: What is the advantage of bacterial plastics over plastic-cornstarch mixtures?

Fermentation

Have you ever baked bread? If so, you've used a process called fermentation. **Fermentation** is a process that gives off energy without using oxygen. Yeast breaks down the glucose in the dough. Carbon dioxide and alcohol are released. The bubbles of carbon dioxide cause the dough to rise. The alcohol is released into the air. Yeast and some bacteria use fermentation to get energy.

Cells use both fermentation and respiration to release energy. Respiration uses oxygen and takes place in mitochondria. Sometimes, however, during periods of strenuous activity, muscle cells run low on oxygen. The muscles begin to burn and sting. When oxygen levels are low, the muscle cells begin to release energy from glucose by fermentation. Less energy is produced by fermentation. In addition, carbon dioxide and an organic compound called lactic acid are formed. It is lactic acid that causes the muscles to burn and to be sore and stiff. Fermentation takes place in the cytoplasm of cells.

In summary, you can say that producers capture the sun's energy and store it in the form of food. Consumers eat producers. Cells use the glucose and oxygen made by producers to release energy during respiration and fermentation.

Figure 3-11. During a sprint, oxygen can't be supplied to cells fast enough. Energy is supplied through fermentation and not respiration.

SECTION REVIEW

1. What is metabolism?
2. How are chloroplasts important to photosynthesis?
3. What is the role of mitochondria in respiration?
4. Explain how the energy used by all living things on Earth can be traced back to sunlight.
5. **Apply:** Plants can use carbon monoxide, CO, instead of CO_2 for photosynthesis. CO is a major component of cigarette smoke. How can indoor plants help to purify the air in a room with cigarette smoke?

☑ Comparing and Contrasting

Skill Builder

Make a table that compares and contrasts respiration and fermentation. If you need help, refer to Comparing and Contrasting in the **Skill Handbook** on page 683.

3-4 Nonbiodegradable Materials in Your Environment

New Science Words

biodegradable

Objectives

▶ Explain the consequences of nonbiodegradable substances in the environment.

Recycling and the Environment

Do you ever drop candy or gum wrappers on the ground? It's likely to be a very long time before these wrappers disappear. Materials such as plastic wrappers and aluminum foil take years to break down in the environment.

Substances that do break down easily in the environment are **biodegradable.** A combination of sunlight, weathering, oxygen, bacteria and fungi, and moisture causes them to decompose, or break down, into the elements they are made of. For example, fruit and leaves are biodegradable. They are plant parts in a cycle that returns nutrients to the soil. Aluminum cans, glass bottles, and plastic bags, which are often seen along roadways, are nonbiodegradable. In fact, all of these take a very long time to decompose. A tin can needs 100 years to break down. An aluminum can requires more than 200 years to break down, and some types of plastics may require 450 years or more!

The situation becomes a problem when you consider the huge amounts of these materials that are dumped into the environment each year. The average United States citizen uses and throws away about 299 kilograms of non-biodegradable material each year. At this rate, it probably wouldn't take very long for the trash produced by several people to fill up a space the size of a circus tent.

Are these products so bad that we should just stop producing them? That would be difficult. Nearly every moment of the day, you are in contact with or using some type of plastic, glass, or aluminum! There is no denying that many lives have been saved thanks to plastics in medical equipment and supplies.

We aren't likely to quit using these products, and the best way to control their use may be to use them over and over again and change them into new products. We call this recycling. Many communities are very interested in finding new uses for non-biodegradable materials and have begun recycling programs. Glass, plastic, aluminum, paper, and motor oil can all be recycled. Scientists are developing new forms of previously nonbiodegradable products, such as soap, paint, or trash bags, that decompose more easily. By buying such products and making an effort to recycle the others, we can become part of the effort to keep these materials from accumulating and continuing to cause environmental problems.

SECTION REVIEW

1. Give two ways in which you can help the current problem with nonbiodegradable materials.
2. Discuss how substances decompose naturally, and explain what happens to the materials that are released by decomposition.

You Decide!

Some states have aluminum can deposit laws. Each empty aluminum can is worth five cents. This is one way to help motivate people to keep the roadsides free from litter. Should all states be required to develop recycling programs?

ACTIVITY 3-2
Photosynthesis and Respiration

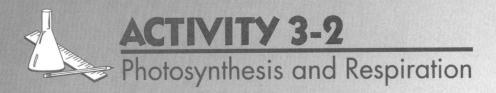

Problem: *When do plants carry on photosynthesis?*

Materials

- test tubes, 16 by 150 mm with stoppers (4)
- test-tube rack
- stirring rod
- balance
- sodium bicarbonate
- bromothymol blue solution in dropping bottle
- aged tap water
- pieces of *Elodea* (2)

Procedure

1. Label the test tubes 1 through 4. Fill each tube about three-fourths full with aged tap water.
2. Add 1 g of sodium bicarbonate to each test tube. Sodium bicarbonate releases carbon dioxide when mixed with water.
3. Add 5 drops of bromothymol blue solution to each test tube. Bromothymol blue turns green to yellow in the presence of an acid.
4. Cut two 10-cm pieces of *Elodea*. Place one piece of *Elodea* in test tube 1 and one piece in test tube 3. Stopper the test tubes. Record the color of the solution in each test tube.
5. Place test tubes 1 and 2 in bright light and test tubes 3 and 4 in the dark for 30 minutes.
6. Observe the test tubes and record the colors.

Analyze

1. What is indicated by the color of the water in all four tubes at the start of the activity?
2. What color were the liquids in tubes 1 and 3 after 30 minutes?
3. What color were the liquids in tubes 2 and 4 after 30 minutes?

Data and Observations

Test tube	Color at start	Color after 30 minutes
1		
2		
3		
4		

Conclude and Apply

4. What was the purpose of tubes 2 and 4?
5. Explain the color of the liquid in tube 1 after 30 minutes.
6. Explain the color of the liquid in tube 3 after 30 minutes.
7. From your observations, when does a green plant carry on photosynthesis?

REVIEW

SUMMARY

3-1: Chemistry of Living Things

1. Everything is made of matter, which is composed of atoms arranged in elements, molecules and compounds.

2. Both inorganic and organic molecules are important to living things.

3. Carbohydrates, lipids, proteins, and nucleic acids are organic compounds. Inorganic compounds do not contain carbon.

3-2: Cell Transport

1. The cell membrane controls what molecules can pass through it.

2. Molecules move by diffusion from areas of greater numbers to areas of lesser numbers. In osmosis, water diffuses through a membrane.

3. The cell expends energy to move molecules by active transport, but not by passive transport.

3-3: Energy in Cells

1. Producers produce energy in the form of food, which consumers eat.

2. Green plants use light energy to make chemical energy in the form of glucose during photosynthesis. In respiration, glucose is broken down and energy is released.

3. Some yeasts, bacteria, and oxygen-deprived cells carry out fermentation to release small amounts of energy from glucose without using oxygen.

3-4: Science and Society: Nonbiodegradable Materials in Your Environment

1. Nonbiodegradable substances do not break down easily in the environment and accumulate as wastes.

KEY SCIENCE WORDS

a. **active transport**
b. **biodegradable**
c. **carbohydrates**
d. **consumers**
e. **diffision**
f. **endocytosis**
g. **enzymes**
h. **equilibrium**
i. **exocytosis**
j. **fermentation**
k. **lipids**
l. **metabolism**
m. **nucleic acids**
n. **osmosis**
o. **passive transport**
p. **photosynthesis**
q. **producers**
r. **proteins**
s. **respiration**

UNDERSTANDING VOCABULARY

Match each phrase with the correct term from the list of Key Science Words.

1. organisms that make their own food

2. the movement of water molecules through a membrane

3. movement of molecules that requires energy

4. substance that is broken down in the environment by bacteria or fungi

5. capable of releasing more energy than carbohydrates can

6. sugar, starch, and cellulose

7. made up of amino acids

8. use of light energy to make food

9. release of a substance from a small sac at the membrane

10. the breakdown of glucose without the presence of oxygen

CHAPTER
REVIEW

CHECKING CONCEPTS

Choose the word or phrase that completes the sentence.

1. Cell energy is used to move molecules by __b__.
   a. diffusion   c. osmosis
   b. active transport   d. passive transport

2. Bacteria are taken into cells by __a__.
   a. osmosis   c. exocytosis
   b. endocytosis d. diffusion

3. An example of an organic compound is __d__.
   a. $C_6H_{12}O_6$ c. H_2O
   b. CO_2 d. all of these

4. __d__ is an example of a carbohydrate.
   a. Cellulose   c. Starch
   b. Glucose   d. all of these

5. Organic compounds in the chromosomes are __d__.
   a. carbohydrates   c. lipids
   b. water molecules d. nucleic acids

   it's the power house

6. The organic molecule that releases the greatest amount of energy is __d__.
   a. carbohydrate   c. lipid
   b. water molecule d. nucleic acid

7. Salt is a(n) __d__ molecule.
   a. organic   c. carbohydrate
   b. lipid   d. inorganic

8. __a__ occurs when molecules are evenly distributed.
   a. Equilibrium   c. Fermentation
   b. Metabolism   d. None of these

9. __c__ are organisms that can't make their own food.
   a. Biodegradables c. Consumers
   b. Producers   d. Enzymes

10. Chlorophyll is needed for __d__.
    a. fermentation   c. metabolism
    b. cellular respiration d. photosynthesis

UNDERSTANDING CONCEPTS

Complete each sentence.

11. Proteins called __enzymes__ are used to speed up chemical reactions.

12. DNA and RNA are examples of chemicals called __Nucleic acids__.

13. __osmosis__ is the diffusion of water through a membrane.

14. Molecules move from one place to another until __equilibrium__ is reached.

15. __enzymes__ are used to help glucose molecules move through cell membranes.

THINK AND WRITE CRITICALLY

16. Compare and contrast diffusion and osmosis. *sheet*

17. Why might there be many more mitochondria in muscle cells than in other types of cells?

18. Explain how some substances, but not others, can pass through the cell membrane. *It's a selectivally permive*

19. Describe how a cell reaches equilibrium with its environment if there are ten water molecules inside and 24 molecules outside. *when they are seperi equally throughall*

20. During the night, what happens to the starch the plant made and stored in its leaves?

APPLY

21. If you could place a single red blood cell into a glass of distilled water and watch it, what do you think you would see? Explain. *[handwritten: equilibrium] [handwritten: It would spread out 30]* *[handwritten: nothing not enough water to]*

22. In snowy states, salt is used to melt ice on the roads. Explain what happens to many roadside plants as a result. *[handwritten: they die]*

23. Explain why sugar dissolves faster in hot tea than in iced tea.

24. Explain what would happen to the consumers in a lake if all the producers died. *[handwritten: consumers would die because they can't make their own food]*

25. Meat tenderizers contain enzymes. How do these enzymes affect protein in meat?

MORE SKILL BUILDERS

If you need help, refer to the Skill Handbook.

1. Interpreting Data: In an experiment that tests the rate of photosynthesis in water plants, the water plants were placed at different distances from a light source. Bubbles of gas coming from the plants were counted to measure the rate. What can you say about how the rate is affected by the light? *[handwritten: further away less bubbles from light]*

Beaker Number	Distance from Light	Bubbles per minute
1	10 cm	45
2	30 cm	30
3	50 cm	19
4	70 cm	6
5	100 cm	1

2. Making and Using Graphs: Use the data from Question 1 to graph the relationship between photosynthesis rate and distance from light.

3. Classifying: Classify these common foods into a category of carbohydrates, lipids, or proteins: butter, bread, candy bar, cereals, cheese, cornstarch, fish, margarine, meats, pasta, peanut butter, shortening, sugar, vegetable oil. *[handwritten: all mixed togeather]*

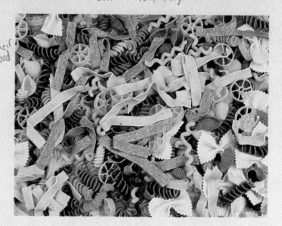

4. Concept Mapping: Sequence the parts of matter from smallest to largest: element, atom, compound in an events chain concept map.

5. Hypothesizing: Make a hypothesis about what will happen to wilted celery when placed into a glass of plain water. *[handwritten: celery would become more fresher]*

PROJECTS

1. Design an experiment to show that respiration takes place in growing lima bean seeds.

2. Make a list of elements found in ten substances in your home. Use the labels to determine the elements each product contains.

4 Cell Reproduction

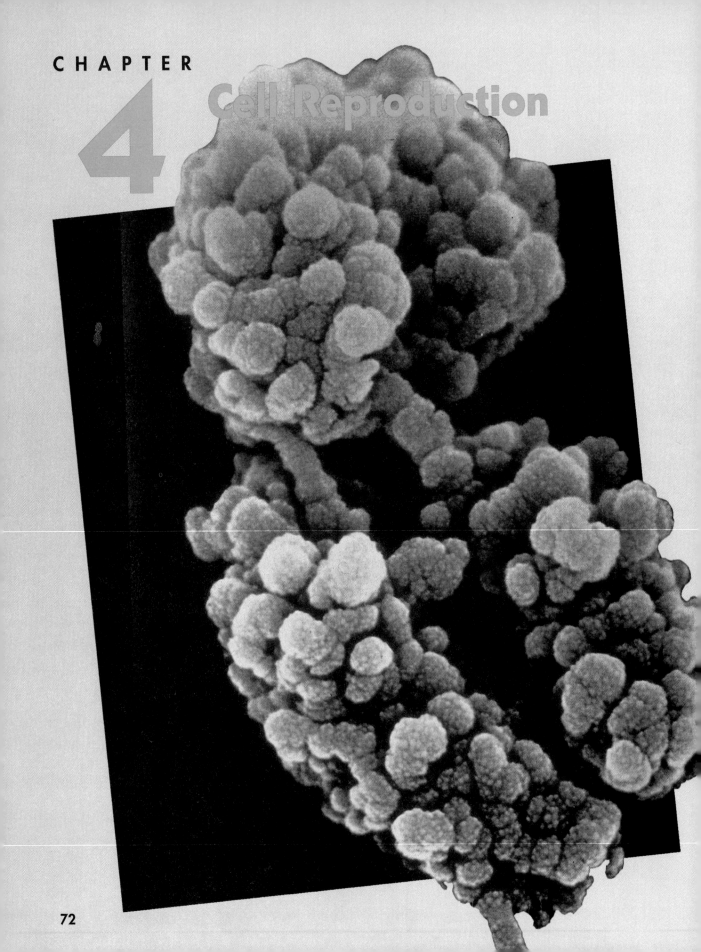

Do you know that your life hangs by a thread? Miles of thread-like DNA and protein condense to make up chromosomes like the one to the left. When cells divide and organisms grow, chromosomes are the carriers of the information that shapes each new cell.

FIND OUT!

Do this activity to see what changes take place in a plant as it develops.

Carefully split open a pinto bean seed that has soaked in water overnight. Look at it with a hand lens. What do you find inside the top part of the seed? Place four other bean seeds in a moist paper towel in a plastic bag. Observe the seeds for a few days. What happens to the tiny plant inside the seed? How did this happen?

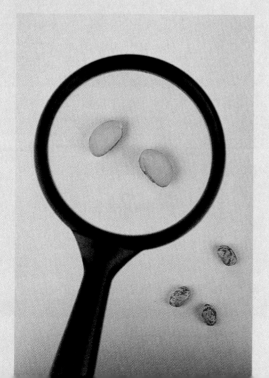

Gearing Up

Previewing the Chapter

Use this outline to help you focus on important ideas in this chapter.

Section 4-1   Cell Growth and Division
  ▶ What Happens When Cells Divide
  ▶ The Cell Cycle
  ▶ Mitosis
  ▶ Types of Reproduction
Section 4-2   Sexual Reproduction and Meiosis
  ▶ Sexual Reproduction
  ▶ The Importance of Gametes
  ▶ Meiosis—Gamete Formation
Section 4-3   DNA
  ▶ What Is DNA?
  ▶ How DNA Copies Itself
  ▶ DNA and Genes
  ▶ Mutations
Section 4-4   Science and Society Inventing Organisms
  ▶ Transgenic Organisms
  ▶ Patenting Life

Previewing Science Skills

▶ In the **Skill Builders,** you will outline and make concept maps.
▶ In the **Activities,** you will observe, infer, experiment and make a model.
▶ In the **MINI-Labs,** you will make a model and sequence events.

What's next?

In this chapter you'll learn how cells divide and how organisms reproduce. You'll also learn about DNA—how it reproduces and controls proteins produced in the cells of an organism.

Cell Growth and Division

New Science Words

mitosis
chromosomes
centromere
asexual reproduction
sexual reproduction

Objectives

▶ Describe mitosis and explain its importance.
▶ Explain differences between mitosis in plant and animal cells.
▶ Distinguish between asexual and sexual reproduction and give two examples of asexual reproduction.

What Happens When Cells Divide

It's very likely that each time you go to the doctor, a nurse measures your height and mass. Over the years, similar data collected from thousands of people have given the medical profession an idea of how people grow. Much of the growth happens because the number of cells in your body increases over the years. Other growth occurs because some cells become larger in size through metabolism.

The fact is that you are constantly changing. You aren't the same now as you were a year ago or even a few hours ago. At this very moment, as you read this page, groups of cells throughout your body are growing, dividing, and dying. Worn-out cells on the palms of your hands and other areas of your skin are being replaced. Cuts and bruises are healing. Red blood cells are being produced in your bones at a rate of about two to three billion per second. Muscles that you exercise are getting larger. Other organisms undergo similar processes. A plant climbs a garden stake as the number of its cells increases. How does this happen?

Figure 4-1. Many-celled organisms, such as the pole-bean plant above, grow by increasing numbers of cells. A one-celled organism reaches a certain size and then divides.

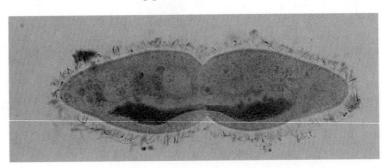

The Cell Cycle

Organisms go through stages, or a life cycle, while they are alive. A simple life cycle is birth, growth and development, and death. Right now, you are in a stage in your life cycle called adolescence, a period of active growth and development. Cells also go through cycles. Most of the life of any cell is spent in a period of growth and development called *interphase*. Cells in your body that no longer divide, such as nerve and muscle cells, are always in interphase. Cells that actively divide, such as your skin cells, have a more complex cell cycle. The cell cycle, as shown in Figure 4-2, is a series of events that takes place in a cell from one division to the next.

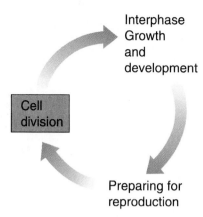

Figure 4-2. A Cell Cycle

Figure 4-3. An organism undergoes many changes as it develops. These photographs show some of the stages in the development of a pelican.

Mitosis

Cells divide in two steps. First the nucleus of the cell divides, and then the cytoplasm divides. **Mitosis** is the process in which a cell nucleus divides into two new nuclei, each of which contain the same number of chromosomes as the parent cell. The parent cell is the cell that undergoes division. Mitosis is described as a series of steps. These steps have been named prophase, metaphase, anaphase, and telophase.

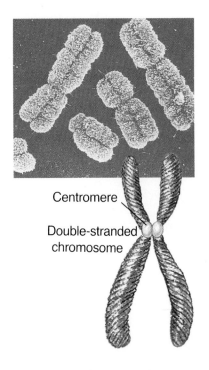

Centromere

Double-stranded
chromosome

Steps of Mitosis

When a cell divides, the chromosomes in the nucleus play the most important part. **Chromosomes** are structures in the nucleus that contain DNA. During *interphase,* you can't see chromosomes but they are actively duplicating themselves. Then they condense and become visible. When the chromosomes appear, they are thick and doubled-stranded as in the illustrations on the left. Each double-stranded chromosome is held together at a region called a **centromere.** Once chromosomes are double-stranded, the cell is ready to begin the process of division. Follow the steps of mitosis in the illustrations in Figure 4-4 on these pages.

During *prophase,* chromosomes become fully visible. The nucleolus and the nuclear membrane fade and disappear. In animal cells, two small structures called centrioles move to opposite ends of the cell. Between the centrioles, threadlike spindle fibers begin to stretch across the cell, making a football-shaped network of fibers. Plant cells don't have centrioles.

Figure 4-4. The steps of mitosis are shown in order on this page and the next.

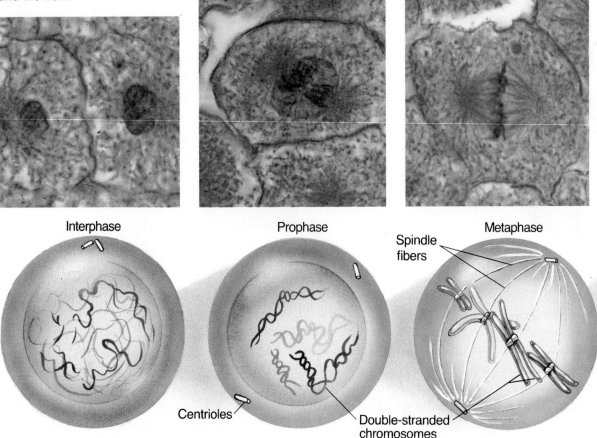

Interphase

Prophase

Metaphase

Spindle fibers

Centrioles

Double-stranded chromosomes

In the second step, *metaphase,* the double-stranded chromosomes line up around the center of the cell. Each centromere becomes attached to a spindle fiber. As the process enters *anaphase,* each centromere divides. The two strands of each chromosome separate. Then, the separate strands begin to move away from each other toward opposite ends of the cell.

In the final step of mitosis, *telophase,* centrioles and spindle fibers start to disappear. The chromosomes stretch out and become harder to see. A nuclear membrane forms around each mass of chromosomes, and a new nucleolus appears in each new nucleus.

In most organisms, once the nucleus has divided, the cytoplasm also separates and two whole new cells are formed. In animal cells, the cytoplasm pinches in to form the new cells. The new cells then begin a period of growth. They will take in water and other nutrients that they need to carry out cell processes.

Science and MATH

If a single cell undergoes mitosis every five minutes, how many cells will result from this single cell after one hour?

During what phase does a new nuclear membrane form?

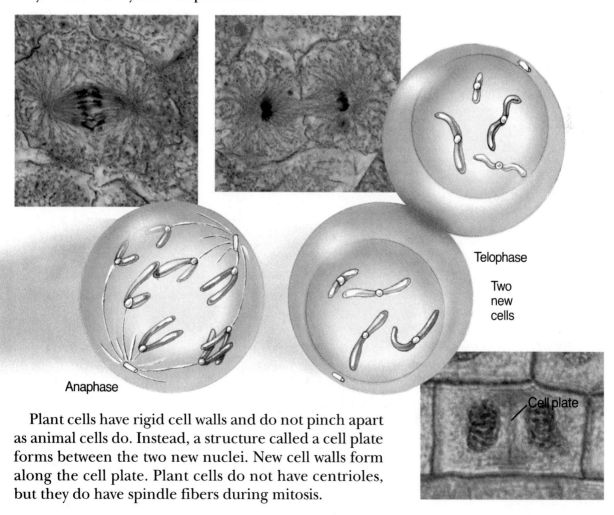

Telophase

Two new cells

Anaphase

Cell plate

Plant cells have rigid cell walls and do not pinch apart as animal cells do. Instead, a structure called a cell plate forms between the two new nuclei. New cell walls form along the cell plate. Plant cells do not have centrioles, but they do have spindle fibers during mitosis.

MINI-Lab

How does one cell become two?

Work in Paired Partners to make models showing the different stages in mitosis. Use a cell with four chromosomes. Show each phase on a separate poster. Use yarn for chromosomes, sewing thread for spindle fibers, and nickel-sized paper dots for centrioles. Put the posters in correct sequence.

There are two important things to remember about mitosis. The first is that mitosis is the division of a nucleus. The second is that mitosis produces two new nuclei that have the same number of chromosomes as the original nucleus. Cells in your skin, like most of the cells in your body, each have 46 chromosomes. Each new skin cell produced by mitosis will also have 46 chromosomes. Cells in fruit flies have eight chromosomes. New fruit fly cells produced by mitosis will each have only eight chromosomes. Table 4-1 shows an additional example.

Table 4-1

CHROMOSOME NUMBERS		
Humans	**Fruit Flies**	**Carrots**
46	8	18
After mitosis	After mitosis	After mitosis
46 46	8 8	18 18

PROBLEM SOLVING

Divide and Repair!

How much have you grown during the past year? Has your height increased by two or three centimeters, or have you gained a kilogram or two? The growth you have experienced is partly the result of millions of new cells forming in your body.

Within certain tissues in your body, cells divide to produce new cells that are just like the original cells.

Christopher, an avid skateboarder, fell and got a burning scrape on his leg. In a few days, the leg had begun to heal. What took place on Chris's leg that helped his leg heal?

Think Critically: If one skin cell divides every 15 minutes, how many cells will there be in two hours?

ACTIVITY 4-1
Mitosis in Plant and Animal Cells

Problem: *How is mitosis in a plant cell different from mitosis in an animal cell?*

Materials
- prepared slide of an onion root tip
- prepared slide of a whitefish embryo
- microscope

Procedure
1. Obtain prepared slides of onion root tip and whitefish embryo.
2. Set your microscope on low power and examine the onion root tip. Move the slide until you can see the area just behind the root tip. Turn the nosepiece to high power.
3. Use Figure 4-4 on pages 76-77 to help you find a cell in interphase. Draw and label the parts of the cell you observe.
4. Repeat Step 3 for prophase, metaphase, anaphase, and telophase.
5. Turn the microscope back to low power. Remove the onion root tip slide.
6. Place the whitefish embryo slide on the microscope stage under low power. Focus and find a region of dividing cells. Turn the microscope to high power.
7. Use Figure 4-4 to help you find a cell in interphase. In a data table, draw and label the parts of the cell you observe.
8. Repeat Step 7 for prophase, metaphase, anaphase, and telophase.
9. Return the nosepiece to low power. Remove the whitefish embryo slide from the microscope stage.

Analyze
1. How are the cells in the region behind the onion root tip different from those in the root tip?
2. What is the shape of the cells in the onion root tip?
3. In which stage do the chromosomes move to the center of the cell?
4. When do the chromosomes move to opposite ends of the cell?
5. What is the shape of the cells in the whitefish embryo?
6. When do the spindle fibers appear in both the onion root tip and the whitefish embryo?

Conclude and Apply
7. How do the whitefish embryo cells and the onion root tip cells compare in size?
8. How does the size of the whitefish embryo chromosomes compare with the size of onion root tip chromosomes?
9. How is mitosis in the onion root tip different from mitosis in the whitefish embryo?

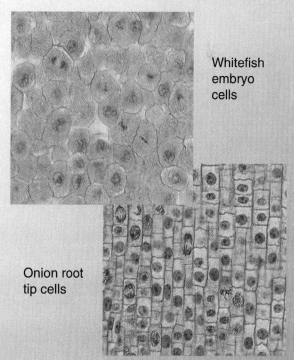

Whitefish embryo cells

Onion root tip cells

How do asexual and sexual reproduction differ?

Figure 4-5. Many organisms produce new parts asexually. Sea star arms and strawberry runners are produced by mitosis.

Types of Reproduction

Your body forms two types of cells—body cells and sex cells. Skin, liver, bones, kidneys, lungs, and muscles are made up of different types of body cells. By far, your body has many more body cells than sex cells. The only sex cells that you have are the eggs or sperm in your reproductive organs.

Reproduction is the process by which an organism produces others of the same kind. Among living organisms, there are two types of reproduction—asexual reproduction and sexual reproduction. In **asexual reproduction,** new organisms are produced from one parent. You've just seen examples of this in the process of mitosis. Offspring produced by asexual reproduction have DNA that is identical to the DNA of the parent organism. In **sexual reproduction,** a new organism is produced when sex cells from two parents combine. The DNA of the offspring is different from either parent. You will learn about the importance of sexual reproduction in Section 4-2.

Several types of asexual reproduction are important in plants and animals. If you've ever grown a sweet potato in a jar of water, you've seen asexual reproduction take place. All the stems and leaves that grow out from the sweet potato have been produced asexually by mitosis. Strawberry runners and grass roots are produced asexually. Bacterial cells reproduce asexually by fission. Fission is division of an organism into two equal parts.

Budding is also a type of asexual reproduction in which a new organism grows from the body of the parent organism. Yeast used in baking reproduces this way. When the bud on the yeast cell becomes large enough, it breaks away to live on its own.

Figure 4-6. Some animals produce whole new body parts by regeneration. A gecko can replace a lost tail by regeneration.

Some organisms produce new organisms through regeneration. During regeneration, a new organism grows from a piece of the parent organism. Sponges and sea stars undergo regeneration. If the cells of a sponge are separated, they collect together and form a whole new sponge body. If a sponge is cut into small pieces, a new sponge develops from each piece. How do you think sponge farmers increase their "crop"?

Through cell division, organisms grow, replace worn-out or damaged cells, and produce whole new organisms. Fission, budding, and regeneration are types of asexual reproduction that result from mitosis and division of the cytoplasm.

Did You Know?

The lining of your digestive system is constantly worn away by the movement of food. As a result, cells divide to replace this lining about every five days.

SECTION REVIEW

1. What is mitosis?
2. What are the stages of mitosis?
3. What is the difference between sexual and asexual reproduction?
4. Describe two types of asexual reproduction.
5. **Apply:** The body cells of a frog contain 26 chromosomes. If these cells undergo mitosis, how many chromosomes will be in each new cell produced?

✉ Outlining

Outline the events in each stage of mitosis in animal cells using the stages of mitosis as heads. Begin with interphase. If you need help, refer to Outlining in the **Skill Handbook** on page 681.

Skill Builder

4-2 Sexual Reproduction and Meiosis

New Science Words

gametes
sperm
egg
meiosis
diploid
haploid
fertilization
zygote

Objectives

▶ Describe the stages of meiosis and its end products.
▶ Name the cells involved in fertilization and explain how fertilization occurs.
▶ Explain the difference between haploid and diploid cells.

Sexual Reproduction

More than 2000 years ago, people debated how a human could grow from a single egg cell. Some thought the cell must contain a tiny, completely formed human. With the development of the microscope, scientists were able to disprove this idea. With the microscope, they were able to learn more about cells, marvel at reproduction, and watch growth take place.

In the last section, you learned that asexual reproduction occurs with only one parent. In contrast, sexual reproduction requires two parents to produce offspring. During sexual reproduction two sex cells, called **gametes,** join to form a new individual. Each gamete is produced by a different parent. The gamete from the male parent is called the **sperm.** The gamete from the female parent is called the **egg.** Gametes are usually different in size from one another. Eggs are usually large and contain food material. Sperm are small with whiplike tails.

A human body cell has 23 pairs of chromosomes, but human gametes have only 23 chromosomes. How does the chromosome number become reduced? How do gametes form? The process of nuclear division that produces gametes is called **meiosis.** Meiosis takes place in cells of reproductive organs both in plants and animals.

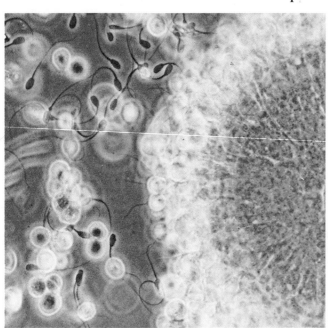

Figure 4-7. The large cell is a human egg cell, or ovum. The smaller cells are human sperm.

The Importance of Gametes

In body cells, chromosomes are found in pairs. The 46 human chromosomes form 23 pairs of chromosomes. The pairs form because the chromosomes are alike. A cell that has two of every kind of chromosome is said to be **diploid.** Gametes, on the other hand, contain only one chromosome from each matched pair. A cell, such as a gamete, that has just one chromosome of each pair is **haploid.** Haploid means "single form." A human gamete has 23 chromosomes, not 23 pairs of chromosomes. Therefore, it is haploid. For corn, the diploid number is 20, and the haploid number is 10. Usually, the haploid number of chromosomes is found only in gametes of an organism.

What is so important about gametes? Sexual reproduction starts with the formation of gametes and ends when one gamete joins with another gamete and a new organism is begun. The joining of an egg and a sperm is called **fertilization.** The cell that forms in fertilization is called a **zygote.** If an egg with 23 chromosomes joins with a sperm that has 23 chromosomes, a zygote forms that has 46 chromosomes, or the diploid chromosome number for that organism. A zygote then begins to undergo mitosis and the organism develops.

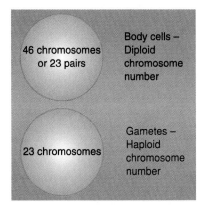

What is the difference between a haploid cell and a diploid cell?

What is fertilization?

Figure 4-8. When gametes join, a zygote forms. The zygote develops into a new individual.

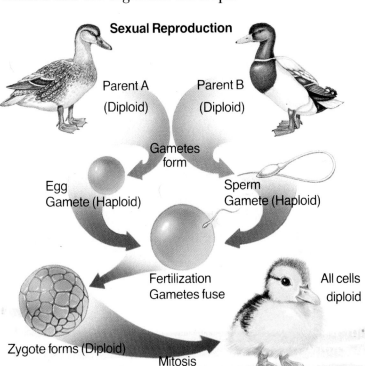

Sexual Reproduction

Parent A (Diploid)

Parent B (Diploid)

Gametes form

Egg Gamete (Haploid)

Sperm Gamete (Haploid)

Fertilization Gametes fuse

All cells diploid

Zygote forms (Diploid)

Mitosis

Meiosis—Gamete Formation

In meiosis, there are two divisions of the nucleus: meiosis I and meiosis II. The different phases of each division have names like those in mitosis, so follow the steps of meiosis I carefully in Figure 4-9. In *prophase I,* double-stranded chromosomes and spindle fibers appear. The nuclear membrane and the nucleolus disappear. Like chromosomes come together in matching pairs.

In *metaphase I,* the pairs of chromosomes line up in the center of the cell. Their centromeres become attached to the spindle fibers. In *anaphase I,* each double-stranded chromosome separates from its matching chromosome. Each one is pulled to opposite ends of the cell. Then in *telophase I,* the cytoplasm divides and two cells form. Each chromosome is still double-stranded.

Figure 4-9. The Steps of Meiosis I

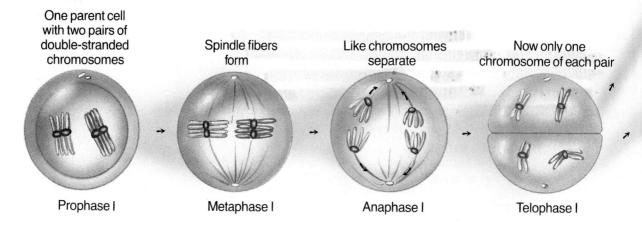

One parent cell with two pairs of double-stranded chromosomes

Spindle fibers form

Like chromosomes separate

Now only one chromosome of each pair

Prophase I

Metaphase I

Anaphase I

Telophase I

Meiosis II begins. In *prophase II,* the double-stranded chromosomes and spindle fibers reappear in each new cell. In *metaphase II,* the double-stranded chromosomes move to the center of the cell. There, the centromeres attach to spindle fibers. During *anaphase II,* the centromere divides, and the two strands of each chromosome separate and move to opposite ends of the cell. As *telophase II* begins, the spindle fibers disappear, and a nuclear membrane forms around the chromosomes at each end of the cell. Each nucleus contains only half the number of chromosomes that were in the original nucleus. A cell with 46 chromosomes at the beginning of meiosis I divides to produce cells that each have only 23 single-stranded chromosomes at the end of meiosis II.

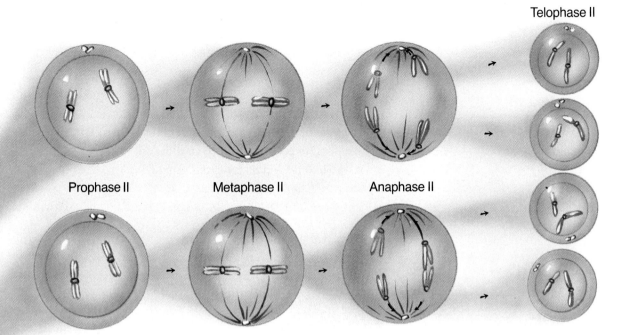

Telophase II

Prophase II   Metaphase II   Anaphase II

When meiosis II is finished, the cytoplasm divides. Meiosis I forms two cells. In meiosis II, both of these cells divide into two cells. The two nuclear divisions result in four cells. Each of these four cells is a gamete. Each cell has one half the number of chromosomes as the original cell.

Figure 4-10. The Steps of Meiosis II

Are gametes haploid or diploid?

SECTION REVIEW

1. Why is meiosis I sometimes called reduction division?
2. How many cells are there at the end of meiosis II?
3. What is a zygote, and how is it formed?
4. How do gametes and body cells differ?
5. **Apply:** If body cells of a horse have 64 chromosomes, how many chromosomes are there in a sperm cell produced by the horse?

☑ Making and Using Tables

Skill Builder

Make a table to compare mitosis and meiosis in humans. Horizontal heads in your table should be: Feature, Mitosis, and Meiosis. Vertical heads under the Feature column should be: What type of cell (Body or Sex), Beginning cell (Haploid or Diploid), Number of cells produced, End-product cell (Haploid or Diploid), and Number of chromosomes in cells produced. If you need help, refer to Making and Using Tables in the **Skill Handbook** on page 688-689.

4-3 DNA

New Science Words

DNA
replication
gene
mRNA
tRNA
mutation

Objectives

▶ Construct and identify the parts of a model of a DNA molecule.
▶ Describe the process of DNA replication.
▶ Describe RNA and its functions.

What Is DNA?

Have you ever sent a message to someone using a code? In order for them to read your message, they had to understand the meaning of the symbols you used in your code. The chromosomes in the nucleus of a cell contain a code. This code is in the form of a chemical called DNA. The DNA code in the nucleus is copied and passed to new cells when mitosis takes place. In this way, new cells receive the same coded information that was in the original cell. **DNA** controls the activities of cells with coded instructions. Every cell that has ever been formed in your body or in any plant or other animal contains DNA.

Figure 4-11. James Watson and Francis Crick with their model of DNA.

Since the mid-1800s, it has been known that the nuclei of cells contain chemicals called nucleic acids. What does DNA look like? Scientist Rosalind Franklin discovered that the DNA molecule was a strand of molecules in a spiral form. By using an X-ray technique, Dr. Franklin showed that the spiral was so large that it was probably made up of two spirals. As it turned out, the structure of DNA is similar to the handrails and steps of a spiral staircase. In 1953, using the work of Franklin and others, scientists James Watson and Francis Crick made a model of a DNA molecule. According to the Watson and Crick model, the sides ("the handrails") of the DNA molecule are made up of two twisted strands of sugar and phosphate molecules. The "stairs" that hold the two sugar-phosphate strands apart are made up of molecules called nitrogen bases. There are four kinds of nitrogen bases. These are adenine, guanine, cytosine, and thymine. In Figure 4-12, the bases are represented by the letters *A, G, C,* and *T.* An American biochemist named Edwin Chargaff had discovered in 1949 that the amount of cytosine in cells always equals the amount of guanine and that the amount of adenine always equals the amount of thymine. This led him to hypothesize that these bases occur in pairs in the molecule. The Watson and Crick model shows that adenine always pairs with thymine, and guanine always pairs with cytosine. Like interlocking pieces of a puzzle, each base pairs up only with its correct partner.

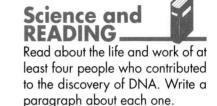

Science and READING

Read about the life and work of at least four people who contributed to the discovery of DNA. Write a paragraph about each one.

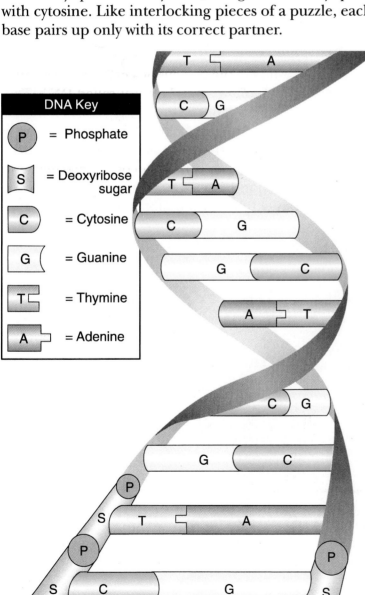

Figure 4-12. The DNA Molecule and Its Parts. DNA stands for *deoxyribonucleic acid.*

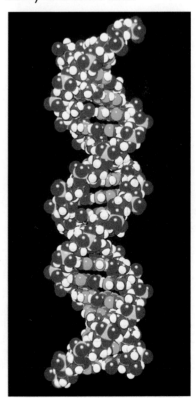

DNA Key

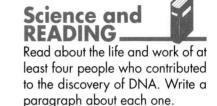

P = Phosphate

S = Deoxyribose sugar

C = Cytosine

G = Guanine

T = Thymine

A = Adenine

How DNA Copies Itself

What is replication?

When chromosomes are doubled at the beginning of mitosis, the amount of DNA in the nucleus is also doubled. **Replication** is the process by which DNA copies itself. The Watson and Crick model can be used to show how replication takes place. The two strands of DNA unwind and separate. Each strand then becomes a pattern on which a new strand is formed. Figure 4-13 follows a strand of DNA as it produces two new DNA strands identical to the original DNA. The events occurring during replication are given below.

Step 1. DNA molecule before replication

Step 2. An enzyme breaks the bonds between the nitrogen bases. The two strands of DNA separate.

Step 3. The bases attached to each strand then pair up with new bases from a supply found in the cytoplasm. Adenine pairs with thymine. Cytosine pairs with guanine. The order of base pairs in each new strand of DNA will match the order of base pairs in the original DNA.

Step 4. Sugar and phosphate groups form the side of each new DNA strand. Each new DNA molecule now contains one strand of the original DNA and one new strand.

Figure 4-13. DNA Replication

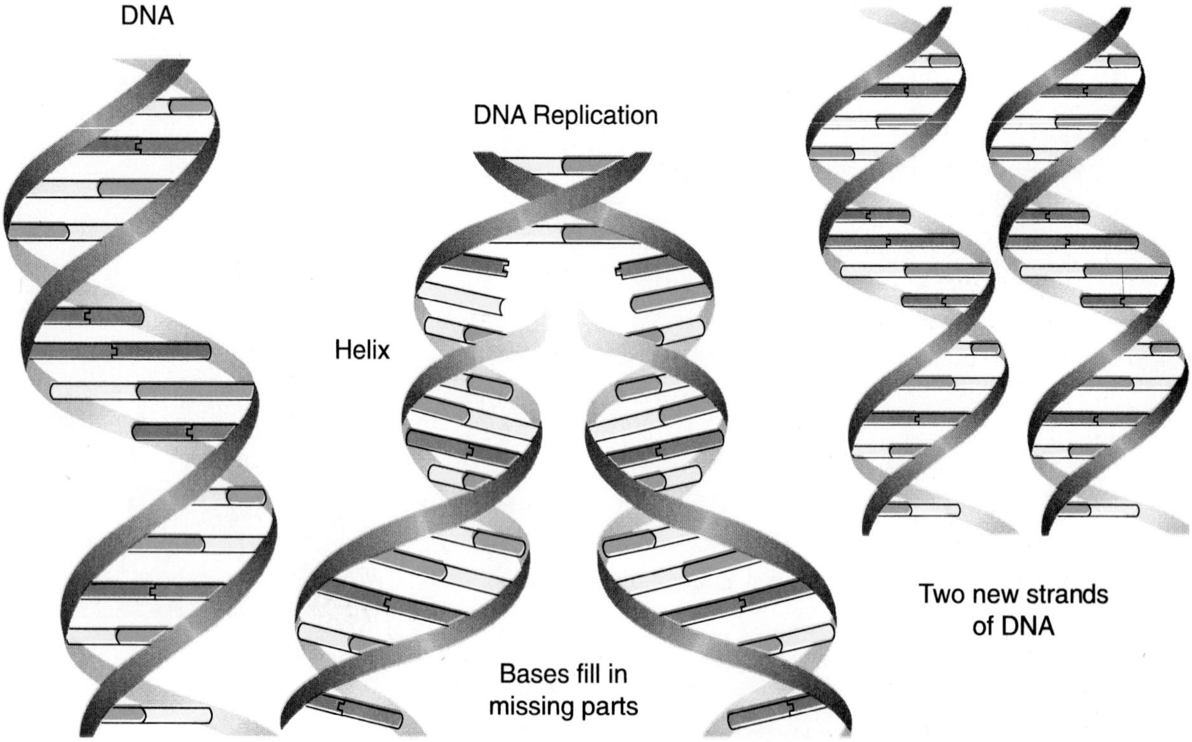

DNA

DNA Replication

Helix

Bases fill in
missing parts

Two new strands
of DNA

TECHNOLOGY

The Bacteria Factory

Bacteria can be turned into factories to produce important substances using recombinant DNA. Small circular molecules in some bacteria, called plasmids, are the key. A fragment of DNA from another source is joined, or spliced, to the plasmid. This modified plasmid is mixed with bacterial cells and a few take in the new plasmid. Quickly, each cell grows into a colony of millions of cells—each producing the desired substance.

Insulin for diabetics and enzymes for making cheese have become common products of recombinant DNA technology. With the help of this technology, sugars in vegetable wastes have been converted into ethanol, a clean-burning fuel.

Think Critically: How would bacteria-produced ethanol be useful in the United States?

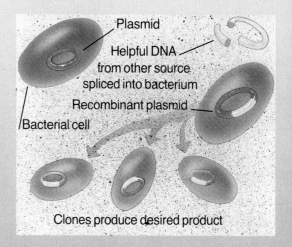

Plasmid

Helpful DNA from other source spliced into bacterium

Recombinant plasmid

Bacterial cell

Clones produce desired product

DNA and Genes

Why is DNA important? All of the characteristics that you have are affected by the DNA that you have in your cells. It controls the color of your eyes, the color of your hair, and whether or not you can digest milk. These characteristics are called traits. How traits appear in you depend on the kinds of proteins your cells make.

Proteins are made of units called amino acids that are linked together in a certain order. A protein may be made of hundreds or thousands of amino acids. Changing the order of the amino acids changes the kind of protein made. DNA stores the blueprints for making proteins. The section of DNA on a chromosome that directs the making of a specific protein is called a **gene.** Genes control proteins that build cells and tissues and work as enzymes. Think about what might happen if an important protein couldn't be made in your cells.

How does a cell know which proteins to make? The gene gives the directions for the order in which amino acids will be arranged. This order produces a particular protein.

What is a gene?

MINI-Lab

How is RNA made?

RNA is made in the nucleus on a pattern supplied by DNA. Look at Figures 4-12 and 4-13 to see the structure of DNA and how these strands separate to make new DNA. When RNA is made, the two DNA strands separate and one is used as a pattern for making a strand of RNA. Suppose a molecule of DNA untwists and separates and the left strand is used to make RNA. If the order of the bases in the DNA strand is T C A G A T C G A, what, in correct order, will be the bases in the RNA? If the new strand of RNA that you just made were a piece of mRNA, what tRNA bases would link up with it in the cytoplasm?

In Chapter 2 you learned that proteins are made on ribosomes in cytoplasm. How does the code in the nucleus reach the ribosomes out in the cytoplasm? The codes for making proteins are carried from the nucleus to the ribosomes by a second type of nucleic acid, called ribonucleic acid (RNA). RNA is different from DNA in that it is made up of only one strand, and it contains a nitrogen base called uracil (U) in place of thymine. RNA is made in the nucleus on a DNA pattern.

Two different kinds of RNA are made from DNA in the nucleus—messenger RNA (mRNA) and transfer RNA (tRNA). Protein assembly begins as **mRNA** moves out of the nucleus and attaches to ribosomes in the cytoplasm. Pieces of **tRNA** pick up amino acids in the cytoplasm and bring them to the ribosomes. There, tRNA temporarily matches with mRNA and the amino acids become arranged according to the code carried by mRNA. The amino acids become bonded together, and a protein molecule begins to form.

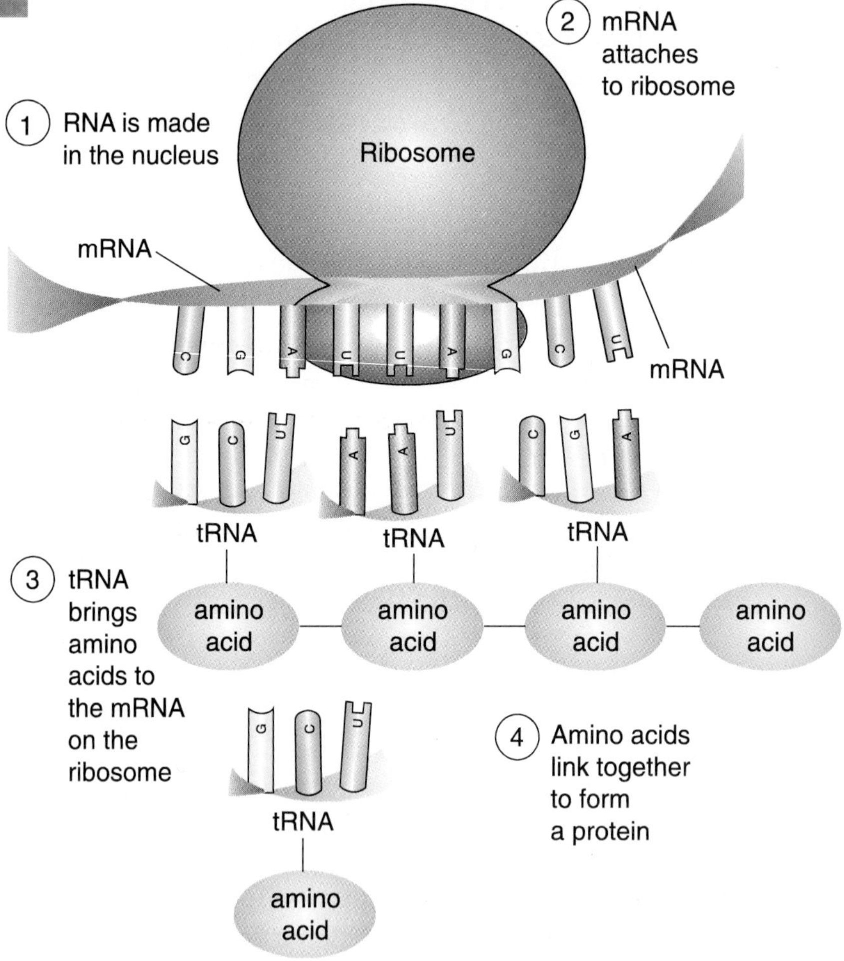

Figure 4-14. RNA carries the code for a protein from the nucleus to the ribosome. There, its message is translated into a specific protein.

Mutations

Genes control the traits you inherit. Without correctly coded proteins, an organism can't grow, repair, or maintain itself. If a change occurs in a gene or chromosome, the traits of that organism are changed. Sometimes during replication an error is made in copying a gene. Occasionally, a cell receives an entire extra chromosome. Outside factors such as X rays and chemicals have been known to change or break chromosomes. Any permanent change in a gene or chromosome of a cell is called a **mutation.** If the mutation occurs in a body cell, it may or may not be life threatening to the organism. If, however, a mutation occurs in a gamete, then all the cells that are formed from that gamete will have that mutation. Down syndrome in humans occurs when a gamete forms with an extra number 21 chromosome, so that the zygote that forms has three number 21 chromosomes. Many mutations are harmful to organisms. Many times, an organism with a mutation doesn't survive. But mutations also add variety to a species.

Figure 4-15. Albinism is an example of a mutation.

SECTION REVIEW

1. Which bases form pairs in a DNA molecule?
2. How is the structure of DNA like a spiral staircase?
3. Why is protein production important in a cell?
4. How does DNA make a copy of itself?
5. **Apply:** A single strand of DNA has the bases AGTAAC. Using letters, show what bases would match up to form an RNA strand from this DNA pattern.

☒ Concept Mapping

Using a network tree concept map, show how DNA and RNA are alike and how they are different. If you need help, refer to Concept Mapping in the **Skill Handbook** on pages 688 and 689.

Skill Builder

4-4 Inventing Organisms

New Science Words

transgenic organisms

Objectives

▶ Explain the term *transgenic organism.*
▶ Explain some advantages and disadvantages of patenting organisms.

Transgenic Organisms

Have you ever thought of actually being able to invent an organism? Today, scientists are doing just that. Through genetic engineering, they are able to produce **transgenic organisms,** organisms that contain genetic information from another species. Making a transgenic organism involves taking a gene from one organism and placing it in another. This technology provides many opportunities for research in medicine and agriculture. For example, a mouse received a human gene that resulted in the animal being very susceptible to human cancers. Because this mouse can develop certain types of tumors, it is a very valuable tool for cancer research. Using this organism, tests can be conducted to detect substances that cause cancer. Potential anti-cancer drugs can also be tested. In agriculture, a gene from bacteria can be transplanted into crops to prevent certain insect pests from eating them.

Patenting Life

Biologists are now asking for patents on genetically engineered organisms that they develop in the laboratory. A patent is a license issued by the government that gives the owner the legal right to control the manufacture and sale of an invention. In 1988, the United States government gave the first transgenic organism patent to Harvard University for its transgenic mouse.

The development of transgenic organisms and the patenting of these organisms have met some opposition. People who are concerned about the consequences of such genetic technology worry that transgenic organisms may become pests or burdens to society. Some think that transgenic plants and animals might have the same effect on society as organisms introduced into the United States from other countries. Certain species of rats, fish, and insects have taken over or destroyed many native organisms. In addition, many people are opposed to the idea of having legal ownership of living organisms. Although the patents are designed to protect the biotechnology industry, some scientists see the patent as a barrier to the tradition of sharing information within the scientific community.

As technology continues to grow and play an important role in society, new developments may present new risks to the environment. People will have to compare these risks with the benefits that they may provide.

SECTION REVIEW

1. What is a transgenic organism?
2. List two risks of developing transgenic organisms.
3. What rights does a patent owner have?

You Decide!

SCIENCE & SOCIETY

After hospital patients have had surgery to remove tumors or tissues, these cells are sometimes saved. They are kept alive in the laboratory. Sometimes these cells, or products made from these cells, are sold for use in research. Patients are now claiming that they should have profits from products made from their own body tissues. Research companies that develop the products disagree. They argue that the cells all by themselves are useless without the time and skills of the researchers. Should patients be paid for products made from their cells?

ACTIVITY 4-2
Making a Model

Problem: *What does a model of DNA look like?*

Materials

- tracing paper
- scissors
- heavy paper
- crayons

Procedure

1. Trace the four DNA parts shown below.
2. Cut out the four tracings. **CAUTION:** *Always be careful when using scissors.*
3. Copy each of the tracings onto heavy paper six times. Label each tracing as shown below.
4. Color the phosphate brown. Color the sugar orange. Color the A bases red, the T bases blue, the C bases green, and the G bases yellow.
5. Cut out all 24 parts.
6. Use the following order of bases to make a DNA molecule: ATCCGT. Use your desk as a work space.
7. Separate the bases in the molecule and replicate the original molecule.

8. Use any combination of DNA parts to create other molecules. Compare your molecules with those of your classmates.

Analyze

1. What does each DNA part represent?
2. What does the A base pair with?
3. What does the C base pair with?
4. What is the order of bases in the second strand of the DNA molecule in Step 6?
5. Were the molecules you created in Step 8 the same as your classmates'? Why?

Conclude and Apply

6. Using the model, explain why T only matches with A.
7. Why does a DNA molecule seldom replicate incorrectly?
8. Why do scientists use models?

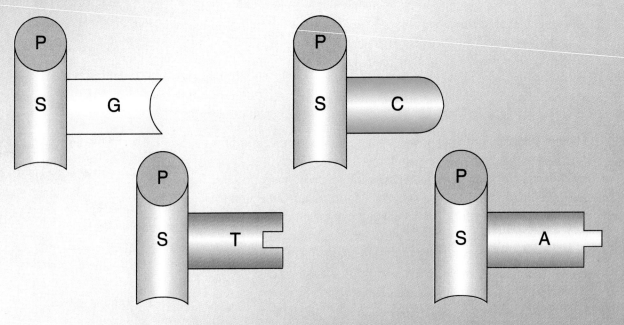

CHAPTER
REVIEW

4-1: Cell Growth and Division

1. Cells divide to form new cells by mitosis and divisions of cytoplasm. There are four stages of mitosis, during which chromosomes copy themselves, separate, and become part of new nuclei.
2. Animal cells have centrioles. New animal cells form when the cytoplasm pinches in. Plant cells lack centrioles; cytoplasm is separated by a cell plate following mitosis.
3. Asexual reproduction requires only one parent. Sexual reproduction requires two parents to produce a new individual. Fission, budding, and regeneration are all methods of asexual reproduction.

4-2: Sexual Reproduction and Meiosis

1. Sexual reproduction involves the production of gametes through the process of meiosis.
2. Gametes from two parents fuse during fertilization to produce a zygote, a cell with the diploid chromosome number.
3. Meiosis is a division of nuclei in reproductive cells that results in gametes, four cells with the haploid chromosome number.

4-3: DNA

1. DNA is made up of bases that appear in specific sequences, and it directs all activities of a cell. DNA can copy itself and is the framework on which RNA is made.
2. mRNA and tRNA assemble in the cytoplasm based on instructions from genes in the nucleus.
3. Mutations are changes in an organism's DNA. Most are harmful to the organism, but some are known to be beneficial.

4-4: Science and Society: Inventing Organisms

1. Transgenic organisms contain genes from an organism of another species.
2. Transgenic organisms can be used in research, but may become pests in nature.

KEY SCIENCE WORDS

a. **asexual reproduction**
b. **centromere**
c. **chromosomes**
d. **diploid**
e. **DNA**
f. **egg**
g. **fertilization**
h. **gametes**
i. **gene**
j. **haploid**
k. **meiosis**
l. **mitosis**
m. **mRNA**
n. **mutation**
o. **replication**
p. **sexual reproduction**
q. **sperm**
r. **transgenic organisms**
s. **tRNA**
t. **zygote**

UNDERSTANDING VOCABULARY

Match each phrase with the correct term from the list of Key Science Words.

1. nuclear structures containing DNA
2. DNA makes a copy of itself
3. segments of DNA controlling production of one protein
4. deoxyribonucleic acid
5. formation of two new nuclei with identical chromosomes
6. fusion of an egg and a sperm
7. nuclear division that forms sex cells
8. a change in an organism's DNA
9. an organism containing genetic information from another species
10. form of RNA that transports amino acids to the ribosomes

CELL REPRODUCTION **95**

CHAPTER
REVIEW

CHECKING CONCEPTS

Choose the word or phrase that completes the sentence.

1. The DNA molecule _____.
   a. is a double spiral
   b. contains nitrogen bases
   c. has two strands
   d. is all of these

2. RNA differs from DNA in that it contains _____.
   a. thymine   c. adenine
   b. thyroid   d. uracil

3. The RNA that carries the blueprint for building a protein to the ribosomes is _____.
   a. mRNA   c. tRNA
   b. single RNA   d. all of these

4. Chromosomes are doubled during _____.
   a. anaphase   c. interphase
   b. metaphase   d. telophase

5. During _____ in mitosis, double-stranded chromosomes separate.
   a. anaphase   c. metaphase
   b. prophase   d. telophase

6. The chromosome number in cells after mitosis is _____ the parent cell number.
   a. the same as
   b. half
   c. twice
   d. four times

7. _____ is a form of asexual reproduction.
   a. budding   c. regeneration
   b. fission   d. all of these

8. Mutations affect _____.
   a. genes   c. traits
   b. chromosomes   d. all of the above

9. Meiosis produces _____.
   a. cells with the diploid chromosome number
   b. cells with identical chromosomes
   c. gametes
   d. a zygote

10. One difference between RNA and DNA is _____.
    a. the bases they contain
    b. the numbers of sugar-phosphate strands
    c. the sugars they contain
    d. all of these are differences

UNDERSTANDING CONCEPTS

Complete each sentence.

11. There are _____ chromosomes in human body cells.

12. A _____ is formed by the fusion of an egg and a sperm.

13. A human gamete has _____ chromosomes.

14. Reproduction that requires two parents is called _____.

15. _____ reproduction is a result of mitosis.

THINK AND WRITE CRITICALLY

16. What is the difference between genes and chromosomes?

17. What are the differences between offspring formed by sexual reproduction and asexual reproduction?

18. What do spindle fibers do during mitosis and meiosis?

19. In what cells do mitosis and meiosis take place?

20. Why is more known about harmful mutations than beneficial ones?

21. If one strand of DNA had bases ordered ATCCGTC, what would be the bases of its other strand?
22. A strand of mRNA matching the DNA strand ATCCGTC would have what base sequence?
23. A mutation takes place in a human skin cell. Will this mutation be passed on to the person's offspring? Explain your answer.
24. What processes in mitosis provide both new cells with identical DNA?
25. How could a zygote end up with an extra chromosome?

MORE SKILL BUILDERS

If you need help, refer to the Skill Handbook.

1. **Making and Using Tables:** Compare and contrast DNA and RNA in a table.

Nucleic acid	DNA	RNA
Number of stands	Use a separate sheet of paper to complete your table.	
Type of sugar		
Letter names of bases		
Where found?		

2. **Hypothesizing:** Make a hypothesis about the effect of an incorrect mitotic division on the new cells produced.

3. **Comparing and Contrasting:** Compare and contrast mitosis and meiosis as to: number of divisions, numbers of cells produced, numbers of chromosomes in parent cells and in gametes.
4. **Concept Mapping:** Complete the events chain concept map of DNA synthesis.

DNA unwinds → [ ] → Two new strands of DNA form

5. **Sequencing:** Sequence the events that occur in sexual reproduction. Start with interphase in the parent cell and follow it through production of a sex cell by meiosis. End with the formation of the zygote. Tell whether the number of chromosomes present at each stage is haploid or diploid.

PROJECTS

1. Research the events involved in exploring DNA since it was first removed from a cell nucleus in 1869. Show your results on a time line.
2. Write a one-page paper about growth hormones called gibberellins and their use.

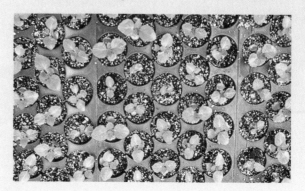

UNIT 1
GLOBAL CONNECTIONS

Life

In this unit, you have studied life and the characteristics of living things. What is the relationship between life science and other subjects you will encounter in your lifetime?

120°   60°

BIOLOGY

CHROMOSOME SURGERY
University of California, Irvine, California
Chromosome surgery? Sounds impossible! Where would anyone find a scalpel small enough? Scientists at the University of California use a laser beam focused through a microscope to remove one part of a chromosome at a time. What can scientists learn from examining separate parts of chromosomes?

METEOROLOGY

LIFE FROM THE SKY?
Woods Hole, Massachusetts
Ships of Woods Hole Oceanographic Institute explore the sea, studying ocean life-forms, charting currents and ocean depths, and studying the relationship between the ocean and rainfall. Why is rainfall important to living organisms?

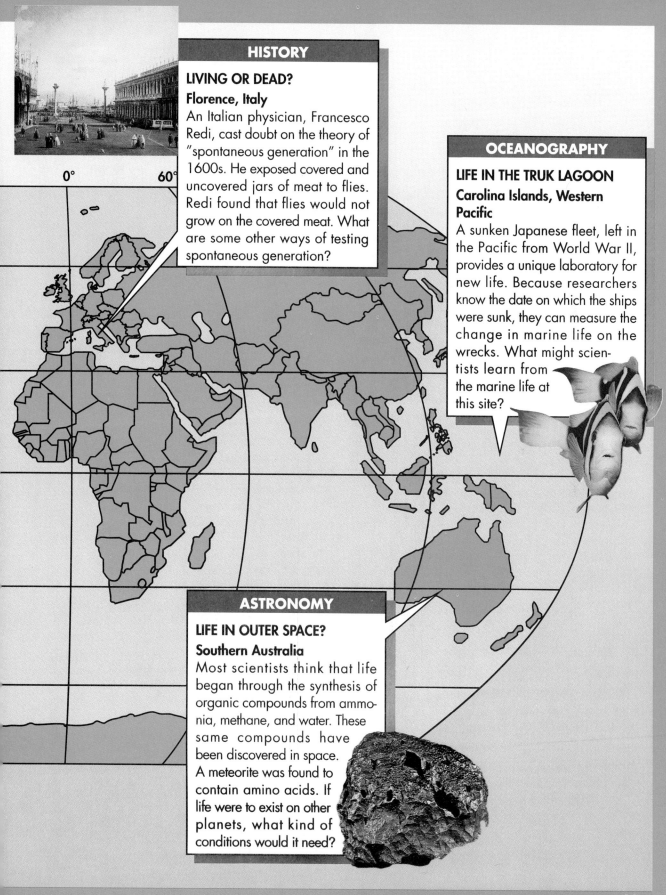

HISTORY

LIVING OR DEAD?
Florence, Italy
An Italian physician, Francesco Redi, cast doubt on the theory of "spontaneous generation" in the 1600s. He exposed covered and uncovered jars of meat to flies. Redi found that flies would not grow on the covered meat. What are some other ways of testing spontaneous generation?

OCEANOGRAPHY

LIFE IN THE TRUK LAGOON
Carolina Islands, Western Pacific
A sunken Japanese fleet, left in the Pacific from World War II, provides a unique laboratory for new life. Because researchers know the date on which the ships were sunk, they can measure the change in marine life on the wrecks. What might scientists learn from the marine life at this site?

ASTRONOMY

LIFE IN OUTER SPACE?
Southern Australia
Most scientists think that life began through the synthesis of organic compounds from ammonia, methane, and water. These same compounds have been discovered in space. A meteorite was found to contain amino acids. If life were to exist on other planets, what kind of conditions would it need?

0°   60°

CAREERS

LABORATORY TECHNICIAN

A *laboratory technician* provides daily care for laboratory experiments. Education requirements vary. Most laboratory technicians must have three years of work-related experience. Some laboratories may require one or two years of college-level courses in basic biology and English.

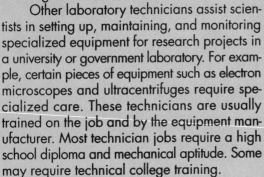

Other laboratory technicians assist scientists in setting up, maintaining, and monitoring specialized equipment for research projects in a university or government laboratory. For example, certain pieces of equipment such as electron microscopes and ultracentrifuges require specialized care. These technicians are usually trained on the job and by the equipment manufacturer. Most technician jobs require a high school diploma and mechanical aptitude. Some may require technical college training.

For Additional Information
Clinical Laboratory Technology, 818 Olive St. Suite 918, St. Louis, MO 63101

UNIT READINGS

▶ Asimov, Isaac. *How Did We Find Out About the Beginning of Life?* Houston: Walker Publishing Co., 1982.
▶ "The Year in Science." *Discover*, January 1991, pp. 22-51.

RESEARCH BIOLOGIST

A *research biologist* is a scientist who works in research and development biology. He or she may be involved with research that increases knowledge of living things or applied research that uses that knowledge to develop new medicines, increase crop production, or improve the environment.

Research biologists work in laboratories with instruments such as an electron microscope, computer, or electronic instruments. Research may be done outside the laboratory too.

A Ph.D. is usually required for persons who want to do independent research or who are in charge of research facilities. A master's degree is necessary for applied research and management positions. A bachelor's degree will qualify a graduate to become a biological scientist in testing and inspection.

For Additional Information
American Institute of Biological Science, Office of Career Services, 730 11th St. NW, Washington D.C. 20001-4584

Essays

by Sir Francis Bacon

Sir Francis Bacon wrote this essay in 1605 to illustrate the problems early scholars had developing scientific methods.

In the year of our Lord 1432, there arose a grievous quarrel among the brethren over the number of teeth in the mouth of a horse. For 13 days the disputation raged without ceasing. All the ancient books and chronicles were fetched out, and wonderful and ponderous erudition, such as was never before heard of in this region, was made manifest.

At the beginning of the 14th day, a youthful friar of goodly bearing asked his learned superiors for permission to add a word, and straightway, to the wonderment of the disputants, whose deep wisdom he sore vexed, he beseeched them to unbend in a manner coarse and unheard-of, and to look in the open mouth of a horse and find the answer to their questionings. At this, their dignity being grievously hurt, they waxed exceedingly wroth; and, joining in the mighty uproar, they flew upon him and smote him hip and thigh, and cast him out forthwith. For, said they, surely Satan hath tempted this bold neophyte to declare unholy and unheard-of ways of finding truth contrary to all the teachings of the fathers.

After many days more of grievous strife the dove of peace sat on the assembly, and they as one man, declaring the problem to be an everlasting mystery because of a grievous dearth of historical and theological evidence thereof, so ordered the same writ down."

In Your Own Words

▶ Write a report explaining what part of the scientific method the "youthful friar" wanted his superiors to use. Explain how this problem might be approached by researchers today.

2 HEREDITY AND EVOLUTION

What's Happening Here?

What do cockroaches, crocodiles, and horseshoe crabs have in common? None of them has changed much since their first appearance on Earth. The horseshoe crabs on this beach are often called living fossils. In many ways they still resemble their trilobite ancestor shown in the small picture. What does this tell you about their ability to adapt? Nearly 99 percent of all species that have ever lived are now extinct, yet the horseshoe crab remains unchanged. Is it just luck? Is there some evolutionary principle at work here? In this unit, you'll learn more about heredity and evolution.

UNIT CONTENTS

Chapter 5   Heredity
Chapter 6   Evolution
Chapter 7   Classification of Living Things

5 Heredity

The tigers in the photo to the left have so many traits in common that they look almost identical. Most traits found in organisms have at least two forms, such as free and attached earlobes in humans. How are these and other traits distributed among your classmates?

FIND OUT!

Do this activity to find out about the types of earlobes in your class.

Some people have earlobes that are attached, whereas others have earlobes that swing free. Count the number of your classmates who have attached earlobes. How many have free earlobes? Record the number of people in your class who have each type. What does your data tell you about the earlobe trait in your class? Do you have enough data to say which form of earlobe is more common in the human population?

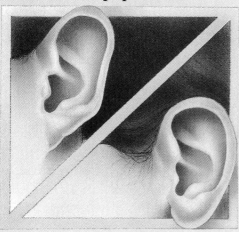

Gearing Up
Previewing the Chapter
Use this outline to help you focus on important ideas in this chapter.

Section 5-1   What Is Genetics?
▶ What Have You Inherited?
▶ The Father of Genetics
▶ Mendel's Experiments
▶ Using a Punnett Square

Section 5-2   Genetics Since Mendel
▶ Incomplete Dominance
▶ Multiple Alleles
▶ Multiple Genes

Section 5-3   Human Genetics
▶ Genes and Health
▶ Sex Determination
▶ Sex-linked Disorders
▶ Why Is Genetics Important?

Section 5-4   Science and Society
The Human Genome
▶ Tracking Human Genes

Previewing Science Skills
▶ In the **Skill Builders,** you will observe and infer, compare and contrast, and use a concept map.
▶ In the **Activities,** you will experiment, hypothesize, and collect and analyze data.
▶ In the **MINI-Labs,** you will observe, collect and analyze data.

What's next?

Now that you have seen that a single human trait can have more than one form, learn about some of the ways in which these traits are inherited, and learn about the importance of genetics in your life.

5-1   What Is Genetics?

New Science Words

heredity
alleles
genetics
purebred
dominant
recessive
probability
Punnett square
genotype
homozygous
heterozygous
phenotype

Objectives

▶ Explain how traits are inherited and explain Mendel's role in the history of genetics.
▶ Use a Punnett square to predict the results of crosses.
▶ Explain the difference between genotype and phenotype.

What Have You Inherited?

What's the first thing you think about when you hear the word *inheritance*? Money? A new home? People inherit all sorts of things. It might be a set of dishes or a set of tools. Of course, a lot of people will never inherit things like this. But there is a type of inheritance that all living things receive. For you, this inheritance is in the nucleus of each cell of your body in the form of pairs of genes.

For centuries, people have been interested in why one generation looks like another. A new baby may look much like one of its parents. It may be the shape of its nose or its earlobes. In either case, a trait is being noticed. Every organism is a collection of traits, all inherited from its parents. **Heredity** (huh RED ut ee) is the passing of traits from parent to offspring. How does this take place? These traits are controlled by genes.

In 1933, an American scientist, Thomas Hunt Morgan, stated that genes are found on chromosomes. Genes, as you learned in Chapter 4, are made up of DNA. They control all the traits that show up in an organism. When pairs of chromosomes separate into gametes during meiosis, pairs of genes also separate from one another. As a result, each gamete winds up with one form of a gene for each trait that an organism shows. If the trait is for earlobes, then the gene in one gamete may control one form of the trait, such as attached earlobes. The gene for earlobes in the other gamete may control the other form of the trait, such as free earlobes. The different forms a gene may have for a trait are its **alleles** (uh LEELZ). In life science, the study of how alleles affect generations of offspring is **genetics.**

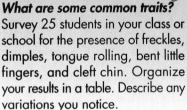

MINI-Lab

What are some common traits?
Survey 25 students in your class or school for the presence of freckles, dimples, tongue rolling, bent little fingers, and cleft chin. Organize your results in a table. Describe any variations you notice.

What is an allele?

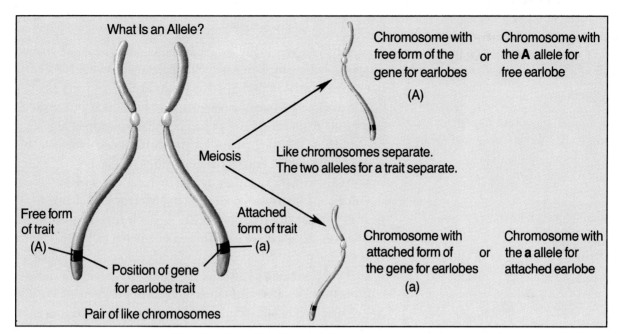

What Is an Allele?

Meiosis

Like chromosomes separate.
The two alleles for a trait separate.

Chromosome with free form of the gene for earlobes (A) or Chromosome with the **A** allele for free earlobe

Chromosome with attached form of the gene for earlobes (a) or Chromosome with the **a** allele for attached earlobe

Free form of trait (A)

Attached form of trait (a)

Position of gene for earlobe trait

Pair of like chromosomes

The Father of Genetics

The first thorough scientific study of how traits pass from one generation to the next was done by a monk, Gregor Mendel. Mendel lived in the 1800s in a section of Eastern Europe that is now part of Czechoslovakia. His father taught him about plants in the family's small orchard. Although everyone expected him to become a farmer, he became a priest. He studied science and math and eventually worked many years as a substitute teacher in local schools. In connection with his teaching, Mendel took over a small garden plot at the monastery. There he experimented with plants. His observations of his father's orchard made him think that it was possible to predict the kinds of flowers and fruit a plant would produce. But enough had to be known about the parents of the plant. Mendel made extremely careful use of scientific methods in his research. In 1866, after eight years of work on inheritance in plants, Mendel presented the results of his research to a group of scientists. Unfortunately, they didn't understand anything he was talking about. Mendel died in 1884, still not knowing if his work would ever be understood.

In 1900, Mendel's work was rediscovered. By then, other scientists had come to the same conclusions that he had reached. Since then he has become known as the Father of Genetics.

Figure 5-1. An allele is one form of a gene. Alleles separate into gametes during meiosis.

Figure 5-2. Through experiments, Mendel discovered basic laws of inheritance.

Figure 5-3. Many people breed dogs for specific pure traits.

Mendel's Experiments

Mendel chose ordinary green peas, like the ones you've eaten for dinner, for his experiments. Peas are easy to breed for pure traits. You've heard of purebred horses and purebred dogs. An organism that always produces the same traits in its offspring is pure, or **purebred.** Tall plants that always produce tall plants are pure for the trait of tall height. Altogether, Mendel studied seven purebred traits of peas, which are shown in Table 5-1.

In one of his first experiments, Mendel crossbred tall plants with short plants. He took pollen from the male reproductive structure of flowers of pure tall plants and placed it on the female reproductive structures of flowers of pure short plants. This process is called cross-pollination. The results of this cross are shown in Figure 5-4. Notice that tall plants crossed with short plants produce all tall plants. It seemed as if whatever had caused the plants to be short had disappeared.

Mendel called the tall height form that appeared the **dominant** factor, because it seemed to dominate or cover up the short height form. In this case, the tall height form was dominant. He called the form that seemed to disappear the **recessive** factor. But what had happened to the recessive form? He experimented to find out.

Mendel allowed the new tall plants to cross-pollinate. Then he collected the seeds from these tall plants and planted them. To his surprise, the plants that grew from these seeds were tall and short. The recessive form had reappeared. Mendel saw that for every three tall plants

Figure 5-4. A cross between pure tall plants and pure short plants (a) produces a generation of all tall plants (b). When the first generation tall plants are crossed with each other, a second generation is produced with three tall plants for every one short plant (c).

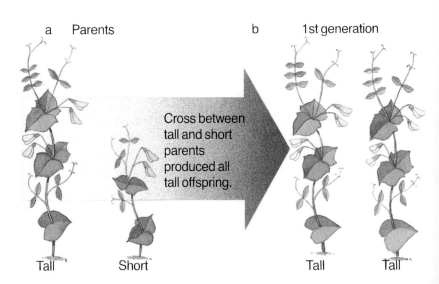

a   Parents

b   1st generation

Cross between tall and short parents produced all tall offspring.

Tall   Short

Tall   Tall

Table 5-1

TRAITS COMPARED BY MENDEL						
Shape of seeds	**Color of seeds**	**Color of seed coats**	**Color of pods**	**Shape of pods**	**Plant height**	**Position of flowers**
Round	Yellow	Green	Green	Full	Tall	On side branches
Wrinkled	Green	White	Yellow	Flat or Constricted	Short	At tips of branches

there was one short plant, or a 3:1 ratio. He saw this 3:1 ratio often enough that he knew he could predict his results when he started a test. He knew that the *probability* was great that he would get that same outcome each time.

Probability is a science that helps you determine the chance that something will take place. Suppose your cat comes running every time you open a can of cat food. If the cat acts this way every day for a year, then you can say that the probability of the cat acting that way every day for the next year is very great. As a matter of fact, the probability is 100 percent. You can predict it.

Mendel also dealt with probabilities. One of the things that made his predictions accurate was that he worked with large numbers. He counted every plant and thousands of seeds. Now, this may not sound like fun, but by doing so, Mendel increased his chances of having accurate results. Scientific research is based on accurate, repeatable results.

What is probability?

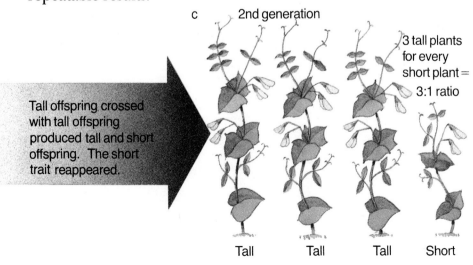

c   2nd generation

3 tall plants for every short plant = 3:1 ratio

Tall offspring crossed with tall offspring produced tall and short offspring. The short trait reappeared.

Tall   Tall   Tall   Short

Using a Punnett Square

A handy tool used to predict results in genetics is the **Punnett square.** It uses your knowledge of alleles. Dominant and recessive alleles are represented by letters. A capital letter (*T*) stands for a dominant allele. A small letter (*t*) stands for a recessive allele. The letters are a form of shorthand. They show the genetic make-up, or **genotype,** of an organism. Once you understand what the letters mean, you can tell a lot about the inheritance of a trait in an organism.

Every cell in your body has two alleles for every trait. An organism with two alleles for a trait that are exactly the same is called **homozygous** (ho muh ZI gus). This would be written as *TT* or *tt*. An organism that has two different alleles for a trait is called **heterozygous** (het uh roh ZI gus). This condition would be written *Tt*. The purebred pea plants that Mendel used were homozygous for tall, or *TT*, and homozygous for short, or *tt*. The hybrid plants he produced were all heterozygous, or *Tt*.

The physical trait that shows as a result of a particular genotype is its **phenotype** (FEE nuh tipe). Red is the phenotype for red flowering plants. Short is the phenotype for short plants. If you have brown hair, then the phenotype for your hair color is brown.

Science and MATH

Suppose Mendel's tall plants sell for $20 per dozen. The short ones sell for $10 per dozen. If you sold all of the 100 dozen offspring plants from the first generation cross, how much money would you make?

Explain the difference between heterozygous and homozygous.

Figure 5-5. A Punnett square shows you all the ways in which alleles can combine. A Punnett square does *not* tell you how many offspring will be produced.

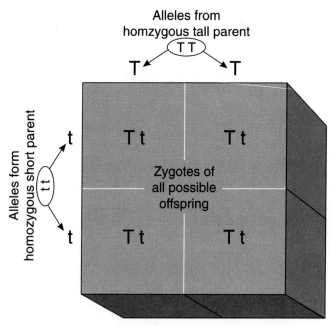

Alleles from homzygous tall parent

T T

T T

Alleles form homozygous short parent

t t

t

t

Tt Tt

Zygotes of all possible offspring

Tt Tt

Genotypes of offspring: All Tt
Phenotypes of offspring: All tall

Look at the Punnett square in Figure 5-5. The letters representing the two alleles from one parent are written along the top of the square. Those of the second parent are placed along the side of the square. Each square in the middle is filled in much like a multiplication problem with one allele donated by each parent. The letters that you use to fill in each of the squares represent the genotypes of zygotes that the parents *could* produce.

The Punnett square in Figure 5-5 represents the first type of cross-pollination experiment by Mendel. You can see that each homozygous parent plant has two alleles for height. One parent is homozygous for tall (*TT*). The other parent is homozygous for short (*tt*). The alleles inside the squares are the genotypes of the possible offspring. All of them have the genotype *Tt*. They all have tall as a phenotype. Notice that you can't always figure out a genotype just by looking at the phenotype. The combination of *TT* or *Tt* both produce tall plants when *T* is dominant to *t*. Study the additional sample problems given below.

Figure 5-6. The color phenotype of this hibiscus flower is red.

EXAMPLE PROBLEMS: Using Punnett Squares

Problem 1: Color in Peas
Yellow color in peas is dominant to green peas. A homozygous yellow pea plant is crossed with a homozygous green pea plant. What will the genotypes of all the possible offspring be?

Outcome:
Genotypes of all possible offspring: All Yy
Phenotypes of offspring: All yellow

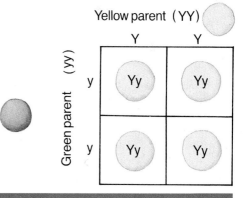

Problem 2: Wing Length in Fruit Flies
In fruit flies, long wings (L) are dominant to short wings (l). Two heterozygous long-winged fruit flies (both Ll) are crossed. What are the possible genotypes of their offspring? What are the phenotypes?

Outcome:
Genotypes of all possible offspring: LL, Ll, and ll
Phenotypes of all possible offspring:
LL and Ll = long wings
ll = short wings

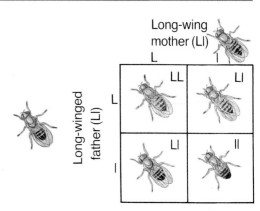

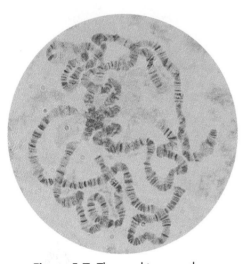

Figure 5-7. The markings on these chromosomes show where DNA is located.

Table 5-2

MENDELIAN INHERITANCE
1. Traits are controlled by alleles on chromosomes.
2. An allele may be dominant or recessive in form.
3. When a pair of chromosomes separates during meiosis, the different alleles for a trait move into separate gametes.

Gregor Mendel didn't know anything about DNA, genes, or chromosomes. He did figure out that "factors" in the plants caused certain traits to appear. He also figured out that these factors separated when the plant reproduced. Now we refer to these factors as alleles. Mendel arrived at his conclusions by patient observation and careful analysis. His work is summed up briefly in Table 5-2.

SECTION REVIEW

1. How are alleles and traits related?
2. Explain the difference between genotype and phenotype, and give an example of each.
3. Explain Mendel's contribution to genetics.
4. **Apply:** Make a Punnett square showing a cross between two dogs. One dog is homozygous for black coat, and the other dog is homozygous for white coat. Black is dominant to white. Use *B* for the dominant allele and *b* for the recessive allele. What are the genotypes of the parents and the genotypes and phenotypes of the puppies?

Skill Builder

☑ Observing and Inferring

Hairline shape is an inherited trait in humans. A widow's peak is a V-shaped hairline in the middle of the forehead. People lacking the trait have a straight hairline. The widow's peak allele is dominant and the straight hairline allele is homozygous recessive. From your study of Mendel's experiments, infer how parents with widow's peaks could have a child without the trait. If you need help, refer to Observing and Inferring in the **Skill Handbook** on page 682.

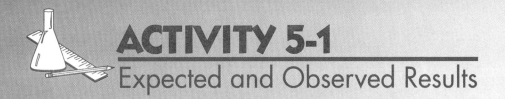

ACTIVITY 5-1
Expected and Observed Results

Problem: *How does chance affect the combination of genes?*

Materials
- 2 paper bags
- 100 red beans
- 100 white beans

Procedure
1. Place 50 red beans and 50 white beans into a paper bag. Place 50 red beans and 50 white beans into a second bag. The beans represent alleles for flower color.
2. Label one of the bags "female" for the female parent. Label the other bag "male" for the male parent.
3. Use a Punnett square to predict how many red/red, to red/white, to white/white combinations will be selected.
4. Without looking inside the bags, remove one bean from each bag. The two beans represent the alleles that combine when sperm and egg join.
5. Make a table like the one shown with room for 100 data entries. Record the color combination of the beans each time you remove two beans. Then return them to their original bags and shake the bags.
6. Repeat Steps 5 and 6 *ninety-nine* times.
7. Count and record the total numbers of red/red, red/white, and white/white bean combinations in your data table.
8. Compile and record the class totals.

Data and Observations

Beans	Red/Red	Red/White	White/White
Total			
Class Total			

Analyze
1. Which combination occurred most often?
2. If red is dominant and white is recessive, how many plants have hybrid or heterozygous genes?
3. How did your predicted (expected) results of selected combinations compare with your observed (actual) results?
4. What was the ratio of red/red to red/white to white/white?

Conclude and Apply
5. What are the chances of selecting the same color in a pair of alleles each time?
6. How does chance affect allele combination?
7. How do the results of a small sample compare with the results of a large sample?

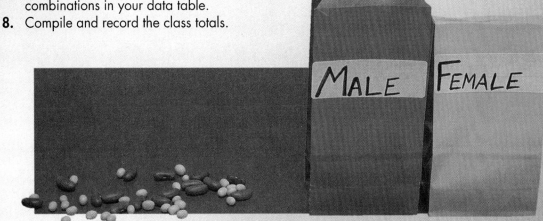

5-2 Genetics Since Mendel

New Science Words

incomplete dominance
multiple alleles
polygenic inheritance

Objectives

▶ Explain incomplete dominance.
▶ Compare multiple allele and polygenic inheritance, and give examples of both.

Science and WRITING

Write a brief report on Barbara McClintock. Find out about her work with genes that change position on chromosomes.

Figure 5-8. The diagram below shows how color in four o'clock flowers is inherited by incomplete dominance. The first generation plants (a) are crossed with each other to obtain the second generation (b).

Incomplete Dominance

When Mendel's work was rediscovered, scientists repeated his experiments. Mendel's results proved true for peas and other plants again and again. One scientist, Karl Correns, crossed pure red four o'clock plants with pure white four o'clocks. He expected to get all red flowers. But to his surprise, all the flowers were pink as in Figure 5-8a. Neither allele for flower color seemed dominant. Had the colors become blended like paint colors? He crossed the pink flowered plants with each other and red, pink, and white flowers were produced as in Figure 5-8b. The red and white alleles had not become "blended." When *both* alleles are expressed in offspring, the condition is called **incomplete dominance.** Coat color in cattle and horses and blood type in humans are examples of incomplete dominance.

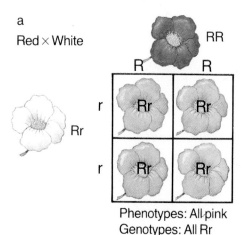

a
Red × White

Phenotypes: All-pink
Genotypes: All Rr

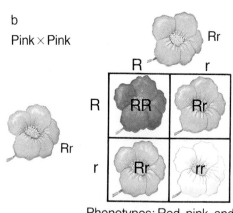

b
Pink × Pink

Phenotypes: Red, pink, and white
Genotypes: RR, Rr, and rr

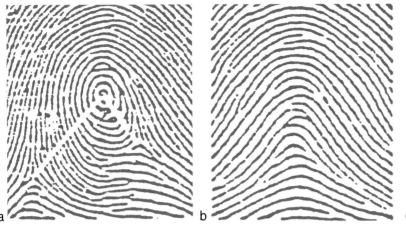
a
b

c

Figure 5-9. Fingerprints in your class will probably show varieties of the whorl (a), arch (b), and loop (c), patterns.

Multiple Alleles

Mendel studied traits in peas that had two alleles controlling a trait. However, many traits have more than two alleles, or **multiple alleles,** that control them. In the human population, blood type is a trait that has three alleles.

In 1900, Dr. Karl Landsteiner found three blood types in the human population. He called them A, B, and O. A and B alleles are inherited by incomplete dominance. A person with AB blood type shows both alleles in his or her phenotype. However, both A and B alleles are dominant to the O allele, which is recessive.

Table 5-3 shows the ways in which the alleles for blood type can combine. Notice that a person with phenotype A blood has inherited either the genotype AA or AO. A person with phenotype B blood has inherited either genotype BB or BO. For a person to have type AB blood, an A allele is inherited from one parent and a B allele is inherited from the other parent. Finally, a person with phenotype O blood has inherited an O allele from each parent and has the genotype OO.

MINI-Lab

What are fingerprints?
Fingerprints are formed before birth. The whorl pattern shown in Figure 5-9 is *LL;* the arch pattern is *ll;* the hybrid, or heterozygous, condition is *Ll* and shows a looped pattern. Collect data to see which patterns appear in your class. Explain what type of inheritance is in action in fingerprints.

Table 5-3

HUMAN BLOOD TYPES	
Phenotype	**Genotype**
A	AA or AO
B	BB or BO
AB	AB
O	OO

Multiple Genes

How many different shades of blue or brown eye color can you detect among your classmates? Eye color is an example of a single trait that is produced by a combination of many pairs of genes. **Polygenic** (pahl ih JEHN ihk) **inheritance** occurs when a group of gene pairs act together to produce a single trait. The effect of each allele may be small, but the combination produces a wide variety. You'll probably have trouble classifying all the different shades of blue or brown eyes in your class.

Many human traits are controlled by polygenic inheritance. Height, weight, body build, and shape of eyes, lips, and ears are traits controlled by polygenic inheritance. It is estimated that skin color is controlled by three to six pairs of genes. Even more gene pairs may control the color of your hair and eyes.

Polygenic inheritance is, of course, not limited to human traits. Grain color in wheat, milk production in cows, and egg production in chickens are polygenic traits also.

The study of genes is no longer a simple look at a single trait controlled by one pair of alleles. Mendel would be astounded if he could see the amount of information that has come from his beginning work.

Figure 5-10. Eye color in humans is the result of more than one pair of genes.

SECTION REVIEW

1. How is multiple allele inheritance different from polygenic inheritance?
2. Explain why a trait inherited by incomplete dominance is not a blend of two alleles.
3. **Apply:** A chicken that is purebred for black feathers is crossed with one that is purebred for white feathers. All the offspring produced have shiny blue feathers. Explain how you could determine whether this was a case of incomplete dominance.

Skill Builder

☒ Comparing and Contrasting

Using the information on pages 115 and 116, compare and contrast multiple alleles and multiple genes to explain differences between the two concepts. Include examples of each. If you need help, refer to Comparing and Contrasting in the **Skill Handbook** on page 683.

Human Genetics

Objectives

▶ Describe two human genetic disorders.
▶ Explain inheritance of sex-linked traits.
▶ Explain the importance of genetic engineering.

New Science Words

sex-linked gene
pedigree
genetic engineering

Genes and Health

Sometimes a gene undergoes mutation and results in an unwanted trait. If this happens in a sex cell, then all cells in future generations are affected. In Chapter 4, you learned that there are several types of mutations. Not all mutations are harmful, but some have resulted in genetic disorders among humans. In Chapter 4, you learned that Down syndrome results from an extra chromosome. Two disorders discussed here are the result of alterations in DNA and are therefore gene mutations.

Sickle-cell anemia (uh NEE mee uh) is a homozygous recessive disorder in which red blood cells are sickle-shaped instead of disc-shaped. Sickle cells can't deliver enough oxygen to the cells in the body. In addition, the misshapen cells don't move through blood vessels easily. Body tissues may be damaged due to insufficient oxygen. Sickle-cell anemia is found in tropical areas and in a small percentage of Afro-Americans.

Cystic fibrosis is another homozygous recessive disorder. Thick mucus is produced in the lungs and digestive system. Mucus in the lungs restricts oxygen intake. In the digestive system, enzymes can't reach food to break it down. Nutrients needed by the body aren't absorbed by body cells. However, with physical therapy exercises and improved medication, the lives of cystic fibrosis patients are being extended.

Did You Know?

In Africa, people who are heterozygous for sickle-cell condition appear to be better protected against malaria than people with normal disc-shaped red blood cells.

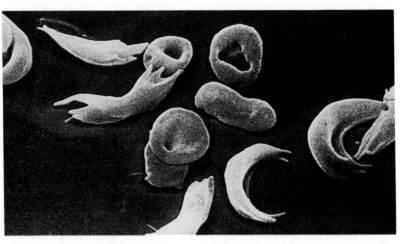

Figure 5-11. In sickle-cell anemia, red blood cells are misshapen.

Figure 5-12. Sex in many organisms is determined by X and Y chromosomes.

Sex Determination

What determines the sex of an individual? Information on sex inheritance in many organisms, including humans, came from a study of fruit flies. Fruit flies have eight large chromosomes in their cells. They contain an X chromosome and a Y chromosome. In 1910, Thomas Hunt Morgan concluded that the X and Y chromosomes contained genes that determine the sex of an individual. Females have two X chromosomes in their cells. Males have an X chromosome and a Y chromosome.

Females produce gametes that have only an X chromosome. Males, on the other hand, produce X containing gametes and Y containing gametes. When an X gamete from a female is fertilized by an X gamete from a male, the offspring is XX, a female. When an X gamete from a female is fertilized by a Y gamete from a male, the zygote produced is XY, and the offspring is a male. What pair of sex chromosomes is in each of your cells?

PROBLEM SOLVING

Boy or Girl?

What is the probability of all children in a family being girls? Probability refers to the chance that an event will occur. For example, if you flip a coin, it will land in only one of two ways—heads or tails. The probability of the coin landing heads or tails is one out of two, or one-half, or 50 percent.

If you were to toss two coins at the same time, each coin still has only a one-half probability of landing with heads or tails up. Look at the combinations that could occur in a two-coin toss. The probability of each combination is the product of the probability of each. In the two-coin toss, the probability of both coins turning up heads is the product of the two, or:

$$1/2 \times 1/2 = 1/4$$

Jennifer's mother is going to have a baby. Jennifer already has a sister, so she really hopes this baby is a boy. What is the probability of the baby being a boy?

Think Critically: What is the probability of Jennifer's parents having three girls in a row?

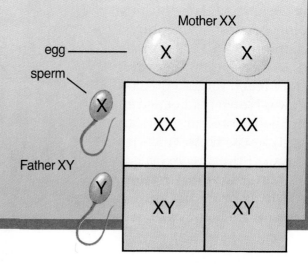

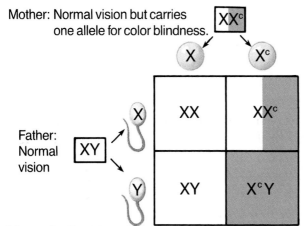

Mother: Normal vision but carries one allele for color blindness.

Father: Normal vision

Possible results: Daughters have normal vision, but may be carriers 50% chance of sons being normal or color blind.

a

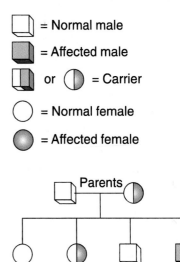

b

Figure 5-13. Color blindness is a sex-linked trait. Females who are heterozygous see colors normally, but their sons may be color-blind (a). In an eye examination, a color-blind person will see a different number in the disc above (b) than a person with normal color vision.

Sex-linked Disorders

Some inherited conditions are closely linked with the X and Y chromosomes that determine the sex of an individual. A story is told that a young boy appeared to have normal intelligence, but couldn't be taught to pick ripe cherries on the family farm. His parents took him to a doctor. After observing him, the doctor concluded that the boy couldn't tell the difference between the colors red and green. Individuals who are red-green color-blind have inherited an allele on the X chromosome that prevents them from seeing these colors.

An allele inherited on a sex chromosome is a **sex-linked gene.** More males are color-blind that females. Can you figure out why? If a male inherits an X chromosome with the color-blind allele from his mother, he will be color-blind. Color-blind females are rare.

Another sex-linked gene disease is hemophilia (hee muh FIHL ee uh), a disorder in which blood does not clot properly. A small scrape can be life threatening. Like color-blindness, males who inherit the X chromosome with the hemophilia allele will have the disorder. For a female to be a hemophiliac, she must inherit the defective allele on both X chromosomes. Hemophilia occurs in fewer than 1 out of 100 males and even less in females.

A **pedigree** is a tool for tracing a trait in a family. Males are represented by squares and females by circles. A solid circle or square shows that the person has the condition. Half colored circles or squares indicate carriers. A carrier has an allele for a trait, but does not show the trait. A horizontal line indicates a mating.

Figure 5-14. Pedigrees show the occurrence of a trait in a family.

☐ = Normal male

◼ = Affected male

◧ or ◐ = Carrier

○ = Normal female

● = Affected female

Parents

Children

Why Is Genetics Important?

If Mendel were to pick up a daily newspaper in most countries today, he probably wouldn't believe his eyes. There is hardly a day that goes by anymore that there isn't a news article about the latest information on genetic research. The word *gene* has become a household word. In this chapter, you have learned that every trait that you have inherited is the result of genes expressing themselves. The same laws that govern inheritance of traits in humans govern the inheritance of traits in watermelons, wheat, and mice as well.

In this section on human genetics, you've seen that there are inherited disorders that affect the human population. You may even know someone with one of these disorders. Many genetic disorders are controlled by diet and preventive measures. Genetics is no longer something that you can read about only in textbooks.

T E C H N O L O G Y

Karyotyping

Karyotyping is a process that allows scientists to study the chromosomes of an individual, sometimes even before birth.

Chromosomes are best seen during prophase in mitosis when they are tightly coiled. Skin cells divide frequently, so these cells are good to use for making a karyotype. The cells are fixed on microscope slides and dyed so that light and dark bands appear showing the position of DNA along the chromosomes. Then a photograph is taken of the chromosomes. The photograph is cut up into individual chromosomes. Scientists use the pattern of the stained bands, chromosome length, and the position of centromeres to identify pairs of matching chromosomes. Each pair is also numbered. The bands enable scientists to see if chromosomes have missing or duplicated parts.

Some genetic disorders can be identified just by looking at the karyotype of an individual. Sometimes this is done before birth when cells are taken from fluid around a fetus.

Think Critically: Why would a missing part of a chromosome affect the traits an individual would have?

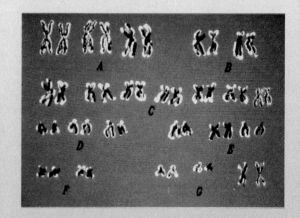

Figure 5-15. Genetically engineered bacteria are being developed to clean up environmental problems such as oil spills.

Knowing how genes are inherited is now causing some people to seek the advice of genetic counselors before having children. For those who have children with genetic disorders, there is a high degree of interest in research that might cure these conditions.

Through **genetic engineering**, scientists are experimenting with methods that allow them to go into cells to change or correct specific damaged or mutated genes. Genetic engineering is already used to help produce large quantities of medicine, such as insulin, to meet the needs of people with the disease diabetes. In addition, genetic engineering research is being used to find new ways to provide people with more nutritious food. Genetics is becoming more a part of your life every day.

Science and WRITING

Use resources in your library to research the work of Hugh de Vries, Walter Sutton, and Thomas Hunt Morgan in the field of genetics. Summarize their work in a written report.

What is genetic engineering?

SECTION REVIEW

1. List two genetic disorders.
2. Explain why males are affected more often than females by sex-linked genetic disorders?
3. Describe the importance of genetic engineering.
4. **Apply:** Use a Punnett square to explain how a woman who is a carrier for color blindness can have a daughter who is color-blind.

☑ Concept Mapping

Use a network tree concept map to show how X and Y gametes can combine to form zygotes. Begin with female gametes each containing an X chromosome. Use two male gametes. Indicate one with an X chromosome and one with a Y chromosome. If you need help, refer to Concept Mapping in the **Skill Handbook** on pages 688 and 689.

Skill Builder

5-4 The Human Genome

New Science Words

genome

Objectives

▶ Describe the goal of the Human Genome Project.
▶ Explain some advantages and disadvantages of genetic research.

What is a genome?

EcoTip

Each animal and plant has a unique set of genes. Keeping the environment pollution-free helps them to survive.

Tracking Human Genes

Think of the DNA that makes up your chromosomes. It is somewhat like a long railroad track. Just as railroad engineers use maps showing the various towns along rail routes, genetic engineers also are now able to locate particular genes along each chromosome. The resulting chromosome map, or **genome,** is a chart that shows the location of individual genes on a chromosome. A project called the *Human Genome Project* is aimed at mapping all the genes on all the human chromosomes. In all, there are about 100 000 genes on the 46 chromosomes in each of the body cells of your body. About 1000 of these genes have been mapped so far.

Much like a railroad engineer who stops at a specific station, scientists who study chromosomes are able to follow a piece of DNA and stop at the spot where a gene is located. Using chromosome maps, they can identify genes responsible for specific traits.

Why would such a map be useful? More than 3000 human disorders are known to be inherited, including cystic fibrosis, muscular dystrophy, and cancers caused by chemicals that change DNA. By examining a few drops of blood, scientists will be able to examine all chromosomes and find genes that code for certain disorders. After examining a person's genes, a doctor can tell if that person has a certain disorder. Doctors are then able to suggest measures to avoid development of the disorder. A person showing an inherited heart disease may begin a stress management program to reduce the chances of having a heart attack. Someone else might decide not to have children based on the information in the genome.

This information may save lives, but there are other facets to consider with this new technology. For example, what if company officials wanted to examine the genome of anyone who applied to them for a job? This information might be able to identify inherited traits that would affect job performance. An airline company might be unwilling to hire a person who is genetically inclined to suffer from alcoholism. This technology may help prevent the development of many disorders, but is it fair to deny a job to someone who *may* develop a disorder?

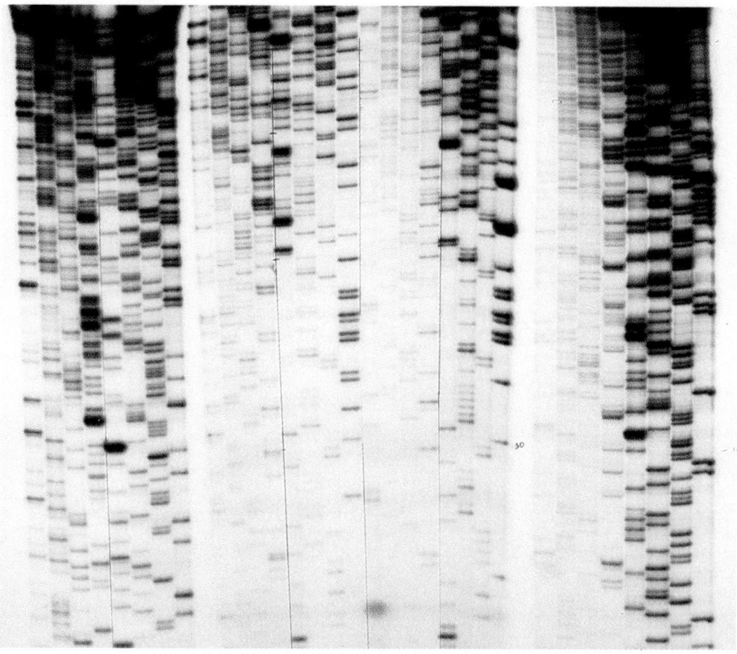

What if a handicap or an inheritable disorder could be spotted while a child is still young? Early detection would allow therapy that could permit a much more enjoyable life.

Most scientists agree that the benefits of the Human Genome Project will far outweigh the costs. Such large research projects almost always result in other technologies that can be used in other sciences. Knowing the location and DNA code of some genes may even make it possible to cure human genetic disorders in the future.

Figure 5-16. Studies of parts of chromosomes can be used to produce chromosome maps that show where specific genes are located.

SECTION REVIEW

1. What is the purpose of the Human Genome Project?
2. List one possible advantage and one possible disadvantage of this type of technology.

You Decide!

Although the human genome initiative could mean good things for people with genetic disorders, the use of such technology may cause problems. Some genetic traits may hinder an individual's ability to perform a job safely. Do you feel that an employer should be given the right to use genetic information to judge an individual's ability to perform a job?

SCIENCE & SOCIETY

ACTIVITY 5-2
Determining Polygenic Inheritance

Problem: *How can the effect of polygenic inheritance be determined?*

Materials
- metric ruler
- graph paper
- pencil

Procedure
1. Make a hypothesis about what a bar graph will look like that shows the heights of the students in your class.
2. Measure the height of every student in the class to the nearest centimeter.
3. Record the height of each student.
4. Make a table on your paper like the one shown. Count the number of students for each interval and complete the table.
5. Plot the results from the table on a bar graph. The height should be graphed on the vertical axis and the number of students of each height along the horizontal axis.

6. The *range* of a set of data is the difference between the greatest measurement and the smallest measurement. The *median* is the middle number when the data are placed in order. The *mean* is the sum of all the data divided by the number of addends. The *mode* is the number that appears most often in the measurements. Calculate each of these numbers.

Analyze
1. What is the range of the heights in your class?
2. What is the median height in your class?
3. What is the mean of the heights in your class?
4. What is the mode of the heights in your class?

Conclude and Apply
5. What does the bar graph look like?
6. How can you tell if a trait is controlled by more than one gene?
7. Do the data indicate that height is controlled by more than two genes?

Data and Observations

Height in cm	Number of Students
101 - 110	
111 - 120	
121 - 130	
131 - 140	
141 - 150	
151 - 160	
161 - 170	
171 - 180	

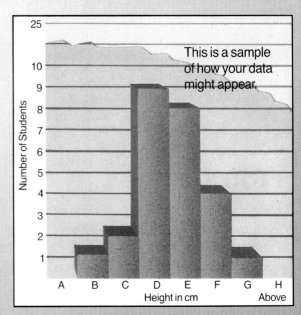

This is a sample of how your data might appear.

CHAPTER
REVIEW

5-1: What Is Genetics?

1. Traits are inherited through alleles passed from one generation to the next. Gregor Mendel determined the basic laws of genetics through controlled experiments.

2. The probability of types of offspring from parents can be predicted by using Punnett squares.

3. Genotype is the genetic makeup of an organism for a trait. Phenotype is the physical appearance that results from the genotype.

5-2: Genetics Since Mendel

1. When a trait is inherited by incomplete dominance, neither allele is completely dominant.

2. With multiple alleles, there are more than two alleles controlling a trait. In polygenic inheritance, more than one pair of alleles controls a trait. Eye and hair color are determined by polygenic inheritance.

5-3: Human Genetics

1. Hemophilia and cystic fibrosis are genetic disorders.

2. Color blindness and hemophilia are located on the X chromosomes. Males express sex-linked traits more than females. Pedigrees may show patterns of inheritance in a family.

3. Genetic engineering may be used to correct mutated genes, cure disease, and produce medicine and food.

5-4: Science and Society: The Human Genome

1. The Human Genome Project seeks to locate and identify all the genes on human chromosomes.

2. Genome information may help pinpoint specific genetic disorders.

KEY SCIENCE WORDS

a. alleles
b. dominant
c. genetic engineering
d. genetics
e. genome
f. genotype
g. heredity
h. heterozygous
i. homozygous
j. incomplete dominance
k. multiple alleles
l. pedigree
m. phenotype
n. polygenic inheritance
o. probability
p. Punnett square
q. purebred
r. recessive
s. sex-linked gene

UNDERSTANDING VOCABULARY

Match each phrase with the correct term from the list of Key Science Words.

1. technology for changing a gene
2. gene located on the X chromosome
3. the allele that is hidden
4. different forms of the same gene
5. the chance that an event will take place
6. an allele that does not show completely
7. the study of heredity
8. more than one pair of alleles controls a trait
9. shows the pattern of gene inheritance in a family
10. all the genes in a species

CHAPTER
REVIEW

CHECKING CONCEPTS

Choose the word or phrase that completes the sentence.

1. _____ are located on chromosomes.
   a. DNA codes   c. Genes
   b. Alleles   d. All of the above
2. Color blindness results from an allele that is
   _____.
   a. dominant
   b. on the Y chromosome
   c. on the X chromosome
   d. all of these
3. _____ results when two alleles both show in the phenotype.
   a. Incomplete dominance
   b. Polygenic inheritance
   c. Multiple alleles
   d. Sex-linked genes
4. During meiosis, _____ for the same trait became separated.
   a. proteins   c. alleles
   b. cells   d. pedigrees
5. Genes _____.
   a. are on chromosomes
   b. control protein
   c. regulate other genes
   d. all of these
6. Blood type is an example of a trait inherited through _____.
   a. polygenic inheritance
   b. multiple alleles
   c. incomplete dominance
   d. recessive genes
7. Sickle-cell anemia is an example of a trait inherited through _____.
   a. polygenic inheritance
   b. multiple alleles
   c. incomplete dominance
   d. recessive genes

8. Eye color is a trait inherited through _____.
   a. polygenic inheritance
   b. multiple alleles
   c. incomplete dominance
   d. recessive genes
9. A female is produced if the egg unites with a sperm containing _____.
   a. an X chromosome   c. a Y chromosome
   b. XX chromosomes   d. XY chromosomes
10. Punnett squares are used to _____ the outcome of crosses of traits.
   a. dominate   c. assure
   b. predict   d. number

UNDERSTANDING CONCEPTS

Complete each sentence.

11. A(n) _____ trait hides a recessive trait.
12. A heterozygous condition has _____ different alleles.
13. _____ is the passing of traits from one generation to the next.
14. More than one pair of genes act together to produce _____ traits.
15. A disorder in blood clotting is a sex-linked trait called _____.

THINK AND WRITE CRITICALLY

16. Compare and contrast multiple allele inheritance and polygenic inheritance.
17. Explain the importance of Mendel's experimental methods.
18. Using an example, explain how blood typing could be used to detect the correct parent of a newborn if there was a mix-up in a nursery.

19. What is the difference between homozygous and heterozygous?
20. Explain why dominant traits might not necessarily be the traits that show up most frequently.

APPLY

21. A pure black guinea pig is crossed with a pure white guinea. All the offspring are black. What are the genotypes of the parents and the offspring?
22. In breeding Andalusian variety chickens, farmers found that chickens with black feathers always had chicks with black feathers, and chickens with white feathers always had chicks with white feathers. But, mating a black with a white chicken produced some chickens with blue feathers. How can this trait be explained?
23. Explain the relationship between DNA, genes, alleles, and chromosomes.
24. How will finding the location of disease-causing genes on chromosomes help to cure genetic diseases?
25. Explain how an organism that has a genotype *Gg* could have the same phenotype as an organism with the genotype *GG*.

MORE SKILL BUILDERS

If you need help, refer to the Skill Handbook.

1. **Experimenting:** Design an experiment to determine if a trait is transmitted by a dominant or recessive gene.
2. **Recognizing Cause and Effect:** A mutation in the gene for normal production of a plant's chlorophyll results in a plant with no chlorophyll. Explain the consequences.

3. **Classifying:** Classify the type of inheritance of each human trait by making a chart: blood type, color blindness, eye color, height, hemophilia, sickle-cell anemia, weight.
4. **Interpreting Scientific Illustrations:** What genotypes and phenotypes would be produced if you crossed a red offspring with a pink offspring from Figure 5-8b on page 114?
5. **Concept Mapping:** On a separate sheet of paper, use the following terms to complete the network tree concept map below: phenotype, recessive genes, dominant.

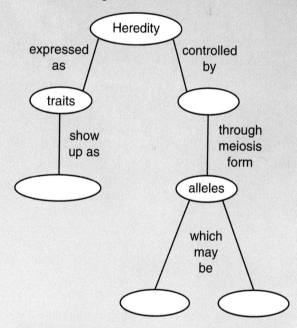

PROJECTS

1. Research a genetic disease such as cystic fibrosis. How is it inherited? Who does it affect? How can it be detected? What are its symptoms? How can it be treated? Share your findings with the class in a written report.
2. Research sex determination in birds, butterflies, and reptiles to find out how it differs from sex inheritance in humans.

CHAPTER

6 Evolution

Have you ever wondered why some grasshoppers are green? Do you know why polar bears are white and grizzly bears brown?

FIND OUT!

Do this simple activity to find out why some organisms are the color they are.

Spread out a sheet of newspaper want ads on the floor. Cut ten 5 cm by 5 cm squares out of another sheet of newspaper want ads, a sheet of black paper, and a sheet of white paper. Scatter the 30 squares randomly across the sheet of newspaper on the floor. Have a partner time you for 10 seconds, and pick up squares from the newspaper. Count and record the number of squares of each color you picked up. Return the squares to the newspaper. Repeat this process three times and average your results. If the squares represented organisms in their environment, which ones would most likely not be found? Now why do you think grasshoppers are green?

Gearing Up

Previewing the Chapter
Use this outline to help you focus on important ideas in this chapter.

Section 6-1   Mechanisms of Evolution
▶ Early Theories of Evolution
▶ Evolution by Natural Selection
▶ Adaptation and Variation
▶ How Fast Does Evolution Occur?
Section 6-2   Evidence for Evolution
▶ Fossil Evidence
▶ The Fossil Record
▶ Other Evidence for Evolution
**Section 6-3   Science and Society
Plant and Animal Extinction**
▶ Causes of Extinction
▶ Ways to Prevent Extinction
Section 6-4   Human Evolution
▶ Primates
▶ Human Ancestors
▶ Modern Humans

Previewing Science Skills
▶ In the **Skill Builders**, you will classify, use tables, and make a concept map.
▶ In the **Activities**, you will collect and organize data, interpret data, and formulate models.
▶ In the **MINI-Labs**, you will experiment and predict.

What's next?

In nature, organisms that are well suited to their environment have a better chance of surviving than those that aren't. In this chapter, you will learn why organisms live where they do and how organisms change. You will also learn about the process of evolution.

6-1 Mechanisms of Evolution

New Science Words

species
evolution
natural selection
variation
population
gradualism
punctuated equilibrium

Objectives

▶ Compare and contrast Lamarck's theory of evolution with Darwin's.
▶ Explain the importance of variations in organisms.
▶ Relate how gradualism and punctuated equilibrium describe the rate of evolution.

Early Theories of Evolution

On Earth today there are millions of different types of organisms. Included among these are different species of plants, animals, bacteria, fungi, and protozoa. A **species** is a group of organisms whose members look alike and successfully reproduce among themselves. Have any of these species of organisms changed since they first appeared on Earth? Are they still changing today? Evidence from observation and experimentation shows that living things have changed through time and are still changing. Change in the hereditary features of a type of organism over time is **evolution.** Figure 6-1 shows how the horse has changed over time.

Figure 6-1. The evolution of the horse. Notice the change from several toes to a single hoof.

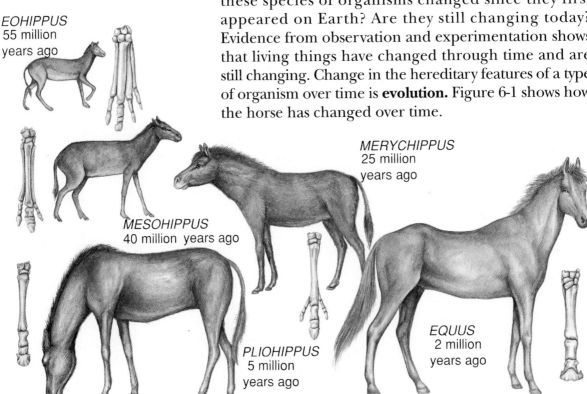

EOHIPPUS
55 million
years ago

MESOHIPPUS
40 million years ago

MERYCHIPPUS
25 million
years ago

PLIOHIPPUS
5 million
years ago

EQUUS
2 million
years ago

Figure 6-2. It takes years of practice and lessons for most people to know how to play an instrument.

In 1809, Jean Baptiste de Lamarck, a French scientist, proposed one of the first theories to explain how species evolve or change. Lamarck hypothesized that species evolve by keeping traits that their parents developed during their life. According to Larmarck, if one of your parents was a bodybuilder and had large muscles, then you would be born with large muscles. Lamarck's theory of evolution is often called the theory of acquired characteristics. Characteristics that were not used were lost from the species.

From your study of Chapter 5, you know that genes on chromosomes control the inheritance of traits. The traits you develop from your life-style, such as strong muscles from bodybuilding, are not inherited. After scientists collected large amounts of data on the inheritance of acquired characteristics, Lamarck's theory wasn't accepted. The data showed that characteristics an organism develops during its life aren't passed on to its offspring.

Evolution by Natural Selection

In the mid-1800s, Charles Darwin developed the theory of evolution still accepted today. At the age of 22, Darwin, after trying several other careers, became the ship's naturalist aboard the *HMS Beagle*. The *Beagle* was on a trip to survey the east and west coasts of South America. The ship sailed from England in December 1831. Darwin was responsible for recording information about all the plants and animals he observed during the journey.

Figure 6-3. According to Lamarck the necks of giraffes became longer when they stretched to reach high branches, and this acquired trait was passed on to their offspring.

Darwin collected many plants, animals, and fossils. He was amazed by the unique plants and animals he found in the Galapagos Islands. The Galapagos Islands are located off the coast of Ecuador in South America. He observed giant cactus trees, 14 species of very similar finches, and huge land tortoises. Darwin was very interested in the finches. He wondered how so many different, but closely related, species of finches could live in areas so near each other.

For 20 years after the voyage Darwin continued studying his collections. He thought about his observations and conducted further studies. He collected evidence of variations among species by breeding pigeons for racing. He also studied breeds of dogs, and other animals and varieties of flowers. Darwin knew that people used artificial selection in breeding plants and animals. They chose parents that the traits they wanted in the offspring.

Darwin concluded from his research that individuals with traits most favorable for a specific environment survived and passed on these traits to their offspring. This is the theory of **natural selection.** The factors Darwin identified that govern natural selection are:

1. Organisms produce more offspring than can survive.
2. Variations are found among individuals of a species.
3. Some variations are better for survival and reproduction than others.
4. Over time, offspring of individuals with advantageous variations make up more of the population.

Figure 6-4. A map of Darwin's voyage, and some of the unique organisms he found in the Galapagos Islands: (a) a tree cactus, (b) marine iguana, (c) the blue-footed booby, and (d) a Hood Island saddleback tortoise.

PROBLEM SOLVING

Why Isn't Earth Covered with Pumpkins and Pike?

Assume that there are 70 seeds in one pumpkin and that this is the typical number for the species. The 70 seeds are planted and each seed grows into a plant that produces two pumpkins. The first year 70 seeds are planted. The number of seeds produced in three years can be calculated by multiplying the number of seeds times two pumpkins for each plant times 70 seeds in each pumpkin:

Year 1: 70 x 2 x 70 = 9800
Year 2: 9800 x 2 x 70 = 1 372 000
Year 3: 1 372 000 x 2 x 70
　　　　　　　　 = 192 080 000 seeds

The largest possible number of offspring produced by one individual is known as the biotic potential of a species.

If the ovaries of a pike contain 42 000 eggs, all the eggs are fertilized and hatched, all the young survive to reproduce, and one-half of the young are females, how many pike would there be after two more generations?

Think Critically: Why is the maximum rate of biotic potential never reached?

Natural selection results in organisms with traits best suited to the environment. This theory is also called "survival of the fittest."

Darwin wrote a book describing his theory of evolution by natural selection. His book *On the Origin of Species by Means of Natural Selection* was published in 1859. Although minor changes have been made to Darwin's theory as new information has been gathered, his theory is one of the most important concepts in the study of life science.

Adaptation and Variation

One of the points in Darwin's theory of evolution is that variations are found among individuals of a species. What are variations? A **variation** is an appearance of an inherited trait that makes an individual different from other members of the same species. Variations can be small, such as differences in the number of petals of a

What is a variation?

MINI-Lab

How does evolution occur?

Below are diagrams representing different species that came from the same ancestor. Determine which is the ancestor and then put the species in order, from simplest to most complex. Use one change in structure at a time. Each structural change is a variation and a new species forms. How does this help illustrate how evolution occurs?

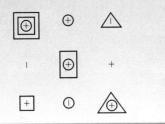

Figure 6-5. Some organisms blend into their environment. Variations among kittens occur in the same litter.

flower, or large, such as an albino deer or a fruit without seeds. Variations are important in populations of organisms. A **population** is a group of organisms of one species that live in an area. If enough variations spread through a population, a new species may evolve from the existing species. Evolution of a new species isn't often seen because it usually takes many generations.

Remember from Chapter 1 that an adaptation is any variation that makes an organism better suited to its environment. The variations that result in adaptation can be in an organism's color, shape, behavior, or chemical makeup. An organism whose color or shape provides camouflage is more likely to survive and reproduce. Camouflage is a protective adaptation that lets an organism blend into its environment. Organisms that can't be easily seen are more likely to survive and reproduce. These types of variations result from mutations, changes in an organism's DNA. Mutations are the source of variation among organisms.

Several other factors bring about evolution. The movement of individuals into or out of a population brings in new genes and variations. Have you ever had a foreign exchange student come to your class? If you have, you know the student brought new ideas, maybe a new style of dress, and even a new language. When new individuals come into an existing population, they can bring in new genes and variations in much the same way. The isolation of some individuals from others by geography and changes in climate can also result in evolutionary change. Each of these factors affects how fast evolution occurs.

How Fast Does Evolution Occur?

How fast does evolution occur? Scientists are debating that question. Most scientists hypothesize that evolution occurs very slowly, perhaps taking tens or hundreds of millions of years. Other scientists hypothesize that evolution may occur very quickly, perhaps in a million years.

Darwin hypothesized that the rate of evolution was steady, slow, and continuous. The model that describes evolution as a slow change of one species to another new species is known as **gradualism.** In this theory there should be intermediate forms of all species.

Another model, the **punctuated equilibrium** model, states that rapid evolution of species comes about by the mutation of a few genes. This is a steplike pattern of evolution. These mutations produce large changes in body form in a short period of time. Without a doubt, many examples in the fossil record give evidence for this type of evolution.

What is the rate of evolution? There is no one convincing answer yet. As you study the evidence for evolution in the next section, you will see that the evidence supports a combination of the two models.

Gradualism

Punctuated equilibrium

Figure 6-6. Evolution can occur very slowly or very rapidly.

SECTION REVIEW

1. Compare Lamarck's theory of evolution with Darwin's.
2. How are variations important in a population?
3. Explain how the gradualism model of evolution differs from the punctuated equilibrium model.
4. **Apply:** Which of the following variations would be beneficial to an animal living in the Arctic; thick fur, large size, large ears? Why?

☑ Classifying

Classify the following variations as being in an organism's shape, color, chemical makeup, or behavior.
1. Two species mate and don't produce offspring.
2. One species has large forelimbs and another species has short forelimbs.
3. Two species of birds build nests in different places.

If you need help, refer to Classifying in the **Skill Handbook** on page 680.

Skill Builder

6-2 Evidence for Evolution

New Science Words

fossils
sedimentary rock
relative dating
radioactive elements
homologous
vestigial structure
embryology

Objectives

▶ Describe the importance of fossils as evidence of evolution.
▶ Explain how relative and radioactive dating are used to date the fossil record.
▶ Give examples of five types of evidence for evolution.

Fossil Evidence

On a hot day in July 1975, in North Central Texas, a young couple was strolling along the breezy shores of Lake Lavon. The couple came across some odd-looking rocks projecting from the muddy shore. They noticed the rocks seemed different from the surrounding limestone rocks. They took a few of the rocks to Dr. Harold Laughlin, a local scientist specializing in reptiles and amphibians. Dr. Laughlin recognized the rocks as pieces of the skull of a fossil mosasaur (MA sah sawr), an extinct lizard that lived in salt water.

Figure 6-7. Uncovering fossils requires careful work.

Figure 6-8. Several types of fossils: (a) an imprint made by a leaf, (b) a cast of an ancient mollusk, and (c) an insect caught in plant resin.

Dr. Laughlin contacted Professor Slaughter, a scientist who studies fossils, at Southern Methodist University. With the help of students, Professor Slaughter and Dr. Laughlin returned to the site and carefully dug up the rest of the fossil mosasaur. It took one of Slaughter's graduate students almost a year to study, preserve, and reassemble the 1.75 meter skull of the 15-meter-long fossil mosasaur. This find provides evidence that about 120 million years ago the North Texas area—now more than 500 kilometers from the Gulf of Mexico—was covered by a shallow sea.

The most abundant evidence for evolution comes from fossils like those found on the shore of Lake Lavon in Texas. **Fossils** are any remains of life from an earlier time. Examples of fossils include:

1. the imprint of a leaf, animal, or feather in rock;
2. a cast made of minerals that filled in the hollows of an animal track or mollusk shell;
3. a piece of wood or bone replaced by minerals;
4. an animal or plant frozen in ice; and
5. an insect or reptile trapped in plant resin.

Sedimentary rock contains most fossils. **Sedimentary rock** is a rock type formed by mud, sand, or other fine particles that settle out of a liquid. Limestone, sandstone, and shale are all examples of sedimentary rock. Fossils are found more often in limestone than in any other kind of sedimentary rock.

The Fossil Record

You learned that the mosasaur fossil found in Texas was 120 million years old. How was that date obtained? Scientists have divided Earth's history into eras and periods. These divisions make up the geologic time scale as shown in Table 6-1. Unique rock layers and fossils give information about the geology, weather, and life forms of each time period. There are two basic methods for reading the record of past life. When these methods are used together, accurate estimates of the ages of certain rocks and fossils are made.

One method often used to determine the approximate age of a rock layer, or fossils within the layer, is to look at where the particular rock layer is. In undisturbed areas, older rock layers lie below successively younger rock layers. Fossils found in the lower layers of rock are older than those in upper layers. This method of dating fossils is known as **relative dating.** Relative dating can only estimate the age of a fossil.

A method used to give a more accurate age to a rock layer or fossil is radioactive dating using radioactive elements. **Radioactive elements** are elements whose atoms give off radiation, a form of atomic energy. Uranium and a radioactive form of carbon are used in radioactive dating. Radioactive elements change to more stable products as they give off radiation. The radiation is given off at a constant rate, and the rate is different for each element. Scientists can measure how much of a radioactive element has changed. They can accurately determine the age of the rock by comparing the amount of stable product with the amount of radioactive element still present. For example, the radioactive element uranium changes to lead as it ages. Scientists can determine how old a fossil in a rock sample is by measuring the amounts of uranium and lead in the sample. The more lead there is, the older the fossil.

Figure 6-9. Fossils found in lower layers of sedimentary rock are usually older than fossils in upper layers.

How are fossils dated using radioactive elements?

Table 6-1

GEOLOGIC TIME SCALE

ERA	PERIOD	MILLION YEARS AGO	MAJOR EVOLUTIONARY EVENTS	REPRESENTATIVE ORGANISMS
Cenozoic	Quaternary		Humans evolve	
Cenozoic	Tertiary	5	First placental mammals	
Mesozoic	Cretaceous	65	Flowering plants dominant	
Mesozoic	Jurassic	144	First birds First mammals First flowering plants	
Mesozoic	Triassic	213	First dinosaurs	
Paleozoic	Permian	248	Cone-bearing plants dominant	
Paleozoic	Carboniferous	286 320	First reptiles Great coal deposits form First seed plants	
Paleozoic	Devonian	360	First Amphibians	
Paleozoic	Silurian	408	First land plants First jawed fish	
Paleozoic	Ordovician	438	Algae dominant First vertebrates	
Paleozoic	Cambrian	505	Simple invertebrates	
Precambrian		590	Life diversifies	
Precambrian			Eukaryotes	
Precambrian			Prokaryotes	
Precambrian			Life evolves	
Precambrian		3500		

An Ostrich Egg Timer

A dating technique called amino acid racemization (AAR), used to date the age of fossil objects, may turn ordinary eggshells into geologic clocks.

AAR uses amino acids left in materials produced by living things, to figure out how old the materials are. Over time, amino acids change into a slightly different form of their original form. By measuring the ratio of the original amino acids to the changed amino acids in an eggshell, the age of the shell can be determined. The technique works better in cold climates. In warm climates the rate of amino acid change is affected by temperature and by moisture.

Scientists are excited by AAR because it can be used to date objects that can't be dated by radioactive dating, such as eggshells, bits of rock, and tooth enamel. Ostrich eggshells are very common in many archeological sites. Early humans ate the eggs, and then used the shells as water con-tainers. Using AAR to date the eggshells helps scientists determine the age of the site.

AAR is an important technique because it allows scientists to date back 200 000 years at warm-weather sites, and one million years at cold-weather sites. Current radioactive carbon dating methods can't date back this far.

Think Critically: How can AAR dating help us understand human evolution?

Fossils are a record of organisms that lived in the past. But the fossil record is incomplete, much like a book with some pages missing. Because every living thing doesn't or can't become fossilized, the record will never be complete. By looking at fossils, scientists have determined that many simpler forms of life existed earlier in Earth's history, and more complex forms of life appeared later. The oldest fossil bacteria appeared 3.8 billion years ago. Simple plants did not appear until the Ordovician period about 430 million years ago. The first mammals and birds did not appear until the Jurassic period about 190 million years ago. The fossil record gives scientists convincing evidence that living things have evolved. There are still other types of evidence that support the theory of evolution.

Other Evidence for Evolution

Besides fossils, what other evidence is there for evolution? Scientists have found more evidence by looking at similarities in the chemical makeup, the development, and the structure among organisms. You know that the functions of your arm, a dolphin's flipper, a bat's wing, and a bird's wing are all very different. Yet, as you can see in Figure 6-10, they are all made up of the same bones. Each has about the same number of bones, muscles, and blood vessels. Each of these limbs developed from similar tissues in the embryo. Body parts that are similar in origin and structure are called **homologous.** Homologous structures give evidence that two or more species share comon ancestors.

Vestigial structures also give evidence for evolution. A **vestigial structure** is a body part that is reduced in size and doesn't seem to have a function. Examples of vestigial organs in humans are the appendix and the muscles that move the ear. Scientists think vestigial structures are leftover parts that once functioned in an ancestor.

Figure 6-10. A bird wing, bat wing, dolphin flipper, and human arm are homologous. Each has about the same number of bones, muscles, and blood vessels.

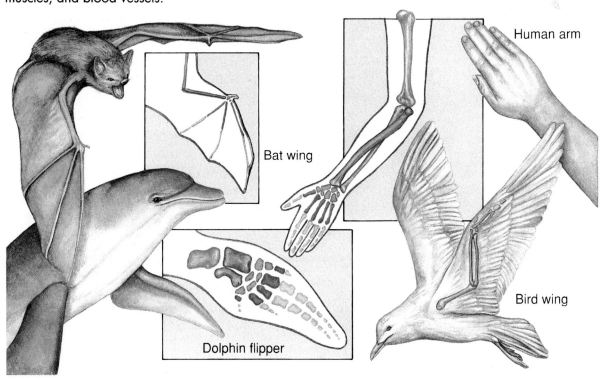

Bat wing

Human arm

Dolphin flipper

Bird wing

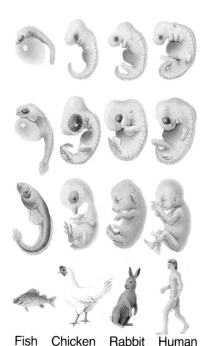

Fish   Chicken   Rabbit   Human

Figure 6-11. Similarities in the embryos of fish, chickens, rabbits, and humans show evidence of evolution.

The study of the development of embryos is called **embryology.** An embryo is an organism in its earliest stages of development. Compare the embryos of the organisms in Figure 6-11. Do you see similarities? In the early stages of development, the embryos of fish, reptiles, birds, and mammals have a tail and gills or gill slits. Fish keep their gills, but the other organisms lose them as their development continues. In humans, the tail disappears, but fish, birds, and lizards keep theirs. These similarities suggest an evolutionary relationship among all vertebrate species. This supports evidence from the fossil record that shows aquatic, gill-breathing organisms came before air-breathing land vertebrates.

Remember from Chapter 4 that DNA is the molecule that controls heredity. Scientists can also determine whether or not organisms are closely related by comparing their DNA. Organisms that are close relatives share more similarities in DNA with each other than with distant relatives. For example, by studying DNA, scientists have determined that dogs are the closest relatives of bears. You would probably not be surprised that gorillas and chimpanzees also have DNA that is very similar.

SECTION REVIEW

1. How do fossils give evidence for evolution?
2. How is radioactive dating used to interpret the fossil record?
3. List five examples of evidence that support the theory of evolution.
4. **Apply:** Fossil leaves are found in the top layer, fossils of shells are found in the bottom layer, and fish bones are in the middle layer of three undisturbed beds of sedimentary rock. List the fossil types from oldest to youngest.

Skill Builder

⊠ Making and Using Tables

Use Table 6-1, The Geologic Time Scale, to answer the following questions. During which periods did the first mammals and flowering plants appear? Which was the longest period of the Paleozoic era? If you need help, refer to Making and Using Tables in the **Skill Handbook** on page 690.

ACTIVITY 6-1
A Radioactive Dating Model

Problem: *How can a radioactive element be used to determine a fossil's age?*

Materials
- 100 pennies
- cardboard box with lid
- graph paper
- pencil

Procedure
1. A rock or fossil may be dated by measuring the relative amount of a stable element with its radioactive parent element. As the rock ages, the amount of radioactive element decreases and the amount of stable element increases. Examine the graph below to see the decrease of a radioactive element over time.
2. Make a data table like the one shown.
3. Place 100 pennies face up in the cardboard box and replace the lid.
4. Shake the coins in the box for 10 seconds.
5. Take off the lid and remove all coins that are face down.
6. Record the number of coins removed.
7. Repeat Steps 4 through 6 until all the coins have been removed.

Analyze
1. What happens to the number of coins remaining after each trial?
2. Construct a graph of your results. Plot the number of coins remaining face up on the y-axis, and plot the trials on the x-axis. How does your graph compare with the graph below?
3. How does shaking the box represent the energy given off by radioactive elements when they become stable?

Conclude and Apply
4. How is this model similar to the decay of a radioactive element?
5. How is this model unlike the decay of a radioactive element?
6. Why do you think radioactive dating is considered more accurate than dates calculated from fossil beds?
7. Why are different radioactive elements used to date rocks and fossils?

Data and Observations

Trial #	0	1	2	3	4	5	6	7	8
Coins Left	100								
# Removed	0								

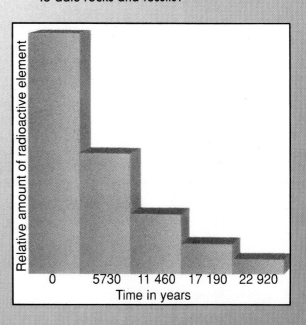

Plant and Animal Extinction

New Science Words

extinction
endangered species

Objectives

▶ Define extinction and identify some causes of extinction.
▶ Name two ways in which endangered species may be saved from extinction.

EcoTip

Extinction is forever. Don't buy products made from the skins and other parts of endangered animals.

Causes of Extinction

By the time you finish reading this paragraph, one more animal or plant species may have joined the thousands that have become extinct. Some scientists estimate that one-fourth of all animal and plant species alive in the world today will be extinct in only 25 years! What's going on?

Extinction, the dying out of a species, is a natural event. Extinction occurs naturally because the environment is always changing. To survive, each species must adapt to it. In nature, only those species that can best adapt to the changing environment will escape extinction. Through the slow process of natural selection, those species that are genetically unable to change along with the environment are naturally removed.

The rate of extinction has increased greatly due to destruction of natural habitats by humans. Not only have humans destroyed many species of plants and animals, but we also have destroyed habitats and food supplies that organisms depend on. With no home or food supply, a species will eventually die.

Figure 6-12. Plant and animal habitats are being destroyed by development.

Ways to Prevent Extinction

How can extinction be prevented? One way is to preserve the remaining natural areas in which endangered plants and animals live. An **endangered species** is one whose numbers are so low that it is in danger of becoming extinct. By preserving areas that have not yet been destroyed, we can keep organisms in their natural homes and let them rebuild their populations. Organizations, such as the Nature Conservancy, are working hard to save what untouched natural areas remain.

Another way to prevent extinction is to remove endangered animals from their natural habitats and breed them in captivity. After helping animals reproduce in a setting that provides food, shelter, and protection, researchers may then release them into the wild. Zoos have become very important in these types of programs.

Researchers are battling the extinction of Bengal tigers in this way. Only 3000 to 5000 of these tigers remain in the wild. This endangered species may be saved by a technique known as in vitro fertilization, joining an egg and sperm together in a test tube. An embryo results from the joining of an egg and sperm. Embryo transfer, the placing of the embryo in a female, then follows. If the procedure is successful, the embryo develops into a baby tiger. Zoos have been successful in breeding Bengal tigers by placing the embryo in a female Siberian tiger. Through surgery, the developed kittens were removed from the foster mother.

Figure 6-13. Bengal tigers are being bred in captivity to help save them from extinction.

It is hoped that in vitro fertilization can be used to help many other endangered animal species. By protecting the natural areas that are not yet destroyed and by breeding animals in captivity, preservationists are working to slow the current rate of extinction and preserve the species that remain.

SECTION REVIEW

1. Why is extinction not always a bad event?
2. Describe two ways in which we can work to save endangered species.

You Decide!

A lot of energy and money is put into programs that help us save endangered species from extinction. Are these species really worth our time and effort? Should we be concerned about saving an animal or plant that we'll never see?

6-4 Human Evolution

New Science Words

primates
hominids
Homo sapiens

Objectives

▶ Describe the evidence that monkeys, apes, and humans evolved from a common ancestor.
▶ Describe the ancestors of humans.
▶ Trace the evolutionary history of humans.

Primates

Monkeys, apes, and humans belong to the group of mammals called **primates.** The primates share several characteristics that led scientists to think all primates evolved from a common ancestor. All primates have opposable thumbs that allow them to reach out and bring food to the mouth. Having an opposable thumb allows you to cross your thumb across your palm and touch your fingers. Think of the problems you might have if you didn't have this type of thumb!

Another important primate characteristic is binocular vision. Binocular vision permits a primate to judge depth or distance with its eyes. All primates have flexible shoulders and rotating forelimbs. These allow tree-dwelling primates to swing easily from branch to branch, and allow you to swing on a jungle gym. Each of these characteristics provides evidence that the primates have common ancestry.

Figure 6-14. An opposable thumb allows tree-dwelling primates to hold onto branches. It also allows you to use your hand in many ways.

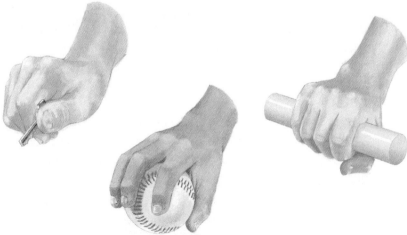

a   b

Figure 6-15. Lemurs (a) and tarsiers (b) belong to a subgroup of primates called the prosimians, which means "before apes."

Genetic evidence also supports the view that monkeys, apes, and humans all evolved from a common ancestor. The DNA of chimpanzees, gorillas, and humans is very similar. In addition, primates share many of the same proteins. Hemoglobin is a protein in red blood cells that carries oxygen. Many primates have hemoglobin that is almost identical.

Human Ancestors

Primates are divided into two major groups. The first group includes organisms such as lemurs and tarsiers. These animals have large eyes and are most active at night. The second group, the higher primates, includes monkeys, apes, and humans. About 6 million years ago the hominids, our earliest ancestors, branched off from the other higher primates. **Hominids** are humanlike primates that eat both meat and vegetables and walk upright on two feet. Hominids share some common characteristics with gorillas, orangutans, and chimpanzees. A larger brain size along with the characteristics mentioned above separated them from other great apes.

In 1924 Raymond Dart, a South African scientist, discovered an unusual fossil skull in a quarry in South Africa. The skull had a small brain cavity but humanlike jaw and teeth. Dart named his discovery *Australopithecus*. *Australopithecus*, one of the earliest hominid groups discovered, means "southern ape." In 1974, an almost complete skeleton of *Australopithecus* was discovered by an American scientist, Donald Johanson, and his colleagues. They named the fossil, estimated to be 2.9 to 3.4 million years old, Lucy. Lucy had a small brain but walked upright. Many scientists today believe humans evolved in Africa from ancestors similar to Lucy.

Figure 6-16. The fossil remains of Lucy, a hominid estimated to be 2.9 to 3.4 million years old.

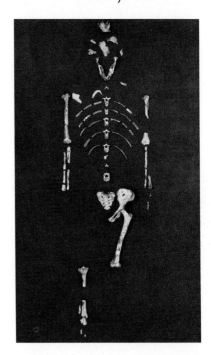

Science and WRITING

Using what you know of the characteristics of Neanderthal man, write an advertisement for *The Neanderthal News* for a modern-day product that you think humans might have been able to use back then.

About 40 years after the discovery of *Australopithecus,* a discovery was made in East Africa by Louis, Mary, and Richard Leakey. The Leakeys discovered a fossil more similar to present-day humans than *Australopithecus.* They named this hominid *Homo habilis,* the "handy man," because they found simple stone tools near him. Scientists estimate *Homo habilis* to be 1.5 to 2 million years old. Homo habilis is thought to be a direct ancestor of humans because it had a larger brain and was more similar in form to humans than *Australopithecus.*

Modern Humans

Our species is named ***Homo sapiens,*** meaning "wise human." The fossil record shows that the human species, a very recent arrival on Earth, evolved about 300 000 years ago. By about 125 000 years ago, two early groups of *Homo sapiens,* Neanderthal human and Cro-Magnon human, probably lived at the same time in parts of Africa and Europe.

Neanderthal humans had short, heavy bodies with thick massive bones, small chins, and heavy brow ridges. The Neanderthal humans lived in family groups in caves and hunted mammoths, deer, and other large animals with well-made stone tools. For reasons that are not clear, Neanderthal humans disappeared from the fossil record about 35 000 years ago.

Cro-Magnon fossils have been found in Europe, Asia, and Australia. These fossils are dated from 40 000 to about 10 000 years ago. Cro-Magnon humans are thought to

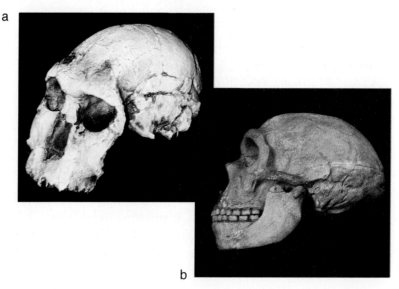

Figure 6-17. Fossil skulls of (a) *Homo habilis* and (b) Neanderthal. Notice the larger brain area in the Neanderthal skull.

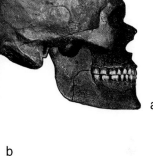

Figure 6-18. A Cro-Magnon skull (a) thought to be 10 000 to 40 000 years old. (b) Cave paintings done by Cro-Magnon man.

a

b

be the direct ancestors of modern humans. The oldest recorded art dates from the caves of France where Cro-Magnon humans first painted bison, horses, and spear-carrying people. Cro-Magnon humans lived in caves, made stone carvings, cared for their elderly, and buried their dead. Standing about 1.8 m tall, the physical appearance of Cro-Magnon people was almost identical to that of modern humans.

Science and MATH

Your grandfather's grandfather is your great, great grandfather. If a generation is 25 years, how many "greats" would there be in the title of your Cro-Magnon ancestor?

SECTION REVIEW

1. Describe at least three kinds of evidence that suggests all primates shared a common ancestor.
2. What is the importance of *Australopithecus*?
3. Describe the differences between Neanderthal humans, Cro-Magnon humans, and modern humans.
4. **Apply:** How was an opposable thumb important in human evolution?

☑ Concept Mapping

Using information is this section, make a concept map to show the sequence of human ancestors. Use the following terms: Neanderthal human, lemurs and tarsiers, *Homo habilis*, *Australopithecus*, modern *Homo sapiens*, Cro-Magnon human. If you need help, refer to Concept Mapping in the **Skill Handbook** on pages 688 and 689.

Skill Builder

ACTIVITY 6-2
Making a Time Line

Problem: *How can a time line represent events in the fossil record?*

Materials
- metric ruler
- pencil
- typing paper (3 sheets)
- tape

Procedure
1. Turn each paper on its side, so that the long side goes from right to left.
2. Put the papers end to end, and tape the ends of the papers together.
3. Turn the papers over so that no tape shows.
4. Draw a line 60 cm long through the middle of your papers from right to left.
5. Make a point on the line every centimeter.
6. Each centimeter represents 10 million years on the time line. Begin with the point on the right end and label it 0 for the present. Label each centimeter point with 10, 20, etc., until you get to the left end.
7. Plot the major events from Table 6-1, The Geologic Time Scale, on your time line.

Analyze
1. Which event occurred closest to present?
2. Which event occurred about midway along your time line?
3. In what geologic era did life begin?

Conclude and Apply
4. What pattern occurs with the complexity of organisms on the time line?
5. What happens to the spacing of events on the time line?
6. Why is a time line more helpful than a table when comparing events?

Data and Observations

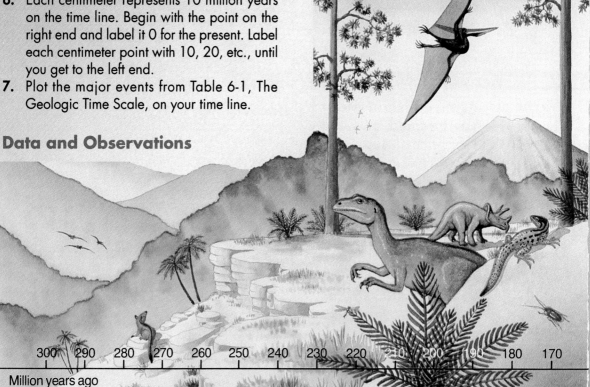

300 290 280 270 260 250 240 230 220 210 200 190 180 170

Million years ago

CHAPTER
REVIEW

SUMMARY

6-1: Mechanisms of Evolution
1. Hereditary features of a species of organisms evolve or change over time.
2. Lamarck developed the theory of acquired characteristics to explain evolution. His theory implied that characteristics parents developed during their lives were passed on to their offspring. Charles Darwin developed the natural selection theory of evolution. According to this theory, organisms best adapted to their environments survive and reproduce.
3. Variations are differences in inherited traits among members of the same species. Variations can allow an organism to be better suited to its environment.

6-2: Evidence for Evolution
1. Fossils are remains of life from an earlier time. They give important evidence of evolution.
2. The age of a fossil can be found by using relative dating or radioactive dating. In relative dating, the age of a fossil is found by looking where it is in the rock layers. Radioactive dating determines the age of a fossil by comparing amounts of radioactive and stable substances in a fossil.
3. Evidence for evolution is obtained by comparing embryology, homologous structures, chemical similarities, and vestigial structures.

6-3: Science and Society: Plant and Animal Extinction
1. Extinction is the dying out of a species due to changes in the environment.
2. Endangered species can be saved from extinction by preserving their environments and by breeding them in captivity.

6-4: Human Evolution
1. Primates share several common characteristics including opposable thumbs, binocular vision, and flexible shoulders and rotating forearms.
2. The earliest known hominid is *Australopithecus*. Hominids are humanlike primates. The hominid *Homo habilis* is thought to be the direct ancestor of humans.
3. Modern humans, *Homo sapiens*, evolved 300 000 years ago. They most likely evolved from Cro-Magnon humans.

KEY SCIENCE WORDS

a. embryology
b. evolution
c. endangered species
d. extinction
e. fossils
f. gradualism
g. hominids
h. *Homo sapiens*
i. homologous
j. natural selection
k. population
l. primates
m. punctuated equilibrium
n. radioactive elements
o. relative dating
p. sedimentary rock
q. species
r. variation
s. vestigial structure

UNDERSTANDING VOCABULARY

Match each phrase with the correct term from the list of Key Science Words.

1. remains of once-living things
2. leftover structure with no use
3. similar organisms that successfully reproduce
4. body structures that are similar in origin
5. change in hereditary feature over time
6. a difference in an inherited trait
7. all the members of one species in an area
8. model of evolution showing slow change
9. the study of stages of an organism's early development
10. group containing monkeys, apes, and humans

CHAPTER
REVIEW

Choose the word or phrase that completes the sentence or answers the questions.

1. _____ is the death of all members of a species.
   a. Evolution   c. Gradualism
   b. Extinction   d. Variation

2. The most accurate age of a fossil can be found using _____.
   a. natural selection   c. relative dating
   b. radioactive elements   d. camouflage

3. Which of the following provides evidence of evolution?
   a. homologous structures c. fossils
   b. vestigial structures   d. all of these

4. A factor that governs natural selection is _____.
   a. inheritance of acquired traits
   b. unused traits are lost from the species
   c. organisms produce more offspring than can survive
   d. all of these

5. A new species may evolve from a series of _____.
   a. adaptations   c. variations
   b. mutations   d. all of these

6. Scientists think that _____ is the ancestor of modern humans.
   a. *Australopithecus*
   b. Neanderthal humans
   c. Cro-Magnon humans
   d. none of these

7. Organisms adapted to their environment will _____.
   a. become extinct
   b. develop vestigial structures
   c. survive and reproduce
   d. none of these

8. In order for evolution to occur, some change takes place in _____.
   a. an individual organism c. a population
   b. an embryo   d. none of these

9. Opposable thumbs and flexible shoulders are characteristics of _____.
   a. all primates   c. humans only
   b. hominids   d. monkeys and apes

10. The earliest paintings were done by _____.
    a. *Australopithecus*
    b. Cro-Magnon humans
    c. *Homo sapiens*
    d. Neanderthal humans

UNDERSTANDING CONCEPTS

Complete each sentence.

11. Many fossils are found in limestone, a type of _____ rock.

12. _____ was the scientist who developed the theory of acquired characteristics.

13. The model of _____ states that the mutation of a few genes causes rapid evolution.

14. Darwin's theory of _____ explains the shaping of adaptations by the environment.

15. According to the geologic time scale, life appeared on Earth in the _____ era.

THINK AND WRITE CRITICALLY

16. Use Darwin's theory of natural selection to explain how the giraffe got its long neck.

17. Describe what causes variations and how the resulting adaptations help explain evolution.

18. What could happen if members of a population became completely separated from each other?

19. Compare gradualism and punctuated equilibrium.
20. Compare relative dating to radioactive dating of fossils. Which do you think is more accurate and why?

APPLY

21. Explain how Lamarck and Darwin would have explained a duck's webbed feet.
22. Using an example, explain how a new species of organism could evolve. (HINT: isolation, change in climate)
23. How is the coloration of chameleons an adaptation to their environment?
24. Describe the process a scientist would use to figure out the age of a fossil.
25. Explain how an organism could become extinct. Give an example.

MORE SKILL BUILDERS

If you need help, refer to the Skill Handbook.

1. **Observing and Inferring:** Observe the birds' beaks pictured below. Describe each. Infer the types of food each would eat and explain why.

2. **Hypothesizing:** Frog eggs are common in ponds in spring. Make a hypothesis as to why ponds are not overpopulated by frogs in the summer. Use the ideas of natural selection to help you.
3. **Comparing and Contrasting:** Compare and contrast Cro-Magnon humans and Neanderthal humans.
4. **Outlining:** Outline the events that led Charles Darwin to his theory of natural selection.
5. **Interpreting Data:** Interpret the following data. The chemicals present in certain bacteria were studied. Listed below are the chemicals found in each type. Each letter represents a different chemical. Use this information to determine which of the bacteria are closely related.

Chemicals Present	
Bacteria 1	A, G, T, C, L, E, S, H
Bacteria 2	A, G, T, C, L, D, H
Bacteria 3	A, G, T, C, L, D, P, U, S, R, I, V
Bacteria 4	A, G, T, C, L, D, H

PROJECTS

1. Find drawings of *Australopithecus*, Cro-Magnon humans, Neanderthal humans, and *Homo habilis*. Describe the humanlike features you see.
2. Research the journey of Charles Darwin aboard the *Beagle*. Chart his voyage on a map of the world. Present a report to the class highlighting Darwin's adventures.

You might have visited a zoo and discovered creatures you didn't even know existed. Do you remember how you decided if an animal was a type of monkey or a type of bear? Or if it was a bird or an insect?

FIND OUT!

Do this simple activity to find out how you might determine relationships between organisms.

Examine the organisms on the opposite page. Notice that all of the organisms are insects, all have wings, and all of them can fly. Now look closely at each of the organisms. Group them based on specific traits that are shared. For example, organisms that have feathery antenna can be grouped together. You may also group the organisms based on color, size, shape, or any other traits you observe. You might find organisms that can't be grouped with the others. Now try to divide your groups into smaller, more specific groups. Were you able to group similar organisms together based on physical traits?

Gearing Up

Previewing the Chapter

Use this outline to help you focus on important ideas in this chapter.

Section 7-1   What Is Classification?
▶ Classifying
▶ Early History of Classification
▶ Scientific Naming

Section 7-2   Modern Classification
▶ Five-Kingdom System
▶ Prokaryotes and Eukaryotes
▶ Groups within Kingdoms

Section 7-3   Science and Society
The Rain Forest Crisis
▶ Undiscovered Treasures
▶ The Consequences

Section 7-4   Identifying Organisms
▶ Common versus Scientific Names
▶ Making and Using Dichotomous Keys

Previewing Science Skills

▶ In the **Skill Builders,** you will observe and infer, make a concept map, and classify.
▶ In the **Activities,** you will classify and observe.
▶ In the **MINI-Labs,** you will classify, make models, and apply knowledge.

What's next?

Now you know that life scientists can look at physical traits to categorize living things. In this chapter you will learn more about how and why scientists categorize living things. You will learn about the history of this process and scientists who have developed widely used classification methods. You will also learn about the five kingdoms of living things and the groups within the kingdoms.

7-1 What Is Classification?

New Science Words

classify
taxonomy
kingdom
binomial nomenclature
species
genus

Objectives

▶ Give examples that show the need for classification systems.
▶ Describe Aristotle's system of classification.
▶ Explain Linnaeus's system of classification.

Classifying

When you go into a grocery store do you usually go to one aisle to get milk, to another part of the store to get margarine, and to a third area to get yogurt? No, most grocery stores group similar items. The dairy products mentioned in the example above would be found together. By placing similar items together, you are classifying. To **classify** means to group ideas, information, or objects based on similarities.

Classification is a necessary part of life. Grocery stores, bookstores, and department stores group similar items together. Can you think of other places in which classification is important?

Early History of Classification

More than 2000 years ago Aristotle, a Greek philosopher, developed a system to group living things. The science of grouping and naming organisms is called **taxonomy** (tak SAHN uh mee). Aristotle began his system of taxonomy by dividing organisms into two large kingdoms, the plant and animal kingdoms. A **kingdom** is the largest of the taxonomic categories. Aristotle then divided the animal kingdom into smaller groups based on where animals live. Animals that live on land were in one group, animals that live in water were in another group,

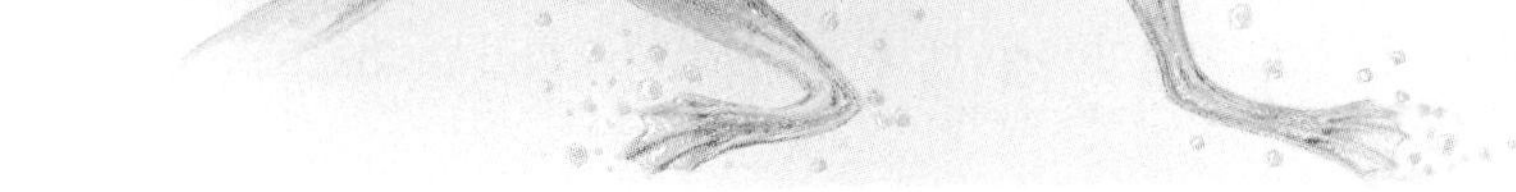

MINI-Lab

How can leaves be classified?
Collect a variety of types of leaves. Place the leaves between sheets of newspaper and press in a heavy book. Classify the leaves based on similarities. Glue the leaves onto poster board in their groups. Present your collection to the class, and explain how you classified the leaves.

Figure 7-1. Frogs did not fit into Aristotle's system of classification. They live both on land and in water.

and animals that fly through the air were in a third group. The plant kingdom was also divided into three groups based on size and structure.

Eventually scientists began to criticize Aristotle's system because it had many exceptions. Animals were classified according to where they live, but what about frogs? Frogs spend part of their lives in water and part on land. There was a problem with Aristotle's classification of plants also. Trees aren't all related just because they're trees. For example, an apple tree is more closely related to a rose bush than to a maple tree. A more logical classification system was needed.

Scientific Naming

Like Aristotle, Carolus Linnaeus (luh NAY us), a Swedish physician and naturalist, created a system to classify organisms based on similarities in body structures and systems, size, shape, color, and methods of obtaining food.

Linnaeus's system gives a two-word name to every organism. The two-word naming system is called **binomial nomenclature.** *Binomial* means "two names." The two-word name is commonly called the organism's scientific name or Latin name. The first name of an organism's scientific name is the genus, and the second is the species. **Species** is the smallest, most specific classification category. A **genus** is the next largest category. It is a group of different species that are similar. Organisms that belong to the same genus have common ancestors.

An example of a two-word, or scientific, name is *Felis catus.* This is a common house cat. Notice that the first name, the genus name, always begins with a capital letter. The second name, the species, begins with a lowercase letter. Both words in a scientific name are written in italic or underlined. Linnaeus chose the Latin language for his naming system because the meanings for Latin words are the same around the world and the language is unchanging. Another important result of Linnaeus's system is that no two organisms have the same scientific name. Because of Linnaeus's system and the use of Latin, scientists around the world recognize *Felis catus* as a house cat and not a Bengal tiger, *Felis tigris.*

Figure 7-2. The top photo shows a housecat, *Felis catus.* Other members of the genus Felis are the cougar, *Felis concolor* (middle), and the bobcat, *Felis rufa* (bottom).

PROBLEM SOLVING

Whose Shoe?

After the bell had rung, Mrs. Spencer announced, "Yesterday, we discussed how scientists classify organisms. Today, I want you to report to your learning groups and develop a classification system for the shoes of the members of your group."

Dani's group divided the shoes into two kingdoms, one with shoelaces and one without. Then, the group divided the laces group into white and nonwhite shoes. Because Dani's white shoes had rubber soles and Mike's had leather soles, the type of sole was the characteristic the groups chose to subdivide the white shoe group. The group then divided the nonwhite shoes group into brown for Colleen's shoe and black for Albert's shoe.

The kingdom without laces was easy to divide. Maria's shoe was a penny loafer,

and Lauren's shoe was a white sandal.

Whose shoe is a white shoe with laces and a leather sole?

Think Critically: Diagram the classification system developed by Dani's group.

SECTION REVIEW

1. What is the purpose of classification?
2. Why didn't Aristotle's classification system work?
3. Why did Linnaeus choose to name species in Latin terms?
4. What is binomial nomenclature?
5. **Apply:** List two examples of things that are classified based on their similarities.

Skill Builder

☒ Observing and Inferring

What could you infer about the following species of oaks: *Quercus alba, Quercus rubra, Quercus suber, Quercus macrocaroa.* If you need help, refer to Observing and Inferring in the **Skill Handbook** on page 682.

ACTIVITY 7-1
Classifying Seeds

Problem: *In what ways can seeds be classified?*

Materials
- packet of 10 different seeds
- hand lens
- metric ruler
- 2 sheets of paper

Procedure
1. Empty the packet of seeds on a sheet of paper. Examine each seed carefully.
2. Divide the 10 seeds into two groups, I and II. The seeds in each group must have at least one thing in common. For example, you could classify round seeds in Group I and seeds that are not round in Group II.
3. Record the characteristic that Group I seeds have in common in a chart like the one shown. Record the characteristics that Group II seeds have in common.
4. Now, divide the Group I seeds into two groups. Again, the seeds in a group must have something in common. Record in the chart the characteristics that the seeds in each group have in common.

5. Divide the seeds into two groups again. Record the characteristic that the seeds in each group have in common.
6. Repeat Step 5 two more times.
7. Repeat Step 4 through 6 with Group II.
8. Give the seed packet and chart to another person. Ask that person to identify each seed using your classification system.

Analyze
1. What characteristic did you use to divide the seeds into the first two groups?
2. Are there several ways to classify seeds?

Conclude and Apply
3. How is classifying helpful?
4. In what ways can seeds be classified?
5. Why is it an advantage to scientists to use standardized classification systems? What observations did you make that support your answer?

Data and Observations

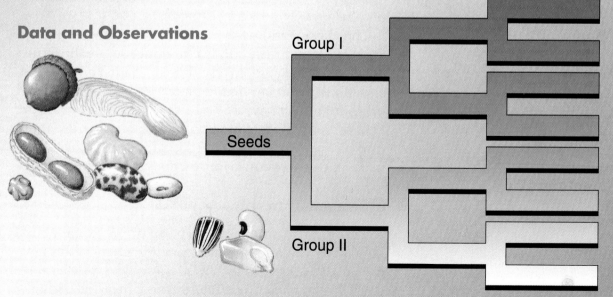

Modern Classification

New Science Words

phylogeny
prokaryotes
eukaryotes
phylum
division
classes
orders
families

Objectives

▶ Name the five kingdoms of living things.
▶ Identify characteristics and members of each kingdom.
▶ Identify the differences between prokaryotes and eukaryotes.
▶ List the groups within each kingdom.

Five-Kingdom System

How does the classification system used today by scientists differ from those of the past? Aristotle and Linnaeus developed their systems of classification using only characteristics of organisms that were easily observed. Besides external characteristics, scientists today look at several other things to classify organisms. They look at the chemical makeup of the organism and its ancestors. Scientists can find relationships among organisms by looking at similarities in genes and body structure. They also study fossils and the way the embryos of an organism develop. By studying all these things scientists can determine an organism's phylogeny. The **phylogeny** of an organism is its evolutionary history. It tells scientists who the ancestors of an organism were and helps them classify it. Today classification of many organisms is based on phylogeny.

The classification system most commonly used today separates organisms into five major groups called kingdoms. The five kingdoms are Animal, Plant, Fungi, Protist, and Monera. Organisms are placed into a kingdom based on four characteristics. The first is whether or not the cells of the organism have a nucleus. Second, are there one or many cells present? Third, does the organism make its own food? And fourth, does the organism move?

Figure 7-3. These colorful mushrooms are members of the Kingdom Fungi.

Prokaryotes and Eukaryotes

The Kingdom Monera is made up of single-celled organisms with a simple structure. Members of this kingdom include bacteria such as streptococcus, which causes strep throat, and cyanobacteria, a single-celled plantlike

TECHNOLOGY

Beyond Appearances

Besides looking at an animal's physical traits, scientists are checking out an animal's DNA to classify it. The more similar the DNA is between two animals, the closer they are related. By using DNA information, scientists can tell which similar animals are actually separate species. They can also study how geographic separation and other factors affect populations. The information scientists gather helps zoos and wildlife programs conserve many species of animals.

Genetic studies are also changing the way some organisms are classified. By studying DNA scientists have found that pandas really are bears, and not relatives of the raccoon as they once thought. The "Asiatic" lions in U.S. zoos are not truly from Asia. They have African genes as well.

White rhinos in North and South Africa are genetically the same in spite of being separated by 2000 miles. Some gray foxes living on islands off California's coast vary genetically from each other.
Think Critically: How can scientists use DNA to classify organisms?

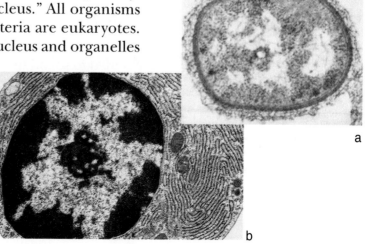

organism found in lakes and ponds. Unlike members of the other kingdoms, monerans don't have an organized nucleus surrounded by a membrane. They are also missing cell organelles. Because monerans don't have an organized nucleus or organelles they are called **prokaryotes.** *Prokaryote* means "before nucleus." All organisms other than bacteria and cyanobacteria are eukaryotes. **Eukaryotes** are organisms with a nucleus and organelles surrounded by membranes. *Eukaryote* means "true nucleus." Figure 7-4 shows the differences between prokaryotes and eukaryotes. Table 7-1 on page 162 gives examples and basic information about each of the five kingdoms. You will learn more about each kingdom in coming chapters.

Figure 7-4. A prokaryotic cell (a) has no nucleus. A nucleus is seen in the eukaryotic cell (b).

a

b

Table 7-1

LIFE'S FIVE KINGDOMS

	Monera	Protist	Fungi	Plant	Animal
Type of cells	Prokaryotic	Eukaryotic	Eukaryotic	Eukaryotic	Eukaryotic
One-celled or Many-celled	One-celled	One- and many-celled	One- and many-celled	Many-celled	Many-celled
Movement	Some move	Some move	Don't move	Don't move	Move
Nutrition	Some members make their own food, others obtain it from other organisms.	Some members make their own food, others obtain it from other organisms.	All members obtain food from other organisms.	Members make their own food.	Members eat plants or other animals.
Examples					

Science and WRITING

Go to the reference section of the library and find information on each of the five kingdoms. Rank the following according to the number of existing species: animals, mammals, flowering plants, insects, birds, fish, reptiles, and nonflowering plants.

Groups within Kingdoms

Imagine you received ten dollars for your birthday. You decided to spend the money on the new tape you've been wanting, so you go to the mall and to the record store. Now what do you do? Will you look through all the tapes in the store until you find the one you're looking for? You don't have to because the tapes are divided into categories of similar types of music such as rock, soul, classical, country, and jazz. Within each category the tapes are divided by artists, and into specific titles by the artist. Because of this system you can easily find the tape you want.

Scientists classify organisms into groups in just the same way. Organisms are placed into kingdoms. Each kingdom is divided into six groups, each smaller than the one before it. The largest group within a kingdom is a **phylum.** In the plant and fungi kingdoms, the word **division** is used in place of phylum. Each phylum or division is divided into **classes.** Classes are divided into **orders,** and orders are divided into **families.** A genus is a group within a family. A genus can have one or more species.

Scientists go through this series of categories to name a specific organism the same way you went through a series of categories to find a specific tape. To understand how an organism is classified, look at the classification of the Arctic wolf in Figure 7-5. Each grouping shows organisms that have more in common. Each grouping also contains fewer organisms. When you reach species, a specific organism has been named, in this case, the Arctic wolf.

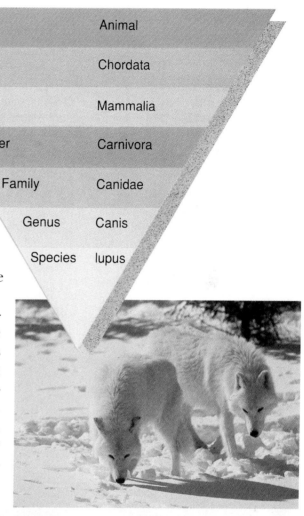

Kingdom	Animal
Phylum	Chordata
Class	Mammalia
Order	Carnivora
Family	Canidae
Genus	Canis
Species	lupus

Figure 7-5. The classification of the Arctic wolf shows its genus and species to be *Canis lupus.*

SECTION REVIEW

1. What are the five kingdoms of living things?
2. Describe each kingdom. Identify one member of each.
3. Why are there smaller groups within each kingdom?
4. Describe prokaryotic and eukaryotic cells.
5. **Apply:** What kingdom does a single-celled, eukaryotic organism that makes its own food belong in?

☑ Concept Mapping

Skill Builder

Use the following terms to make a network tree concept map. Provide your own linking words. *Cells, cell organelles, eukaryote, prokaryote, plants, animals, cyanobacteria, bacteria, no cell organelles, no nucleus, fungi, protists, organized nucleus.* If you need help, refer to Concept Mapping in the **Skill Handbook** on pages 688 and 689.

7-3 The Rain Forest Crisis

New Science Words

deforestation
species diversity

Objectives

▶ Identify two dangerous effects of tropical deforestation.
▶ Explain the importance of the rain forest to us and to the people who live there.

Undiscovered Treasures

There are still places on Earth that have escaped the effects of human technology. Places such as bright green jungles hold thousands of undiscovered and unnamed species of plants and animals. The tropical rain forests of South America are just those places. Life there has gone on undisturbed for thousands of years, but this may all soon come to an end. There is a crisis occurring at this very moment.

There is no time to waste. Every minute, more than 50 more acres of rain forest is cleared for farming, or cut for timber. Many organizations are hard at work to explore these mysterious rain forests and help stop **deforestation,** the destruction of forests. Each year, hundreds of field biologists hunt through the dense tropical forests to unlock its mysteries. They want to learn as much as possible about the plants and animals that live there before these

Figure 7-6. Many species of animals and plants will be lost if deforestation continues.

organisms become extinct. Scientists believe that only about 15 percent of all the species of plants and animals there have been identified. The rest may never be discovered. This great variety of plants and animals, or **species diversity,** in the rain forests of the world is being destroyed by humans at a rapid rate. In the next 30 years we may lose one-fourth of all the species alive today.

The Consequences

Will the destruction of the rain forest really affect you? Is the effort to save the forest really necessary? Scientists think so. Along with saving species of animals, saving the trees and plants is also very important. Our atmosphere is very dependent on them to remove carbon dioxide and produce oxygen. The air that we breath in the United States will be affected by the loss of tropical forests. The damaged atmosphere may cause changes in weather patterns and dangerous storms. The climate of areas of the United States could also change. The northeastern region could have the tropical climate of Florida. And the southeast may become a desert.

Wild animals and plants aren't the only ones dependent on the rain forest lands for survival. The native people depend on farming these areas for survival. Remember how the pioneers settled America? They were starving to death and many died before they cleared thousands of acres and mastered farming. The people of South America are in the same situation. They are dependent on farming or logging for their income and survival. Farming is very destructive to rain forests because they have poor soils. An area can be farmed for only a few years before it is no longer fit to raise crops. A new piece of forest must then be cleared to be used for farming. Every few years the people must cut a new area of forest to grow crops to survive.

EcoTip

When you are a visitor in our National Parks and Forests, take all your trash out with you. These forests are home for more than 130 endangered species.

Figure 7-7. Rain forests are cleared for farming.

SECTION REVIEW

1. Why is tropical deforestation a concern of those of us in North America?
2. How are the native people dependent on rain forest lands?

You Decide!

Much of the research on the tropical rain forests is being conducted by scientists from countries outside the rain forest, such as the United States. Is it right for the United States to purchase and preserve land that other people depend upon for survival? Should another society walk into their homeland and demand that the rain forest destruction stop?

SCIENCE & SOCIETY

New Science Words

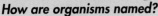

dichotomous keys

Objectives

▶ List reasons scientific names are more useful to scientists than common names.
▶ Identify the function of a dichotomous key.
▶ Demonstrate how to use a dichotomous key.

MINI-Lab

How are organisms named?

Make a fictitious organism out of clay. Give your organism a scientific name. Be sure the name is Latinized and gives information about your species. Present your organism and its name to the class.

Figure 7-8. These three robins have the same common name, yet they are three different species.

Common versus Scientific Names

Have you ever seen a bird like the one in Figure 7-8a? What do you call it? Have you heard anyone call this bird a *Turdus migratorius*? In much of the United States this bird is commonly called a robin, or a robin redbreast. However, people who live in England call the bird in Figure 7-8b a robin. In much of Europe the same bird is called a redbreast. If you lived in Australia, you'd call the bird in Figure 7-8c a robin, or yellow robin. Are these the same species of bird? No, these birds are obviously very different from one another. Yet they all have the same or a similar common name. If you were talking informally to someone in your area who knew the same birds you did, you could use common names. But the common names for the different birds could be confusing if you were in another country or in another area of the same country.

If life scientists used only common names, they would have trouble sharing information about the organisms they study. Many errors in understanding would probably result from the confusion. The system of binomial nomenclature developed by Linnaeus gives each of these birds

a

b

c

a unique scientific name. The scientific name for the bird in 7-8a is *Turdus migratorius*. The name for the bird in 7-8b is *Erithacus rubecula*. The name for the bird in 7-8c is *Eopsaltria australis*.

Scientific names serve four basic functions. First, scientific names help life scientists avoid errors in communication. A life scientist who studied yellow robins, *Eopsaltria australis*, would not be confused by information he or she read about *Turdus migratorius*, the American robin. Second, organisms with similar evolutionary histories are classified together. Because of this you know that organisms that share the same genus name are more related than those that don't. Third, the scientific name gives descriptive information about the species. What can you tell from the species name *Turdus migratorius*? It tells you that this bird must migrate from place to place. Fourth, the scientific names allow information about organisms to be organized and found easily and efficiently. Scientific names are used in guides to organisms called dichotomous (DI kaaht uh mus) keys.

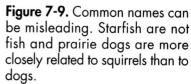
How do scientific names help scientists?

Figure 7-9. Common names can be misleading. Starfish are not fish and prairie dogs are more closely related to squirrels than to dogs.

Making and Using Dichotomous Keys

How would you go about finding out the name of an insect like the one pictured on page 168 in Table 7-2? The easiest way would be to ask an expert on insects from your local area. However, no one knows, or is even expected to know, all of the insects or any other major taxonomic group. The best the expert can do is tell you that the insect is some kind of staghorn beetle. So, after you've trekked to the local natural history museum, you are still stumped. Should you give up? No, your next step should be to consult a manual or field guide that contains descriptive guides or keys as an aid to identification. These can be found in a bookstore or library.

The keys found in most field guides are divided into steps with two descriptions at each step. These keys are called **dichotomous keys.** Look at the dichotomous key for staghorn beetles in Table 7-2. Notice that the descriptions are labeled 1a and 1b, 2a and 2b, and so on. To use the key, you must always begin with a choice from the first pair of descriptions. Notice that the end of each description is either the name of a species or directions to go on to another step. If you use the dichotomous key properly, you will eventually wind up with the correct name for your species.

Science and READING

Field guides are available to help you identify most animals. Pick a phylum (birds, insects, etc.) and see how many different species you can find in your neighborhood. Try to find species from the greatest variety of genera, families, orders, and classes.

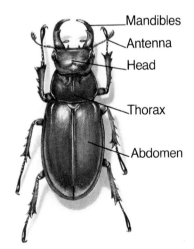

Figure 7-10. The external structures of a staghorn beetle.

(labels: Mandibles, Antenna, Head, Thorax, Abdomen)

Table 7-2

STAGHORN BEETLES OF NORTH AMERICA
1a If the beetle is longer than 20 mm, go to Step 2.
1b If the beetle is less than 20 mm long, go to Step 5.
2a If it is reddish brown, go to Step 3.
2b If it is dark brown or black, go to Step 4.
3a If the beetle is 22-35 mm long with an oval patch of golden hairs on the front legs, it is commonly called a pinching bug, or *Pseudolucanus capreolus.*
3b If the beetle is 20-32 mm long, with silky hairs between segments on the bottom surface, it is also called a pinching bug, or *Pseudolucanus placidus.*
4a If it is 20-26 mm long and the mandibles do not overlap, it is commonly called an antelope beetle, *Dorcus parallelus.*
4b If it is 45-60 mm long with large overlapping mandibles, it is commonly called the elephant staghorn beetle or giant staghorn beetle, *Lucanus elaphus.*
5a If the head is as wide as the thorax and it is reddish black, it is an oak stag beetle, *Platycerus agassizi.*
5b If the head is much narrower than the thorax with a backward-directed horn, it is a rugose staghorn beetle, *Sinodendron rugosum.*

Figure 7-11. Each of these staghorn beetles is a different species.

Let's identify the staghorn beetle in Table 7-2. Start at Step 1 of the key. Your beetle is much longer than 20 mm, so you go to Step 2. The beetle is black, so you skip Step 3 and go to Step 4. Your beetle is about 50 mm long with overlapping mouth parts, so you choose 4b. The dichotomous key tells you that the insect is *Lucanus elaphus,* commonly called an elephant staghorn beetle or giant staghorn beetle.

There are many kinds of field guides containing dichotomous keys. There are field guides to plants, mushrooms, fish, butterflies, and every other kind of organism. You could find the name of more than a million named species by following the descriptions in the proper dichotomous key.

SECTION REVIEW

1. List four reasons biologists use scientific names in their communications.
2. When would it be permissible to use common names for organisms?
3. What is the function of a dichotomous key?
4. **Apply:** How could you tell if two species that look similar share a common evolutionary history?

☒ Classifying

Classify the beetles in Figure 7-11, using the dichotomous key in Table 7-2. If you need help, refer to Classifying in the **Skill Handbook** on page 680.

Skill · Builder

ACTIVITY 7-2
Using a Dichotomous Key

Problem: How can a dichotomous key be used to identify jays?

Materials
- paper and pencil

Procedure
1. Look at the jays pictured below.
2. Begin with Step 1 of the dichotomous Key to Jays of North America. Use the key to identify the bird below labeled A.
3. On your paper, make a data table like the one shown. Write the common name and scientific name for the jay.
4. Use the same procedure to identify the species of jay labeled B.

Data and Observations

Jay	Scientific Name	Common Name
A		
B		

Analyze
1. According to the key, how many species of jay are in North America?
2. How many genera can be identified with this key?

Conclude and Apply
3. How do you know that this key doesn't contain all the species of jays in the world?
4. Why couldn't you be successful in identifying a robin using this key?
5. Why wouldn't it be a good idea to begin in the middle of a key, instead of with the first step?

KEY TO JAYS OF NORTH AMERICA

1a If the jay has a crest on the head, go to Step 2.
1b If the jay has no crest, go to Step 3.
2a If the jay has white on the tail and wings, it is a blue jay, *Cyanocitta cristata*.
2b If the jay has a gray or brown crest, it is a stellar's jay, *Cyanocitta stelleri*.
3a If the jay is mostly blue, go to Step 4.
3b If the jay has little or no blue, go to Step 6.
4a If the jay has a white throat, it is a scrub jay, *Aphelocoma coerulescens*.
4b If the throat is not white, outlined in blue, go to Step 5.
5a If the jay has a dark eye mask and gray breast, it is a gray-breasted jay, *Aphelocoma ultramarinus*.
5b If the jay is all steel-blue and has a short tail, it is a pinyon jay, *Gymnorhrinus cyanocephalus*.
6a If the jay is mostly gray and has black and white head markings, it is a gray jay, *Perisorenus canadensis*.
6b If the jay is not gray, go to Step 7.
7a If the jay has a brilliant green body with some blue on the head, it is a green jay, *Cyanocorax yucas*.
7b If the jay has a plain brown body, it is a brown jay, *Cyanocorax moria*.

A   B

CHAPTER
REVIEW

7-1: What Is Classification?

1. To *classify* means to group ideas, information, or objects based on similarities. Taxonomy is the study of grouping and naming organisms.
2. Aristotle was the first to develop a system to classify organisms.
3. Linnaeus developed a two-word system to name organisms.
4. Binomial nomenclature is a two-word naming system that gives every organism its own scientific name.

7-2: Modern Classification

1. The five kingdoms of living things are Monera, Protist, Fungi, Plant, and Animal.
2. Monerans, such as bacteria and cyanobacteria, are single-celled prokaryotes. The Kingdom Protist contains a variety of single-celled and many-celled eukaryotic organisms. Fungi are eukaryotic, many-celled organisms that can't make their own food. Plants and animals are both eukaryotic, many-celled organisms. Plants can make their own food, animals can't.
3. Organisms without an organized nucleus and cell organelles are prokaryotes. Eukaryotes have a nucleus and organelles.

4. Organisms are classified into seven categories. They are kingdom, phylum, class, order, family, genus, and species. The genus and species names a specific organism.

7-3: Science and Society: The Rain Forest Crisis

1. Many species of plants and animals are lost due to the deforestation of rain forests. The world's atmosphere may be damaged by the loss of the oxygen-producing trees.
2. Native people depend on rain forests for timber and farming to survive.

7-4: Identifying Organisms

1. Scientific names help scientists communicate. They also allow organisms with similar evolutionary histories to be classified together. Scientific names give descriptive information about the species and allow information about organisms to be organized.
2. Dichotomous keys are used to identify specific organisms.
3. Dichotomous keys are made up of steps of paired descriptions.

KEY SCIENCE WORDS

a. **binomial nomenclature**
b. **classes**
c. **classify**
d. **deforestation**
e. **dichotomous keys**
f. **division**
g. **eukaryotes**
h. **families**
i. **genus**
j. **kingdom**
k. **orders**
l. **phylogeny**
m. **phylum**
n. **prokaryotes**
o. **species**
p. **species diversity**
q. **taxonomy**

UNDERSTANDING VOCABULARY

Match each phrase with the correct term from the list of Key Science Words.

1. to put similar organisms in groups
2. a group of similar species
3. the science of classification
4. system of naming organisms with two names
5. evolutionary history of organisms
6. cells without organelles or a nucleus
7. subdivisions of a class
8. largest group within the Plant kingdom
9. cells with a nucleus and organelles
10. the second of an organism's scientific names

CHAPTER
REVIEW

CHECKING CONCEPTS

Choose the word or phrase that completes the sentence.

1. The group with the most members is a _____.
   - **a.** family
   - **b.** kingdom
   - **c.** genus
   - **d.** order

2. Organisms that are the most similar belong in a _____.
   - **a.** family
   - **b.** class
   - **c.** genus
   - **d.** species

3. The most complex organisms are _____.
   - **a.** animals
   - **b.** monerans
   - **c.** plants
   - **d.** protists

4. The closest relative of *Canis lupus* is _____.
   - **a.** *Quercus alba*
   - **b.** *Equus zebra*
   - **c.** *Felis tigris*
   - **d.** *Canis familiaris*

5. The scientific name is written as _____.
   - **a.** *Genus Species*
   - **b.** genus species
   - **c.** genus Species
   - **d.** *Genus species*

6. The kingdom bacteria belong to is _____.
   - **a.** Animal
   - **b.** Fungi
   - **c.** Monera
   - **d.** Plant

7. The _____ do not have eukaryotic cells.
   - **a.** animals
   - **b.** fungi
   - **c.** monerans
   - **d.** plants

8. The simplest eukaryotes are _____.
   - **a.** animals
   - **b.** fungi
   - **c.** monerans
   - **d.** protists

9. Trees and flowers are _____.
   - **a.** animals
   - **b.** plants
   - **c.** monerans
   - **d.** protists

10. Cells without an organized nucleus are _____.
    - **a.** eukaryotes
    - **b.** phylogeny
    - **c.** species
    - **d.** prokaryotes

UNDERSTANDING CONCEPTS

Complete each sentence.

11. Members of the _____ kingdom make their own food, are eukaryotic, and cannot move.

12. _____ help life scientists avoid errors in communication.

13. _____ cells do not have a nucleus.

14. _____ are plantlike but lack chlorophyll and cannot make their own food.

15. The scientific name is written in the _____ language.

THINK AND WRITE CRITICALLY

16. Use an example to explain the problems with Aristotle's classification system.

17. Two organisms belonging to the family also belong to what other same classification groups?

18. How do embryology and similar structures help classify organisms?

19. Why is it important to maintain the species diversity found in tropical rain forests?

20. Members of the Kingdom Protist are often called "misfits." Can you explain why?

21. How could you distinguish between prokaryotes and eukaryotes under the microscope?
22. Name each of the five kingdoms, and identify a member of each kingdom.
23. Write a short dichotomous key to identify the members of your family. Use such things as sex, hair color, eye color, and weight in your key. Each individual's first and last name will make up the person's genus and species.
24. Discuss the relationship between tigers and lions, members of *Felis*.
25. Scientific names often describe a characteristic of the organism. What does *Lathyrus odoratus* tell you about a sweet pea?

MORE SKILL BUILDERS

If you need help, refer to the Skill Handbook.

1. **Comparing and Contrasting:** Compare the number and variety of organisms in a kingdom and genus.
2. **Classifying:** Use the Key to Jays of North America on page 170 to identify these birds.

a

b

c

3. **Observing:** You observe an organism you don't know. How would you go about determining its classification?
4. **Making Graphs:** Make a pie graph to show the number of species in each kingdom.

Kingdom	Number of Species
Moneran	4000
Protist	51 000
Fungi	100 000
Plant	285 000
Animal	1 million

5. **Concept Mapping:** Use the information found in Sections 7-1 and 7-2 to make an events chain concept map to show the events leading up to the modern system of classification. (HINT: Start with Aristotle.)

PROJECTS

1. Make a poster of the five kingdoms to display in the classroom. You may want to draw organisms found in each kingdom, or make a collage using pictures from newspapers or magazines.
2. Research the life of Carolus Linnaeus. Find as much interesting information as possible. Present your report to the class.

GLOBAL CONNECTIONS

Heredity and Evolution

In this unit, you have studied the principles and importance of heredity and evolution. Now see how heredity and evolution influence people, places, and events throughout the world.

120°   60°

60°

30°

0°

ASTRONOMY

LOOKING FOR THE BIG BANG
Mauna Kea, Hawaii
Fourteen thousand feet above the Pacific Ocean, at the Mauna Kea Observatory, six telescopes search the night skies to learn more about the origin of the universe. Why do you think there are six telescopes? What will they find?

BIOLOGY

MYSTERY OF THE JUMPING GENE
Cold Spring Harbor, New York
Geneticist Barbara McClintock puzzled over the different colors of Indian corn husks. Through her studies, she learned that genes often change their positions on a single chromosome. She called them "jumping genes." Why are genes important?

HISTORY

AN IDEA WHOSE TIME HAD COME
Monmouth, England
Alfred Russel Wallace, a naturalist and philosopher, developed a theory of evolution by natural selection separately from Charles Darwin. His ideas and Darwin's were presented together at a scientific meeting in London in 1858. Why do you think Alfred Wallace is not as well known as Darwin?

BIOLOGY

A LIVING FOSSIL
The Republic of Comoros
The Indian Ocean, off the east coast of Africa near Madagascar, teems with life. It was there that a "living fossil" called the coelacanth was discovered by Melanie Courtenay-Latinerin. Find out why the discovery of a coelacanth is important to science.

PALEONTOLOGY

FOOTPRINTS IN TIME
Olduvai Gorge, Tanzania
Three million, six hundred thousand years ago, someone walked across the muddy southern Serengeti Plains. Their tracks, and other evidence of ancient people, have been discovered by Mary Leakey and her family. The tracks show that ancient people walked erect. What would be important about walking erect?

0°

GENETIC COUNSELOR

Genetic counselors work in the field of medicine. They do genetic testing to help doctors understand the genetic background of a patient. Knowing a patient's genetic background can help doctors make a diagnosis or predict the risks of an inherited disease occurring. For instance, the risk for certain types of breast cancer can show in a person's genes. The risk of bearing a child with a genetic illness worries many people. With genetic testing, they can learn whether they have a good chance of having a healthy child. A person who is interested in becoming a genetic counselor should have a background in science, especially biology and genetics. A genetic counselor must have a master's degree and be certified by one of the health accrediting agencies. He or she should enjoy working with people.

For Additional Information

Contact the American Institute of Biological Sciences, Office of Career Service, 730 11th St. NW., Washington, DC 20001-4584

FARMER

Farmers who raise animals such as cattle or hogs or horses keep records of the health and inheritance of these animals. By breeding the best of their animals, they improve their livestock. Most farmers are also aware of the benefits of genetically improved crop plants such as corn and soybeans. Many farmers learn farming through work on the family farm. Farmers spend much of their time working outdoors. They need to be in good physical health, because farm work involves hard physical labor. Because farming is changing, many farmers attend four-year college programs to learn advanced farming methods and business management. Organizations such as the National Farm Bureau and County Extension Agencies offer programs on livestock and crop production.

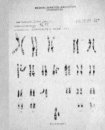

For Additional Information

Contact the National FFA Organization, Box 15160, 5632 Mt. Vernon Memorial Hwy., Alexandria, VA 22309; or the American Farm Bureau Federation, 225 Touhy Ave., Park Ridge, IL 60068.

UNIT READINGS

▶ "The Telltale Gene." *Consumer Reports*, July, 1990, pp. 483-488.
▶ "An Earlier Cancer Warning." *Newsweek*, Dec. 31, 1990, p. 68.

The Voyage of the Beagle

by Charles Darwin

The following passage recounts Darwin's observations of tortoises on the Galapagos Islands in September 1835.

The tortoise is very fond of water, drinking large quantities, and wallowing in the mud. The larger islands alone possess springs. Near the springs it was a curious spectacle to behold many of these huge creatures, one set eagerly traveling onwards with their outstretched necks, and another set returning, after having drunk their fill. When the tortoise arrives at the spring, quite regardless of any spectator, he buries his head in the water above his eyes, and greedily swallows great mouthfulls, at the rate of about ten in a minute. The animal probably regulates them (its visits) according to the nature of the food on which it has lived. It is, however, certain, that tortoises can subsist even on these islands where there is no other water than what falls during a few rainy days in the year....

During the breeding season, when the male and female are together, the male utters a hoarse roar or bellowing, which, it is said, can be heard at the distance of more than a hundred yards. The female never uses her voice, and the male only at these times; so that when the people hear this noise, they know the two are together. They were at this time (October) laying their eggs.... The young tortoises, as soon as they are hatched, fall a prey in great numbers to the carrion-feeding buzzard. The old ones seem generally to die from accidents, as from falling down precipices: at least, several of the inhabitants told me, that they never found one dead without some evident cause.

The inhabitants believe that these animals are absolutely deaf; certainly do not overhear a person walking close behind them. I was always amused when overtaking one of these great monsters, as it was quietly pacing along, to see how suddenly, the instant I passed, it would draw in its head and legs, and uttering a deep hiss fall to the ground with a heavy sound, as if struck dead. I frequently got on their backs, and then giving a few raps on the hinder part of their shells, they would rise up and walk away, but I found it very difficult to keep my balance.

In Your Own Words

▶ In a brief essay, state the aspects of the tortoise's behavior that you may have found surprising.

3 SIMPLE LIVING THINGS

What's Happening Here?

When 11 million gallons of oil spilled in Prince William Sound in Alaska, scientists scrambled for ways to clean up the beaches where much of the oil came to rest. In a treatment known as bioremediation, beaches were sprayed with fertilizer. Bacteria that lived on the beaches rapidly reproduced and began to break down the oil into carbon dioxide and water. Three weeks later, the beach was oil-free to a depth of about 30 cm. Bacteria have been used for 50 years to treat wastewater. Without these simple living things, the world would be covered with garbage, for bacteria are necessary for turning organic matter back into nutrients needed by all living things.

UNIT CONTENTS

Chapter 8   Viruses and Monerans
Chapter 9   Protists and Fungi

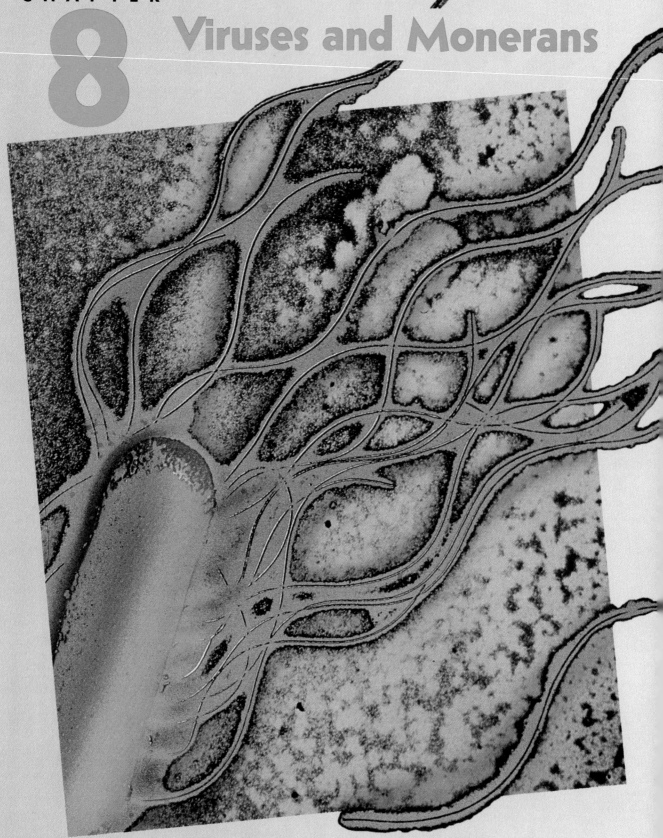

Bacteria, like the one on the opposite page that causes food poisoning, are so small that you need a microscope to see them. Viruses are even smaller. Hundreds of virus particles can fit inside a single bacterium. Isn't it amazing that something so small can make you feel so bad? But are all bacteria harmful?

FIND OUT!

Do this activity to find out what some bacteria look like.

Bacteria are used to turn milk into yogurt. In a small dish, mix a small drop of yogurt with a drop of water. Now add a drop of methylene blue dye. Methylene blue stains the bacteria so that you can see them. Put a tiny drop of the mixture on a glass slide, set a coverslip on top, and view the bacteria under low and then high magnification. What do these bacteria look like?

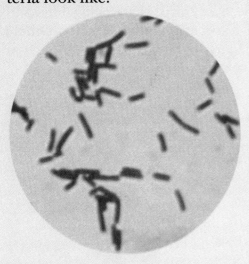

Gearing Up

Previewing the Chapter

Use this outline to help you focus on important ideas in this chapter.

Section 8-1   Viruses: Are They Alive?
▶ What Is a Virus?
▶ Making More Viruses
▶ Viruses Affect All Organisms
▶ Preventing Diseases
▶ Are There Any Good Viruses?

**Section 8-2   Science and Society
The Cost of Curing a Disease**
▶ AIDS

Section 8-3   Kingdom Monera
▶ What Is a Moneran?
▶ Bacteria
▶ Cyanobacteria

Section 8-4   Monerans in Your Life
▶ Helpful Monerans
▶ Harmful Monerans

Previewing Science Skills

▶ In the **Skill Builders**, you will hypothesize, make a concept map, and measure in SI.
▶ In the **Activities**, you will observe, collect and organize data, and experiment.
▶ In the **MINI-Labs**, you will research and experiment.

What's next?

You have just seen what some live bacteria look like. In this chapter, you will learn more about bacteria. You will also learn about viruses, particles that are not living, but that affect you and most other organisms. Are all bacteria and viruses harmful? How are some of them helpful? Find out.

8-1 Viruses: Are They Alive?

New Science Words

viruses
parasite
latent virus
vaccine
interferon

Objectives

▶ Describe the structure of a virus and explain how viruses reproduce and cause disease.
▶ Explain the uses of vaccines and the role of interferon in viral diseases.
▶ Describe some helpful uses of viruses.

What Is a Virus?

Imagine something that doesn't grow, respond, or eat, yet it can reproduce itself. This something, which appears to be neither living or nonliving, is a virus. **Viruses** are microscopic particles made up of either a DNA or RNA core covered by a protein coat. Viruses are so small that an electron microscope is needed to see them.

Viruses are not classified in any kingdom because they are not cells. They show almost none of the characteristics of living things. Some viruses can be made into crystals and stored in a jar on a shelf for years. Then, if they are put into an organism, presto, they reproduce and cause new infections.

The classification of viruses is based on the virus' shape, the kind of nucleic acid it contains, and the kind of organism that the virus infects. The protein coat of a virus gives the particle its shape. Some viruses are many-sided and look somewhat like a soccer ball with 20 sides. Others look like rods. Some viruses have tails. Others, such as the AIDS virus, are spherical like a basketball.

What is a virus?

Figure 8-1. Viruses have a variety of shapes. The photograph at the bottom shows a virus that infects bacterial cells.

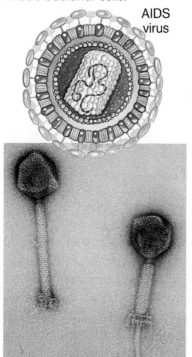

AIDS virus

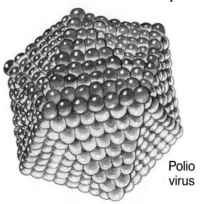

Polio virus

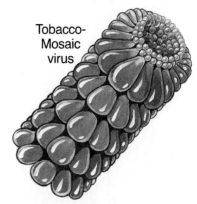

Tobacco-Mosaic virus

Making More Viruses

When most people hear the word *virus*, they relate it to a cold, AIDS, or a cold sore—anything but a pleasant experience. That's because viruses are generally destructive. They are a type of parasite. A **parasite** is anything that depends on an organism or cell to survive and may harm the thing on which it depends. As parasites, viruses depend on living cells. A virus has to be inside a cell in order to reproduce. The cell or organism that a virus depends on is called a host. Once a virus is in a host cell, the virus can act in two ways. It can either be active, or it can become part of the cell for a while.

Active Viruses

If a virus enters a cell and becomes active right away, it causes the cell to make new viruses and destroys the host cell. Figure 8-2a shows the steps an active virus takes to reproduce itself inside a bacterial cell:

1. **Attach:** A specific virus attaches to the surface of a specific bacterial cell.
2. **Invade:** The nucleic acid of the virus injects itself into the cell.
3. **Copy:** The viral nucleic acid takes control of the cell, and the cell begins to make new virus particles.
4. **Release:** The cell bursts open, and hundreds of new virus particles are released from the cell. These new viruses go on to infect other cells.

Latent Viruses

Some viruses are called latent viruses. A **latent virus** enters a cell and becomes part of the cell's DNA without destroying the cell or making new viruses. The viral nucleic acid becomes part of the cell's own DNA as in Figure 8-2b. As the cell divides, the virus is reproduced right along with it. Latent viruses can hide inside host cells for a long time. Then, without warning, the virus becomes active. It forms new virus particles and destroys the cell. If you have ever had a cold sore, you've experienced a virus going from the latent phase into the active phase. The painful cold sore on your lip is a sign that the virus is active. It's destroying thousands of cells in your lip. Stress factors, such as too much sun or a cold, may cause a virus to become active. When the cold sore disappears, the virus has become latent again. The virus is still in your body, you just don't realize it.

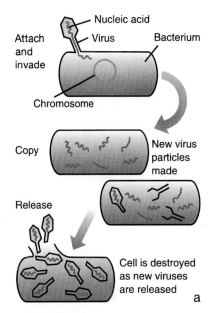

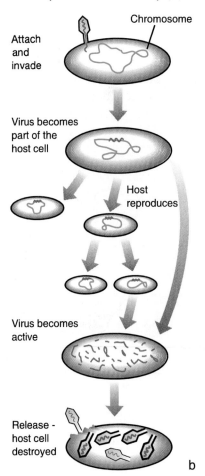

Figure 8-2. An active virus reproduces and destroys the cell (a). A latent virus, below, may not destroy a cell immediately (b).

Figure 8-3. Edward Jenner developed the first vaccine in 1798.

Viruses Affect All Organisms

Viruses cause disease in plants, animals, fungi, bacteria, and protists. Tobacco mosaic virus infects tobacco plants and tomato plants. Animal viruses that you might know about are rabies, chicken pox, and mumps. If you have a cat, you might also know about the feline leukemia virus. Some viruses called oncogenes change normal cells into cancerous tumor cells.

Preventing Diseases

There are no medications to *cure* viral diseases. But some viral diseases can be *prevented* by vaccines. A **vaccine** is made from damaged particles that can't cause disease anymore. Vaccines have been developed for measles and polio, and for bacterial diseases as well.

The first vaccine was developed in 1798 by Edward Jenner, an English doctor. Jenner developed a vaccine for smallpox, a disease that was greatly feared, even into the twentieth century. Jenner noticed that people who milked cows and came down with a disease called cowpox didn't get smallpox. He prepared a vaccine from the sores of milkmaids who had cowpox. When injected into healthy people, the cowpox vaccine seemed to protect them from smallpox. Did Jenner know he was fighting a virus? No. At that time, no one understood what caused disease or how the body fought disease.

The body's natural system for fighting viral infections is called interferon. **Interferon** is produced in animal cells and stops viruses from infecting other cells in that animal. A cell that is infected by a virus produces interferon. The interferon acts like a warning messenger. It travels to uninfected cells and "interferes" with the production of viruses in those cells.

Table 8-1

VACCINES AGAINST DISEASE	
Caused by Viruses	**Caused by Bacteria**
Flu	Whooping cough
Measles	Diphtheria
German measles	Tuberculosis
Smallpox	Gangrene
Polio	Tetanus
Rabies	Typhoid fever
Mumps	Cholera

Are There Any Good Viruses?

Most of what you hear about viruses makes you think that viruses always act in a harmful way. However, there are some cases where, through research, scientists are discovering uses for viruses that may make them helpful.

One method, called gene therapy, involves substituting correctly coded DNA for a cell's incorrect DNA. The new DNA is enclosed in a virus. The virus then acts like an ambulance, taking the strand of DNA into defective cells to replace the incorrect DNA.

Using gene therapy, scientists hope to help people with genetic disorders. For example, some people have the genetic disorder sickle-cell anemia. Because of a defective gene, hemoglobin in their red blood cells does not release oxygen when it reaches body tissues. With the help of a virus, a repaired gene was allowed to "infect" blood cells in a mouse, and the mouse blood cells began to produce the correct substance. Researchers are hoping to use similar techniques for cancer patients.

Figure 8-4. The streaked color pattern in this tulip is the result of a viral infection. If the virus stops infecting the tulip, it will develop a more solid color.

SECTION REVIEW

1. Describe two ways viruses reproduce.
2. Explain how interferon and vaccines work.
3. Describe the structure of viruses. Explain why viruses are not classified in any kingdom.
4. Explain how viruses may be helpful in the process of gene therapy.
5. **Apply:** Explain why the doctor might not give you any medication if you had a cold caused by a virus.

☑ Hypothesizing

You are a researcher in a laboratory. The bacterial cells in an experiment you have been working on have reproduced in large numbers. Then, all of a sudden, most of the bacteria begin to die. You need to find out what caused the deaths of the bacteria. What hypothesis can you make about what is happening to the bacteria? If you need help, refer to Hypothesizing in the **Skill Handbook** on page 686.

Skill Builder

8-2 The Cost of Curing a Disease

New Science Words

AIDS

Objectives

▶ Define AIDS and explain how it attacks the body.
▶ Estimate the cost of curing AIDS.

AIDS

AIDS, acquired immune deficiency syndrome, is an incurable human disease caused by an RNA virus. Within a decade of its discovery, AIDS became an epidemic, causing more than 300 000 deaths throughout the world. In 1990, as many as 650 000 people in the United States were thought to be infected. Some scientists predict that by the year 2000, as many as 40 000 people may die from AIDS each year in the United States.

From an intensive study of the AIDS virus (referred to as HIV), scientists know that the virus is spread in body fluids. Most people get the AIDS virus through sexual contact. You can't get the virus through casual contact such as hugging, kissing, or shaking hands. Many drug users get AIDS by using contaminated syringes. A pregnant or nursing woman with AIDS can pass the virus to her child. Others have been infected through contaminated blood transfusions. After getting the virus, it may be years before any signs of disease appear.

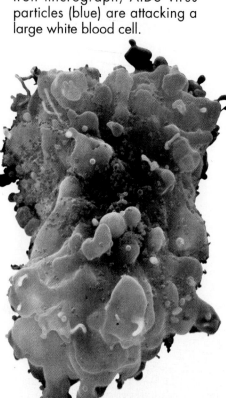

Figure 8-5. In this scanning electron micrograph, AIDS virus particles (blue) are attacking a large white blood cell.

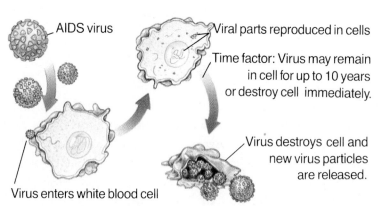

AIDS virus

Viral parts reproduced in cells

Time factor: Virus may remain in cell for up to 10 years or destroy cell immediately.

Virus destroys cell and new virus particles are released.

Virus enters white blood cell

The AIDS virus attacks certain white blood cells that normally protect the body from infection. Because the virus disables the body's immune system, a person with the AIDS virus becomes unable to protect him or herself from other types of viruses or bacteria that cause infections. People with AIDS often develop pneumonia, tuberculosis, and certain forms of cancer. These diseases are called secondary infections. People with AIDS die from the secondary infections rather than the AIDS virus itself.

Scientists and medical doctors are trying to combat AIDS by studying the virus and by using new drug therapies. No vaccine has yet been developed. One drug, AZT, or zidovudine, interferes with the reproductive cycle of the AIDS virus. AZT seems to slow down the AIDS infection but does not cure it.

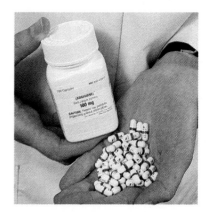

Figure 8-6. AZT is a drug used to combat AIDS infection.

Many people believe the reaction to AIDS has been blown out of proportion to the threat of the disease. They point out that more money is usually spent on prevention of disease than on a cure, but the opposite is true for AIDS. Also, the U.S. Food and Drug Administration has made exceptions to its own rules by approving drugs for use in the fight against AIDS. AZT won approval of use in less than four months. Normally it takes an average of two years for a new drug to be approved for use.

About $1.6 billion was spent on AIDS research in 1990. This was more than the amount spent on cancer, which kills more than 500 000 people per year. The amount was more than twice the money spent on heart disease, which is the nation's top killer.

Science and WRITING

Write a one-page paper explaining why it is important to know the facts about AIDS.

SECTION REVIEW

1. What is AIDS and how is it spread?
2. How does the AIDS virus attack the body?
3. Why are people with AIDS likely to come down with secondary infections?

You Decide!

AIDS research presently costs taxpayers more than one billion dollars a year. Treatment of AIDS patients costs much more than research. If you were in control of the federal budget, how would you determine how much money to spend on AIDS research and treatment?

SCIENCE & SOCIETY

8-3 Kingdom Monera

New Science Words

flagellum
fission
aerobes
obligate anaerobes

Objectives

▶ Describe the characteristics of moneran cells.
▶ Compare aerobic and anaerobic organisms.

What Is a Moneran?

In Chapter 2, you read about two types of cells—prokaryotic cells and eukaryotic cells. Prokaryotes are organisms whose cells have no membrane-bound organelles. Monerans are simple-looking, one-celled organisms. They are prokaryotes. Their nuclear material consists of a single circular chromosome. Monerans don't have organelles such as mitochondria or chloroplasts but they do contain ribosomes.

Monerans have a few plantlike characteristics. They have a cell wall as plants do. Some monerans contain chlorophyll. This enables them to use carbon dioxide and sunlight to make their own food.

Most monerans, however, don't make their own food. That means they have to rely on other organisms to provide food. These monerans have to break down, or decompose, other living things to obtain energy. If you've ever helped clean out the refrigerator, you've probably run into some things that smelled bad. A moneran was at work decomposing a forgotten leftover. In nature, monerans and fungi keep the world free of wastes by breaking them down. In doing so, they also release nutrients into the soil for use again. There are two groups of monerans. One you know as bacteria; the other is cyanobacteria.

How do monerans obtain energy?

Figure 8-7. Bacteria are decomposers. They break down living tissues.

Bacteria

When most people hear the word *bacteria*, they probably associate it with sore throats or gum disease. However, very few bacteria cause illness. Most are important for other reasons. Bacteria are almost everywhere—in the air you breathe, the food you eat, and the water you drink. A shovelful of soil contains billions of them. Hundreds of thousands of bacteria live on and in your body. Most are beneficial to you.

The bacteria that normally inhabit your home and body have three basic shapes—spheres, rods, and spirals. Sphere-shaped bacteria are called *cocci*, rod-shaped bacteria are called *bacilli*, and spiral-shaped bacteria are called *spirilla*. The general characteristics of bacteria can be seen in the bacillus shown in Figure 8-9b. It contains cytoplasm, surrounded by a cell membrane and wall. The nuclear material is in the form of a single chromosome strand. Some bacteria have a thick gel-like capsule around the cell wall. The capsule helps the bacterium stick to surfaces. How would a capsule help a bacterium to survive?

Many bacteria float freely in the environment on air and water currents, your hands, your shoes, and the family dog or cat. Many that live in very moist conditions have a whiplike tail called a **flagellum** to help them move.

Most bacteria reproduce by fission, as shown in Figure 8-9a. **Fission** produces two cells with genetic material exactly like the parent cell's. Some bacteria also reproduce by a simple form of sexual reproduction. Two bacteria line up beside each other and exchange some DNA through a fine tube. This produces cells with different genetic material that may have an advantage in surviving in their environment.

Figure 8-8. Bacteria that grow in plaque in your mouth produce acids that break down tooth enamel.

Figure 8-9. In the photograph, a bacterium is undergoing fission (a). The characteristics and common shapes of bacteria are also shown (b).

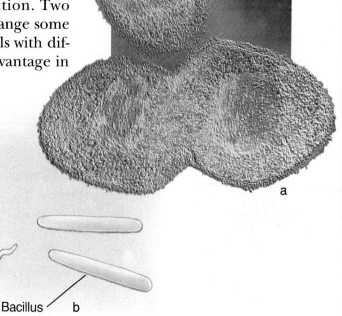

Flagellum
Jellylike capsule
Cell wall
Cell membrane
Nuclear material
Cytoplasm
Bacterial cell
Cocci
Spirillum
Bacillus
a
b

Most bacteria live in places where there is a supply of oxygen. Organisms that use oxygen for respiration are called **aerobes.** You are an aerobic organism. In contrast, organisms that are poisoned when exposed to oxygen are called **obligate anaerobes.** Bacteria that live in your intestines are obligate anaerobes.

Certain types of obligate anaerobe bacteria are thought to have existed for millions of years. They are found in boiling hot springs, extremely salty lakes, muddy swamps, the intestines of cattle, and near vents deep in the ocean where sunlight doesn't penetrate.

Figure 8-10. Bacteria that can survive in hot springs are similar to ancient forms.

PROBLEM SOLVING

How Are *E. coli* Bacteria Helpful?

Sarah's class was studying bacteria in life science. The teacher mentioned a common bacterium called *Escherichia coli,* which is found in the intestines of humans and other animals. The teacher explained that these bacteria help break down foods that otherwise would not be digested and produce materials such as vitamins.

While watching the news on TV, Sarah learned that people in a flooded area of her state were being told to boil their water. A test had shown high levels of *E. coli* bacteria in the water. She wondered why the water had been tested for *E. coli* and not for other disease-causing bacteria.

Think Critically: Why were the people in the flood area told to boil their water? Why are *E. coli* bacteria used to show that water is harmful to drink?

Cyanobacteria

Cyanobacteria are monerans that are producers. They make their own food using carbon dioxide and sunlight. Cyanobacteria contain chlorophyll, which is a green pigment, and another pigment that is blue. The green and blue pigment combination gives cyanobacteria their common name, blue-green bacteria. But, in fact, not all cyanobacteria are blue-green. Some are yellow or black or red. The Red Sea gets its name from a red cyanobacterium.

All species of cyanobacteria are one-celled organisms. However, some of these organisms live together in long chains or filaments. Many are covered with a gel-like substance. This allows them to live in globular groups called colonies. Individual cells reproduce by fission. They do not contain mitochondria, chloroplasts, or nuclei. Cyanobacteria are important for food production in lakes and ponds. Because cyanobacteria can make food and energy from the sunlight, fish in a healthy pond can eat them and utilize that energy.

Have you ever seen a pond covered with smelly, green, bubbly slime? When large amounts of nutrients enter a pond, cyanobacteria increase in number and produce a matlike growth called a bloom. The cyanobacteria die. Bacteria feed on them and use up all the oxygen in the water. As a result, fish and other organisms die.

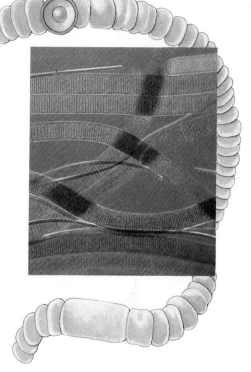

Figure 8-11. Some species of cyanobacteria exist as filaments. The photograph shows *Oscillatoria,* which grows on damp soil and can make stones slick in damp areas. The drawing is of *Anabaena,* commonly found in ponds.

SECTION REVIEW

1. What are the characteristics of monerans?
2. Describe three shapes of bacteria.
3. What pigments are found in cyanobacteria?
4. How do aerobic and obligate anaerobic organisms differ from one another?
5. **Apply:** A mat of cyanobacteria is found growing on a lake with dead fish floating along the edge. What has caused this to occur?

⊠ Concept Mapping

Use an events chain concept map to show what happens in a pond when a bloom of cyanobacteria dies. If you need help, refer to Concept Mapping in the **Skill Handbook** on pages 688 and 689.

Skill Builder

ACTIVITY 8-1
Observing Cyanobacteria

Problem: *What do cyanobacteria look like?*

Materials

- microscope
- prepared slides of *Gloeocapsa* and *Anabaena*
- living cultures of *Nostoc* and *Oscillatoria*

Procedure

1. Make a data table like the one shown. Indicate whether each cyanobacteria sample is in group or colony form or chain form. Write a + or − for the presence or absence of each characteristic in each type of cyanobacteria observed.
2. Observe the prepared slides of *Gloeocapsa* and *Anabaena* under the low and high power of the microscope. Notice the difference in the arrangement of the cells. The large cells in the *Anabaena* filaments fix nitrogen. The jelly-like capsules around *Gloeocapsa* cells help them to stick together in a group. Draw and label a few cells of each cyanobacterium.
3. Make a wet mount of each living culture. Observe under low and high power of the microscope. Notice how the filaments of *Oscillatoria* sway back and forth. Watch for larger nitrogen-fixing cells in *Nostoc*. Draw and label a few cells of each cyanobacterium.
4. Return all slides with living material to your teacher for correct disposal.
5. Wash your hands before continuing.

Analyze

1. How does the color of cyanobacteria compare with the color of leaves on trees?
2. Which of the cyanobacteria has a greener color than the others?
3. What is the purpose of the jelly-like layers around some cyanobacteria?

Conclude and Apply

4. How can you tell by observing them through a microscope that cyanobacteria belong to Kingdom Monera?
5. Describe the general appearance of cyanobacteria.

Data and Observations

Structure	Ana-baena	Gloeo-caspa	Nostoc	Oscill-atoria
Filament or colony				
Nucleus				
Chlorophyll				
Jelly-like layer				
Nitrogen-fixing cells				

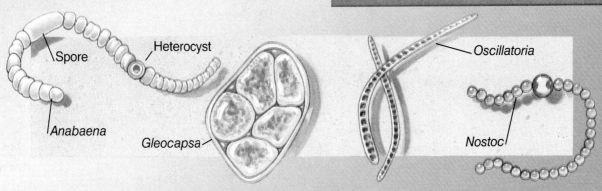

Spore Heterocyst Oscillatoria

Anabaena Gleocapsa Nostoc

Monerans in Your Life

Objectives

▶ Identify some ways bacteria are helpful.
▶ Explain the importance of nitrogen-fixing bacteria.
▶ Explain how some monerans cause disease.

Helpful Monerans

Have you had any bacteria for lunch lately? Anytime you eat cheese, butter, or yogurt, you eat some bacteria. Bacteria break down substances in milk to make these everyday products. If you have eaten sauerkraut, you ate a product made with cabbage and a bacterial culture. Vinegar is also made by a bacterium.

Many industries rely on bacteria. Biotechnology has put bacteria to use in making medicines, enzymes, cleansers, adhesives, and other products. Bacteria have been extremely important in helping to clean up the extensive oil spills in Alaska, California, and Texas.

Monerans called saprophytes (SAP ruh fitz) help maintain nature's balance. A **saprophyte** is any organism that uses dead material as a food and energy source. Saprophytes digest dead organisms and recycle nutrients so that they are available for use by other organisms. Without the saprophytic monerans, there would be layers of dead material deeper than you are tall spread over all of Earth.

New Science Words

saprophyte
nitrogen-fixing bacteria
pathogen
antibiotic
toxins
endospores

MINI-Lab
How do you make yogurt?
Bring a quart of milk almost to a boil in a saucepan. **CAUTION:** *Always be careful when using a stove or hot plate.* Remove the pan from the burner. Cool the milk to lukewarm. Add one or two heaping tablespoons of yogurt starter and stir. Pour the mixture into a clean thermos bottle and put on the lid. The thermos bottle will keep the mixture at a constant temperature. Let stand for six hours and then refrigerate. Add fruit when cool.

Figure 8-12. Helpful monerans are used in food production.

The roots of plants such as peanuts and peas contain **nitrogen-fixing bacteria** in growths called nodules. These bacteria change nitrogen from the air into forms useful for plants and animals. Plants benefit by using the nitrogen, and the bacteria benefit by having a place to live. It is estimated that nitrogen-fixing bacteria save United States farmers several million dollars in fertilizer costs every year.

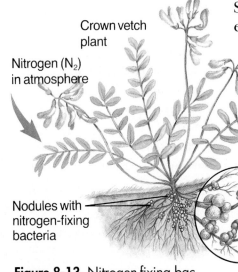

Crown vetch plant

Nitrogen (N_2) in atmosphere

Bacteria in nodules change N_2 to organic nitrogen

Nodules with nitrogen-fixing bacteria

Usable nitrogen compounds form first in plants then in animals.

Figure 8-13. Nitrogen-fixing bacteria live in nodules on roots.

Harmful Monerans

Monerans that cause disease are pathogens. A **pathogen** is any organism that produces disease. If you have ever had strep throat, you have had firsthand experience with a bacterial pathogen. Other pathogenic bacteria are anthrax in cattle, and diphtheria, tetanus, and whooping cough in humans. Bacterial diseases in animals are treated effectively with antibiotics. An **antibiotic** is a substance produced by one organism that inhibits or kills another organism. Penicillin, a well-known antibiotic, prevents bacteria from making cell walls.

Some pathogens produce poisons called **toxins.** Botulism, a type of food poisoning, is caused by a toxin that can cause paralysis and death. Many bacteria that produce toxins are able to produce thick walls around themselves and make themselves resistant to heat or drying. These thick-walled structures are called **endospores.** Botulism endospores require long exposure to heat to be destroyed. Once the endospores are inside the canned food, the bacteria can change back to regular cells and start producing toxins. Botulism bacteria are able to grow inside cans because they are anaerobes and cannot use oxygen to live. Botulism toxins can be destroyed by heat.

Figure 8-14. Bacterial endospores are heat-resistant structures.

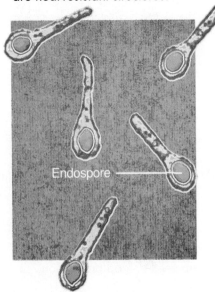

Endospore

TECHNOLOGY

Hungry Bacteria

Scientists are exploring a new way to remove poisons from soil and water. They are using bacteria to eat away the problem in a technique called *bioremediation*. The name refers to using living organisms to remove pollutants.

To clean a toxic site, large populations of resistant bacteria are brought to a problem area. The bacteria reproduce rapidly and eat away the pollutant over several years. When the pollutant is gone, so is the bacteria's food source, and they die off. Bioremediation has been used to clean up oil, gasoline, PCBs, and pesticides.

Think Critically: What are the disadvantages of bioremediation?

Pasteurization, a process of heating food to a temperature that kills harmful bacteria, is used in the food industry. You are most familiar with it in pasteurized milk, but beer and fruit juices are also pasteurized. The term comes from Louis Pasteur, who first formulated the process for the wine industry in the 19th century in France.

SECTION REVIEW

1. Why are saprophytes helpful?
2. Which foods require bacteria to be produced?
3. What is a pathogen?
4. Why are nitrogen-fixing bacteria important?
5. **Apply:** Why is botulism associated with canned foods and not fresh foods?

EcoTip

Put vegetable scraps in a compost heap. Saprophytic bacteria will break them down and valuable nutrients will be returned to the soil.

☑ Measuring in SI

Air may have more than 3500 bacteria per cubic meter. How many bacteria might be in your classroom? If you need help, refer to Measuring in SI in the **Skill Handbook** on pages 684 and 685.

Skill Builder

ACTIVITY 8-2
Observing and Culturing Bacteria

Problem: *How can bacteria be observed and cultured?*

Materials

- 600-mL beaker
- microscope
- cotton swabs
- petri dishes (4)
- prepared slide with different types of bacteria

- fork or tongs
- potato
- hot plate
- hot mitts
- knife
- soap and water

Procedure

1. Observe the prepared slide of bacteria under the microscope. Draw and label what you see.
2. Make a data table like the one shown. Label petri dishes 1, 2, 3, and 4.
3. Peel a potato. Cut it into slices 2 cm thick and put four or five slices in a beaker.
4. Place a fork in the beaker with the potato slices, add water to cover, and boil for five minutes.
5. At the end of five minutes of boiling, use the kitchen mitts to transfer one piece of potato to each petri dish. Cover each dish and *let the slices* cool down. **CAUTION:** *All materials will be hot! Use kitchen mitts to hold the beaker and fork while transferring the potato slices to petri dishes.*
6. Use one swab to innoculate one potato slice with dust. Cover the dish. Touch the inside of your cheek with another swab, then rub the swab on the second slice. Cover the dish immediately. Rub your finger on the third slice once it is just warm. Leave the fourth potato slice in its dish.
7. Wash your hands with soap and water.
8. Wait three days. Observe the potato slices and record your data. **CAUTION:** *At the end of the experiment, give all materials to your teacher for disposal.*

Data and Observations

Treatment	Number and appearance of colonies
Dust	
Cheek	
Finger	
Control	

Analyze

1. What were the shapes of the bacteria on the prepared slide?
2. Which potato slice has the most colonies?
3. Which slice had the fewest colonies?

Conclude and Apply

4. Explain why dish 4 was the control.
5. How can you tell different species of bacteria by their colonies?
6. Where can you find bacteria?
7. Why did you boil the fork and the potato?

SUMMARY

8-1: Viruses: Are They Alive?

1. A virus is a structure containing nucleic acid surrounded by a protein coat. A virus can reproduce only inside a living cell. It may destroy a cell immediately or be latent.

2. Vaccines prevent viral infections. Interferon blocks viruses from reproducing.

3. Viruses are used in gene therapy to replace defective DNA with correctly coded DNA.

8-2: Science and Society: The Cost of Curing a Disease

1. AIDS is a deadly human viral disease affecting the immune system.

2. AIDS detroys the body's ability to combat disease, leaving a person with AIDS defenseless. Death results from other infections.

3. The cost of treating and curing AIDS is more than that spent on diseases that affect many more people, such as heart disease, diabetes, and cancer.

8-3: Kingdom Monera

1. Monerans are cells that contain DNA, ribosomes, and cytoplasm; they lack organelles. Most reproduce by fission.

2. Cyanobacteria are monerans that make their own food.

3. The oldest types of monerans are anaerobic, whereas more complex cells need oxygen and are called aerobes.

8-4: Monerans in Your Life

1. Monerans are helpful through recycling nutrients, nitrogen fixation, and use in food production.

2. Some bacteria are harmful because they cause disease. Some diseases are anthrax, tetanus, and botulism.

3. A process like pasteurization keeps food and the environment free of harmful bacteria.

KEY SCIENCE WORDS

a. **aerobes**
b. **AIDS**
c. **antibiotic**
d. **endospores**
e. **fission**
f. **flagellum**
g. **interferon**
h. **latent virus**
i. **nitrogen-fixing bacteria**
j. **obligate anaerobes**
k. **parasite**
l. **pathogen**
m. **saprophyte**
n. **toxins**
o. **vaccine**
p. **viruses**

UNDERSTANDING VOCABULARY

Match each phrase with the correct term from the list of Key Science Words.

1. organisms that decompose dead organisms
2. structure by which some organisms move
3. heat-resistant structures in bacteria
4. chemical that stops a virus from reproducing in the body
5. something that does harm to its host
6. incurable disease caused by an RNA virus
7. organisms that live without oxygen
8. substance that prevents a viral disease from beginning
9. bacteria in roots that make nitrogen available to organisms
10. microscopic particles that are not alive

CHAPTER
REVIEW

CHECKING CONCEPTS

Choose the word or phrase that completes the sentence.

1. _____ is an example of a viral disease.
   a. Tuberculosis   c. Smallpox
   b. Anthrax   d. Tetanus

2. Moneran cells contain _____.
   a. nuclei   c. mitochondria
   b. DNA   d. all of these

3. Monerans that make their own food have _____.
   a. chlorophyll   c. Golgi bodies
   b. lysosomes   d. mitochondria

4. A function of monerans is _____.
   a. photosynthesis c. nitrogen fixation
   b. decomposition   d. all of these

5. Bacteria that are rod shaped are _____.
   a. bacilli   c. spirilli
   b. cocci   d. all of these

6. The structure that allows a bacterium to stick to surfaces is _____.
   a. capsule   c. capsid
   b. flagella   d. envelope

7. Blooms in ponds are caused by _____.
   a. archaebacteria c. cocci
   b. cyanobacteria   d. viruses

8. Nutrients and carbon dioxide are returned to the environment by _____.
   a. producers   c. saprophytes
   b. consumers   d. pathogens

9. An example of a problem caused by a pathogenic moneran is _____.
   a. anthrax   c. botulism
   b. diphtheria   d. all of these

10. Organisms poisoned by oxygen are _____.
    a. anaerobes   c. saprophytes
    b. aerobes   d. viruses

UNDERSTANDING CONCEPTS

Complete each sentence.

11. Bacteria reproduce asexually by _____.
12. Viral infections can be prevented only with _____.
13. Whiplike tails of bacteria are called _____.
14. A(n) _____ is a form that allows bacteria to survive extreme conditions.
15. _____ live in growths on the roots of certain plants.

THINK AND WRITE CRITICALLY

16. Why aren't viruses classified in a kingdom?
17. Milk produced by cows is free of bacteria, yet several hours later, it needs to be pasteurized. Why?
18. Why do most AIDS victims die from secondary infections?
19. How can cyanobacteria be both beneficial and harmful in a lake?
20. Explain why monerans are prokaryotes.

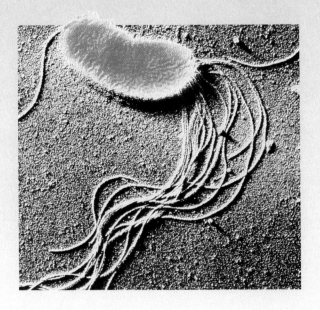

21. What would happen if nitrogen-fixing bacteria could no longer live on the roots of plants?
22. Why are bacteria capable of surviving in all environments of the world?
23. Why is it difficult to get rid of viruses?
24. The organism that causes bacterial pneumonia is called *Pneumococcus*. What is its shape?
25. What precautions can be taken to prevent food poisoning?

MORE SKILL BUILDERS

If you need help, refer to the Skill Handbook.

1. **Sequencing:** Sequence the events of a virus actively infecting a cell.
2. **Making and Using Graphs:** Graph the data of viruses reproducing at different temperatures in a human body.

Virus Reproduction	
Body Temperature °C	**Millions of Viruses**
36.9	1.0
37.2	1.0
37.5	0.5
37.8	0.25
38.3	0.10
38.9	0.05

3. **Interpreting Data:** What can you conclude about the effect of rising temperature on the viruses in Question 2?

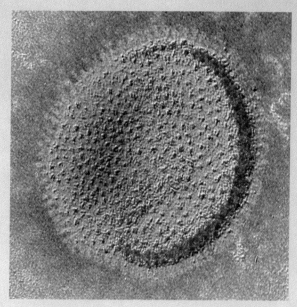

4. **Concept Mapping:** Make an events chain concept map to show what happens when a latent virus becomes active.
5. **Comparing and Contrasting:** In a table, compare and contrast a virus, a bacterial cell, and a eukaryote cell according to the structures they contain.

PROJECTS

1. Find out about the history of vaccination. Look up the term *variolation* in a library reference book and read about early attempts to protect people from disease.
2. Make a poster showing five human bacterial diseases. The poster should include the names of the diseases, the organisms that cause them, their symptoms, and how they are cured.

Have you ever seen mushrooms growing in your yard or a field? You may have eaten mushrooms in a salad, or in a casserole or sauce. But have you ever looked closely at a mushroom?

FIND OUT!

Do this simple activity to find out more about one of the members of the Kingdom Fungi.

Examine a mushroom purchased from the produce section of a grocery store. Carefully pull the cap off the stalk and lay it aside. Use your fingers to pull the stalk apart lengthwise. Continue to pull the stalk apart until the pieces are as small as you can get them. What do you see? Before the mushroom was picked, the stalk was connected to an underground structure by thin strands of tubelike cells. The strands of cells grew up from the ground to form the stalk.

Now look at the underside of the cap. Observe the many thin membranes. The brown color comes from the covering of spores on the membranes. The spores are a part of the life cycle of a mushroom and many other fungi.

Gearing Up
Previewing the Chapter
Use this outline to help you focus on important ideas in this chapter.

Section 9-1   Kingdom Protista
▶ What Is a Protist?
▶ Plantlike Protists
▶ Animal-like Protists
▶ Funguslike Protists

Section 9-2   Kingdom Fungi
▶ What Are Fungi?
▶ Divisions of Fungi

Section 9-3   Science and Society
Fungus—Can't Live Without It
▶ Beneficial Fungi

Previewing Science Skills
▶ In the **Skill Builders,** you will make and use tables and use variables, constants, and controls.
▶ In the **Activities,** you will observe and compare and contrast.
▶ In the **MINI-Labs,** you will make observations and experiment.

What's next?

The many kinds of mushrooms make up only one group of fungi. You will learn more about the organisms in the Kingdom Fungi in this chapter. But first you will learn about the different types of organisms in the protist kingdom.

9-1 Kingdom Protista

New Science Words

protists
algae
protozoa
pseudopods
cilia

Objectives

▶ Identify the characteristics shared by all protists.
▶ Describe the three groups of protists.
▶ Compare and contrast the protist groups.

What Is a Protist?

Look at the organisms in Figure 9-1. Do you see any similarities between them? Believe it or not, all these organisms belong to the same kingdom, the protist kingdom. The Kingdom Protista (pruh TIHS tuh) contains many different types of organisms that share more characteristics with each other than with members of any other kingdom. All **protists** have a nucleus and therefore are eukaryotic. Some protists are one-celled, and others are many-celled. Although some protists contain many cells, none shares the complex organization found in plants and animals. Some protists contain chlorophyll and make their own food and others don't. Protists can be plantlike, animal-like, or funguslike.

Most scientists think that protists evolved from the monerans because protists are more complex in structure than monerans. Bacteria are thought to be the ancestors of animal-like and funguslike protists because these organisms can't make their own food. Plantlike protists probably evolved from cyanobacteria because both are able to produce their own food.

Scientists hypothesize that protists are ancestors of the fungi, plant, and animal kingdoms. The green algae are the most probable ancestors of plants. Protozoans are hypothesized to be the ancestors of animals because they have so many animal characteristics. Our knowledge of the evolution of protists is incomplete because many lack hard parts and, as a result, there aren't very many fossils of these organisms.

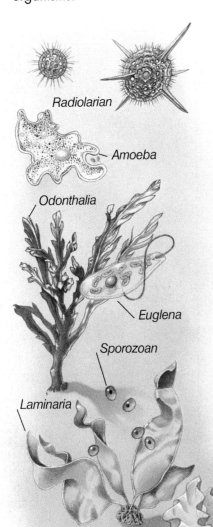

Figure 9-1. The Protist Kingdom is made up of a diverse group of organisms.

Radiolarian

Amoeba

Odonthalia

Euglena

Sporozoan

Laminaria

Volvox

Slime mold

Ulva

Vorticella

Plantlike Protists

Plantlike protists are known as **algae.** Some species of algae are one-celled and others are many-celled. All algae can make their own food because they contain the pigment chlorophyll in their chloroplasts. Remember pigments are colored materials that absorb certain wavelengths of light. Chlorophyll is a green pigment. Even though all algae have chlorophyll, not all algae are green. Many have other pigments that cover up their chlorophyll. Species of algae are grouped into phyla mainly according to the pigments and the food storage compounds they have. There are six main phyla of algae. Each phylum has its own unique characteristics.

Euglenas

Algae that belong to the phylum Euglenophyta have characteristics of both plants and animals. A typical euglena is the bright green *Euglena gracilis,* shown in Figure 9-2. Like plants, these one-celled algae have chloroplasts and are able to produce their own food. When light is not present, euglenas can be heterotrophs. Many euglenas move by using one or more flagella. Although euglenas have no cell walls, they do have a strong, flexible covering over their cell membrane that helps the organism move and change shape. Another animal-like characteristic of euglenas is they have a simple structure called an eyespot used to detect light. The reddish eyespot helps the euglena locate light it needs to produce food by photosynthesis.

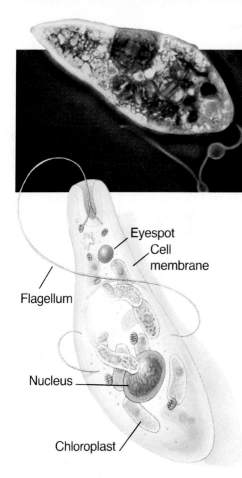

Eyespot
Cell membrane
Flagellum
Nucleus
Chloroplast

Figure 9-2. Euglenas are protists that have both plantlike and animal-like characteristics.

Diatoms

The most numerous of all the algae are the diatoms. They belong to the phylum Chrysophyta (kruh SAHF uh tuh). *Chryso* means "golden brown." Diatoms are photosynthetic one-celled algae. They have a golden-brown pigment that covers the green chlorophyll. The shells of diatoms contain silica, the main element in glass. The body of a diatom is like a small box with a lid. One half of the shell fits inside the other half. Figure 9-3 shows that diatom shells are covered with many markings and pits in the form of beautiful patterns.

You can find diatoms living in both freshwater and saltwater habitats. They are an important food source for many aquatic organisms.

Figure 9-3. The glassy cell walls of diatoms are covered with many beautiful markings.

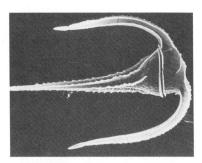

Figure 9-4. A scanning electron micrograph of a dinoflagellate.

Figure 9-5. There are many different shapes among the species of green algae. Phytoplankton (a) and Spirogyra (b) are shown here.

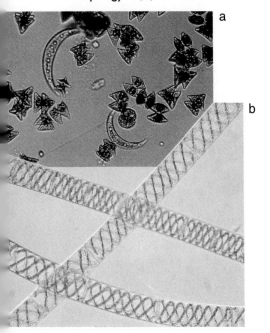

a

b

Diatoms reproduce in unbelievably large numbers. When the organisms die, their small shells sink to the floor of the body of water and collect in very large numbers. The earth made of these diatoms is mined with power shovels and used for insulation, filters, and road paint. The diatoms produce the sparkle in the paint that makes the road lines visible at night.

Dinoflagellates

Phylum Pyrrophyta (puh RAHF uh tuh), the "fire" algae, contains species of one-celled algae called dinoflagellates that contain red pigments. The name *dinoflagellate* means "spinning flagellates." One of the flagella moves the cell, and the other circles the cell, causing it to spin with a motion similar to a top. The dinoflagellate shown in Figure 9-4 shows the arrangement of these flagella.

Almost all dinoflagellates live in salt water. They are important food sources for many saltwater organisms. For unknown reasons, every once in awhile the population of certain species of dinoflagellates increases very rapidly. Red pigments in these algae cause the water to look red. This explosion of algae is known as a "red tide." Some dinoflagellates that cause red tides contain a nerve poison that can kill fish. People who eat fish or shellfish that have absorbed the poisons produced by these algae can become ill and sometimes die.

Green Algae

Species of green algae form the phylum Chlorophyta (kloh RAHF uh tuh). As you can tell from the name, the chlorophyll of the green algae is not covered up by other pigments. There are many different forms of green algae, as shown in Figure 9-5. Although most green algae live in water, others can live in many other environments, including trunks of trees and even on other organisms! Green algae can be one-celled or many-celled. *Chlamydomonas* is an example of a one-celled green alga, and *Ulva,* also called sea lettuce, is a many-celled saltwater alga that forms sheets. Many-celled species of green algae can be either chainlike or form colonies. *Spirogyra* is a chainlike freshwater alga that has spiral-shaped chloroplasts. *Volvox* is a freshwater form that occurs in ball-shaped colonies. The colony rolls through the water using its flagella.

Red Algae

The red algae belong to the phylum Rhodophyta (roh DAHF uh tuh). *Rhodo* means "red" and describes the color of members of this phylum. If you've ever eaten pudding, or used toothpaste, you have used something made with red algae! A carbohydrate called carrageenan found in red algae is used to give toothpaste and pudding their smooth, creamy texture. Most red algae are many-celled. Some species of red algae can live up to 175 meters deep in the ocean. Their red pigment allows them to absorb the few wavelengths of light that penetrate to those depths.

Brown Algae

Brown algae make up the phylum Phaeophyta (fee AHF uh tuh). Members of this phylum are many-celled and vary greatly in size. Large brown algae called kelps may be as much as 100 meters long. Many kelps are important food sources for fish and invertebrates. They form a dense mat of stalks and leaflike blades where many small fish and other animals live.

People in many parts of the world eat brown algae. The thick texture of food such as ice cream and marshmallows is produced by a carbohydrate called algin found in this alga. Brown algae are also used to make fertilizer for food crops.

Science and WRITING

Choose one species of plantlike protist and imagine that you become that protist for a day. Research the protist and decribe your day as that organism.

Table 9-1

THE PLANTLIKE PROTISTS

Phylum	Example	Pigments	Other Characteristics
Euglenophyta Euglenas		Chlorophyll	One-celled algae that move with a flagellum; has eyespot to detect light.
Chrysophyta Diatoms		Golden Brown	One-celled algae with body made of two halves. Cell walls contain silica.
Pyrrophyta Dinoflagellates		Red	One-celled algae with two flagella. Flagella cause cell to spin. Some species cause red tide.
Chlorophyta Green Algae		Chlorophyll	One- and many-celled species. Most live in water, some live out of water, in or on other organisms.
Rhodophyta Red Algae		Red	Many-celled algae; carbohydrate in red algae is used to give some foods a creamy texture.
Phaeophyta Brown Algae		Brown	Many-celled algae, most live in salt water; important food source in aquatic environments.

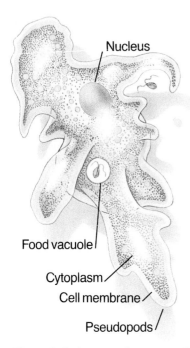

Figure 9-6. An amoeba constantly changes shape as it moves.

Figure 9-7. Many of the saltwater sarcodines have skeletons made of a chalklike material called calcium carbonate. The White Cliffs of Dover in England are made almost entirely of the shells of billions of these organisms. The photo at the right shows the shells of some sarcodines.

Animal-like Protists

One-celled animal-like protists are known as **protozoa** (proht uh ZOH uh). These complex organisms live in water, soil, and dead organisms. Many types of protozoans live as parasites. Remember that a parasite is an organism that lives in or on another organism. The parasite harms the other organism. In addition to the usual cell organelles, protozoans contain special vacuoles for digesting food and getting rid of excess water. Species of protozoan are classified based on their method of movement.

Sarcodines

The first protozoans were probably similar to members of the phylum Sarcodina (sar kuh DI nuh). The *Amoeba* shown in Figure 9-6 is a typical species of this phylum. Sarcodines move about and feed using temporary bulges of their cytoplasm called **pseudopods** (SEWD uh pahdz). The word *pseudopod* means "false foot." Pseudopods are footlike extensions of cytoplasm the organism uses to move and to trap food. An amoeba extends the cytoplasm of a pseudopod on either side of a bit of food such as a bacterium. The two ends of the pseudopod close like two fingers. As the fingers of cytoplasm close, the bacterium is trapped. A vacuole forms around the food and it is digested. Sarcodines are found in freshwater or saltwater environments and in other animals as parasites. You may have been told not to drink the water if you have visited a foreign country. This is because many areas of the world have a kind of amoeba in the water that can cause dysentery. Dysentery is a disease that can produce a severe form of diarrhea.

Flagellates

Protozoans that move using flagella are called flagellates (FLAJ uh layts) and belong to the phylum Mastigophora (mas tuh GAHF un ruh). All of the flagellates have one or many long flagella that whip through a watery environment to move the organism along. Many species of flagellates live in fresh water, but some are parasites.

Trypanosoma is a flagellate that causes African sleeping sickness in humans and animals. It is spread by the tsetse fly in Africa. The disease causes fever, swollen glands, and extreme sleepiness. Another type of flagellate lives in the digestive system of termites. These flagellates are beneficial to the termites, because they produce enzymes that digest the wood the termites eat. The termites can't digest the wood without the flagellates.

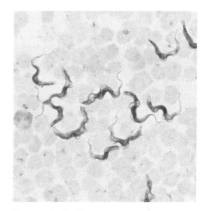

Figure 9-8. *Trypanosoma* is a parasitic flagellate that causes African sleeping sickness.

Ciliates

The most complex protozoans belong to the phylum Ciliophora. Members of this phylum move by using cilia. **Cilia** are short, oarlike structures that extend from the cell membrane. Ciliates may be covered with cilia, or have cilia grouped in special areas of the cell. The beating of the cilia is organized so the organism can move in any direction.

A typical ciliate is the *Paramecium* in Figure 9-9. In the *Paramecium* you can see another characteristic of the ciliates: they have two nuclei, a macronucleus and a micronucleus. The large macronucleus controls the everyday functions of the cell. The smaller micronucleus functions in reproduction. Paramecia usually feed on bacteria swept into the oral groove. Once the food is inside the cell, a food vacuole forms and the food is digested. The contractile vacuole removes excess water from the cell. Wastes are removed through the anal pore.

Figure 9-9. The *Paramecium* is a typical ciliate.

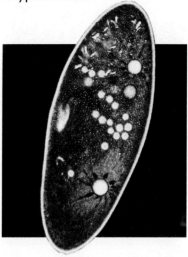

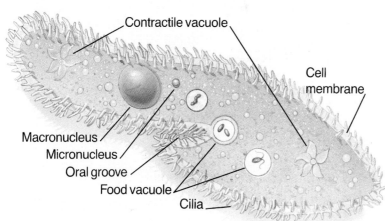

Contractile vacuole

Cell membrane

Macronucleus

Micronucleus

Oral groove

Food vacuole

Cilia

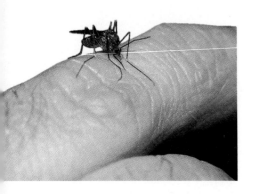

Figure 9-10. Female *Anopheles* mosquitoes spread the sporozoan that causes malaria.

Sporozoans

The phylum Sporozoa contains only small, parasitic protozoans. Sporozoans have no means of movement. All are parasites that live in and feed on the blood of humans, and other animals.

Figure 9-10 shows *Plasmodium,* a sporozoan that is common in tropical climates. This sporozoan causes malaria in humans. Malaria is spread when an infected mosquito bites a human. The disease causes recurring bouts of high fever, followed by chills and sweating.

Funguslike Protists

The funguslike protists include several small phyla of protists that have features of both protists and fungi. Slime molds and water molds are funguslike protists. Slime molds are much more attractive than their name sounds. Many are very brightly colored. They form a delicate weblike structure on the surface of their food supply. They obtain energy by decomposing organic materials.

PROBLEM SOLVING

Puzzled about Slime

Stan and his cousin, Aaron, were walking through the woods near Stan's home when Stan discovered some orange growth underneath a fallen log. Stan told Aaron it was slime mold. His class had been studying protists, and he had seen some slime mold at school. He had read that slime molds were classified in the protist kingdom because they are similar to amoebas and used pseudopods to move and ingest food.

Aaron said, "You're wrong. My textbook classifies slime molds in the fungus kingdom. Slime molds have sporangia just like fungi."

The two boys were puzzled as to why slime molds were placed in the protist kingdom in one book and in the fungus kingdom in another. What evidence is there that slime molds are protists?

Think Critically: Why do some scientists classify slime molds as protists and others classify them as fungi?

Slime Molds

Slime molds like the one pictured in Problem Solving have some protozoan characteristics. During part of their life cycle, the cells of slime molds move by means of pseudopods and resemble amoebas. Slime molds reproduce with spores the way fungi do. You will learn about reproduction in fungi in the next section.

Although most slime molds live on decaying logs or dead leaves in moist, cool, shady woods, one common slime mold is sometimes found crawling across a city lawn. It creeps along using amoeboid movement, feeding on small organisms. When conditions become unfavorable, reproductive structures are formed on stalks and spores are reproduced.

Water Molds and Mildew

Water molds, downy mildews, and white rusts make up another phylum of funguslike protists. The most well-known member of this phylum is the water mold that caused the Irish potato famine in 1846 and 1847. Potatoes were Ireland's main crop and the main food source for the people. Nearly two million people died in the famine.

Water molds have cell walls as do fungi, but their relatively simple cells are more like those of protozoans. Figure 9-11 shows a parasitic water mold that grows on decaying fish. If you have an aquarium, you may see water molds attack a fish and cause its death.

MINI-Lab

What do slime molds look like?
Obtain materials for growing the slime mold *Physarum* from your teacher. Follow the instructions for growing the mold. Keep daily observations of the appearance of the mold as it grows.

Figure 9-11. A parasitic water mold growing on a fish.

SECTION REVIEW

1. What are the characteristics of protists?
2. Describe the main characteristics of the three groups of protists.
3. Describe the funguslike protists.
4. **Apply:** Why aren't there many fossils of the different groups of protists?

⊠ Making and Using Tables

Make a table that compares the characteristics of the four phyla of protozoans. Include phylum, example species, mode of locomotion, and other characteristics. If you need help, refer to Making and Using Tables in the **Skill Handbook** on pages 690-691.

Skill Builder

ACTIVITY 9-1
Comparing Algae and Protozoa

Problem: *What are the differences between algae and protozoans?*

Materials
- cultures of *Paramecium, Amoeba, Euglena, Spirogyra,* and *Micrasterias*
- prepared slide of slime mold
- 5 coverslips
- microscope
- dropper
- 5 microscope slides

Procedure
1. Make a data table for your drawings. Use another sheet of paper to write your observations of each protist.
2. Make a wet mount of the *Paramecium* culture.
3. Observe the wet mount under both low and high power. Draw and label the organism. Write your observations on another sheet.
4. Repeat Steps 2 and 3 with the other cultures. Return all preparations to your teacher and wash your hands.
5. Observe the slide of slime mold under low and high power. Record your observations.

Analyze
1. For each organism that could move, list the structure that enabled the movement.
2. Which protists could not move? Why?
3. Which protists make their own food?
4. Describe whether each protist had one cell or many cells.

Conclude and Apply
5. Which protists had plant characteristics?
6. Which protists had animal characteristics?
7. Which protists had fungus characteristics?
8. What are the characteristics of protists?

Data and Observations

	Paramecium	Amoeba	Euglena	Spirogyra	Micrasterias
Drawing					

Kingdom Fungi

Objectives

▶ Identify the characteristics shared by all fungi.
▶ Classify fungi into groups based on their methods of reproduction.
▶ Describe the difference between the imperfect fungi and all other fungi.

New Science Words

hyphae	budding
chitin	basidium
spores	lichen
sporangia	symbiosis
asci	mutualistic

What Are Fungi?

Do you believe you can find members of the Kingdom Fungi in a quick trip around your house or apartment? Well, you probably can. You can find fungi in your kitchen if you have canned mushrooms, mushroom soup, or fresh mushrooms. You may also find mold, a type of fungus, growing on an old loaf of bread, or mildew, another fungus, growing on your shower curtain. Yeasts are a type of fungi used to make bread rise, as well as in the making of cheese and beer and wine.

As important as fungi seem in the production of different foods, they are most important in their role as organisms that decompose or break down organic materials. Food scraps, clothing, dead plants, and animals are all made of organic material. Fungi work to decompose, or break down, all these materials and return them to the soil. The materials returned to the soil are then used by plants to grow. Fungi help to keep Earth from becoming buried under mountains of waste materials.

Fungi were once classified as plants. Unlike plants, fungi do not make their own food or have the specialized tissues and organs of plants. You will learn about plant structures in the next unit. Most species of fungi are many-celled. The body of a fungus is usually a mass of many-celled, threadlike tubes called **hyphae** (HI fee). The mat of hyphae is called a mycelium (mi SEE lee um). The cell walls of hyphae are made of **chitin,** a strong, flexible carbohydrate that is also found in the body covering and wings of insects.

Mycelium Hyphae

Figure 9-12. A fungus is made up of many threadlike tubes called hyphae.

Figure 9-13. Fungi reproduce by spores. This puffball mushroom releases many spores at once.

Fungi don't contain chlorophyll and can't make their own food. Most fungi feed on dead organisms. Organisms that obtain food in this way are called saprophytes. Fungi release enzymes to digest food outside the cells, then the cells absorb the digested food. Some fungi, such as the ones that cause athlete's foot and ringworm, are parasites. They obtain their food directly from living things.

Fungi grow best in warm, humid areas. The tropical regions of the world are home for many types of fungi because they provide the best environment.

Look at the mushroom in Figure 9-13. The puff of smoke above it is actually made of the structures fungi use for reproduction, spores. **Spores** are reproductive cells that form new organisms without fertilization. The structures in which a fungus produces spores are used to classify fungi into one of four divisions.

Divisions of Fungi

Zygote Fungi

The fuzzy black mold that you sometimes find growing on an old loaf of bread is a type of zygote fungus. Fungi that belong to this division, the division Zygomycota (zi goh mi KOH tuh), produce spores in round spore cases called **sporangia** on the tips of upright hyphae. The sporangia turn black as they mature. The black fuzz you see on the bread is actually a mass of mature spore cases. When each sporangium splits open, hundreds of spores are released into the air. Each spore will grow into more mold if it lands where there is enough moisture, a warm temperature, and a food supply.

How are fungi classified?

Figure 9-14. In zygote fungi spores are produced in round black spore cases on the tips of upright hyphae. The photo shows the zygote fungus *Rhizopus* growing on bread.

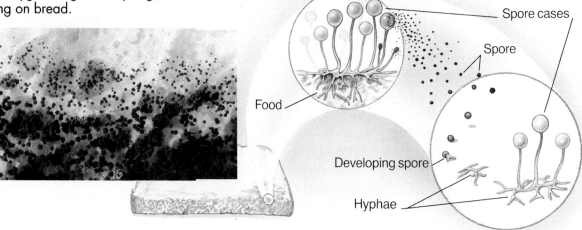

Spore cases

Spore

Food

Developing spore

Hyphae

Sac Fungi

Yeasts, molds, morels, and truffles are all examples of sac fungi. The spores of these fungi are produced in little sacs called **asci.** The division Ascomycota is named for these sacs. The ascospores are released when the tip of an ascus is broken open.

Many sac fungi are well known by farmers because they destroy plant crops. Diseases caused by sac fungi are Dutch elm disease, apple scab, and ergot disease of rye.

Yeast is an economically important sac fungus. Yeasts don't always reproduce by forming spores. They also reproduce asexually by budding. **Budding** is a form of asexual reproduction in which a new organism grows off the side of the parent. Yeasts are used in the baking industry. As yeasts grow, they use sugar for energy and produce alcohol and carbon dioxide as waste products. The carbon dioxide causes bread to rise. All the little holes you see in a slice of bread were formed from little bubbles of carbon dioxide produced by yeast.

Figure 9-15. Yeasts can reproduce by forming buds off the side of the parents. The bud pinches off and forms an identical cell.

T E C H N O L O G Y

A Yeast Library

Scientists have a goal to map the entire human DNA pattern, or genome, within fifteen years. Surprisingly, yeast may be an important tool. The genome maps the order of all the bases in human DNA and allows scientists to locate a particular gene on a specific piece of DNA. The gene can then be analyzed to find the exact bases involved and their order. Yeast artificial chromosomes (YAC) are providing a library for storing human DNA segments.

Human DNA is cut into pieces, and these pieces are inserted into yeast chromosomes. Scientists then try to reorder the DNA as it would appear on a human chromosome and map the nucleotide bases present. YACs are useful because one YAC holds more than ten times as many bases as other artificial chromosomes. The longer the sequence of bases in a segment, the easier it is to piece segments together. The most complete YAC collection of human DNA contains 60 000 YACs.

Think Critically: How would knowing the human genome help us?

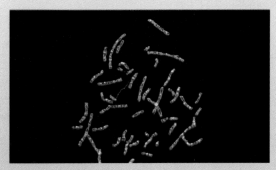

Figure 9-16. A mushroom is the spore-producing structure of a club fungus. Spores are contained in many club-shaped basidia that line the gills of a mushroom cap.

Club Fungi

The mushroom shown in Figure 9-16 is a member of the division Basidiomycota (buh SIHD ee uh mi koht uh). These fungi are commonly known as club fungi. The spores of these fungi are produced in a club-shaped structure called a **basidium.** Under the cap of a mushroom, the reproductive structure of the fungus, are thin sheets of tissue called gills. The tiny club-shaped structures line the gills. The spores you observed on the gills of the mushroom in the Find Out activity at the beginning of this chapter were actually produced in microscopic basidia. Puffball mushrooms, the mushrooms you eat on pizza, and the bracket, or shelf, fungi that grow on the trunks of trees are club fungi.

Many of the club fungi are economically important. Rusts and smuts damage billions of dollars of food crops each year. Mushrooms are an important food crop, but you should never eat a wild mushroom because many are poisonous. Even experts at fungi identification sometimes find it difficult to tell the difference between an edible and a poisonous mushroom. Mistakes in identification can be fatal!

Imperfect Fungi

The imperfect fungi, division Deuteromycota, is composed of species of fungi in which the sexual stage has never been observed. When the sexual stage of a fungus is observed, the species is immediately classified as one of the other three phyla. *Penicillium* is one example from this group. Penicillin, an antibiotic, is an important product of these fungi. Other examples of imperfect fungi are species that cause ringworm and athlete's foot.

Lichens

The colorful organisms in Figure 9-17 are lichens. A **lichen** is an organism that is made of a fungus and green alga or a cyanobacterium. When two organisms live together, they often have a symbiotic relationship. **Symbiosis,** a close relationship between two organisms, can have several results. The fungus and cyanobacterium or green alga both benefit from living together, and they are said to have a **mutualistic** relationship.

The cells of the alga live tangled up in the threadlike strands that make up the fungus. The alga gets a moist, protected place to live, and the fungus gets food from the alga.

Lichens are an important food source for many animals. Reindeer and caribou feed on reindeer moss, a lichen that grows in arctic regions. Many lichens are easily affected by air pollution. Lichen growth on tree trunks and stone buildings can be used to monitor pollution levels.

Figure 9-17. Lichens can grow upright like the British soldier lichen (left), appear leafy (right), or be very flat.

SECTION REVIEW

1. How do fungi obtain food?
2. Why are Ascomycota called sac fungi?
3. Which fungi can't reproduce sexually?
4. In a lichen, how do both the fungus and cyanobacterium or alga benefit from living together?
5. **Apply:** If an imperfect fungus were found to produce basidia under some circumstances, how would the fungus be reclassified?

☑ Using Variables, Constants, and Controls

Skill Builder

In an experiment, yeasts were cultured at different temperatures in a particular concentration of syrup and water. Different amounts of carbon dioxide were produced at each temperature. Identify the constant and variables in this experiment. If you need help, refer to Using Variables, Constants, and Controls in the **Skill Handbook** on page 686.

9-3 Fungus—Can't Live Without It

Objectives

▶ State two types of drugs that are produced from fungi.
▶ Appreciate the role of fungi in medicine.

Beneficial Fungi

Did you know that fungus has probably saved your life? In fact, this may have happened several times! Before the introduction of antibiotic drugs during the 1940s, many deaths occurred due to diseases caused by bacteria. It was common at that time for people to die of pneumonia, tuberculosis, and other infections. Today, however, antibiotics, chemicals that have a harmful effect on bacteria, are used to treat these infections. Many antibiotics are produced from fungi that grow in the soil. You have probably heard of penicillin, the most famous antibiotic. It is produced by a fungus, *Penicillium chrysogenum.* You may have seen this fungus growing on a moldy orange.

Antibiotics prevent bacterial diseases by preventing bacteria from reproducing and growing. Most bacterial infections can be cured with antibiotics. Unfortunately, some people cannot be treated with certain antibiotics because of allergic reactions.

Now scientists face a new problem: bacteria are able to develop new strains that are not affected by antibiotics. For example, at one time, penicillin was effective against many types of bacteria. Today, it has no effect on most of these bacteria. Other antibiotics that have this same problem are streptomycin, tetracycline, and erythromycin. This is keeping scientists working continuously to develop new antibiotics to work against these harmful types of bacteria.

Antiviral drugs are used to treat infections caused by viruses. However, they were much more difficult to develop. This is because viruses do not have enzymes or organelles to destroy. Drugs developed to treat viral infections often resulted in being harmful to the patient as well.

Encephalitis is an inflammation of the brain, spinal cord, and the nerves leading from the spinal cord. It is carried by mosquitoes and can be deadly. In 1978, an antiviral drug, vidarabine, was finally approved by the United States Food and Drug Administration for treatment of encephalitis. This was the very first antiviral drug. It was produced from a species of fungi.

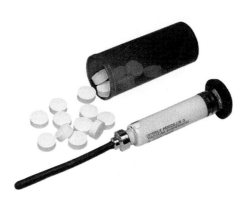

In 1983 another drug produced from fungi was approved for use. The drug cyclosporine was approved for use in organ transplant patients. Cyclosporine is made from an imperfect fungus. The drug helps prevent the rejection of transplanted organs. Because of cyclosporine, organ transplants have become routine. One problem is that the patient must take cyclosporine for life, and it can become expensive. It can also have some bad side effects, such as kidney failure.

Due to the great expense of research programs that were needed to develop these drugs, some people argue that more effort should be made to prevent these diseases rather than cure them. Encephalitis, for example, could be prevented by controlling the mosquitoes that transmit it. Society must work with science if such medical problems are to be prevented.

SECTION REVIEW

1. State two types of drugs that are products of fungi.
2. Why have fungi become so important to medicine?

You Decide!

In the fall of 1990, there was an outbreak of encephalitis spread by mosquitoes in central and southern Florida. Health officials urged people to limit evening activities outdoors because mosquitoes are most active and feeding then. By keeping people away from the mosquitoes, they hoped to limit the spread of encephalitis. Why do you think it was important for people to stay away from the mosquitoes when there is a drug to fight the disease? Would you have taken the advice of the health officials?

ACTIVITY 9-2
Observing Bread Mold

Problem: *How can molds be cultured on bread?*

Materials
- coverslip
- forceps or tweezers
- magnifying glass
- microscope
- wet mount solution
- microscope slide
- plastic sealable bag
- prepared slide of molds
- slice of stale bread

Procedure
1. Sprinkle a little water on the slice of bread. Leave uncovered for several hours.
2. Sprinkle a little water on the bread again and place it in the plastic bag.
3. Blow some air into the bag and seal.
4. Make a data table like the one shown.
5. Observe the bag for five or six days. Add a sprinkle of water if dry.
6. Examine the prepared slide first on low then high power. Look at all three kinds of molds. Draw and label hyphae, sporangia, and spores.
7. Observe your mold with the magnifying glass.
8. Prepare a wet mount using a small portion of your mold. Try to get a piece with a stalk containing spores. Remove it with forceps and place it in a drop of solution. Cover and observe first on low power and then on high power. Draw and label what you see.

Analyze
1. Why did you leave the bread uncovered?
2. Where did the mold come from?
3. Describe your observations with the magnifying glass.

Conclude and Apply
4. How are hyphae different from stalks?
5. Why are the sporangia on stalks?
6. What provides food for the mold?
7. When did mold first appear on your bread?

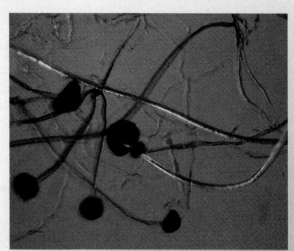

Data and Observations

Day	Observations
1	
2	
3	
4	
5	
6	

9-1: Kingdom Protista

1. Protists are eukaryotic organisms. They can be one- or many-celled but do not have the complex organization found in plants and animals.

2. The protist kingdom is made up of a variety of organisms. Some are plantlike, others are animal-like, and others are funguslike.

3. Algae are photosynthetic and classified according to their pigments. Other protists, like flagellates and ciliates, are animal-like and have special means of locomotion. Funguslike protists include slime molds and water molds.

9-2: Kingdom Fungi

1. Fungi are saprophytes. They reproduce by spores. The structures in which a fungus produces spores are used to classify fungi into one of four divisions.

2. Zygote fungi produce spores in small round spore cases on the tips of upright hyphae. Bread mold is a zygote fungus. Sac fungi produce spores in small sacs called asci. Yeast is an example of a sac fungus. Mushrooms are club fungi. Club fungi produce spores in a club-shaped structure called a basidium. These structures line the gills of a mushroom cap.

3. Imperfect fungi are those for which no sexual stage has been observed. When it is observed, they are classified into one of the other groups. Penicillin is an important product of these fungi.

9-3: Science and Society: Fungus— Can't Live Without It

1. Fungi are important sources of drugs such as penicillin, streptomycin, vidarabine, and cyclosporine.

2. Medicines produced from fungus products have saved the lives of millions of people with diseases such as pneumonia and tuberculosis, as well as those who have had organ transplants.

KEY SCIENCE WORDS

a. algae
b. asci
c. basidium
d. budding
e. chitin
f. cilia
g. hyphae
h. lichen
i. mutualistic
j. protists
k. protozoa
l. pseudopods
m. sporangia
n. spores
o. symbiosis

UNDERSTANDING VOCABULARY

Match each phrase with the correct term from the list of Key Science Words.

1. footlike cytoplasmic extensions
2. reproductive cells of fungi
3. eukaryotic organisms that are animal-like, plantlike, or funguslike
4. animal-like protists
5. plantlike protists
6. oarlike structures used for movement
7. a close relationship between two organisms
8. threadlike strings of a fungus
9. contain spores in zygote fungi
10. strong carbohydrate in fungus' cell walls

CHECKING CONCEPTS

Choose the word or phrase that completes the sentence.

1. _____ are examples of one-celled algae.
   a. Euglenas   c. Diatoms
   b. Dinoflagellates   d. All of these

2. Members of phylum Chrysophyta are _____ in color.
   a. green   c. golden-brown
   b. red   d. brown

3. Large numbers of _____ cause red tides.
   a. *Euglena*   c. *Ulva*
   b. diatoms   d. dinoflagellates

4. Brown algae belong to phylum _____.
   a. Rhodophyta   c. Phaeophyta
   b. Chrysophyta   d. Pyrrophyta

5. _____ moves by using cilia.
   a. *Amoeba*   c. *Plasmodium*
   b. *Paramecium*   d. All of these

6. Funguslike protists live _____.
   a. on decaying logs   c. on fish
   b. in shady woods   d. all of these

7. An important role fungi play is to _____.
   a. decompose   c. make dough rise
   b. make cheese   d. all of these

8. An example of a sac fungus is _____.
   a. mushroom   c. rust
   b. yeast   d. none of these

9. _____ produce the spores in mushrooms.
   a. Sporangia   c. Asci
   b. Basidia   d. None of these

10. An example of an imperfect fungi is _____.
    a. mushroom   c. *Penicillium*
    b. yeast   d. lichen

UNDERSTANDING CONCEPTS

Complete each sentence.

11. A(n) _____ is colored material that absorbs light.
12. Light is detected by the _____ of *Euglena*.
13. Diatoms have cell walls made of _____.
14. _____ are reproductive cells of fungi.
15. The spore case of bread mold is called a(n) _____.

THINK AND WRITE CRITICALLY

16. List the ways in which algae are plantlike.
17. List several of the products that are made with algae.
18. How are fungi important to the environment?
19. How are protozoans like animals?
20. What are the causes and effects of a red tide?

21. Why is *Spirogyra* a good name for this green algae?
22. Compare and contrast unicellular, colonial, chain, and multicellular algae.
23. Discuss why scientists find it difficult to trace the origin of fungi. Why are fossils of fungi rare?
24. Explain the adaptations of fungi that allow them to get food.
25. What kind of environment is needed to prevent fungal growth?

MORE SKILL BUILDERS

If you need help, refer to the Skill Handbook.

1. **Inferring:** Match the color or meaning with each prefix of the algae names. Prefixes: *Chloro-, Chryso-, Phaeo-, Pyrro-, Rhodo.* Color meaning: brown, green, fire, gold, red.
2. **Concept Mapping:** Complete the following concept map.

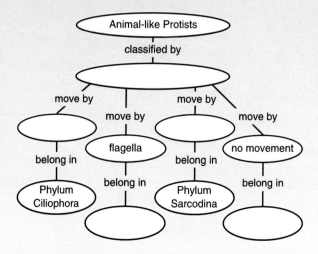

3. **Comparing and Contrasting:** Make a chart comparing and contrasting sac fungi, zygote fungi, and club fungi.
4. **Classifying:** Classify the organisms based on their method of movement. *Euglena, Amoeba,* dinoflagellates, *Paramecium, Plasmodium,* slime molds, *Trypanosoma, Volvox.*
5. **Observing:** The figure below shows some of the structures and specialized adaptations of kelp, including the stipe, blade, holdfast, and gas floats. Why do you think these structures are important for kelp?

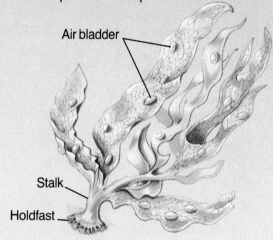

PROJECTS

1. Bring in labels of foods that contain carrageenans. Find out what protist these are from.
2. Find out the names of poisonous fungi. Do any inhabit your area? Bring a list to school.

GLOBAL CONNECTIONS

The Simplest Living Things

In this unit, you have studied viruses and simple organisms. Now find out the effects of viruses, bacteria, protists, and fungi around the world.

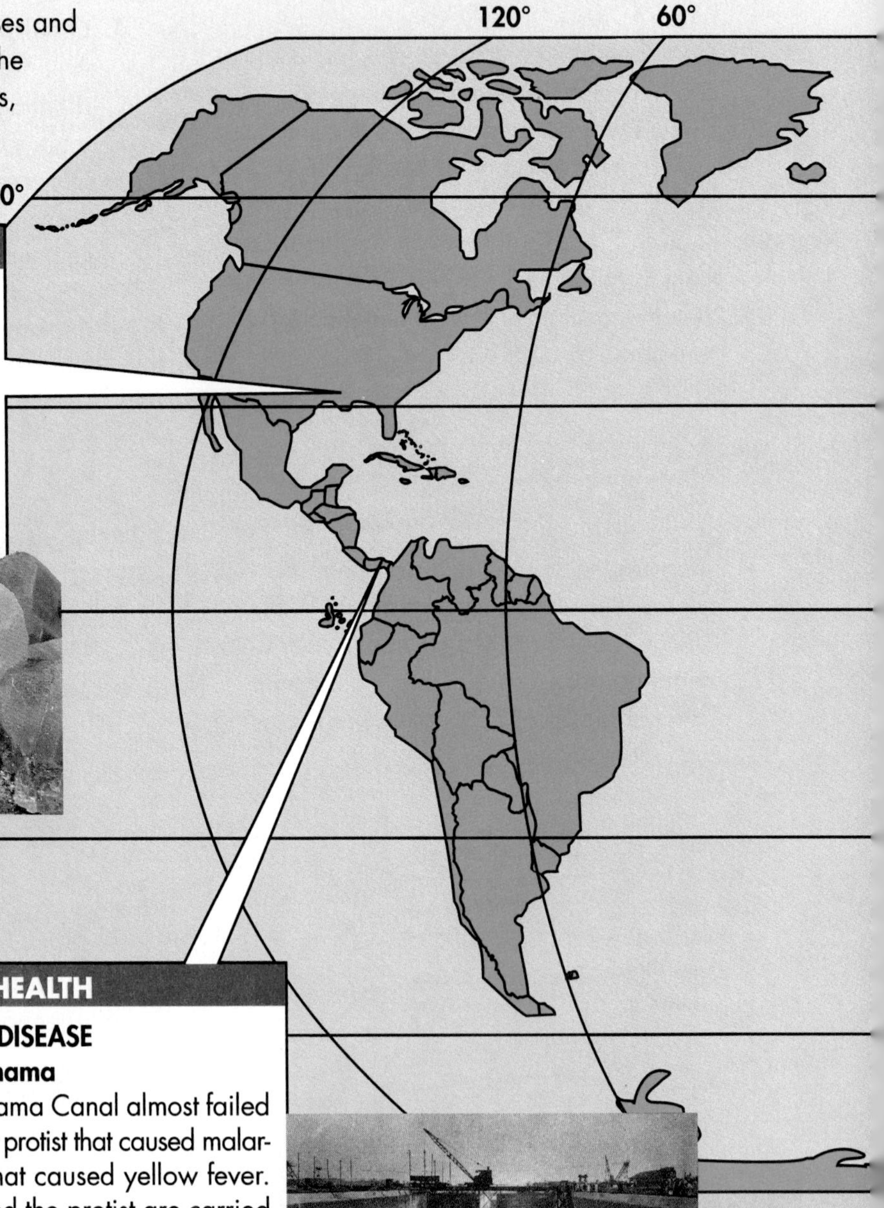

120° 60°

60°

GEOLOGY

SULFUR BACTERIA
Sulphur, Louisiana
Bacteria play an important role in producing sulfur. Bacterial sulfur has been found in rocks that are 800 million years old. What can you tell about bacteria as an early life form?

30°

HEALTH

VICTORY OVER DISEASE
Canal Zone, Panama
Building the Panama Canal almost failed because of a tiny protist that caused malaria and a virus that caused yellow fever. Both the virus and the protist are carried by mosquitoes. How could these diseases be controlled?

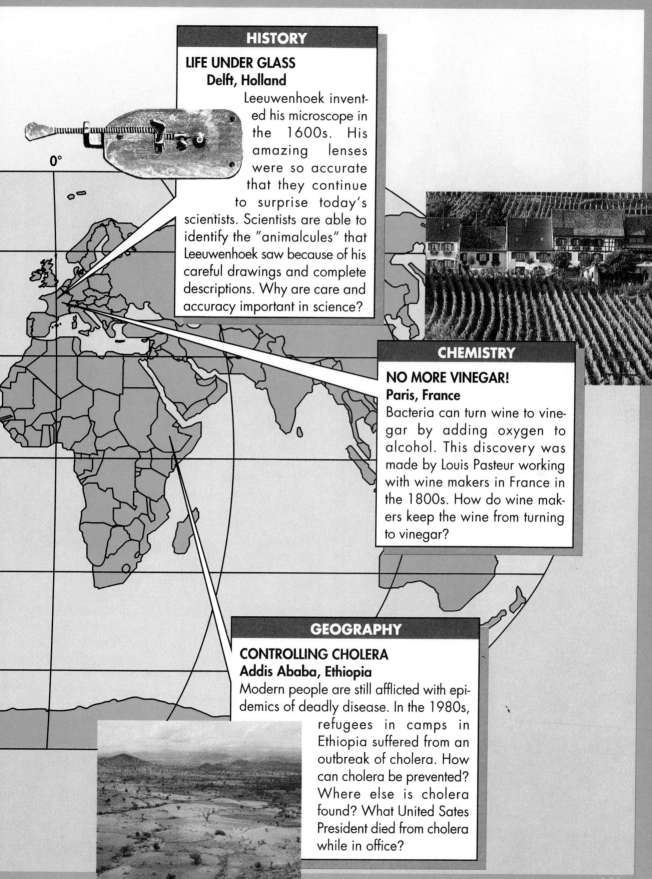

HISTORY

LIFE UNDER GLASS
Delft, Holland

Leeuwenhoek invented his microscope in the 1600s. His amazing lenses were so accurate that they continue to surprise today's scientists. Scientists are able to identify the "animalcules" that Leeuwenhoek saw because of his careful drawings and complete descriptions. Why are care and accuracy important in science?

0°

CHEMISTRY

NO MORE VINEGAR!
Paris, France

Bacteria can turn wine to vinegar by adding oxygen to alcohol. This discovery was made by Louis Pasteur working with wine makers in France in the 1800s. How do wine makers keep the wine from turning to vinegar?

GEOGRAPHY

CONTROLLING CHOLERA
Addis Ababa, Ethiopia

Modern people are still afflicted with epidemics of deadly disease. In the 1980s, refugees in camps in Ethiopia suffered from an outbreak of cholera. How can cholera be prevented? Where else is cholera found? What United Sates President died from cholera while in office?

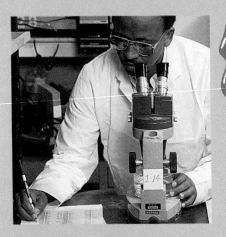

EPIDEMIOLOGIST

An *epidemiologist* studies the causes and spread of infectious diseases that affect large numbers of people. He or she may work in a laboratory, or at the site of an outbreak of a disease. A student interested in becoming an epidemiologist should study biology and chemistry in high school.

An epidemiologist will need four years of college plus graduate work in the fields of microbiology, biochemistry, physiology, and biotechnology. Many epidemiologists are medical doctors or people with doctorates who work in pathology laboratories. They may work in a national disease control center or in a university laboratory.

For Additional Information

Contact the American Society for Microbiology, Office of Education and Professional Recognition, 1913 I Street, Washington, DC 20006.

MUSHROOM FARMER

A *mushroom farmer* must have a knowledge of soils, as well as the growing conditions that mushrooms require. He or she will also need a knowledge of the varieties of mushrooms. Many new varieties of mushrooms are being cultivated because of the increase in ethnic cooking and specialty restaurants.

Most of the training a mushroom farmer needs can be learned on-the-job. To advance, these farmers should have some training in small business management. Such training can be obtained at trade schools or through community college programs. Usually, small business training programs take two years.

For Additional Information

Contact the American Farm Bureau Federation, 225 Touhy Ave., Park Ridge, IL 60068.

UNIT READINGS

▶Lee, Douglas. "Slime Mold: The Fungus That Walks." *National Geographic*, July 1981.
▶de Kruif, Paul. *Microbe Hunters*. Orlando, FL: Harcourt, Brace, 1926. This classic details the lives of pioneers in microbiology and their search for the cause of disease.

The Sea Around Us

by Rachel Carson

The following passage is taken from a chapter titled The Changing Year, which describes life in the sea as the seasons change.

In the sea, as on land, spring is a time for renewal of life. During the long months of winter in the temperate zones the surface waters have been absorbing cold. Now the heavy water begins to sink, slipping down and displacing the warmer layers below. Rich stores of minerals have been accumulating on the floor of the continental shelf—some freighted down by the rivers from the lands; some derived from sea creatures that have died and whose remains have drifted down to the bottom; some from the shells that once encased a diatom, the streaming protoplasm of a radiolarian, or the transparent tissues of a pteropod. Nothing is wasted in the sea; every particle of material is used over and over again, first by one creature, then by another. And when in spring the waters are deeply stirred, the warm bottom water brings to the surface a rich supply of minerals ready for use by new forms of life.

Just as land plants depend on minerals in the soil for their growth, every marine plant, even the smallest, is dependent upon the nutrient salts or minerals in the sea water. Diatoms must have silica, the element of which their fragile cells are fashioned. For these and all other microplants, phosphorus is an indispensable mineral. Some of these elements are in short supply and in winter may be reduced below the minimum necessary for growth. The diatom population must tide itself over this season as best it can. It faces a stark problem of survival, with no opportunity to increase, a problem of keeping alive the spark of life by forming tough protective spores against the stringency of winter, a matter of existing in a dormant state in which no demands shall be made on an environment that already withholds all but the most meager necessities of life. So the diatoms holds their place in the winter sea, like seeds of wheat in a field under snow and ice, the seeds from which the spring growth will come.

In Your Own Words

▶ Many of the simplest living things survive unfavorable living conditions as spores. Describe how this allows these life forms to survive. Write a brief essay describing the characteristics of spores. Tell what problems in the environment may cause an organism to form a spore. Also tell what must happen for the spore to resume normal growth and development.

UNIT

4 PLANTS

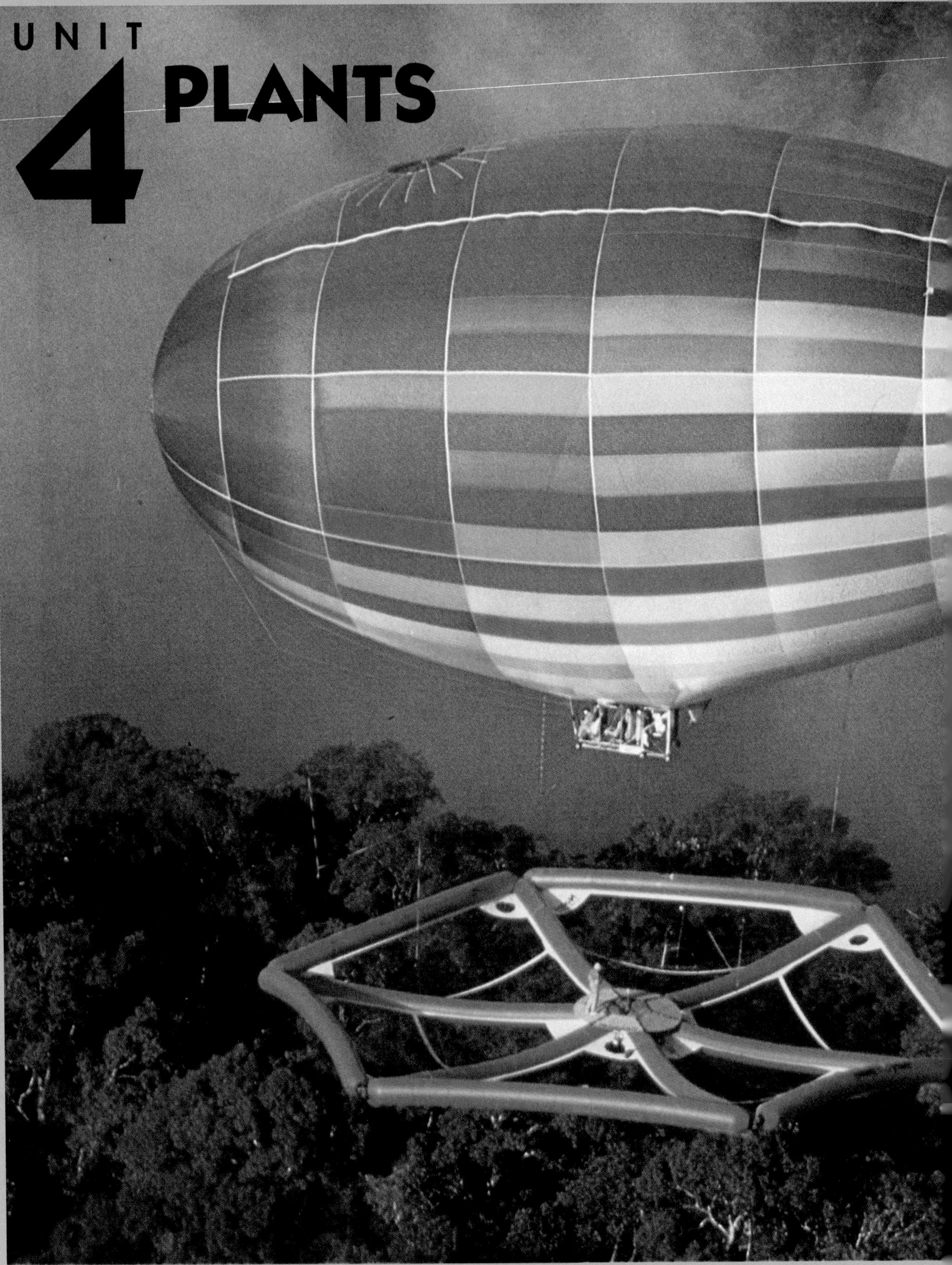

What's Happening Here?

How do you collect specimens 150 meters in the air? In 1989, a daring group of French scientists cleverly solved this problem by lowering a raft onto the trees of the rain forest from the air. The scientists tethered themselves to the raft for safety and then worked, ate, and slept in their unique, elevated research lab. What did they hope to learn? As rain forests are destroyed at an increasing rate, there is less time to learn about their treasures. The raft helped the scientists to find out if the plants and animals that live on the floor of the forest are different from those at home in the upper story.

UNIT CONTENTS

Chapter 10   Introduction to Plants
Chapter 11   The Seed Plants
Chapter 12   Plant Processes

Do you ever eat salads? A salad can contain almost any kind of plant you can think of. What plants would you choose for a salad? What part of the plant would you be eating?

FIND OUT!

Do this simple activity to find out what plant parts you eat.

Make a list of five things that you might find in a garden salad. Compare your list with a classmate's list. Did you choose different things? Now decide what part of the plant each salad item is. Did you choose carrots? Carrots are roots. If you chose lettuce, you would be eating leaves. What about some sprigs of parsley? They are stems. Bean sprouts, pineapple fruit, and sunflower seeds are other parts of plants you might find in a salad.

Gearing Up

Previewing the Chapter

Use this outline to help you focus on important ideas in this chapter.

Section 10-1   Characteristics of Plants
- ▶ What Is a Plant?
- ▶ Origin and Evolution of Plants
- ▶ Classification of Plants

Section 10-2   Seedless Plants
- ▶ Nonvascular Plants
- ▶ Seedless Vascular Plants

Section 10-3   Science and Society
Peat Moss as Fuel
- ▶ What's In a Bog?

Previewing Science Skills

- ▶ In the Skill Builders, you will outline and hypothesize and make a concept map.
- ▶ In the Activities, you will observe, collect data, and classify.
- ▶ In the MINI-Labs, you will observe, measure, and infer.

What's next?

So far, you have identified some plant parts. In this chapter you will learn more about the characteristics of plants and how plants are adapted to life on land.

10-1 Characteristics of Plants

New Science Words

carotenoids
cellulose
cuticle
vascular plants
nonvascular plants

Objectives

▶ List the characteristics of plants.
▶ Describe adaptations of plants that made it possible for them to survive on land.
▶ Describe the differences between vascular and nonvascular plants.

What Is a Plant?

Have you ever walked in a park like the one shown in Figure 10-1? You may have taken off your shoes and wriggled your toes in the cool grass. Perhaps you climbed a tree and looked at the sky through green leaves. Or you may have walked down a nature trail to a low, damp place where ferns grew. The grass, trees, and ferns all are members of the plant kingdom.

Now look at Figure 10-2. These organisms have common characteristics that help identify them as plants, too. What do they have in common with grass, trees, and ferns?

All plants are many celled and most contain the green pigment chlorophyll. Cell walls surround plant cells and give them structure. Most plants have roots or rootlike

Figure 10-1. All plants are many-celled and contain chlorophyll. Grass, trees, and ferns all are members of the Plant Kingdom.

fibers that hold them in the ground, so plants usually do not move around. Plants are eukaryotes that have adapted to life on land. In fact, they have adapted so well that they are found in nearly every environment on Earth. From the frigid, ice-bound land of Antarctica to the hot, dry deserts of Africa, there are plants that have evolved to survive even the most extreme conditions.

Most plants live on land, but many live in or near water. Plants range in size from tiny water ferns that require a hand lens for close observation, to the giant sequoia trees of the western United States, some of which are nearly a thousand years old.

About 285 000 plant species have been identified, and scientists believe there are many more still to be found, primarily in tropical rain forests. If you were asked to make a list of all the plants you could name, you probably would name vegetables, fruits, and field crops like wheat, rice, or corn. These plants are important food sources to people and other consumers. Without green plants, life on Earth as we know it would not be possible.

Figure 10-2. Simple plants include mosses and liverworts like these.

Why are green plants important to consumers?

Origin and Evolution of Plants

Where did the first plants come from? Like all life, early plants probably came from the sea, evolving from the plantlike protists. What evidence is there that this occurred? Both plants and plantlike protists have two different types of chlorophyll as well as carotenoids (kuh RAT uh noydz) in their cells. **Carotenoids** are red, yellow, or orange pigments found in chloroplasts and in all cyanobacteria. Carrots are orange in color because of these pigments.

One way of understanding the evolution of plants is to look at the fossil record. Unfortunately, the fossil record for plants is not as good as that for animals. Plants usually decay before they form fossils. The oldest fossil plants are from the Devonian period and are about 400 million years old. Available fossils show that early plants were very similar to the plantlike protists. Fossils of *Rhynia major* represent the earliest land plants known. This fossil plant is shown in Figure 10-3. These plants had no leaves, and their stems grew underground. Scientists hypothesize that these kinds of plants evolved into the simple plants of today.

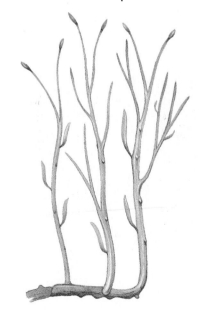

Figure 10-3. *Rhynia major* is one of the earliest land plants known.

What do you think are some of the adaptations found in early plants that allowed them to survive on land? Imagine life for a one-celled green alga floating in a shallow pool. The water in the pool surrounds and supports the alga cell. It can make its own food through the process of photosynthesis, and materials move freely into and out of the cell membrane by osmosis and diffusion. The alga has everything it needs to survive.

Now imagine a summer drought. The pool begins to dry up. Soon the alga lies on the damp mud that once was the bottom of the pool. What will happen to the alga? It can still make its own food, so it won't starve. As long as the ground stays damp, the alga can move materials in and out through the cell membrane. But it is no longer supported or protected by the pool's water. What will happen to the alga if the land continues to dry up? The alga will lose water through the cell membrane by osmosis. Remember that in osmosis, water molecules diffuse through a membrane from an area of higher water concentration to one of lower concentration. Water will diffuse out of the alga to the drier pond bottom. Without water, the alga cannot continue photosynthesis. Eventually it will die.

Can you think of an adaptation that would make it possible for plants to survive on land? Loss of water is the major problem plants faced in adapting to life on land. Plant cells have cell membranes like the protists do, but

Figure 10-4. Green algae (a) produce their own food and move materials in and out through the cell membrane. Without water, algae connot produce food, so they eventually die (b).

Figure 10-5. Cell walls and waxy cuticles are adaptations that enable plants to survive on land.

they also have rigid outer cell walls. Cell walls are made of **cellulose,** an organic compound made up of long chains of sugar molecules. Wood used for furniture and construction is about 50 percent cellulose. Cotton fiber is almost pure cellulose. Cell walls help prevent plant cells from drying out and provide structure and support. Most land plants also have a waxy, protective layer on stems and leaves called a **cuticle.** The next time it rains, go outside and see how raindrops bead up on the surface of most plant leaves. The rain rolls right off beause of the waxy cuticle. The cuticle is another adaptation that helped plants to conserve water and survive on land.

How does a cuticle help a plant adapt to life on land?

Another problem plants faced on land was reproduction. Plants evolved from organisms that reproduced in water, and simple plants still require water to reproduce. You will learn more about reproduction in simple plants in Section 10-2. More complex plants evolved ways to reproduce that do not require water. Reproduction in these plants is discussed in Chapter 11.

There are some advantages to life on land for plants. For one thing, there's a lot more sunlight available for photosynthesis on land than in the water. Another advantage of life on land is the availability of carbon dioxide. There is much more carbon dioxide in the air than in the water. Carbon dioxide is a gas that plants use to produce food. All plants still need water to carry nutrients into and waste products out of their cells. They also need some kind of structure to support their weight on land.

Classification of Plants

Today, plants usually are classified into major groups called divisions. A division is the same level as the phylum you've studied in the Protist Kingdom. The simplest plants—mosses and liverworts—are placed in the division Bryophyta (bri uh FITE uh).

Bryophytes are usually just a few cells thick, so they are able to absorb water directly through their cell walls. Bryophytes are small plants found in damp environments like the forest floor, the edges of ponds and streams, and near the ocean. Plants in the other divisions of the Plant Kingdom have systems in which water and nutrients are transported through the plant in a tubelike system of vessels. These vessels are similar to your own blood vessels. Vessels transport materials to all plant cells. Plants with vessels can be more than a few cells thick. Plants that have vessels are **vascular plants.** Most of the plants you are familiar with, such as trees, bushes, and flowers, are vascular plants. Plants without vessels, the bryophytes, are often called **nonvascular plants.** Why are nonvascular plants small and found in damp environments?

What are plants with and without vessels called?

Figure 10-6. The Plant Kingdom

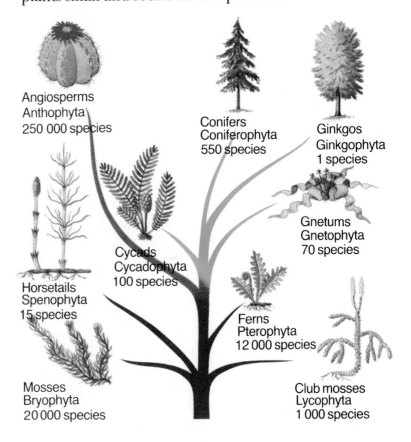

Angiosperms
Anthophyta
250 000 species

Conifers
Coniferophyta
550 species

Ginkgos
Ginkgophyta
1 species

Gnetums
Gnetophyta
70 species

Cycads
Cycadophyta
100 species

Horsetails
Spenophyta
15 species

Ferns
Pterophyta
12 000 species

Mosses
Bryophyta
20 000 species

Club mosses
Lycophyta
1 000 species

TECHNOLOGY

Oil from Desert Plants

The jojoba (ho HO bah), a desert plant, produces brown, peanut-sized seeds that contain an oil very similar to sperm whale oil. Trade in sperm whale oil was banned in the United States in 1970. Sperm whale oil was used in many products, from face creams to transmission fluids. Without sperm whale oil, industries tried new oils, including jojoba oil.

Jojoba seeds contain 50 percent oil by weight. This oil has a very high boiling point (398°C) and is valuable for lubricating machinery. Jojoba oil has no cholesterol and can be a healthy substitute for other cooking oils. Used also in soap and cosmetics, jojoba has a promising future.

However, it is expensive because, until recently, most oil was extracted from seeds collected in the desert. Only a few thousand hectares have been planted commercially so far.

Think Critically: How does the availability of jojoba oil affect its usefulness to industry?

SECTION REVIEW

1. List the characteristics of plants.
2. Describe the adaptations that made life on land possible for plants. What are some advantages of life on land for plants?
3. What organisms did plants probably evolve from?
4. Explain the main difference between vascular and nonvascular plants.
5. **Apply:** If you left a board lying on the grass for a few days, what would happen to the grass underneath the board? Why?

⊠ Hypothesizing

From what you have learned about adaptations necessary for life on land, make a hypothesis as to what types of adaptations land plants would need if they had to survive submerged in water. If you need help, refer to Hypothesizing in the **Skill Handbook** on page 686.

10-2 Seedless Plants

New Science Words

moss
rhizoids
liverwort
sporophyte
gametophyte
alternation of generations
pioneer species
vascular tissue
epiphyte
rhizome
frond
sori
prothallus

What is a moss?

Objectives

▶ Describe the life cycles of mosses and ferns.
▶ Compare simple nonvascular plants with simple vascular plants.
▶ State the importance of simple nonvascular and vascular plants.

Nonvascular Plants

If you were asked to name the parts of a plant, you probably would list roots, stems, leaves, and perhaps flowers. You may also know that many plants grow from seeds. But did you know that some simple plants have none of these parts? Nonvascular plants, the bryophytes, do not have roots, stems, or leaves. They do have rootlike fibers, stalks that look like stems, and leaflike green growths. Instead of growing from seeds, bryophytes grow from spores. The nonvascular plants include the mosses and liverworts. Figure 10-7 shows some common types of nonvascular plants.

A **moss** is a simple rootless plant with leaflike growths in a spiral around a stalk. Moss plants are held in place by rootlike filaments or threads made up of only a few long cells called **rhizoids.** A **liverwort** is a simple, rootless plant that has a flattened, leaflike body. Liverworts get their

Figure 10-7. The nonvascular plants include the mosses (a) and the liverworts (b).

name from their shape. A liverwort looks like a liver. In the ninth century, liverworts were thought to be useful in treating diseases of the liver. The ending, *-wort,* means "herb," so the word *liverwort* means "herb for the liver." In liverworts, each rhizoid is made up of just one cell. Both mosses and liverworts are small plants that grow in damp areas. They range in size from 2 to 20 centimeters in height.

Of approximately 20 000 species of nonvascular plants, most are classified as mosses. Have you ever seen mosses growing on tree trunks, rocks, or the ground in damp or humid areas? Sometimes mosses grow right on the sides of wood houses.

The Moss Life Cycle

A typical growth of moss plants looks like a soft, green carpet on the forest floor, as shown in Figure 10-7a. Now look at the closeup of the moss plants in Figure 10-8. Can you see the structures sticking up out of the leaflike plants? These are the moss sporophytes. A **sporophyte** includes a stalk and a capsule where spores are produced by the process of meiosis.

Figure 10-8. The leafy green gametophytes of moss support the stalks and capsules of the moss sporophytes.

What is a gametophyte?

Recall from Chapter 4 that meiosis results in gametes that are haploid. When a haploid spore lands on wet soil or rocks, it germinates into a thin, threadlike green structure called a protonema. Within a few days, small gametophyte moss plants begin to grow here and there along the protonema. A **gametophyte** is the form of a moss plant that produces gametes. Sometimes a moss gametophyte produces only male or female gametes, but often both types are produced. During a heavy dew or rain, the male gametes get splashed onto the female gametophyte. They swim to the female gametes. When the male and female gametes unite, they form a diploid zygote. The zygote divides by mitosis to form an embryo, which in turn develops into a sporophyte, and the cycle begins again. This continual cycle that alternates between the sporophyte and gametophyte of the moss plant is called **alternation of generations** and represents sexual reproduction in mosses. In bryophytes, the most common plant is the green, leaflike gametophyte. The life cycle of a moss, including the alternation of generations, is shown in Figure 10-9. Liverworts have a life cycle similar to that of the mosses.

In addition to the alternation of generations, both mosses and liverworts reproduce asexually. New moss plants can develop when a small section of the parent plant breaks off. Liverworts develop small balls of cells within cuplike structures on the surface of the leaflike body. These balls of cells can be carried by water to new areas where they grow into new plants.

Like mosses and liverworts, all plants have a life cycle in which the sporophyte and gametophyte alternate. In other words, all plants go through a diploid and a haploid stage in sexual reproduction. In nonvascular plants, the sporophytes depend on the gametophytes for water and nutrients. In the more complex vascular plants, the sporophyte is independent of the gametophyte. In fact, the gametophyte is no more than a small structure on the sporophyte plant itself.

Figure 10-9. The Moss Life Cycle

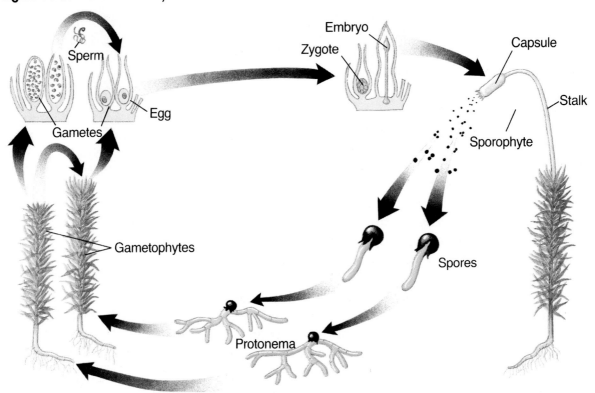

Pioneer Plants
in Lava

Figure 10-10. Mosses and liverworts are pioneer plants that often are among the first living things to inhabit a new environment like this lava field.

Importance of Mosses and Liverworts

Mosses and liverworts are important in the ecology of many areas. They are often among the first plants to grow in new environments, such as lava fields, or disturbed environments, such as forests destroyed by fire. When a volcano erupts, the lava covers the land and destroys the plants living there. After the lava cools, the spores of mosses and liverworts are carried to the new rocks by the wind and begin to grow wherever there is enough water. When they grow on rocks, their rhizoids can actually begin to penetrate tiny cracks in the rocks' surfaces. Weathering of rocks often begins when mosses release chemicals that begin to break rocks down. Organisms that are the first to grow in new or disturbed areas like these are called **pioneer species.** Pioneer plant species grow and die and begin to build up decaying plant material that provides nutrients for other, less hardy, plants. That is, these pioneer plants change the conditions in the environment so that other plants can grow there, too. Larger vascular plants then begin to grow, sending their roots down through the decaying plants and into the rocks underneath. As the roots grow, they crack the rocks apart even more, and the weathering process slowly turns the rocks into new soil.

What are pioneer species?

Science and READING

Surtsey, an island near Iceland, is an important scientific laboratory. Read about this island and find out why. Report to your class on what's being found there.

ACTIVITY 10-1
Comparing Mosses and Liverworts

Problem: *How are mosses and liverworts similar?*

Materials

- hand lens
- forceps
- dropper
- 2 microscope slides
- microscope
- dissecting needle
- prepared slides of moss and liverwort gametophytes

- mosses
- liverworts
- water
- 2 coverslips

Data and Observations

Structure	Liverwort	Moss
Sporophyte		
Gametophyte		
Spores		

Procedure

1. Obtain a moss. The leafy part of the moss is the gametophyte. With a hand lens, observe the leafy body of the moss. Locate and observe the rhizoids.
2. Remove a piece of the leafy portion of the moss with a forceps and make a wet mount. Observe under low power and examine the cell layers.
3. Examine prepared slides of sections of the sporophyte and gametophyte moss plants under low and high power. Draw.
4. On the moss gametophyte, locate the capsule at the tip of the stalk. Remove the capsule and place it in a drop of water on a slide. Place a coverslip on the capsule. Using the eraser of your pencil, gently crush the capsule to release the spores. **CAUTION:** *Do not break the coverslip.* Observe the spores under low and high power. Draw and label the spores.
5. Obtain a liverwort. Repeat Steps 1-3.

Analyze

1. How many cell layers were you able to observe in the moss? in the liverwort?
2. What function do the rhizoids have?
3. Where are spores formed in a moss?
4. Where are spores formed in a liverwort?

Mosses

Liverworts

Conclude and Apply

5. Compare the leafy structures of the mosses and liverworts.
6. Compare the rhizoids of mosses and liverworts.
7. How are the reproductive structures of the mosses and liverworts different?
8. How are the sporophytes of the mosses and liverworts different?
9. How can you tell the difference between a moss and a liverwort?

Seedless Vascular Plants

A second and larger group of simple plants includes the seedless vascular plants. These plants differ from the bryophytes primarily because they have vascular tissue, and from other vascular plants because they produce spores rather than seeds. The **vascular tissue** in the seedless vascular plants is made up of long cells in the form of tubes. These cells carry water, minerals, and nutrients to all the cells throughout the plant. Why would having cells like these be an advantage to plants? Remember that bryophytes are only a few cells thick. Each cell has to be able to absorb water directly from the environment. As a result, these plants cannot grow very big. Plants with vascular tissue can grow bigger and thicker because each cell gets water and nutrients through the vascular tissue.

Seedless vascular plants include the club mosses, spike mosses, horsetails, and ferns. Today, there are about 1000 species of club mosses, spike mosses, and horsetails. Ferns are more abundant, with at least 12 000 species known. During the Paleozoic era, there were many species that we know of only from fossils. In the warm, moist Paleozoic era, some species of horsetails grew up to 15 meters tall. In contrast, none of the simple vascular plant species today reach more than 1 or 2 meters in height.

What is vascular tissue?

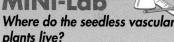

MINI-Lab

Where do the seedless vascular plants live?
Use the available pictures your teacher has provided. How can the club mosses live in the desert? Why are horsetails found in the tropics? How can the water fern live in the water? What is the advantage of mosquito ferns forming dense mats? Why are ferns good houseplants?

Figure 10-11. The seedless vascular plants include club mosses, spike mosses, horsetails, and ferns.

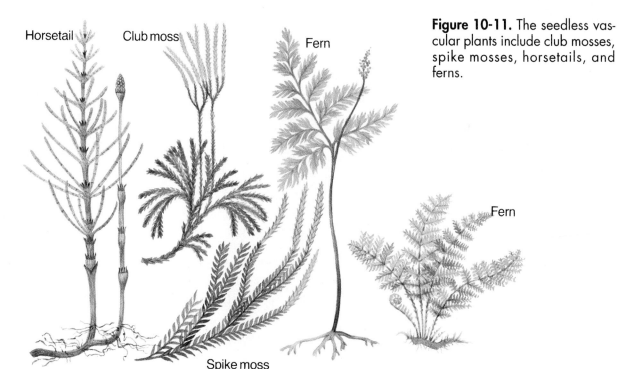

Horsetail   Club moss   Fern

Spike moss

Fern

Club Mosses and Spike Mosses

Look at the photographs of club mosses and spike mosses in Figure 10-12. Club mosses produce spores at the end of the stems in structures that look like tiny pine cones. The upright stems of club mosses have needlelike leaves. One kind of club moss, *Lycopodium*, is called the ground pine because it looks like a miniature pine tree. *Lycopodium* is found from arctic regions to the tropics, but never in large numbers. In some areas *Lycopodium* is endangered because of overcollection. Most tropical species of *Lycopodium* are epiphytes. An **epiphyte** is a plant that grows on other plants for support.

Spike mosses look similar to club mosses. One species of spike moss, the resurrection plant, is adapted to desert conditions. When water isn't available, the plant curls up and looks dead. But when water falls in the desert, the resurrection plant unfurls its green leaves and begins making food again. The plant can go through this process many times if necessary.

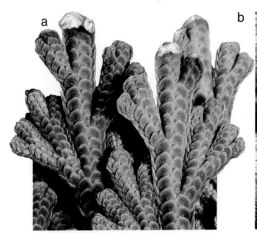

Figure 10-12. Club mosses (a) and spike mosses (b) produce spores at the end of stems in structures similar to pine cones.

Horsetails

Horsetails have a stem structure unique among the vascular plants. Their stems are jointed and have a hollow center surrounded by a ring of vascular tissue. Leaves grow in a spiral around each joint. In Figure 10-13 you can see these joints easily. If you pull on a horsetail stem it will pop apart in sections. Spores grow in a structure at the tip of the stems, as in the club mosses. The stems of the horsetails contain silica, a gritty substance found in sand. In the days when

Figure 10-13. Horsetails contain silica and were used by pioneers in the United States to scrub pots and pans.

pioneers traveled westward across the United States, horsetail stems were used to scour pots and pans. The common name of *Equisetum* today is still "scouring rush."

Ferns

The largest group of seedless vascular plants is the division Pterophyta (teh ruh FITE uh), the ferns. There are about 12 000 living species of ferns, but like the other divisions of vascular plants, many more species are known only as fossils.

During the Carboniferous period of the Paleozoic era, most ferns grew much larger than any fern species alive at present. Species of tree ferns found today in tropical areas may reach 3 to 5 meters in height, but ancient tree ferns living in the swamps of the Carboniferous grew as high as 25 meters. When they died, tree ferns and other plant species were submerged in water and mud before they could decompose. This plant material built up, became compacted and compressed, and eventually turned into coal. Today, this same process can be seen in peat bogs. Coal and peat are two types of fuel used in many parts of the world today for energy. Coal, peat, petroleum, and natural gas all are known as fossil fuels because they were formed from the plants and other organisms of the Carboniferous period.

Figure 10-14. The unusual cinnamon fern bears its spores on separate stalks rather than in sori on the fronds.

What are four types of fossil fuels?

Figure 10-15. The Carboniferous swamp forest contained many more species of club mosses, spike mosses, horsetails, and ferns than are alive today.

The Fern Life Cycle

In the life cycle of a fern, the gametophyte and sporophyte are independent of each other. This means that both forms of the fern plant can produce their own food. The fern plants that you may have seen growing in the woods or in pots in your classroom are the sporophytes. A fern has leaves that grow above the ground from an underground stem called a **rhizome.** Roots grow from the rhizome to anchor the plant in the soil. The leaf of a fern is called a **frond.** Young fronds are often called fiddleheads because their curled shape looks similar to the tops of violins, or fiddles. Ferns produce spores in structures called **sori** (*sing.* sorus) on the lower sides of the mature fronds. The sori are usually a dusty brown color and may look like crusty bumps. When a sorus opens, spores are released at incredible speeds. They land on damp soil or rocks and germinate into small, green, heart-shaped gametophytes. The gametophyte is called a **prothallus.** The prothallus produces gametes that unite to form the zygote. The zygote develops into the embryo, then sporophyte, as in the mosses. But in ferns, the gametophyte also produces new rhizomes, which can grow into the separate sporophyte fern plants you are familiar with. You can see the life cycle of a fern in Figure 10-16.

Ferns are interesting plants to scientists because they have characteristics of both nonvascular and vascular plants. Like the bryophytes, ferns produce spores, yet

What is a frond?

Figure 10-16. The Fern Life Cycle

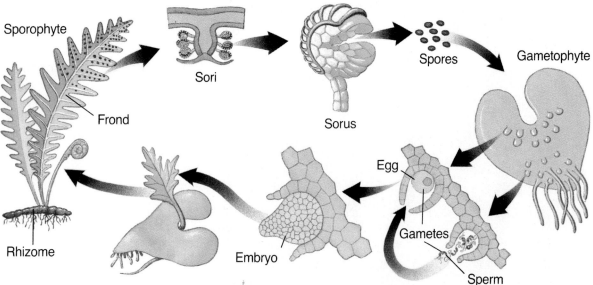

Sporophyte

Sori

Spores

Gametophyte

Frond

Sorus

Egg

Gametes

Rhizome

Embryo

Sperm

What Are the Brown Spots on the Leaves?

Marites was a member of the Nature Club at her elementary school. One Saturday the Nature Club visited the arboretum to learn about local plants. The teacher led the group. As the group was examining a clump of large leaves growing in a moist, shady area, Marites noticed a bunch of brown bugs on the underside of the leaves. Joseph didn't think the leaves had bugs. He thought the plant had some kind of disease. Sarah said, "You're both wrong. I think the brown spots are seeds."

Think Critically: How might the teacher explain what the brown spots on the leaves really are?

they have vascular tissue like seed-bearing plants. Ferns also have leaves (the fronds), stems (the rhizomes), and roots. If you were a scientist, would you classify ferns as nonvascular or vascular plants? Why?

SECTION REVIEW

1. Describe the life cycle of mosses.
2. How are club and spike mosses similar to mosses?
3. Explain the stages in the life cycle of a fern.
4. Explain why a fern is classified as a vascular rather than a nonvascular plant.
5. **Apply:** List three ways simple plants affect your life each day. (HINT: How is your home heated? Where does the electricity to run your television set come from?) Explain.

⊠ Concept Mapping

Make a concept map showing how nonvascular and vascular plants are related. Include these terms in the concept map: *plant kingdom, bryophytes, liverworts, mosses, seedless plants, nonvascular plants, seedless vascular plants, club mosses, ferns, horsetails,* and *spike mosses.* If you need help, refer to Concept Mapping in the **Skill Handbook** on pages 688 and 689.

Skill Builder

SCIENCE & SOCIETY

10-3 Peat Moss as Fuel

New Science Words

bogs

Objectives

▶ State two advantages of using peat as fuel.
▶ Understand the environmental cost of using peat as fuel.

What's In a Bog?

What is a bog?

Bogs are very mysterious places. Human bodies 7000 years old have been recovered from these wet areas all over the world. Sound like the beginning of a horror movie? What exactly is a bog? **Bogs** are poorly drained areas with spongy, wet ground that is composed mainly of dead and decaying plants. The principal plants in bogs are nonvascular plants that belong to the genus *Sphagnum*. *Sphagnum* moss forms large mats on top of the water surface in bogs. The water in a bog is very acidic and has very low levels of oxygen. These conditions slow down or stop the growth of the bacteria responsible for decomposing dead organic matter such as plants. As a result, moss and other plants that die in bogs don't decay. Dead peat moss builds up in the bog and is compressed by the weight of the water above. Gradually the peat moss becomes peat, a combination of partially decaying sphagnum moss and other organisms. Peat has been used as a low-cost fuel for centuries. Blocks of black peat can be cut out of the bog, dried in the sun, then burned in a stove or furnace to produce heat. Peat is actually the first step in the geological process of turning plant material into coal. Lignite coal is formed when peat has been compressed and heated by the geologic force of Earth.

MINI-Lab

How much water do simple plants hold?

Place a few teaspoons of *Sphagnum* moss on a piece of cheesecloth. Twist the cheesecloth to form a ball and secure with a rubber band. Put 200 mL of water in a beaker. Add the ball to the water. Wait about 15 minutes; remove the ball from the water, placing it on a glass dish. Measure the amount of water left in the beaker. How much water did the *Sphagnum* moss soak up?

246 INTRODUCTION TO PLANTS

Peat has been used as a fuel for many years in Northern Europe, England, and Ireland. It is very cheap and burns slowly for long periods of time. After it is dried, the most decomposed peat burns with greater fuel efficiency than wood. Developing countries such as Burundi and Rwanda are looking into the use of peat as an alternative to importing expensive petroleum products. In the United States, geologists estimate that Maine has 300 000 hectares of peat available to use for fuel, whereas Minnesota has about three million hectares. In Maine, America's first peat-fueled power plant is already supplying energy to Boston. This is very economical for the New England area because oil, gas, and coal resources are all very far away.

Have we found the perfect source of fuel? Environmentalists don't think so. They fear that the bogs of the United States are headed toward the same fate as those in Ireland. Today, Ireland generates 21 percent of its electric power with peat. However, in the last 40 years, the Irish have destroyed 95 percent of their bogs. These bogs took nature 10 000 years to build! Why save bogs? They are home to animals and plants that can live no other place in the world. Bogs help control flooding by holding huge amounts of water. Peat moss can hold water in amounts up to 20 times its own dry weight. Bogs also help keep water resources such as rivers and lakes clean by filtering out silt and chemicals. Although peat is a cheap source of energy, it is a nonrenewable fossil fuel, just like coal, petroleum, and natural gas. When it burns, it releases chemicals such as carbon dioxide, sulfur dioxide, and nitrogen oxides, all sources of air pollution.

Figure 10-17. Unique plants of the peat bog include: (a) arethusa, (b) bog rosemary, (c)leather leaf, (d) pitcher plant, (e) false Solomon's seal, (f) sundew, (g) dewthread, (h) cranberry, (i) Labrador tea, and (j) *Sphagnum* moss.

SECTION REVIEW

1. Why is peat considered a good alternative fuel?
2. Why are environmentalists concerned with its use?

You Decide!

The state of Maine has certain environmental standards which the peat harvesters are required to uphold. The Maine peat has little sulfur and emits little sulfur dioxide. Excess water will be captured in ponds to prevent runoff, and vegetation will be restored to the area after the harvest. Are these sufficient trade-offs for losing the bogs that took thousands of years to form?

ACTIVITY 10-2
The Life Cycle of a Fern

Problem: *How can stages in the life cycle of a fern be observed?*

Materials

- fern
- fern frond with spores
- fern spores
- hand lens
- petri dish
- paper towel
- scissors
- water
- prepared slides of fern
- microscope

Procedure

1. Cut a piece of paper towel into a circle that will just fit into the bottom of the petri dish.
2. Soak the paper towel circle with water. Use your fingernail to gently scrape away the protective membrane of the sorus on a fern frond. Tap the sorus to dislodge the spores.
3. Sprinkle a few fern spores on the paper towel and cover the petri dish. Observe the petri dish with a hand lens once each week for 6 weeks. Add water if necessary.
4. Make a data table like the one shown. Draw and label what you see in the petri dish each week. Write your observations in the table.
5. Observe the fronds of the fern plant for evidence that it is a sporophyte.
6. Use the microscope to observe prepared slides of the fern life cycle under low and high power.

Analyze

1. How many stages are there in the life cycle of a fern?
2. In which stage are spores formed?
3. In which stage are sex organs formed?
4. What is the name given to fern leaves?

Data and Observations

Week	Fern Gametophyte	Fern Sporophyte
1		
2		
3		
4		
5		
6		

Conclude and Apply

5. What is the name given to the underground stem of a fern sporophyte?
6. What is the difference between rhizoids and rhizomes?
7. Describe a fern gametophyte.
8. Compare the sporophyte with the gametophyte of a fern.

CHAPTER
REVIEW

10-1: Characteristics of Plants
1. Plants are many-celled eukaryotes adapted to life on land.
2. Plants evolved from the plantlike protists.
3. Simple plants include nonvascular plants, the bryophytes, and vascular plants with vessels to conduct materials to plant cells.

10-2: Seedless Plants
1. Bryophytes—mosses and liverworts—reproduce through the process of alternation of generations, as do all plants.
2. Ferns, club mosses, and horsetails are seedless vascular plants with vascular tissue.
3. Nonvascular plants are pioneer species that help to break down rock into soil for other plants. Simple vascular plants have characteristics of both nonvascular and vascular plants.

10-3: Science and Society: Peat Moss as Fuel
1. Peat is a cheap fuel that burns slowly for long periods of time. It is available in places that are far away from oil, gas, or coal resources.
2. Bogs are important homes for unique organisms, hold water to prevent flooding, and help filter out silt and chemicals in water.

KEY SCIENCE WORDS

a. **alternation of generations**
b. **bogs**
c. **carotenoids**
d. **cellulose**
e. **cuticle**
f. **epiphyte**
g. **frond**
h. **gametophyte**
i. **liverwort**
j. **moss**
k. **nonvascular plants**
l. **pioneer species**
m. **prothallus**
n. **rhizoids**
o. **rhizome**
p. **sori**
q. **sporophyte**
r. **vascular plants**
s. **vascular tissue**

UNDERSTANDING VOCABULARY

Match each phrase with the correct term from the list of Key Science Words.

1. plant that produces gametes
2. small, green, heart-shaped gametophyte
3. plant that produces spores
4. rootlike filaments
5. underground fern stem
6. spore-producing capsules
7. made of tubelike conducting cells
8. plant division including mosses and liverworts
9. the first plants to grow in new environments
10. waxy layer on stems and leaves

CHAPTER
REVIEW

CHECKING CONCEPTS

Choose the word or phrase that completes the sentence.

1. Characteristics of plants include _____.
   a. roots   c. many cells
   b. cell walls   d. all of these

2. Plants probably evolved from _____.
   a. animals   c. fungi
   b. protists   d. none of these

3. _____ are plants only a few cells thick.
   a. Bryophytes   c. Horsetails
   b. Ferns   d. Vascular

4. _____ plants are plants with vessels.
   a. Bryophyte   c. Nonvascular
   b. Moss   d. Vascular

5. Nonvascular plants have all but _____.
   a. zygotes   c. rhizoids
   b. rhizomes   d. protonema

6. Nonvascular plants are _____.
   a. peat formers   c. pioneer species
   b. small   d. all of these

7. Ferns are _____.
   a. spore producers c. seed producers
   b. nonvascular   d. none of these

8. _____ are seedless vascular plants.
   a. Mosses   c. Horsetails
   b. Liverworts   d. None of these

9. Of these, ferns do not have _____.
   a. fronds   c. rhizomes
   b. rhizoids   d. spores

10. All plants have a life cycle with _____.
    a. sporophytes
    b. gametophytes
    c. alternation of generations
    d. all of the above

UNDERSTANDING CONCEPTS

Complete each sentence.

11. The _____ is a waxy protective covering.
12. _____ are groups in plant classification.
13. The life cycle that has sporophyte and gametophyte stages is called _____.
14. The _____ is a fern's gametophyte.
15. A fern's leaf is called a(n) _____.

THINK AND WRITE CRITICALLY

16. Why is it an advantage for simple plants to alternate generations?
17. Why are sporophytes dependent on the gametophytes in bryophytes?
18. Explain which generation of plant you see when you look at a fern in a pot; a moss plant on a tree trunk.
19. What would happen if a land plant's waxy cuticle was destroyed?
20. Compare how the cells of nonvascular and vascular plants get water.

21. Human remains sometimes found in peat bogs are very well-preserved. Explain why this occurs.
22. Discuss the importance of water in reproduction of bryophytes and ferns.
23. Why is *Sphagnum* moss added to garden soil?
24. Explain why mosses are found on moist forest floors.
25. How do mosses change rocky areas so that other plants can take root?

MORE SKILL BUILDERS

If you need help, refer to the Skill Handbook.

1. **Concept Mapping:** Fill in the map showing the divisions of the Plant Kingdom.

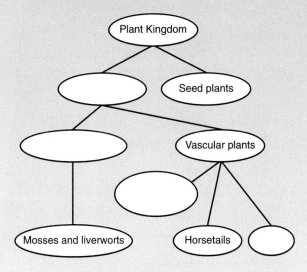

2. **Classifying:** Classify these plants in the correct group, bryophytes or seedless vascular: 1. club moss, 2. fern, 3. liverwort, 4. *Equisetum*, 5. horsetail, 6. *Lycopodium*, 7. moss, 8. spikemoss, 9. *Sphagnum*, 10. peat moss.

3. **Classifying:** Classify as part of the sporophyte or gametophyte generation of a moss:
    1. produces gametes
    2. produces spores
    3. zygote formed
    4. made from protonema
    5. has a capsule on a stalk
    6. produces a protonema
    7. forms from an embryo
4. **Sequencing:** Put the steps of the moss life cycle in sequence starting with the sporophyte stage.
5. **Graphing:** Make a pie graph that shows the number of species of these simple plants:

Simple Plants	Number of Species
Bryophytes	20 000
Club mosses, spike mosses, and horsetails	1000
Ferns	12 000
Total	33 000

PROJECTS

1. Write a report on how coal is formed. Include a map of the parts of the U.S. where coal mines are located.
2. Go for a walk in the woods and see how many different kinds of mosses there are. Bring a list of these plants and where they were located back to class with you.

CHAPTER

11 The Seed Plants

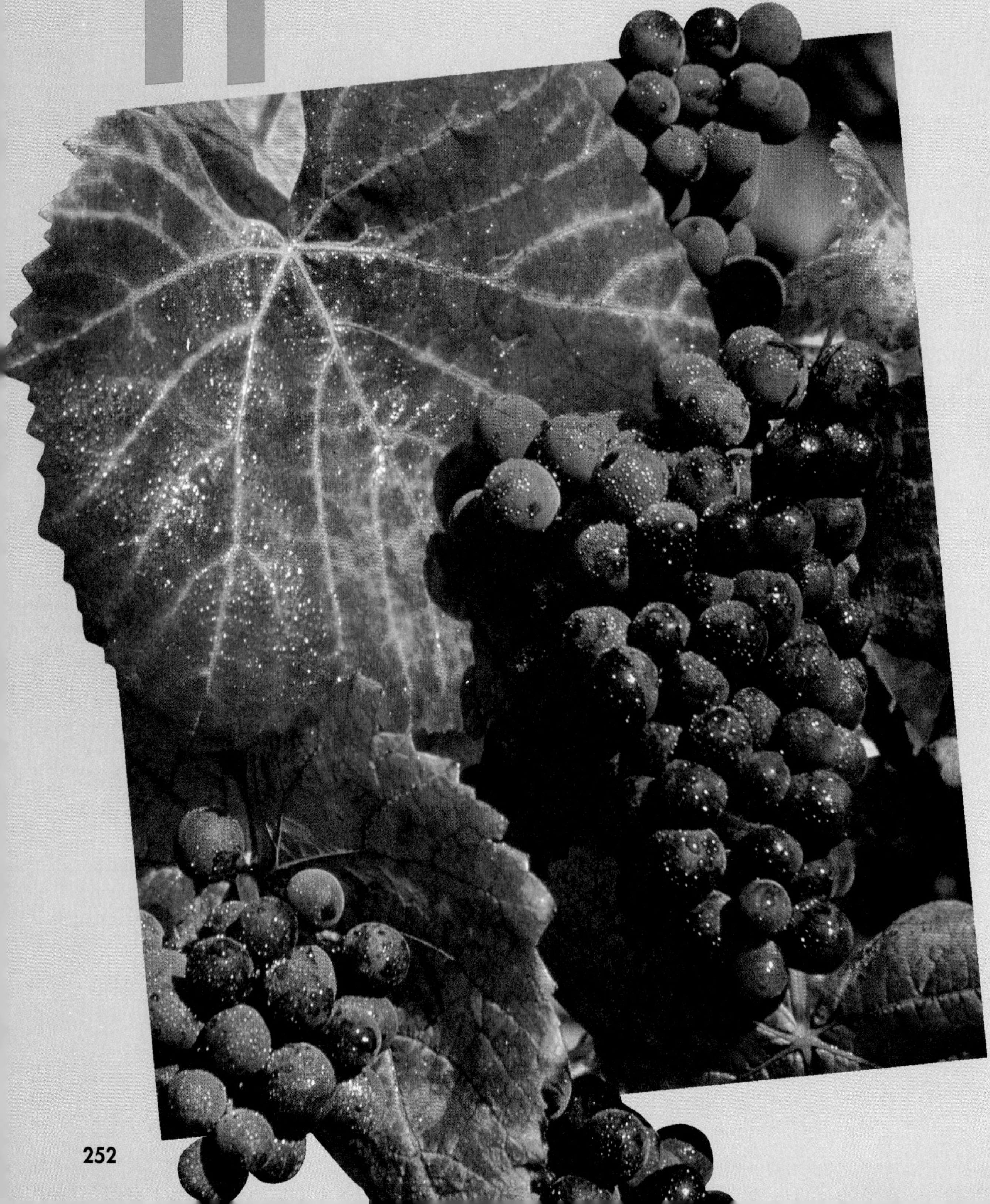

What's inside a seed? Are there green leaves, stems, and roots in a seed? How is a seed like a living plant?

FIND OUT!

Do this simple activity to find out what's in a seed.

Obtain a peanut that is still in its shell. Peanuts are seeds, and shells are dried fruit. Open the shell so you can see the seeds. Take the reddish-brown covering off one of the peanuts. Carefully pull apart the two halves of the peanut. Look for a small bump on one half. This is the embryo plant. Find the parts that you think will become leaves, a stem, or roots.

Gearing Up

Previewing the Chapter

Use this outline to help you focus on important ideas in this chapter.

Section 11-1   Seed Plants
► What Is a Seed Plant?
► Gymnosperms
► Angiosperms
► Origin and Evolution of Seed Plants
► Importance of Seed Plants

Section 11-2   Parts of Complex Plants
► Roots
► Stems
► Leaves

Section 11-3   Seed Plant Reproduction
► Gymnosperm Reproduction
► Angiosperm Reproduction

Section 11-4   Science and Society
Effects of Acid Rain
► Acid Rain: An International Problem

Previewing Science Skills

► In the **Skill Builders**, you will compare and contrast, classify, and observe and infer.
► In the **Activities**, you will examine, observe, analyze, collect data, and interpret data.
► In the **MINI-Labs**, you will experiment, observe, and describe.

What's next?

Now you know that a seed contains an embryo plant. In this chapter you'll learn more about the kinds of plants that can make seeds, how seed plants are important in the environment, and how the evolutionary history of seed plants has affected other organisms.

11-1 Seed Plants

New Science Words

gymnosperms
angiosperms
monocots
dicots

Objectives

▶ List the main characteristics of seed plants.
▶ List the main characteristics of gymnosperms and angiosperms and describe their importance.
▶ Compare the evolution of gymnosperms and angiosperms.

What Is a Seed Plant?

Have you ever eaten Chinese vegetables like those shown in Figure 11-1? These vegetables include bamboo shoots, water chestnuts, and snow peas. In the Philippines and Malaysia, coconut milk and banana flowers are used in many dishes. Corn and beans are staple foods in Mexico. All of these foods came from seed plants. What fruits and vegetables have you eaten today? If you had an apple, a peanut butter and jelly sandwich, and a glass of orange juice for lunch, you ate foods that came from seed plants.

Nearly all the plants you are familiar with are seed plants. There are about 235 000 known species of seed plants in the world. Seed plants have roots, stems, leaves, and vascular tissue. What makes a seed plant different from simple plants is that it grows from a seed. A seed is the reproductive part of a plant that contains a plant embryo and stored food. Within a seed are all the parts needed to produce a new plant.

How are seed plants different from simple plants?

Figure 11-1. Plants like these provide food for humans and most other consumers on Earth.

Most scientists classify seed plants into two major groups, the gymnosperms and angiosperms. Although both of these groups produce seeds, you will see that they exhibit some important differences.

Gymnosperms

The oldest trees alive today are gymnosperms (JIHM nuh spurmz)—in fact, there's one bristlecone pine tree in the White Mountains of eastern California that is 4900 years old. **Gymnosperms** are vascular plants that produce seeds on the scales of cones. The word *gymnosperm* comes from the Greek language and means "naked seed." Seeds of gymnosperms are not protected by a fruit. Gymnosperms do not produce flowers. Leaves of most gymnosperms are needlelike or scalelike. Most gymnosperms are evergreen plants that keep their leaves for several years.

Gymnosperms include four divisions of plants—the conifers, cycads, ginkgos, and gnetophytes. Of these, you are probably most familiar with the pines, firs, spruces, cedars, and junipers in the division Coniferophyta (KAHN uh fur AHF uh tuh). This division contains the greatest number of species of gymnosperms. Some conifers produce male and female cones on separate trees, but other species produce both types of cones on the same tree. Figure 11-2 shows examples of the four divisions of gymnosperms.

What are gymnosperms?

Figure 11-2. The gymnosperms include conifers (a), cycads (b), ginkgos (c), and gnetophytes (d).

Angiosperms

What are angiosperms?

When you bite into a pear or an apple, you are eating part of an angiosperm (AN jee uh spurm). **Angiosperms** are vascular plants in which the seed is enclosed inside a fruit. A fruit is a ripened ovary, the part of the plant where seeds are formed. If you eat most of your pear or apple, you'll find seeds inside. All angiosperms produce flowers and are classified in the division Anthophyta (an THAWF uh tuh). More than half of all known plant species are angiosperms.

There are two classes of angiosperms, or flowering plants: the monocots (MAHN uh kahts) and the dicots (DI kahts). The terms *monocot* and *dicot* are shortened forms of the words monocotyledon and dicotyledon. A cotyledon is a seed leaf inside a seed. **Monocots** have one seed leaf inside their seeds; **dicots** have two. Monocots are flowering plants with flower parts in threes and vascular bundles throughout the stems. The scattered bundles show up as parallel veins in their narrow leaves. If you had cereal for breakfast this morning, you ate a bowlful of monocot seeds! Cereal grains such as corn, rice, oats, and wheat are all monocots.

Dicots are flowering plants with flower parts in fours or fives and vascular bundles in rings inside the stems. The bundles show up as branching, netlike veins in the broad dicot leaves. Examples of dicots include trees like oaks and maples, vegetables like lettuce and beans, fruits like watermelons and oranges, and many garden flowers.

Science and WRITING

The collection of grass clippings as part of garbage placed in landfills has become a big environmental issue. Study the issue, then write a letter to the editor of your local paper supporting one side or the other.

Figure 11-3. The Characteristics of Monocots and Dicots

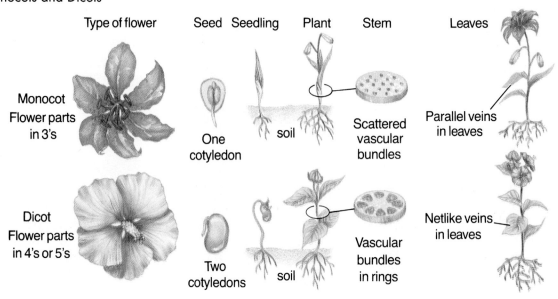

Type of flower   Seed   Seedling   Plant   Stem   Leaves

Monocot Flower parts in 3's

One cotyledon   soil   Scattered vascular bundles   Parallel veins in leaves

Dicot Flower parts in 4's or 5's

Two cotyledons   soil   Vascular bundles in rings   Netlike veins in leaves

Figure 11-4. Grown in terraces like these, rice is a staple food crop for humans worldwide.

Origin and Evolution of Seed Plants

Seed plants have some different requirements from those of simple vascular plants like ferns. For example, ferns need water for reproduction, but seed plants do not. The development of a seed gave these plants the ability to survive on land away from bodies of water. Gymnosperms and angiosperms today are found in tropical, temperate, and even extremely dry or cold environments.

Gymnosperms probably evolved from a group of plants that grew about 350 million years ago. Cycads and conifers have been found in the fossil record since the Paleozoic Era, 200 million years ago. Flowering plants did not exist until the Cretaceous period, about 120 million years ago. Gaps in the fossil record prevent scientists from tracing the exact origins of flowering plants. After their appearance in the Cretaceous period, angiosperms evolved into many different forms. Today they are the most common form of plant life on Earth.

Importance of Seed Plants

Imagine that your class is having a picnic in the park. You cover the picnic table with a red-checked tablecloth and pass out paper cups and plates. You toast hot dogs and buns, eat potato chips, and drink apple cider. Perhaps you collect leaves or flowers for a science project. Later you clean up and put leftovers in paper bags.

Did You Know?

Some seeds are extremely small, and very light in weight. But seeds can be valuable. If you collected one gram of begonia seeds, they would be worth 100 times more than one gram of gold!

Figure 11-5. Linen, a type of cloth, is made from fibers of the flax plant, *Linum usitatissimum.*

Now let's imagine this scene if there were no seed plants on Earth. There would be no picnic table and no pulp to make paper products such as cups, plates, and bags. Bread for buns, apples for cider, and potatoes for chips all come from plants. The tablecloth is made of cotton, a plant. Without seed plants, there would be no picnic!

On a global scale, conifers are the most economically important gymnosperms. Most of the wood used for building construction and for paper production comes from conifers such as pines and spruces. Resin, a waxy substance secreted by conifers, is used to make chemicals found in soap, paint, varnish, and some medicines.

The most common plants on Earth are the angiosperms. They are important to all life because they form the basis for the diets of most animals. Grains such as barley and wheat and legumes such as peas and beans were the first plants ever grown by humans. Angiosperms take in huge amounts of carbon dioxide for photosynthesis and release oxygen needed by other organisms. Many of the fibers used in clothing such as flax and cotton come from angiosperms. Angiosperms are used in the production of medicines, rubber, oils, perfumes, pesticides, and some industrial chemicals.

SECTION REVIEW

1. What are the main characteristics of a seed plant?
2. Make a chart to compare the characteristics of gymnosperms and angiosperms.
3. Explain why scientists cannot trace the evolution of angiosperms.
4. Give three reasons why seed plants are important to humans.
5. **Apply:** The fruit of the ginkgo has an unpleasant smell, so only male trees are planted near homes. Why?

Skill Builder

☑ Comparing and Contrasting

The monocots and dicots have some similarities and differences. Compare and contrast these two classes of plants. If you need help, refer to Comparing and Contrasting in the **Skill Handbook** on page 683.

Parts of Complex Plants

Objectives

▶ Describe the structure of roots, stems, and leaves.
▶ Describe the functions of roots, stems, and leaves.
▶ Explain some unique adaptations of roots, stems, and leaves.

Roots

Imagine a large tree growing alone on top of a hill. What is the largest part? Chances are you named the trunk or the branches. But did you consider the roots? The root systems of most plants are as large or larger than the aboveground stems and leaves. Why do you think root systems are so large?

Roots are very important to plants. All the water and minerals used by a plant enter by way of its roots. Roots have vascular tissue to move water and minerals from the ground up through the stems to the leaves. Roots also anchor plants in soil. If they didn't, plants could be blown away by wind, or washed away by water. Each root system must support all of the plant parts that are above the ground—the stem, branches, and leaves of a tree, for example. You can see how large the root system of a dandelion is in Figure 11-6.

One other function of roots is food storage. When you eat carrots or beets you eat roots swollen with stored food. Root tissues may also perform special functions such as absorption of oxygen and photosynthesis.

Stems

Did you know that the trunk of a tree is really its stem? The main functions of a stem are to support the aboveground parts of the plant and to allow movement of materials between leaves and roots. Some stems also have adaptations that allow them to store food. Potatoes and onions are underground stems with stored food. Sugarcane has an aboveground stem that stores large

New Science Words

xylem
phloem
cambium
stomata
guard cells
palisade layer
spongy layer

Figure 11-6. The Root System of a Dandelion

MINI-Lab

How does water travel in a plant?

Prepare two beakers of water. Add 10 drops of food coloring to each. Cut a fresh stalk of celery in half. Place one piece of celery into each beaker. Let stand overnight. Remove the celery and observe. Describe what you see. What does this tell you about water travel in a stem?

Phloem–transports
sugars throughout plant

Cambium–produces
additional xylem and phloem

Xylem–transports minerals
and water throughout plant

Bark

Wood

Figure 11-7. The vascular tissue
of seed plants includes xylem,
phloem, and cambium.

quantities of food. Stems of cacti are adapted to carry on photosynthesis and make food for the rest of the plant.

Three main tissues comprise the vascular system in the roots, stems, and leaves of plants. **Xylem** (ZI lum) tissue is made up of tubular vessels that transport water and minerals up from the roots throughout the plant. **Phloem** (FLOH em) is a plant tissue made up of tubular cells that move food from leaves and stems, where it is made, to other parts of the plant for direct use or storage. Between xylem and phloem is the cambium (KAM bee um). **Cambium** is a tissue that produces new xylem and phloem cells. All three tissues are shown in Figure 11-7.

Plant stems are either herbaceous (hur BAY shus) or woody. Herbaceous stems are soft and green. The stems of peppers, corn, and tulips are herbaceous.

T E C H N O L O G Y

Plants in Space?

Growing plants without soil is not new, but scientists are moving beyond traditional hydroponics, or the growing of plants in a nutrient solution.

New hydroculture techniques are being developed for use by astronauts on space missions. These techniques allow use of highly nutritious root crops. Instead of immersing roots in nutrient solutions, nutrients are sprayed directly on plant roots. This allows the plants better access to oxygen in the atmosphere, shortening growing time. The environment is carefully controlled, so the vegetables are virtually bacteria-free and pesticides are not needed. Growing trays can be tilted so less room is needed.

These techniques produce good quality vegetables without the need for farmers to worry about seasons, weather, insects, or any other environmental factors.

Think Critically: How might hydroculture be used to help the world food supply?

Oak, birch, and other trees and shrubs have woody stems. Woody stems are hard and rigid.

Leaves

Have you ever rested in the shade of a tree's leaves on a hot, summer day? Leaves are the plant organs that usually trap light and make food for the plant through the process of photosynthesis.

Look at the structure of the leaf shown in Figure 11-8. The epidermis is a thin layer of cells that covers and protects both the upper and lower surfaces of a leaf. A waxy cuticle that protects the plant from wilting or drying out covers the epidermis of many leaves. Another adaptation of leaves are small pores in the leaf surfaces called **stomata** (STOH mut uh). Stomata allow carbon dioxide, water, and oxygen to enter and leave a leaf. The stomata are surrounded by **guard cells** that open and close the pores. The cuticle, stomata, and guard cells all are adaptations that enabled plants to survive on land by conserving water.

Inside a typical leaf are two different types of cells. The **palisade** (pal uh SAYD) **layer** has rows of closely packed cells just below the upper layer of epidermis. Cells of the palisade layer are packed with chloroplasts filled with chlorophyll. Most of the food made by leaves is made in the palisade layer. Between the palisade layer and the lower epidermis is a **spongy layer** of loosely arranged cells and many air spaces. Xylem and phloem tissues are located in the spongy layer.

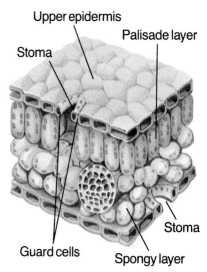

Figure 11-8. The Layers of a Leaf

Where is most plant food made?

SECTION REVIEW

1. What are the functions of roots?
2. How do herbaceous and woody stems differ?
3. Which layer of a leaf is probably responsible for most of the photosynthesis? Why?
4. What are the functions of stems and leaves?
5. **Apply:** The cuticle and epidermis are transparent. Explain why.

☑ Classifying

From what you have learned in this section, classify the following vegetables as roots, stems, or leaves: turnip, lettuce, asparagus, potato, onion, and carrot. If you need help, refer to Classifying in the **Skill Handbook** on page 680.

Skill Builder

11-3 Seed Plant Reproduction

New Science Words

ovules
pollen grains
pollen tube
stamen
pistil
ovary
pollination

Objectives

▶ Sequence the stages in the life cycles of typical gymnosperms and angiosperms.
▶ Describe the structure and function of the flower.
▶ Describe methods of seed dispersal in seed plants.

Gymnosperm Reproduction

Have you ever collected pine cones in the fall to use in making decorations? If you have, you've noticed that pine cones come in many different shapes and sizes. Some people can identify a pine tree just by looking at its cones.

Pine trees are typical gymnosperms. Each pine tree produces male cones and female cones on the sporophyte tree. Female cones consist of a spiral of woody scales on a short stem. Two **ovules** (OHV yewls), or eggs, are produced on top of each scale. As the ovule develops, it releases a sticky fluid. Male cones are smaller and less woody. **Pollen grains** containing the sperm, or male gametophytes, develop on the male cone. Wind carries pollen grains to the female gymnosperm cones. Millions of pollen grains may be released in a great cloud from a single male cone. You can see this in Figure 11-9. Most of this pollen never reaches the female cones because the wind blows it onto other plants, water, and the ground. When a pollen grain does get blown between the scales of a female cone of the same species, it gets caught in the sticky fluid secreted by the ovule. A **pollen tube** grows from the pollen grain to the ovule. A sperm swims down the pollen tube and fertilizes the

Figure 11-9. Male cones release clouds of tiny pollen grains.

ovule. As a result a zygote forms. The zygote develops into a seed.

Female cones of pine trees mature, open, and release their seeds during the fall or winter months. It may take a long time for seeds to be released from a pine cone. From the moment a pollen grain falls on the female cone until the seeds are released may take as long as two years. Once seeds are released from a pine cone, they are carried away, eaten, or buried by animals. The buried seeds may germinate and eventually grow into new pine trees.

Angiosperm Reproduction

Angiosperms all bear flowers. Flowers are important because they are the reproductive organs of angiosperms. Some flowers are not brightly colored, and many don't smell at all. Have you ever looked at the flowers of wheat, rice, or grass? Why do you think there is such variety among flowers?

The Flower

The shape, size, or color of flowers tells you something about the life of the plant. Large flowers with brightly colored petals often attract insects. In turn, these insects help to pollinate the flowers. Flowers that aren't colored are pollinated by the wind. Their petals may be small, or the flowers may have no petals at all! Flowers that open at night often have very strong scents.

Usually the brightly colored parts of a flower are the petals. Outside the petals are some small, leaflike parts called sepals. Sepals are easy to see when a flower is still a bud because the sepals cover the bud. In some flowers the sepals are as colorful as the petals.

What is a flower?

EcoTip

Make fresh-cut flowers last longer. Mix a solution of one part warm water to one part regular lemon-lime soda, and pour it in the vase. The solution provides nutrients for the flowers.

Figure 11-10. Some flowers, like the night-blooming *Datura*, depend on pollinators that are active at night.

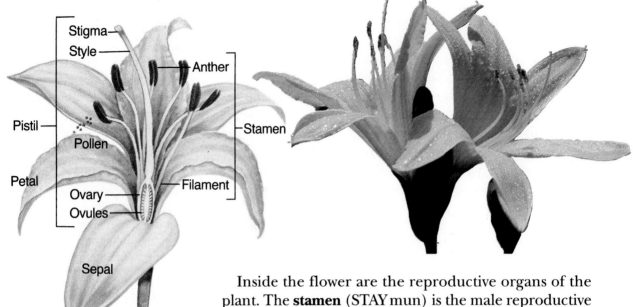

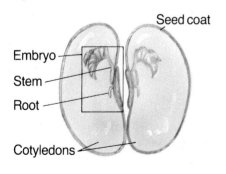

Stigma
Style
Anther
Pistil
Pollen
Stamen
Petal
Filament
Ovary
Ovules
Sepal

Figure 11-11. Parts of a Flower

What is a pistil?

Figure 11-12. The Parts of a Seed

Seed coat
Embryo
Stem
Root
Cotyledons

Inside the flower are the reproductive organs of the plant. The **stamen** (STAY mun) is the male reproductive organ of the flower. Stamens consist of a stalk, or filament, and an anther where pollen grains form. As in gymnosperms, the sperm develops in the pollen grain.

The **pistil** (PIHS tul) is the female reproductive organ of the flower. Pistils consist of a sticky stigma where the pollen grains land, a long stalklike style, and an ovary. In angiosperms, the **ovary** is the swollen base of the pistil where ovules are formed. The female gametophyte, or egg, develops in the ovule. You can see the parts of a typical flower in Figure 11-11.

Development of a Seed

How does a seed develop? Pollen grains reach the ovule in a variety of ways. Pollen is carried by the wind or by animals such as insects, birds, and mammals. A flower is pollinated when pollen grains land on the sticky stigma. The pollen tube grows from the pollen grain down through the style and into the ovary until it reaches the ovules. The sperm then travels down the pollen tube and unites with, or fertilizes, the ovule. This zygote develops into the plant embryo part of the seed. The transfer of pollen grains from the stamen to ovules is the process of **pollination.**

An embryo plant consists of cotyledons, stem, and root. Protected by a seed coat, the embryo also has a supply of stored food called the endosperm. After the embryo germinates, it will use the endosperm until it can begin to produce food on its own. You can see the parts of a seed in Figure 11-12.

Seed Dispersal and Germination

How do seeds get from the flower to the ground for germination? You know that the seeds grow inside the ovary. As an ovary grows larger, it develops into a fruit. Fruits may be either fleshy or dry. Fruits are usually eaten by animals. They eat these fruits and move the seeds to new locations where they can germinate. Have you ever eaten a piece of watermelon and spit out the seeds? You ate the fruit and moved the watermelon seeds to a new place! Both dry and fleshy fruits protect the seeds. Sometimes seeds cannot germinate until the fruit has been digested by an animal, and the seeds are released in the animal's feces. Seeds are also dispersed by the wind or water.

MINI-Lab

How do plants disperse seeds?
Look at the seeds pictured in Figure 11-13. How are the seeds of each plant dispersed—by wind, water, insects, birds, or mammals? Describe the features that tell you how each is dispersed.

Figure 11-13. Seeds can be dispersed by floating (a); attaching to fur, feathers, or clothing (b); or wind (c).

a

b

c

PROBLEM SOLVING

How Can You Tell If Seeds Are Living?

Aurora visited her grandfather, who lived in a nursing home. They went to buy flower seeds to plant in the courtyard of the nursing home. When examining a package of petunia seeds, Aurora noticed that the package said the seeds were 95 percent viable. Her grandfather explained that *viable* meant living. He said that 95 out of 100 seeds would germinate and grow.

They purchased the petunia seeds and several other packages of flower seeds and headed back to the nursing home to plant them. How could Aurora and her grand-father determine if the seeds they planted in the courtyard were viable?

Think Critically: How could Aurora determine if the seed company's claim on the seed package were true?

Figure 11-14. In dicots, the cotyledons raise the seed above the soil. As the endosperm is used the cotyledons shrivel and fall off.

What is germination?

When a seed reaches the soil, it may not germinate right away. Seeds often remain dormant until conditions are right for germination. Some seeds can remain dormant for hundreds of years, yet still be able to grow when environmental conditions become favorable. In 1982 seeds of the East Indian lotus germinated after being dormant for 466 years!

Germination, or the development of a seed into a new plant, begins when water is taken into the seed tissues. Water signals the seed to begin growth. The endosperm provides the energy for the seed to grow. Usually the root begins to elongate and grow out of the seed first. Then the stem lifts the cotyledons above the soil. If the seed is a monocot, the seed containing the endosperm remains below the soil. In a dicot seed, such as a bean, the cotyledons contain most of the endosperm of the seed and raise the seed above the surface. Eventually, as the food is used, the cotyledons shrivel and fall off dicot plants. Then the plant has to take over and make all of its own food by photosynthesis.

SECTION REVIEW

1. Compare the life cycles of angiosperms and gymnosperms.
2. Name the parts of a flower and their functions.
3. List three methods of seed dispersal in plants.
4. **Apply:** Some conifers bear female cones on the top half of the tree and male cones on the bottom half. From what you know about genetics and pollination, what do you think this arrangement of male and female cones on trees helps to prevent? Explain.

Skill Builder

☑ Observing and Inferring

A corn plant produces thousands of pollen grains on top of the plant in incomplete flowers that have no odor or color. The pistils grow from the cob lower down on the plant. Explain how a corn plant is probably pollinated. If you need help, refer to Observing and Inferring in the **Skill Handbook** on page 682.

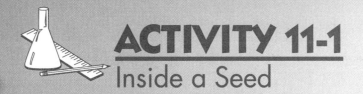

ACTIVITY 11-1
Inside a Seed

Problem: *What parts can you see inside a seed?*

Materials
- soaked lima bean
- soaked seed corn
- forceps
- scalpel
- iodine solution

Procedure
1. Make a data table like the one shown.
2. Examine the soaked corn seed. Place the seed flat on the table and, using a scalpel, cut through the center of the light area on the front of the seed. **CAUTION:** *Always be careful when handling a scalpel.*
3. Place a drop of iodine solution on the cut surface to test for starch. A blue-black color indicates the presence of starch. **CAUTION:** *Iodine is poisonous and may stain and burn the skin.*
4. Locate and observe the embryo corn plant with its single cotyledon. The hypocotyl is the embryo stem and the radicle is the embryo root. Draw the seed in your data table.
5. Using the forceps, carefully remove the outer seed coat from the lima bean.
6. Locate the two thick, fleshy, leaflike cotyledons. Also locate the embryo plant with its tiny first leaves, hypocotyl, and radicle. Draw the seed in your data table.
7. Remove one of the cotyledons, and scratch the covering with the forceps. Test the endosperm for starch.

Data and Observations

	Number of Leaves	Size of Endosperm
Monocot		
Dicot		

Analyze
1. What is the function of the outer covering of the seed?
2. What part of the new plant will the radicle become?
3. Why is a seed that grows within a fruit better adapted for growing on dry land?
4. What parts are contained in both monocot and dicot seeds?

Conclude and Apply
5. What is the function of the endosperm as indicated by the starch test?
6. Which seed had the larger cotyledon? Is there an adaptive advantage for a seed to have a larger cotyledon? Explain.
7. How can you tell the difference between a monocot and a dicot by dissecting the seed?

11-4 Effects of Acid Rain

New Science Words

acid rain
scrubber

Objectives

▶ State the primary causes of acid rain.
▶ Explain why the solution to this problem requires international cooperation.

Acid Rain: An International Problem

Suppose you and your friends go on a camping trip. As you are walking into the forest you are shocked by the death around you. The trees are brown. There are no plants on the forest floor. You can hear no birds or animals. You go fishing in a small lake, but there are no fish there to catch.

In some parts of the United States and Europe, this terrible story is already true. During the 1980s, southeastern Canada, northeastern and northwestern United States, and much of Europe began to experience the effects of acid rain. **Acid rain** is precipitation that falls to Earth after combining with sulfur dioxide and nitrogen oxide in the air. Sulfur dioxide and nitrogen oxide are gases released when fossil fuels such as coal and oil are burned. Sulfur dioxide typically enters the air in emissions from coal-burning power plants, whereas nitrogen oxide is released in the exhuast of automobiles. In the air, sulfur dioxide and nitrogen oxide combine with water vapor to form sulfuric acid and nitric acid. When it rains, snows, or fog covers the ground, these acids land on water or soil. Acid rain is particularly harmful to organisms that live in water.

Hundreds of thousands of lakes in the United States and Canada have been damaged due to acid rain. Forests, buildings, outdoor artwork, and groundwater are also affected by this problem. The maple syrup industry in the United States and Canada

Figure 11-15. Forests affected by acid rain often die from the top down.

has decreased drastically in the last ten years. Many forests in Europe are badly damaged. Acid rain causes the chemistry of the soil to change. Some minerals such as calcium and iron are washed away, while unusual amounts of other minerals such as aluminum are released from the soil and taken up by plants.

Much of the acid rain that falls in the eastern parts of the United States and Canada was actually produced in the Midwest. Scientists in Canada and the United States are working together to try and solve the problem of acid rain. In some parts of Canada, up to 75 percent of the acid rain is due to pollution from the United States. Most of the emissions that result in acid rain in the United States originated here. Studies show that by decreasing the amount of these chemicals released into the air, the damage they cause can be greatly decreased. Many industries in the United States and Canada are using scrubbers to remove some of these chemicals. A **scrubber** is a machine that blows a fine mist of water through gases leaving a power plant's smokestacks. Sulfur dioxide and nitrogen oxide combine with the water in the mist instead of water vapor in the air. The scrubbers are very expensive, yet they prevent much of the sulfur dioxide and nitrogen oxide from being released.

Other means of reducing the emission of the chemicals that cause acid rain are also being developed. It is hoped that each country will develop its own acid rain control program to allow all countries to benefit from an undamaged environment.

Figure 11-16. Installing scrubbers in smokestacks can reduce emissions that result in acid rain.

SECTION REVIEW

1. What chemicals are responsible for acid rain?
2. Why is acid rain an international issue?

You Decide!

SCIENCE & SOCIETY

Some people believe the damaging effects of acid rain are not important enough to discontinue the use of coal and other fossil fuels. Others feel that the use of fossil fuels should be minimized unless expensive scrubbers are used. How do you think the problem should be solved?

ACTIVITY 11-2
Parts of a Flower

Problem: *What are the parts of a flower?*

Materials

- gladiolus flower
- scalpel
- hand lens
- black paper
- microscope
- microscope slide
- coverslip
- dropper
- water

Procedure

1. Make a data table like the one shown.
2. Examine a gladiolus flower. Remove the outer row of colored leaflike parts called the sepals. Use the figure to see how the parts are arranged on a gladiolus flower. Record the number and color of sepals in your data table.
3. The leaflike structures inside the sepals are the petals. Remove the petals and record the number and color.
4. Locate the stamens and remove them. Look at one of the stamens with a hand lens. Observe the top part, called the anther, and the stalk, called the filament. Record the number and color of stamens in your table.
5. Tap the anther against a piece of black paper to knock out the pollen grains. Observe under a microscope and make a simple drawing in your table.
6. The structure that remains is the pistil. Identify the three parts. The three-part stigma is at the top. The stalklike part is the style. The ovary is the swollen base of the pistil. Record the number and color of pistils.
7. Use a scalpel to make a cross section of the ovary. **CAUTION:** *Always be careful with sharp instruments.* Use a hand lens to look at the ovules inside the ovary. Make a simple drawing in your table.

Data and Observations

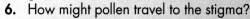

Flower Part	Number	Color
Sepals		
Petals		
Stamens		
Pistils		
Pollen Grains		Ovules

Analyze

1. How do the numbers of stamens, petals, and sepals compare?
2. Describe the appearance of the stigma.
3. How many compartments are in the cross section of the ovary?

Conclude and Apply

4. What functions might the petals have?
5. How is the stigma adapted for trapping pollen grains?
6. How might pollen travel to the stigma?

CHAPTER
REVIEW

SUMMARY

11-1: Seed Plants
1. Seed plants have stems, roots, and leaves, and grow from seeds.
2. Gymnosperms produce seeds on cones; angiosperms produce seeds in flowers.
3. Seed plants provide oxygen, food, clothing, furniture, and many other products.

11-2: Parts of Complex Plants
1. Roots absorb water and minerals, store food, and anchor the plant.
2. Stems transport food and water between roots and leaves and support the plant.
3. The palisade layer of leaves carries out photosynthesis. Xylem and phloem tissues are located in the spongy layer of the leaf.

11-3: Seed Plant Reproduction
1. Wind carries gymnosperm pollen to female cones where fertilization occurs.

2. In angiosperms, pollen reaches the stigma and travels to the ovary to fertilize the ovules.
3. Flowers contain male and female structures. The female pistils consist of the stigma, style, ovary, and ovules. The male stamens consist of the filament and anther, where pollen grains are formed.

11-4: Science and Society: Effects of Acid Rain
1. Acid rain results when sulfur dioxide and nitrogen oxide combine with water vapor in the air to form sulfuric acid and nitric acid.
2. Most acid rain results from emissions from the burning of fossil fuels such as coal and oil.
3. Acid rain may travel far from its source and cause problems in other states or countries. International cooperation is needed to solve this problem.

KEY SCIENCE WORDS

a. **acid rain**
b. **angiosperms**
c. **cambium**
d. **dicots**
e. **guard cells**
f. **gymnosperms**
g. **monocots**
h. **ovary**
i. **ovules**
j. **palisade layer**
k. **phloem**
l. **pistil**
m. **pollen grains**
n. **pollen tube**
o. **pollination**
p. **scrubber**
q. **spongy layer**
r. **stamen**
s. **stomata**
t. **xylem**

UNDERSTANDING VOCABULARY

Match each phrase with the correct term from the list of Key Science Words.

1. transfer of pollen grains to ovules
2. cone-bearing plants
3. male part of a flower
4. small pores in leaf surfaces
5. water containing sulfur dioxide
6. flower-producing plants
7. female part of a flower
8. vessels that transport water
9. plants with one embryo leaf
10. contains most chloroplasts

CHAPTER
REVIEW

Choose the word or phrase that completes the sentence.

1. Gymnosperms include _____.
   a. pines   c. cycads
   b. ginkgos   d. all of these

2. Angiosperms produce _____.
   a. cones   c. needles
   b. flowers   d. none of these

3. Insect-pollinated flowers are _____.
   a. bright   c. not colorful
   b. small   d. all of these

4. A _____ is the sticky part of a flower.
   a. sepal   c. stamen
   b. ovary   d. stigma

5. The _____ contains food for the embryo.
   a. endosperm   c. stigma
   b. pollen grain   d. root

6. The seed leaves of an embryo are _____.
   a. root hairs   c. guard cells
   b. cotyledons   d. stomata

7. The job of a root is to _____.
   a. anchor plant   c. absorb water
   b. store food   d. all of these

8. New xylem and phloem are made from _____.
   a. epidermis   c. stem
   b. cambium   d. none of these

9. Most photosynthesis occurs in the _____.
   a. spongy layer   c. epidermis
   b. palisade layer d. none of these

10. A _____ provides waxy protection for the leaf.
    a. guard cell   c. cuticle
    b. epidermis   d. spongy layer

UNDERSTANDING CONCEPTS

Complete each sentence.

11. Ovules are produced in the _____ of angiosperms.

12. Sperm are contained in the _____ of seed plants.

13. _____ contain two cotyledons.

14. Conifers produce _____, which is used to make soap and paint.

15. The ovary develops into a(n) _____.

THINK AND WRITE CRITICALLY

16. How does the arrangement of cones on a gymnosperm help seed dispersal?

17. List the parts of a plant that store food, giving an example of each.

18. What features of the flower help the process of pollination?

19. Flowers that are pollinated by the wind aren't colorful. Why?

20. Describe the features of the leaf that help prevent water loss.

APPLY

21. What function does resin serve for the gymnosperm that secretes it?

22. Plants called succulents store large amounts of water in their leaves. In what kind of environment would you find succulents?

23. Why do cacti have thick cuticles?

24. Use an example to describe a flower that is pollinated by insects.

25. Classify each fruit as dry or fleshy: acorn, almond, apple, cherry, orange, peanut.

MORE SKILL BUILDERS

If you need help, refer to the Skill Handbook.

1. **Comparing and Contrasting:** Compare the functions of roots, stems, leaves, and seeds in seed plants.

2. **Comparing and Contrasting:** Compare and contrast these structures of monocots and dicots: number of seed leaves, bundles arranged in stems, veins in leaves, flower parts.

3. **Concept Mapping:** Fill in the following concept map to show the sequence of pollination and fertilization.

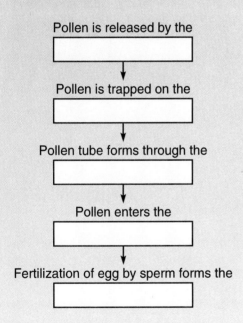

Pollen is released by the

Pollen is trapped on the

Pollen tube forms through the

Pollen enters the

Fertilization of egg by sperm forms the

4. **Interpreting Data:** Interpret the data concerning stomata of these leaf types. What do these data tell you about where gas exchange occurs in each type?

Stomata (per mm^2)	Upper Surface	Lower Surface
Pine	50	71
Bean	40	281
Fir	0	228
Tomato	12	13

5. **Making Observations:** Observe pictures or specimens of flowers and infer how each is pollinated. What features does each flower have to enable the pollination you suggest?

PROJECTS

1. Identify the types of trees in your yard or at your school. You can collect leaves and press them between papers placed inside a phone book. Identify leaves by using a guide book from the library. Bring your collection to school.

2. Find out why leaves change their colors in the fall. Report to your class.

3. Research how hydroponics is used to grow plants. Using this technique, try to grow a plant.

12 Plant Processes

Have you ever forgotten to water a potted plant? Perhaps the plant began to wilt. Why?

FIND OUT!

Do the following activity to find out how water enters and leaves a plant.

Obtain a plastic bag and a potted seedling plant from your teacher. Water the plant, then cover the seedling and its pot with the plastic bag. Seal the bag with tape. Place the bag in a sunny window and observe. Can you see that water collects on the inside of the bag? Where does the water come from? Water vapor goes out of the leaves through tiny pores on leaf surfaces. Carbon dioxide enters leaves through the same pores for photosynthesis. If the water lost by the plant is not replaced, eventually the plant will begin to wilt.

Gearing Up
Previewing the Chapter
Use this outline to help you focus on important ideas in this chapter.

Section 12-1   Photosynthesis and Respiration
▶ Gas Exchange
▶ Photosynthesis
▶ Respiration in Plants

Section 12-2   Plant Responses
▶ What Are Plant Responses?
▶ Plant Responses and Plant Hormones
▶ Photoperiods

Section 12-3   Plant Relationships
▶ Parasitic Relationships
▶ Mutual Relationships
▶ Coevolution

Section 12-4   Science and Society
The Treasure of Tropical Plants
▶ Medical Miracles from the Tropics

Previewing Science Skills
▶ In the **Skill Builders,** you will compare and contrast and hypothesize.
▶ In the **Activities,** you will observe, compare, interpret data, and make and use tables.
▶ In the **MINI-Labs,** you will experiment, observe, infer, and hypothesize.

What's next?

In this chapter you will learn about the process of photosynthesis, the behavior of plants, and the relationships of plants to other living things.

Photosynthesis and Respiration

New Science Words

transpiration
photosynthesis
respiration

Objectives

▶ **Describe the process of gas exchange in plants.**
▶ **Explain the process and importance of photosynthesis.**
▶ **Describe the process and importance of respiration and its relationship to photosynthesis.**

Gas Exchange

Stop right now and take a deep breath. When you breathe in, your lungs remove oxygen from the air. When you exhale, you release carbon dioxide. Gas exchange is one of the ways living things obtain materials they need and get rid of waste products.

Plants need water and carbon dioxide to survive. Recall from Chapter 11 that plants absorb water and minerals through their roots. Water travels up from the roots through the stem to the leaves. Water evaporates from leaf tissues and is released through stomata as water vapor. Carbon dioxide, a gas, gets into plants through stomata on leaf surfaces. Because leaves have more stomata on the lower surface, more carbon dioxide enters the spaces of the spongy layer, as shown in Figure 12-1. Water vapor is also found in the air spaces of the spongy layer. Carbon dioxide and water vapor are exchanged by diffusion through the stomata on leaf surfaces.

How does carbon dioxide enter a leaf? Each stoma is surrounded by two guard cells that con-

Figure 12-1. Carbon dioxide is taken into leaves through stomata. Water vapor is lost to the air when stomata open.

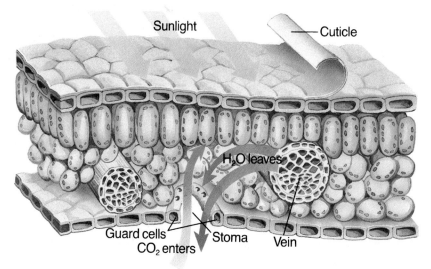

Sunlight

Cuticle

H_2O leaves

Guard cells
CO_2 enters

Stoma

Vein

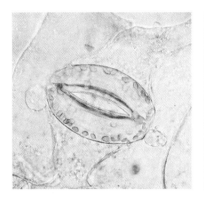
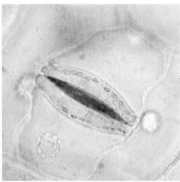

trol the size of the opening. Water moves into and out of guard cells by osmosis. When guard cells absorb water, they swell and the stoma opens, letting carbon dioxide in. Water vapor escapes during the process. When guard cells lose water, they relax and the stoma closes. Figure 12-2 shows open and closed stomata.

Light, water, and carbon dioxide all affect the opening and closing of stomata. Stomata usually are open during the day when photosynthesis is going on. When photosynthesis stops at night, the stomata are usually closed. Less carbon dioxide enters and less water vapor escapes from the leaf when stomata are closed.

Loss of water vapor through stomata of a leaf is called **transpiration.** Far more water is lost through transpiration than is used during photosynthesis. A single wheat plant may transpire 100 liters of water during a growing season. A tree like the date palm may transpire more than 500 liters of water in a single day!

Photosynthesis

Why aren't the leaves of the tree in Figure 12-4 green? If you live in a place that has changing seasons, you know that this photograph was taken in the fall. Many trees and bushes change color as the days get shorter and the weather grows colder. Plants may change from green to red, brown, yellow, or orange. Some show all of these colors at the same time. These colors are the results of pigments like the carotenoids that are present in the green leaves. In the spring and summer, the green pigment chlorophyll is so abundant in the leaves that it covers up, or masks, all other pigments. In the fall, plant cells stop producing chlorophyll, and the other pigments become visible. Chlorophyll is a pigment that traps light

Water lost through transpiration

Water absorbed by roots

Figure 12-3. Every plant loses water through transpiration.

Figure 12-4. Deciduous trees like this red maple change color in the fall, then drop their leaves.

energy for plants to use in making food. **Photosynthesis** is the process in which plants use energy from light to produce food.

What do plants need besides light to make food? In photosynthesis, a plant makes food from light energy, carbon dioxide, and water in a series of chemical reactions. Some of the light energy trapped in the chlorophyll is used to split water molecules into hydrogen and oxygen. Light energy is then used to join hydrogen and carbon dioxide together to form a new molecule of sugar. The sugar formed is glucose, and it is the food a plant uses for maintenance and growth. You can see this process in the following equation:

$$6CO_2 + 6H_2O + \text{light energy} \rightarrow C_6H_{12}O_6 + 6O_2$$

carbon   water   chlorophyll   sugar   oxygen
dioxide

It takes six molecules of carbon dioxide and six molecules of water to form one molecule of sugar, plus six molecules of oxygen. That is, the products of photosynthesis are sugar and oxygen.

TECHNOLOGY

Designer Plants

Using a gun that blasts tiny DNA-coated metal spheres into plant cells, scientists are trying to change the genetic codes of food crops such as wheat, rice, and corn.

Microbeads are the newest and most promising technique for introducing new genetic information into monocot plants like grains. Cell transplants and gene transfers to plant embryos work well on dicots like soybeans, tomatoes, and potatoes. The tomato mosaic virus costs the food industry $50 million each year, but resistant tomato plants are now available. In other tomato plants, a transfer gene provides DNA that blocks production of the chemical that triggers decay. As a result, the tomatoes have a much longer shelf life.

Think Critically: How could these designer plants benefit both farmers and consumers?

What happens to these products in a plant? Plant cells make use of the products of photosynthesis in many ways. Some of the oxygen is used by the plant cells for respiration. The rest of the oxygen is released and leaves the leaf by gas exchange through stomata. Sugar produced by plants is used right away for plant life processes such as growth, or it is stored in the plant as sugar, starch, or other products. When you eat beets, carrots, potatoes, or onions, you are eating stored food.

Why is photosynthesis important to living things? The most important role of photosynthesis is food production. Photosynthetic organisms are producers that provide food for nearly all the consumers on Earth. Secondly, through photosynthesis, plants remove carbon dioxide from the air and produce the oxygen that most organisms need to stay alive. As much as 90 percent of the oxygen entering our atmosphere today probably comes from photosynthesis.

Respiration in Plants

Look at the photographs in Figure 12-5. Do these organisms have anything in common? All of these organisms are similar in that they break down food to produce energy. **Respiration** is the process by which organisms break down food to release energy. Respiration that uses oxygen to break food down chemically is called aerobic respiration. Aerobic respiration occurs in the mitochondria of all eukaryotic cells. The overall chemical equation for aerobic respiration is:

$$C_6H_{12}O_6 \; + \; 6O_2 \; \rightarrow \; 6CO_2 + 6H_2O + energy$$

sugar   oxygen   carbon   water
dioxide

Figure 12-5. Respiration occurs in all cells of all organisms.

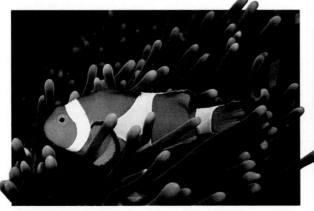

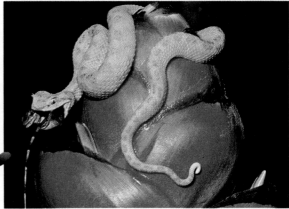

Table 12-1

COMPARING PHOTOSYNTHESIS AND RESPIRATION				
	Energy	**Starting Products**	**End Products**	**In What Cells**
Photosynthesis	stored	light energy, water, carbon dioxide	sugar, oxygen	cells with chlorophyll
Respiration	released	sugar, oxygen	water, carbon dioxide, energy	all cells

Does this equation seem familiar? It is the opposite of the chemical reaction found in photosynthesis. During photosynthesis, energy is stored in food. Photosynthesis occurs only in cells that contain chlorophyll, such as those in the leaves of plants. *Respiration occurs in all cells of all organisms.* Table 12-1 compares the two processes of photosynthesis and respiration.

It's easy to imagine why animal cells need energy, but why do plant cells need energy? Plants use energy to build and repair their cells, tissues, and organs. Sugar is used to make cellulose to build cell walls. Plants use energy from the food they make during photosynthesis for growth and reproduction.

MINI-Lab

How can respiration in yeast be shown?
Pour 10 mL of bromothymol blue into a test tube. Add 20 drops of yeast suspension and 10 drops of sugar solution. What color change is seen after 5 minutes? 10 minutes? 15 minutes? What has caused this color change? Compare the results of the MINI-Lab on page 278 with the results of this MINI-Lab.

SECTION REVIEW

1. Explain how carbon dioxide and water vapor are exchanged in a leaf.
2. Describe the chemical reactions that take place in photosynthesis and respiration.
3. Why are photosynthesis and respiration important to all living things?
4. **Apply:** Humidity is caused by water vapor in the air. Why is humidity high in lush tropical rain forests?

Skill Builder

☑ Comparing and Contrasting

Compare photosynthesis and respiration by describing the starting and end products and what happens to the energy involved in each process. If you need help, refer to Comparing and Contrasting in the **Skill Handbook** on page 683.

ACTIVITY 12-1
Stomata in Leaves

Problem: *How can stomata be observed in lettuce?*

Materials
- lettuce in dish of water
- coverslip
- microscope
- microscope slide
- salt solution
- forceps

Procedure
1. Remove a piece of an outer green leaf of the lettuce. Choose a leaf that is turgid (stiff) from absorbing water in the dish.
2. Bend the leaf back and use the forceps to strip off some of the transparent tissue covering the leaf. This is the epidermis.
3. Prepare a wet mount of a small section of this tissue.
4. Examine the preparation under low and then high power of the microscope. Draw and label the leaf section in your data table.
5. Note the location and spacing of the stomata. Count the number of stomata that are open.
6. Make a second preparation of the lettuce leaf epidermis. Place a few drops of salt solution on the leaf.
7. Examine the preparation under low and then high power of the microscope. Draw and label the leaf section in your data table.
8. Note the location and spacing of the stomata. Count the number of stomata that are open.

Data and Observations

Water Mount	Salt Solution Mount
Number of stomata open	Number of stomata open

Analyze
1. Describe the guard cells around a stoma.
2. How many stomata did you see in each leaf preparation?
3. How were the guard cells different from the other cells of the leaf epidermis?
4. Why did the lettuce leaf become stiff in water?

Conclude and Apply
5. Why were more stomata closed in the salt solution?
6. What is the function of stomata in a leaf?
7. What evidence did you see that shows guard cells engage in photosynthesis?

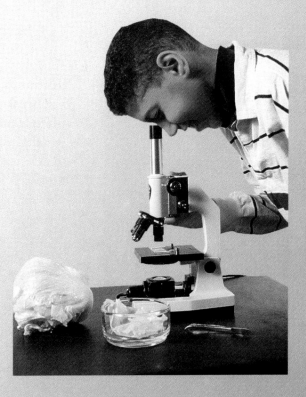

Plant Responses

New Science Words

stimulus
tropism
auxin
photoperiodism
long-day plants
short-day plants
day-neutral plants

Objectives

▶ Explain the relationship between stimuli and tropisms in plants.
▶ Differentiate between long-day and short-day plants.
▶ Explain the relationship between plant hormones and responses.

What Are Plant Responses?

If you touch the leaflets of the *Mimosa pudica* tree in Figure 12-6a, its leaflets will close up, as shown in Figure 12-6b. Why does this happen? The leaflets fold up in response to the stimulus of being touched. A **stimulus** is anything in the environment that affects the behavior of an organism. The response of a plant to a stimulus is called a **tropism.** Most plants respond to stimuli by growing. Tropisms can be positive or negative, that is, result in growth toward or away from the stimulus. Plants respond to stimuli by changing their behavior.

Touch is one stimulus that results in a change in a plant's behavior. Plants also respond to the stimuli of light, gravity, temperature, and amount of water. Some of the responses of plants are the result of plant hormones or chemical reactions in plant cells.

Did you ever notice a plant that appeared to be leaning toward a window? Light is an important stimulus to plants. Plants respond to sunlight by growing toward it. The growth response of a plant to light is called *phototropism.* When the plant responds to light by growing toward it, the response is called positive phototropism. An example of negative phototropism occurs when roots of a plant respond to light by growing away from it.

The growth response of an organism to gravity is called *gravitropism.* Plant roots tend to grow downward and the stems to grow upward. The downward growth of a plant's roots in response to the force of gravity is called positive gravitropism. Upward growth of the plant's stem away from the force of gravity is called negative gravitropism.

Figure 12-6. The *Mimosa* plant's leaflets respond to touch by folding up. The response to touch is called *thigmotropism.*

a

b
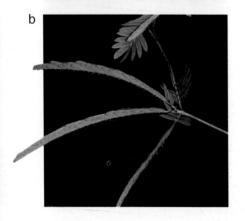

PROBLEM SOLVING

How Do Plants Climb Fences?

While emptying the garbage at the back of his family's restaurant, Hazizi noticed some small plants growing near the fence. Over the next month, Hazizi stopped to look at these plants whenever he helped at the restaurant. As the plants grew, Hazizi noticed little twisted leaves growing out of the sides of the stems. These twisted leaves looked like the metal springs underneath his mattress.

One day Hazizi noticed that a plant seemed to be caught on the fence. He very carefully untwisted the curly leaves that were wrapped around the metal wires of the fence. But the next afternoon, two of the twisted leaves were wrapped around the wires of the fence. This time Hazizi did not try to untangle them.

A week later Hazizi saw that every plant growing near the fence was climbing slowly up the fence by using the special twisted leaves. How were the plants able to cimb the fence?

Think Critically: What caused the plants to twist their leaves around the fence wires?

Plant Responses and Plant Hormones

In garden centers and nurseries like the one in Figure 12-7, horticulturists frequently turn the pots in which seedlings are grown every few days. They do this because the seedlings lean toward the sunlight. As you have learned, this is an example of positive phototropism. But why do the seedlings respond to light in this way?

Plant tropisms are controlled by plant hormones, which are chemical substances that affect growth. An **auxin** is a type of plant hormone. Auxins cause plant stems and leaves to exhibit positive phototropism. If light shines on a plant from one side, the auxin moves to the shaded side of the stem. The auxin causes cells on the shaded side of the stem to grow longer than cells on the lighted side. This causes the stem to curve toward the light.

Ethylene gas, a simple chemical compound of carbon and hydrogen, is another plant hormone. Many plants produce ethylene gas, which causes fruits to ripen.

Figure 12-7. Horticulturists turn pots every few days to make sure seedlings grow straight.

Figure 12-8. Long-day plants such as dill and short-day plants such as primroses flower in response to specific periods of darkness.

When fruits such as oranges, tomatoes, grapes, and bananas are picked before they have ripened, they will stay green because their cells won't produce ethylene. Growers and shippers of fruit found out that it doesn't matter to the fruit where ethylene comes from for ripening. Growers now pick fruit before it is ripe. Shippers treat the picked fruit with ethylene gas during shipping. By the time fruit arrives at the store, it has ripened.

Photoperiods

Sunflowers bloom only in the summer and cherry trees flower only in the spring. Different plant species produce flowers at different times during the year. **Photoperiodism** is the flowering response of a plant to the change in the lengths of light and dark in a day.

Most plants require a specific period of darkness to flower. Plants that require short nights to flower are called **long-day plants.** You may be familiar with long-day plants such as spinach, lettuce, and potatoes. Similarly, plants that require long nights to flower are called **short-day plants.** Some short-day plants are poinsettias, strawberries, and ragweed. Other plants, such as dandelions, corn, and tomatoes, flower over a wide range of night lengths. Plants like these that aren't very sensitive to the number of hours of darkness have a range of flowering times and are called **day-neutral plants.**

SECTION REVIEW

1. Describe the three major forms of tropisms.
2. What is the difference between long-day plants, short-day plants, and day-neutral plants?
3. Explain how auxins cause a plant to show positive phototropism.
4. **Apply:** What is the relationship between plant hormones and tropisms?

Skill Builder

⊠ **Comparing and Contrasting**

Different plant parts exhibit positive and negative tropisms. Compare and contrast the responses of roots, stems, and leaves to light. If you need help, refer to Comparing and Contrasting in the **Skill Handbook** on page 683.

Plant Relationships 12-3

Objectives

▶ Define and give examples of parasitism.
▶ Define and give examples of mutualism.
▶ Describe an example of coevolution.

New Science Words

coevolution

Parasitic Relationships

How does a plant that has no chlorophyll get its food? The dodder plant is a parasite. A parasite is an organism that lives on or in an organism of a different species and gets its nutrients from that organism. Although most plants make their own food by photosynthesis, parasitic plants get nutrients from other plants or animals. Parasitism can occur between any two species of organisms. It is one of the relationships plants have with other organisms.

The Indian Pipe in Figure 12-9 is a ghostly white parasitic plant often mistaken for a fungus. Because it has no chlorophyll, it must get its food from other sources, such as the rotting leaves and stems of other plants.

Several kinds of animals are parasites of plants. Scale insects and aphids suck out the sap from plants. If the scale insect or aphid populations increase to very high levels, plants will eventually die from loss of food and water. Most parasites do not kill their hosts. If they did, the parasites themselves would be left without food.

Did You Know?

Insect-eating plants such as pitcher plants and sundews often grow in areas where heavy rains wash nitrogen from the soil. Few other plants can grow there. How do these plants get the nitrogen they need? They get nitrogen from bodies of insects they trap and eat.

Figure 12-9. Organisms like orange dodder plants (a), scale insects (b), and Indian Pipes (c) are parasites.

a

b

c

Mutual Relationships

What kind of relationship is there between the bat and the flower in Figure 12-10? The bat visits the flower to eat the nectar it produces. When the bat puts its head into the flower, some pollen is rubbed off onto the animal's fur. The bat travels from one flower to the next, pollinating flowers at each stop. Both flowers and bat benefit from their relationship. A relationship between two species that benefits both is called mutualism. Mutualism often occurs between plants and their pollinators. Most angiosperms pollinated by insects, birds, or mammals have mutualistic relationships with their pollinators.

Other mutualistic relationships that do not involve pollination occur between plants and insects. One such relationship has evolved between the thorny acacia trees of Central America and Africa and a species of ant. The ants hollow out and occupy the inside of the acacia tree's thorns. The acacias produce a sweet sap that the ants eat. The tree provides both shelter and food for the ants. The ants attack and bite large insects and herbivores that browse on the acacias so these animals stay away. Acacia trees that do not have these mutualistic relationships with ants grow more slowly and have a higher death rate.

Coevolution

An evolutionary relationship that sometimes occurs between specific plants and animals is coevolution. **Coevolution** occurs when two species of organisms evolve structures and behaviors in response to changes in each other over a long period of time. The pollination of flowers by animals is the most common example of coevolution.

Insects and birds already existed before flowering plants appeared. When dinosaurs died out, so did many gymnosperms, leaving room for new species to emerge. Insects, birds, mammals, and angiosperms evolved together and interacted in ways that improved each species' chances for survival. Today, flowers that depend on bees for pollination often are colored blue, yellow, or ultraviolet. Bees see these colors best and so are attracted to flowers with these colors. Flowers pollinated by moths are usually white, with a strong scent. Moths generally fly at night and may be directed to flowers by scent as well as color. Birds can

Figure 12-10. The bat and the bird and the flowers they pollinate have mutualistic relationships. Relationships like these may be a result of coevolution.

see red and orange very well. They pollinate flowers such as the red and orange bird-of-paradise flower.

Another example of coevolution can be found in the Galapagos Islands once visited by Charles Darwin. Opuntia cacti are found on several of these islands. On some islands, the cacti grow as short bushy forms near ground level. On other islands, this same species of cactus grows as taller, upright tree forms. Galapagos tortoises eat opuntia cactus, but there are no tortoises on islands that have short bushy cacti. Galapagos tortoises are found on islands where the cacti grow as trees. Tortoises on these islands have shells that arch up high above their heads. These tortoises can stretch their necks up high in order to feed. Grazing by the tortoises on these islands apparently eliminated the short opuntias that grew close to the ground. The taller forms survived to reproduce, resulting in the evolution of tall, upright tree forms. As the opuntias evolved into upright forms, the tortoises that had higher shells were able to graze higher in the opuntia trees on their islands. The tortoises with higher shells continued to find food and reproduce. Scientists theorize that these tortoises favored the evolution of taller opuntia cacti, and the taller cacti favored the evolution of tortoises with higher shells. These two species favored the evolution of some adaptations in one another.

Figure 12-11. Short opuntia cacti (a) grow on islands without tortoises, whereas taller tree forms (b) of cacti are only found where tortoises live (c).

a

b

c

SECTION REVIEW

1. What is a parasitic relationship?
2. Describe the features of a mutualistic relationship and give an example.
3. What is coevolution?
4. **Apply:** Some flowers are pollinated by flies that lay eggs on dead or decaying animals. What do you think these flowers smell like?

☑ Hypothesizing

Skill Builder

In a particular relationship between a kind of orchid and a bee, the orchid flower looks and smells like the female bee. The male bee is attracted to the flower and helps in the pollination. Make a hypothesis about the evolutionary history of these species. If you need help, refer to Hypothesizing in the **Skill Handbook** on page 686.

12-4 The Treasure of Tropical Plants

New Science Words

ethnobotany

Objectives

▶ Identify the role of plants in medicine.
▶ Describe how destruction of tropical forests may destroy plant and animal species that could have beneficial uses in modern medicine.

Medical Miracles from the Tropics

Have you ever imagined yourself as the discoverer of a new drug that could be used to treat what was once an incurable disease? Surely, years and years of research are required to develop such miracle drugs! In fact, many of the drugs and medications we use today came from common plants. The knowledge of these plants was gained from ancient cultures in tropical regions of the world. Rosy periwinkle, for example, is a plant that grows on the island of Madagascar off the coast of Africa. A total of 75 chemicals are derived from this plant, including two that are used to successfully treat childhood leukemia and Hodgkin's disease.

Figure 12-12. Rosy periwinkle is the source of 75 chemicals used to treat disease.

Ethnobotany is the study of how people use plants. Most of the plants that are used in drugs and other medication were first discovered through such studies. Today, researchers carefully document the knowledge of traditional healers in tribes that inhabit tropical environments. These healers learned about the qualities of local plants and how they can be used for medical treatment. This information has never been written down. Rather, it has been handed down by word of mouth over thousands of years. Some ethnobotanists live with tribal groups for a few months every year, collecting specimens, seeds, and flowers, as well as writing down information about how each plant is used. Today, the cultures that have used this kind of information are threatened by the destruction of the tropical rain forests where they live.

Thousands of hectares of tropical forests are cut down or burned each day, and as they are, more and more species of animals and plants are lost. Few of the remaining tribes in the tropics have been thoroughly investigated and studied by ethnobotanists. Without documentation of the knowledge of those remaining tribes, the world may suffer great scientific and economic losses.

The National Cancer Institute has seen the urgency of this situation and is taking action. The Institute has awarded millions of dollars to researchers to collect and test species of tropical plants for their ability to stop or slow the growth of tumors. By taking immediate action, researchers may be able to help find the source of such drugs before they are lost forever due to tropical deforestation.

Figure 12-13. Ethnobotantists work with local healers to identify plants with medicinal value.

SECTION REVIEW

1. What are two diseases that can be treated with drugs derived from plants?
2. What work do ethnobotanists do?

You Decide!

SCIENCE & SOCIETY

Some people believe that the people of developing countries could take advantage of the plants that have medicinal value. Factories could be developed to extract the chemicals from these plants. This would make jobs and help the economies of these countries. However, such a life-style change could also greatly change the cultures of tribal groups forever. Should countries get involved in developing the resources of plants with medicinal value?

ACTIVITY 12-2
Plant Tropisms

Problem: *How can tropisms be observed in plant seedlings?*

Materials

- petri dish
- tape
- string
- corn seeds
- paper towel
- water
- ring stand

Procedure

1. Place the bottom of the petri dish on a paper towel, draw around the dish to make a circle, then cut out the circle to fit the dish.
2. Put the paper in the bottom of the dish and tape it to the dish.
3. Arrange ten corn seeds at equal distances around the outer edge of the petri dish with all the points of the seeds pointing to the middle of the dish.
4. Tape the seeds to the paper towel.
5. Wad up another paper towel, wet it, then place it inside the petri dish.
6. Put the cover on the dish and tape it closed.
7. Tape a piece of string to the back of the dish and hang the dish from a ring stand.
8. After 24 hours, unwrap and open the petri dish to check the seeds. Add water if the seeds or paper are dry. Reseal the dish. Repeat this step to check the seeds daily for the next four days. Make a drawing in the data table and record your observations each day.

Analyze

1. When did the seeds begin to germinate?
2. In which direction did the roots appear to grow?
3. In which direction did the stems and leaves appear to grow?
4. Why did you have to add water to the dish?

Data and Observations

Day	Drawing
Day 1	
Day 2	
Day 3	
Day 4	
Day 5	

Conclude and Apply

5. What name would you give to the movement of the roots?
6. What name would you give to the movement of the stems and leaves?
7. What substance probably controlled the tropisms you observed?
8. Design an experiment to prove that this was gravitropism and not phototropism.

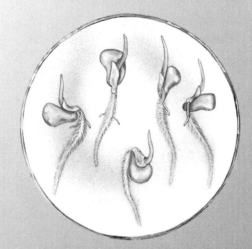

CHAPTER REVIEW

SUMMARY

12-1: Photosynthesis and Respiration

1. Carbon dioxide needed for photosynthesis enters leaves through stomata. Water vapor escapes during this process.

2. Chlorophyll in plants captures sunlight, splits water, and makes glucose and oxygen which are needed by all organisms.

3. Through respiration, energy stored in glucose becomes available for cell activities.

12-2: Plant Responses

1. Plants respond to stimuli by growing toward or away from light, gravity, or water.

2. Plants depend on a critical period of darkness in order to flower.

3. Many tropisms are controlled by hormones produced by plants.

12-3: Plant Relationships

1. Some plants live as parasites, deriving food from other plants.

2. Some plants have mutualistic relationships with other organisms in which both benefit.

3. Plants and animals have coevolved, developing unique relationships with each other.

12-4: Science and Society: The Treasure of Tropical Plants

1. Many medicines used today are derived from common plants.

2. Destroying tropical forests may destroy unknown medicinal plants as well.

KEY SCIENCE WORDS

a. **auxin**
b. **coevolution**
c. **day-neutral plants**
d. **ethnobotany**
e. **long-day plants**
f. **photoperiodism**
g. **photosynthesis**
h. **respiration**
i. **short-day plants**
j. **stimulus**
k. **transpiration**
l. **tropism**

UNDERSTANDING VOCABULARY

Match each phrase with the correct term from the list of Key Science Words.

1. anything in the environment that affects behavior of an organism

2. a plant hormone

3. flowering response of plant to light

4. using light to make glucose and oxygen

5. positive and negative plant responses

6. loss of water through stomata

7. plants that require short nights to flower

8. plants that are not sensitive to hours of darkness

9. releasing energy from food

10. when species evolve together

REVIEW

CHECKING CONCEPTS

Choose the word or phrase that completes the sentence.

1. Stomata open to allow _____.
   a. water in   c. carbon dioxide in
   b. sugar out   d. all of these

2. Products of photosynthesis are _____.
   a. CO_2 c. H_2O
   b. O_2 d. all of these

3. Respiration produces _____.
   a. carbon dioxide   c. energy
   b. water   d. all of these

4. A _____ plant needs short nights to flower.
   a. day-neutral   c. long-day
   b. short-day   d. none of these

5. An example of a stimulus is _____.
   a. light   c. temperature
   b. gravity   d. all of these

6. _____ is a response to gravity.
   a. Phototropism   c. Thigmotropism
   b. Gravitropism   d. None of these

7. Plant hormones affect growth of _____.
   a. stems   c. fruits
   b. roots   d. all of these

8. The _____ is an example of a parasite.
   a. oak   c. dodder
   b. acacia   d. none of these

9. The benefits of ants living on the acacia include _____.
   a. food   c. protection
   b. a place to live   d. all of these

10. Adaptations of cacti and tortoises over time are examples of _____.
    a. coevolution   c. mutualism
    b. parasitism   d. none of these

UNDERSTANDING CONCEPTS

Complete each sentence.

11. _____ is split by light energy trapped in chlorophyll.

12. _____ is the gas made by plants in photosynthesis.

13. Response of roots growing down demonstrates _____.

14. Growing toward light is _____.

15. Hormones that cause plants to bend toward light are _____.

THINK AND WRITE CRITICALLY

16. List the gases stomata allow to enter and exit the leaf.

17. Why is it important that plants grow toward the light?

18. What kind of tropism does *Mimosa pudica* show?

19. Why doesn't the dodder kill its host?

20. What advantage does the Indian Pipe have living off a plant?

21. Growers of bananas pick green bananas, then treat them with ethylene during shipping. Why?

22. Identify the stimulus and response as positive or negative.
    —stem grows up
    —tendrils grow up
    —roots grow down
    —plant grows toward light

23. Scientists who study sedimentary rocks and fossils suggest that oxygen did not occur on Earth until plantlike protists appeared. Why?

24. Give an example of a plant that will flower well in the spring or summer but not in the winter and explain why.

25. Some tropical flowers have fruity odors and are light in color. Bats that are nocturnal eaters have long tongues and fur on their faces. Explain how these two organisms are examples of coevolution.

MORE SKILL BUILDERS

If you need help, refer to the Skill Handbook.

1. **Hypothesizing:** Make a hypothesis as to the action of leaf guard cells in desert plants.

2. **Inferring:** Based on your knowledge of plants, infer the amount and location of stomata in land and water plants.

3. **Classifying:** Classify each as short-day, long-day, or day-neutral plants by making a chart: corn, chrysanthemum, dandelions, dill, iris, poinsettia, red clover, spinach, sunflower, tomato.

4. **Comparing and Contrasting:** Compare and contrast the action of each chemical on a plant: auxin, ethylene.

5. **Designing an Experiment:** Design an experiment concerning the effect of day length on flowering.

PROJECTS

1. Research what tropical plants are being studied for their medicinal value and report on current findings.

2. Find out what chemicals are used in agriculture to help plants carry out photosynthesis. Bring a list to school.

3. Design an experiment to show the rate of yeast respiration at various temperatures.

GLOBAL CONNECTIONS

Plants

In this unit, you have studied about plants. Now find out the importance of plants throughout the world.

120°   60°

CHEMISTRY

GROW YOUR OWN FUEL
Breman, Indiana

Gasohol may be the answer to petroleum woes. Gasohol, or ethanol, as it is more properly called, comes from corn. It is currently blended with gasoline for a lower-cost motor fuel. If gasohol is cheaper than regular gasoline, why isn't it being used more for cars?

30°

GEOLOGY

COAL, A FOSSIL FUEL
Boone's Camp, Kentucky

Coal has long been a valuable fuel for industry around the world. The coal fields of Kentucky had their beginnings 300 million years ago when they were forests of giant fern and club mosses. How do we know coal fields were once forests?

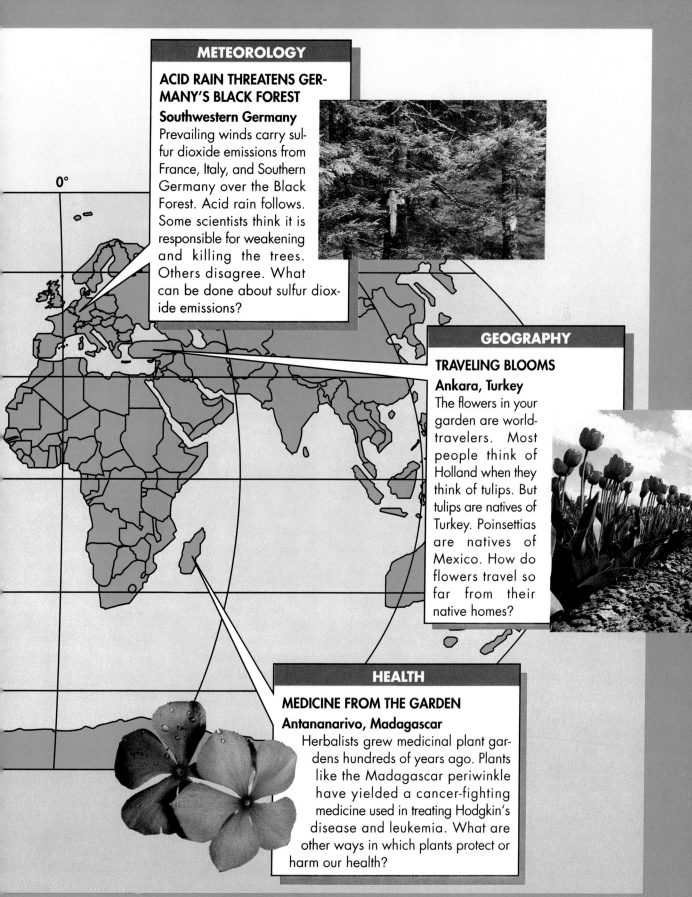

METEOROLOGY

ACID RAIN THREATENS GERMANY'S BLACK FOREST
Southwestern Germany
Prevailing winds carry sulfur dioxide emissions from France, Italy, and Southern Germany over the Black Forest. Acid rain follows. Some scientists think it is responsible for weakening and killing the trees. Others disagree. What can be done about sulfur dioxide emissions?

0°

GEOGRAPHY

TRAVELING BLOOMS
Ankara, Turkey
The flowers in your garden are world-travelers. Most people think of Holland when they think of tulips. But tulips are natives of Turkey. Poinsettias are natives of Mexico. How do flowers travel so far from their native homes?

HEALTH

MEDICINE FROM THE GARDEN
Antananarivo, Madagascar
Herbalists grew medicinal plant gardens hundreds of years ago. Plants like the Madagascar periwinkle have yielded a cancer-fighting medicine used in treating Hodgkin's disease and leukemia. What are other ways in which plants protect or harm our health?

PLANT PATHOLOGIST

A *plant pathologist* studies the diseases of plants. He or she may specialize in the diseases of one particular species of plants, such as spruce trees, or will specialize in one type of plant pathogen such as viruses, bacteria, fungi, insects, or roundworms.

A plant pathologist needs to study biology, botany, and chemistry. Plant pathologists must have a college degree plus graduate work in the field of plant pathology. A plant pathologist may work in a university research lab, for the Department of Agriculture, or for a plant breeder.

For Additional Information

Contact the American Society of Phytopathologists. Dr. G. Anderson, Secretary, Botanical Society of America, Dept. of Ecology and Evolutionary Biology, U-43, 75 North Eagleville Rd., Storrs, CT 06269-3043.

PROFESSIONAL GARDENER

A *professional gardener* should have an interest in plants, landscaping, and the conditions plants need for growing. Professional gardeners need to have a knowledge of the kinds of plants to use in a particular setting and what kinds of grass and trees will grow well in a particular soil. He or she should enjoy working out-of-doors.

Professional gardeners must have a knowledge of gardening tools such as mechanical tree planters, pruning devices, and tillers. A professional gardener can learn much through on-the-job training. Programs are also offered through trade schools, community colleges, or county agricultural extension agencies.

For Additional Information

For additional information, contact the Professional Grounds Management Society, 12 Galloway Ave., Suite 1E, Cockneysville, MD 21030.

UNIT READINGS

▶Meijer, William. "Saving the World's Largest Flower." *National Geographic*, July 1985.
▶McIntyre, Loren. "Humboldt's Way." *National Geographic*, Sept. 1985.

Where the Sky Began,

by John Madson

The following is an excerpt from Where the Sky Began, by John Madson.

Grass and sky would be enough. With only those, the summer prairie would be a smiling, running spread of cloud shadow and wind pattern.

But the tall prairie goes beyond that. From the first greening of spring to the full ripening of autumn, it is spangled by a vivid progression of flowers— a rainbow host that first enamels the burned slopes of early spring and ends months later with great nodding blooms that rise above a man's head. Sometimes as secret and solitary as jewels, but often in broad painted fields, the prairie flowers come on—lavender, indigo, creamy white, pink, coral, gold, magenta, crimson, orange, and palest yellow and blue, their flowers tending from ice to flame....

The prairie flowers come on in waves, each in its own time, some blooming very briefly and others persisting for weeks. Except for a short period early in the growing season, the flowers must compete with a rising tide of grasses. All may begin growing at about the same time; some just mature much later than others, needing months of growth if they are to compete with the towering August bluestem. Spring or fall, prairie flowers are as tall as they need to be.

Most of these earliest prairie flowers appear before mid-May and are never much more than six inches tall. The best known is the pasqueflower, with tulip-like blooms ranging from white to pale lavender, its stem and leaves wearing a dense covering of fine silken hairs. It gives the impression of a small flower trying to keep warm and having a tough time doing so, for pasqueflowers may bloom on bare, exposed crests of old glacial moraines while there are still patches of snow on the sheltered slopes behind them. Brave little flowers, often braver than I. More than once, the lowering clouds and sharp gray winds of late March have hustled me off the prairie before I'd finished photographing the first pasqueflowers. But no matter—at such times their blooms are usually closed anyway.

In Your Own Words

▶ Choose a wildflower, native to your area, and write a brief, descriptive report on its habitat, time of bloom, and any special features of the flower. (Hint: dandelions are not native wildflowers!)

UNIT
5 ANIMALS

What's Happening Here?

These ants aren't preparing to feast on the tiny aphids, but they do get food from them. Ants "farm" aphids for the sweet nectar they produce. The ants keep the aphids in "pens" inside their underground burrows. In another type of relationship, a border collie protects its sheep from predators such as wolves by keeping them together. Animals have many different types of relationships with one another. Many of these relationships work for the benefit of all the animals involved. You'll learn more about animals and about their relationships in this unit.

UNIT CONTENTS

Chapter 13 Introduction to Animals
Chapter 14 Complex Invertebrates
Chapter 15 Cold-Blooded Vertebrates
Chapter 16 Warm-Blooded Vertebrates
Chapter 17 Animal Behavior

Close your eyes and picture an animal. What picture came to your mind? Did you imagine something with four legs and fur, or did you see an insect, worm, or person?

FIND OUT!

Do this simple activity to find out how different members of the Animal Kingdom can be.

Look at the large photograph at the left. On a sheet of paper make a list of all the animals you see in the photo. How many animals are on your list? Did you list five or six? Of course the human and the fish are animals, but so are the corals, sponges, and fan-like organisms. Now close your eyes and picture an animal. Did you picture a different animal?

Gearing Up

Previewing the Chapter

Use this outline to help you focus on important ideas in this chapter.

Section 13-1   What Is an Animal?
► Animal Characteristics
► Animal Classification

**Section 13-2   Science and Society
Experiments Using Animals**
► To Test or Not To Test

Section 13-3   The Simplest Invertebrates
► Sponges
► Origin and Importance of Sponges
► Cnidarians
► Origin and Importance of Cnidarians

Section 13-4   The Simple Worms
► Flatworms
► Roundworms

Previewing Science Skills

► In the **Skill Builders**, you will make a concept map, compare and contrast, and outline.
► In the **Activities**, you will observe, hypothesize, and collect data.
► In the **MINI-Labs**, you will observe and describe.

What's next?

Now that you know that there are many different types of animals, you will learn what makes them different and how they are classified. You will also learn about some invertebrates, sponges, cnidarians, and simple worms.

13-1 What Is an Animal?

New Science Words

vertebrates
invertebrates
radial symmetry
bilateral symmetry

Objectives

▶ Identify the characteristics of animals.
▶ Determine how the body plans of animals differ.
▶ Distinguish between invertebrates and vertebrates.

Animal Characteristics

If someone asked you if it was important to protect giant pandas to keep them from becoming extinct, you would probably say yes. But would you feel the same if you were asked about an endangered worm or beetle or spider? How are animals' relationships to each other and to us important?

Let's look at the characteristics that all animals have in common.

1. Animals cannot make their own food. They depend on other living things in the environment for food. Some eat plants, some eat other animals, and some eat both plants and animals.
2. Animals digest their food. They can't use the proteins, fats, and carbohydrates in foods directly. Instead, food must be broken down into molecules small enough for their bodies to use.
3. Many animals move from place to place. Moving around lets them find food, escape from their enemies, find a better place to live, and find mates. Animals that move very slowly or not at all have adaptations that let them take care of these needs.
4. Animals have many cells. Different cells carry out different functions such as digesting food, reproduction, and getting rid of wastes.
5. Animal cells are eukaryotic. They have a nucleus surrounded by a membrane and organelles surrounded by membranes.

An animal can be defined as a many-celled eukaryotic organism that must find and digest its food.

Figure 13-1. Animals depend on other living things for their food.

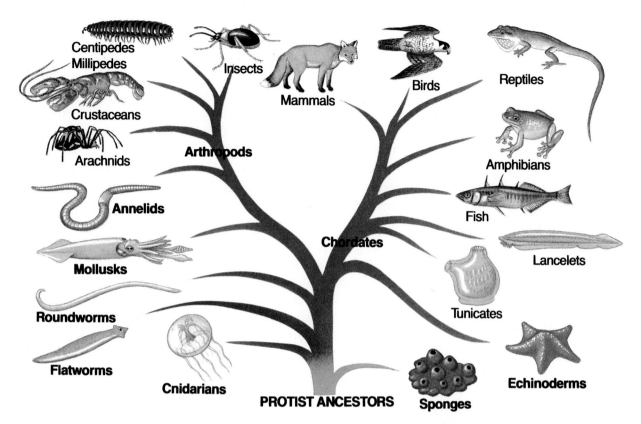

Centipedes
Millipedes
Crustaceans
Arachnids
Arthropods
Insects
Mammals
Birds
Reptiles
Amphibians
Annelids
Chordates
Fish
Mollusks
Lancelets
Roundworms
Flatworms
Tunicates
Cnidarians
PROTIST ANCESTORS
Sponges
Echinoderms

Animal Classification

Scientists have identified and named over one million species of animals. They think there may be as many as three million more to identify and name. There are nine major phyla in the animal kingdom. The phyla are shown in Figure 13-2. All animals have the characteristics listed on page 302, but when a scientist comes across a new animal, how does he or she begin to classify it?

The first thing the scientist can do is look to see if the animal has a backbone. Animals with backbones are called **vertebrates.** Some vertebrate animals are fish, humans, whales, and snakes. About 97 percent of all other animal species are invertebrates. **Invertebrates** are animals that don't have a backbone. Sponges, jellyfish, and clams are all invertebrates.

The next thing the scientist can look at is the arrangement of the animal's body parts. This is called the animal's symmetry. Some animals have body parts arranged in a circle around a central point, the way spokes are arranged around the hub on a bicycle wheel. These animals have **radial symmetry.** Hydra, jellyfish, and sand dollars have radial symmetry.

Figure 13-2. This diagram shows the relationships between different groups in the animal kingdom.

How are vertebrates different from invertebrates?

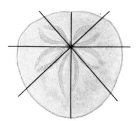

Radial symmetry

Bilateral symmetry

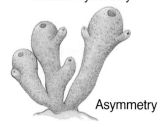

Asymmetry

Figure 13-3. Sand dollars have radial symmetry, butterflies have bilateral symmetry, and sponges are asymmetrical.

Most animals have bilateral symmetry. Look in the mirror. Does your body look the same on both sides? An animal with **bilateral symmetry** has its body parts arranged in the same way on both sides of its body. In Latin the word *bilateral* means "two sides." Bilateral animals can be divided into right and left halves by drawing an imaginary line down the length of the body. Each half is a mirror image of the other half.

Animals with bilateral symmetry have a definite front, or *anterior*, end. They also have a definite back, or *posterior*, end. The upper side of the animal is called the *dorsal* side, and the lower side is called the *ventral* side.

Some organisms have no definite shape and are called asymmetrical. There is no way their bodies can be divided into matching halves. Many sponges are asymmetrical. The three types of symmetry are seen in Figure 13-3.

When the scientist has determined an animal's symmetry and whether it's an invertebrate or vertebrate, he or she will have to identify characteristics it has in common with other animal groups in order to classify it. You learned in Chapter 6 that animals in a group have similar characteristics because they descended from a common ancestor. The evolutionary history and relationships among animal phyla are represented by the diagram in Figure 13-2. It shows what are thought to be some of the major developments in animal evolution that led to the diversity we see today.

SECTION REVIEW

1. What are five characteristics of animals?
2. How do animals obtain food?
3. What are the types of symmetry? Give an example of each type.
4. How are invertebrates different from vertebrates?
5. **Apply:** Identify your dorsal and ventral sides and your anterior and posterior ends.

Skill Builder

☑ Concept Mapping

Using the information on pages 303 and 304, make a chain of events concept map showing the steps a scientist can use to classify a new animal. If you need help, refer to Concept Mapping in the **Skill Handbook** on pages 688 and 689.

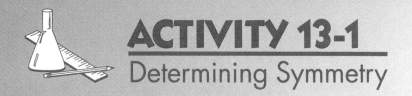

ACTIVITY 13-1
Determining Symmetry

Problem: *What type of symmetry do some animals have?*

Materials

- paper and pencil

Procedure

1. Observe each animal pictured on this page. Decide if the animal has radial symmetry, bilateral symmetry, or does not have symmetry.
2. Record your answers in the data table. If you need help, refer to Section 13-1.
3. Explain how you decided what type of symmetry each animal has in the column labeled "Reason."

Analyze

1. Which animals have radial symmetry?
2. Which animals have bilateral symmetry?
3. Which animal has no symmetry?
4. If an animal has an anterior and a posterior end, what kind of symmetry does it have?

Conclude and Apply

5. What advantages might radial symmetry give an animal?
6. What advantages might bilateral symmetry give an animal?
7. How is type of symmetry related to characteristics of each animal phylum?

Data and Observations

Animals	Symmetry	Reason
Jellyfish		
Crayfish		
Sponge		
Spider		
Starfish		
Oyster		
Snail		
Sea anemone		
Sea urchin		

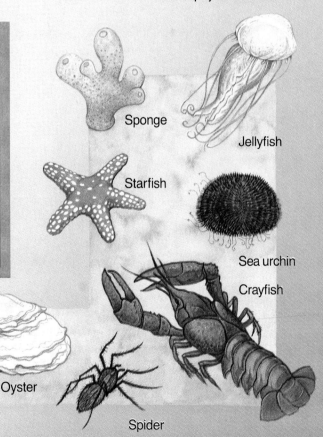

Sponge

Jellyfish

Starfish

Sea urchin

Crayfish

Oyster

Sea anemone

Snail

Spider

13-2 Experiments Using Animals

Objectives

▶ Acknowledge the advancements made due to experimentation with animals.

▶ Develop an idea for a compromise between progress in medicine and the welfare of laboratory animals.

To Test or Not To Test

Did you know that you're probably alive today because of laboratory animals? You may have received a shot of penicillin or a flu vaccine. Such vaccines have wiped out diseases such as polio and smallpox in the United States. Malaria, caused by a microscopic parasite, has killed more people in the world than any other disease. In order to develop an anti-malarial medicine, canaries were infected with malaria to allow scientists to learn more about the parasite. In fact, every surgical technique and drug used today was first tried in animals. But what about the animals? Is it truly necessary to experiment on animals?

It is estimated that each year about 100 million animals are used for research, education, or product testing. Cats are used to learn about the dangerous effects of drug addiction. Digestive enzymes are taken from pig digestive systems and used to help people with cystic fibrosis digest food. Antibiotics are first tested on rats before they are tried on humans. Organ transplants are possible because surgeons first practice on cows and other animals. Dogs and rabbits were used to understand diabetes and in the discovery of insulin. Treatments for cancer, alcoholism, and heart disease have all been greatly improved through experimentation using animals. Due to the advancements in medicine resulting from experiments with animals, a baby born today has a much greater chance of living to a very old age than ever before in the history of the world.

Figure 13-4. Jonas Salk developed the vaccine for polio.

Today animal rights activists are fighting for the rights that they say animals are entitled to. There are about 10 million people in the United States who belong to some 7000 animal rights groups. It's not just the deaths of animals that they are concerned with. Many are opposed to the conditions in which the lab animals are kept. Others feel that dissections of cats, frogs, pigs, and other animals by school-age students are unnecessary.

Some of the tests performed on the animals are very painful. In one experiment, dogs were fed pesticides until they were so sick they could not move. Some reforms are in progress. One of the most common tests for irritancy is the Draize test. In this test, high concentrations of the irritant being tested are squirted into the eyes of rabbits. Many companies are looking for alternatives to this test and are reducing the concentrations of irritant. Researchers believe that saving human lives through research is much more important than the animal lives that are sacrificed. They feel that reforms and regulations may threaten the future of science.

The controversy will surely go on for years. Perhaps a compromise of some type will be reached. Activists often acknowledge the importance of these experiments and argue that only those that are necessary should be allowed. But where can we draw the line? Often basic research that appears unnecessary is later very important in solving a new medical problem. Will a solution ever be reached? Although animal research has saved many lives, pain and distress for the animals often results in their death.

Figure 13-5. Many animals are kept in laboratories and used for research.

SECTION REVIEW

1. Name three diseases for which treatments have been greatly improved due to research using animals.
2. What is the basic belief of animal rights groups?

You Decide!

You have your heart set on a brand new pair of acid washed jeans. Before you go to buy them, you hear on the news that the company that makes your favorite brand uses animals in experiments. To determine if it would irritate humans, the company tests the bleach solution used to lighten the jeans on the eyes and skin of animals. Knowing this, would you still buy the jeans?

The Simplest Invertebrates

New Science Words

sessile
Porifera
filter feeders
collar cells
regeneration
hermaphrodite
larva
cnidarians
tentacles
polyp
medusa

Objectives

▶ Identify the structures that make up sponges and cnidarians.
▶ Describe how sponges and cnidarians obtain food and how they reproduce.

Sponges

Let's take a closer look at the different animal phyla. The "simplest" of the animal groups are sponges, cnidarians (ni DAIR ee uhnz), and simple worms.

Years ago, early scientists thought sponges were plants. The sponge in Figure 13-6 probably doesn't look like an animal to you either, but it is. Sponges make up the group of animals considered to be the simplest in the animal kingdom. They have simple body plans and no body organs or systems.

All sponges live in water. Most are found in warm, shallow salt water near the coast, although some grow almost 1000 meters deep in the ocean. A few species live in freshwater rivers, lakes, and streams. Sponges grow in many shapes, sizes, and colors. Some have radial symmetry, but most are asymmetrical. They may be smaller than a marble or larger than a compact car!

Adult sponges live attached to one place. They are often found with other sponges in colonies that never move, unless they are washed away by a strong wave. Organisms that remain attached to one place during their lifetime are **sessile.** Early scientists classified sponges as plants because they didn't move. As microscopes were improved, scientists observed that sponges couldn't make their own food, and so they classified them as animals.

The body of a sponge is covered with many small openings called pores. It is from the pores that sponges get their phylum name, **Porifera.** Porifera comes from a Latin word meaning "pore-bearing."

Figure 13-6. Some species of sponge can grow to be larger than humans.

Figure 13-7 shows the body plan of a sponge. A sponge's body is a hollow tube closed at the bottom with an opening in the top. The body wall has two cell layers made up of several different types of cells. There are cells that help a sponge get food, cells that digest food for the sponge, cells that carry nutrients to all parts of the sponge, and cells that allow water to flow into the sponge.

Sponges obtain food from water that is pulled in through their pores. They filter bacteria, algae, protozoans, and other materials out of the water. Organisms that obtain food this way are called **filter feeders.** Cells that line the inside of the sponge, called **collar cells,** help water move through the sponge. You can see in Figure 13-7 that collar cells have flagella. The beating of the flagella in these cells brings water into the sponge. The water moving through the sponge also brings oxygen to the cells and carries away wastes.

The bodies of many sponges are made of sharp, pointed structures called spicules. The soft-bodied sponges people use to take baths or to wash their cars have a skeleton of a fibrous material called spongin. Other sponges are supported by both spicules and spongin. Scientists classify sponges based on the kind of material that makes up their skeleton.

Sponges reproduce both asexually and sexually. Sponges can reproduce asexually by forming buds. New sponges can also form from small pieces that break off the parent sponge. Sponge growers actually cut sponges into pieces, attach weights to them, and put them back into the ocean so the sponges can regenerate. **Regeneration** is the ability of an organism to replace body parts.

How do filter feeders obtain food?

Did You Know?

It takes about 50 years for a sponge to grow to the size used in bathing.

Figure 13-7. Sponges are made of several different types of specialized cells. The spicules provide structure for the sponge.

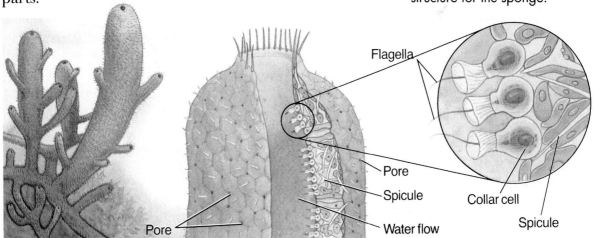

Flagella

Pore

Spicule

Water flow

Pore

Collar cell

Spicule

Sponges reproduce sexually by the joining of egg and sperm. Some species of sponges have separate sexes, but most are hermaphrodites. A **hermaphrodite** (hur MAF ruh dite) is an animal that produces both sperm and eggs. Sperm are released in the water and carried to other sponges where they fertilize the eggs. The fertilized egg develops into a young organism called a **larva.** Larvae usually look very different from the adults. Sponge larvae have cilia which are used to swim about in the water. After a short time, the larva settles down on some object. It will remain there and grow into an adult sponge.

Origin and Importance of Sponges

Sponges appeared on Earth about 600 million years ago in the Cambrian period. Their collar cells are similar to a type of colonial protozoan that is thought to be the ancestor of sponges. No other animal species is known to have evolved from sponges.

TECHNOLOGY

Sea Pharmacy

Eighty percent of all life on Earth lives in the sea. Scientists hope that the 400 000 or more species of ocean plants and animals will provide chemicals to produce new medicines. But with 400 000 plus species, where do scientists start looking? One place is in organisms that use chemicals for protection such as sponges, soft corals, and sea squirts. These chemicals may one day be useful to humans. Sea specimens are also tested for the ability to stimulate the human immune system or to limit the growth of bacteria, viruses, or tumors.

There are many promising leads. The blue blood of horseshoe crabs is used extensively to test for the presence of bacteria that cause infectious diseases. One rare sponge called *Luffariella variabilis* contains a chemical that can block pain and inflammation and may soon be used for patients with arthritis and muscular dystrophy. Algae, sponges, and sea squirts have provided potential anticancer drugs. Poison from puffer fish may one day be used as an anesthetic.

Think Critically: Why are drugs from the sea just beginning to be thoroughly researched?

Sponges provide food for many fish, snails, and starfish. They provide shelter for smaller organisms that live in their bodies. Natural sponges are used in pottery, painting, in other arts and crafts, and as bath sponges. Researchers are collecting and testing sponges as possible sources of medicines.

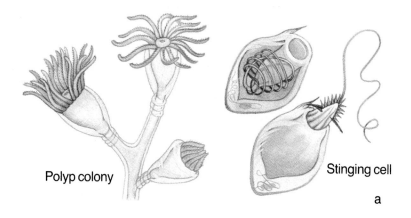

Polyp colony

Stinging cell

a

Cnidarians

The iridescent Portuguese man-of-war, colorful sea anemone, and hydra you see in Figure 13-8 belong to a group of animals called **cnidarians.** This name describes the stinging cells that all members of this phylum have. The word *cnidaria* is Latin for "stinging cells."

Although many types of hydra live in fresh water, most cnidarians live in salt water. Cnidarians live as single organisms and in colonies. All cnidarians have radial symmetry and bodies more complex than those of sponges. They have two cell layers that are arranged into tissues. Cnidarians have a digestive cavity where food is broken down. Most cnidarians have armlike structures called **tentacles** that surround the mouth. The tentacles are armed with the stinging cells that help the organism capture food.

The stinging cells of cnidarians are actually capsules or sacs that contain a coiled harpoonlike thread and poison. Each capsule has a hair that works like a trigger. When a small organism bumps into the hair, the capsule explodes and shoots out its thread and poison. The poison paralyzes the organism until the tentacles wrap around it to pull it into the mouth. Food is digested by enzymes in the digestive cavity. Undigested materials leave through the mouth.

Figure 13-8. The hydra (a), Portuguese man-of-war (b), and sea anemone (c) all contain stinging cells characteristic of the phylum Cnidaria.

b

c

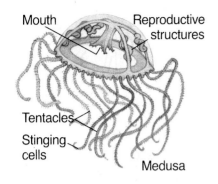

Mouth
Reproductive structures
Tentacles
Stinging cells
Medusa

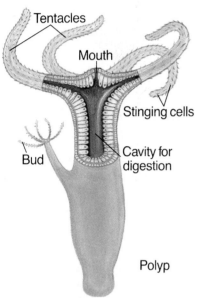

Tentacles
Mouth
Stinging cells
Cavity for digestion
Bud
Polyp

Figure 13-9. The polyp form and medusa form are the two body plans of cnidarians.

Cnidarians have two different body plans. Figure 13-9 shows the two body plans. The **polyp** is shaped like a tube or vase and is usually sessile. The **medusa** is bell-shaped and free swimming. Some cnidarians go through both polyp and medusa stages during their life cycles.

Although the Portuguese man-of-war on page 311 looks like a medusa, it is really a colony of polyps. Some polyps gather food, and others are used for reproduction. The man-of-war has a large, blue, gas-filled float that is used like a sail and moves the colony through the water.

Cnidarians don't have complex nervous systems. They have a system of nerve cells called a nerve net. The nerve net carries impulses and connects all parts of the organism. This makes cnidarians capable of some simple responses and movements. For example, a hydra can somersault away from a threatening situation.

Cnidarians reproduce asexually and sexually. Polyps reproduce asexually by producing buds that eventually fall off the parent and grow into new polyps. Polyps can also reproduce sexually by producing either an egg or sperm. Sperm are released into the water and fertilize the eggs.

Medusa forms of cnidarians have both an asexual stage of reproduction and a sexual one. You can see the cycling between these two stages in Figure 13-10. Free-swimming medusae produce eggs and sperm and release them into the water. The eggs are fertilized and grow into larvae. The larvae eventually settle down and grow into polyps. Young medusae bud off the polyp and the cycle begins again.

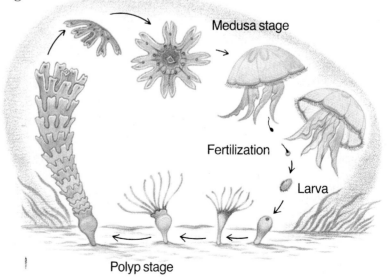

Medusa stage
Fertilization
Larva
Polyp stage

Figure 13-10. Some cnidarians alternate between polyp and medusa forms in their life cycles.

a
b

c

Figure 13-11. Sea rods (a), sea fans (b), and elkhorn coral (c) are all cnidarians that help build coral reefs.

Origin and Importance of Cnidarians

Cnidarians were present on Earth during the Precambrian Era over 600 million years ago. Scientists think that the first form of cnidarian was the medusa. Polyps may have formed from larvae of medusae becoming permanently attached to a surface. Most of the cnidarian fossils found are fossils of corals.

Corals are cnidarian polyp colonies that secrete a hard skeleton around themselves. Many of these polyps living together form coral heads of many different shapes. Some are round, and others look like antlers of elk or deer. Many coral heads together form large coral reefs near shores in warm tropical waters. A large variety of fish and other organisms live on coral reefs. Food and shelter are provided to these organisms by the reef.

Coral reefs protect beaches and shorelines from being washed away by ocean waves. The reefs are also areas of recreation for many people. The beautiful corals and large variety of sea life provide scuba divers and snorklers with a wonderful view of life-forms in a reef.

Science and WRITING

Imagine your class is planning a field study trip to the ocean. Write a section for the student handbook to explain how to deal with jellyfish.

SECTION REVIEW

1. Why is a sponge said to be a simple invertebrate?
2. Describe how sponges get food.
3. What are three characteristics of cnidarians?
4. Describe the two body plans of cnidarians.
5. **Apply:** Why are most fossils of cnidarians fossils of corals?

☒ Comparing and Contrasting

Skill Builder

Compare and contrast the methods of getting food in sponges and cnidarians. If you need help, refer to Comparing and Contrasting in the **Skill Handbook** on page 683.

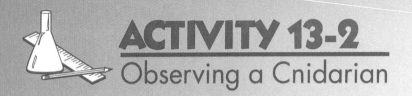

ACTIVITY 13-2
Observing a Cnidarian

Problem: *How does a hydra react?*

Materials

- dropper
- hydra culture
- small dish
- toothpick
- Daphnia or brine shrimp
- stereoscopic microscope

Procedure

1. Use a dropper to place a hydra into a dish along with some of the water in which it is living.
2. Place the dish on the stage of the stereoscopic microscope. Bring the hydra into focus. Record the color of the hydra.
3. Identify and count the number of tentacles. Locate the mouth.
4. Observe the basal disk by which the hydra attaches itself to a surface.
5. Hypothesize what will happen if the hydra is touched with a toothpick. Carefully touch the tentacles. Then gently touch the basal disk. Describe the reactions in the data table.
6. Drop a Daphnia or a small amount of brine shrimp into the dish. Observe how the hydra takes in food. Record your observations.
7. Return the hydra to the culture.

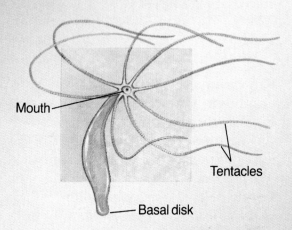

Mouth

Tentacles

Basal disk

Data and Observations

Features	Observations
Color	
Number of tentacles	
Reaction to touch	
Tentacles	
Basal disk	
Reaction to food	

Analyze

1. How many tentacles does the hydra have?
2. Where is the mouth located in relation to the tentacles?
3. How did the hydra react to being touched?
4. How did the hydra react to food?

Conclude and Apply

5. When the hydra was touched, did anything happen to suggest that other areas of the animal were affected?
6. How do the tentacles function in getting food?

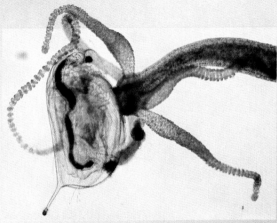

The Simple Worms

Objectives

▶ Describe the body plans of flatworms and roundworms.
▶ Distinguish between free-living and parasitic organisms.
▶ Identify disease-causing flatworms and roundworms.

New Science Words

free-living

anus

cyst

Flatworms

The animal you most likely think of when you hear the word *worm* is the earthworm—the worm that crawls across pavement after a rain, or the worm used to bait a fishing hook. You probably wouldn't think of a tapeworm or any of the other many types of worms in the world. Just what is a worm? Worms are invertebrates with soft bodies and bilateral symmetry. They have three layers of tissues, organs, and organ systems. Worms live in many different environments. Some are very beautiful; others are not so attractive. There are flatworms, roundworms, and worms with segments. In this chapter, you will learn about flatworms and roundworms.

Flatworms are worms with flattened bodies. They are members of the phylum Platyhelminthes (plat ih hel MIHN theez). Members of this phylum include planarians and tapeworms. Some flatworms are free-living but most are parasites. Remember a parasite depends on another organism for food and a place to live. Unlike parasites, **free-living** organisms don't depend on one particular organism for food or a place to live. They find their own. Most flatworms live in salt water, although there are a few species that live in fresh water.

MINI-Lab

How do planarians move?
Use a dropper to transfer a planarian to a watch glass. Add enough water so the worm can move freely. Place the glass under a stereomicroscope and observe. Describe how the organism moves in the dish. Draw the organism.

Figure 13-12. Planarians have a simple body structure.

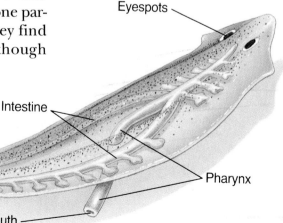

Eyespots

Intestine

Pharynx

Mouth

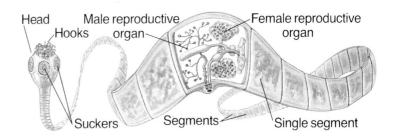

Head   Male reproductive   Female reproductive
   Hooks   organ   organ

Suckers   Segments   Single segment

Figure 13-13. Tapeworms attach to an organism's intestine using hooks and suckers. A section of a tapeworm is made mostly of male and female reproductive structures.

A planarian is an example of a free-living class of flatworms. It has a triangle-shaped head with two eyespots. There is one body opening called the mouth on the ventral side of the body. A muscular tube called the pharynx connects the mouth and the digestive tract. A planarian feeds on small organisms and dead bodies of larger organisms. Most planarians live in fresh water, under rocks, or on plant material. Some live in moist places on land. The body of a planarian is usually about one centimeter long and is covered with cilia. The cilia move the worm along a slimy mucus track secreted from the underside of the planarian.

Planarians reproduce asexually or sexually. They reproduce asexually by simply dividing in two. Planarians also have the ability to regenerate. A planarian can be cut in two, and each piece will grow into a new worm. Planarians reproduce sexually by egg and sperm. Most are hermaphrodites, and they exchange sperm with one another. They lay fertilized eggs that hatch in a few weeks.

Tapeworms are parasitic members of the phylum Platyhelminthes. These worms use hooks and suckers to attach themselves to the intestine of a host organism. Dogs, cats, humans, and other animals act as hosts for tapeworms. Tapeworms don't have a digestive system. Food that has already been digested by the host is absorbed from the intestine of the host by the worm. A tapeworm grows by producing new body segments behind the head. Its ribbonlike body may grow to be 12 meters long.

Each body segment of the tapeworm has both male and female reproductive organs. The segments produce eggs and sperm, and the eggs are fertilized in the segment. Once a segment is filled with fertilized eggs, it breaks off and passes out of the host's body. If a fertilized egg is eaten by another host, the egg hatches and develops into a new worm.

Roundworms

If you own a dog, you've probably had to get medicine from your vet to protect your dog from heartworm. Heartworm is a disease in dogs caused by roundworms. Roundworms make up the largest phylum of worms, the phylum Nematoda. It is estimated that there are more than a half million species of roundworms in the phylum Nematoda. Nematodes are found in soil, in animals, and in fresh water and salt water. Many are parasitic, but most are free-living.

Roundworms are slender and tapered at both ends. The body is a tube within a tube, with fluid in-between. Unlike the organisms you have studied so far, Nematodes have two body openings, a mouth and an anus. The **anus** is an opening at the end of the digestive tract through which wastes leave the body.

Some roundworms are parasites of humans. The most common roundworm parasites of humans are *Ascaris*, hookworm, and *Trichinella*. Humans get hookworms by

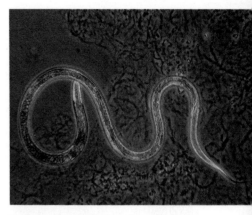

Figure 13-14. This free-living species of roundworm lives among cyanobacteria.

PROBLEM SOLVING

Barbara's New Puppy

Barbara received a new puppy for her birthday. Barbara and her parents took the puppy to a veterinarian for a checkup. After the examination, the veterinarian gave Barbara some medication to give her puppy daily to prevent heartworm disease. He explained how she should increase the dosage as the puppy gains weight.

The vet told her that it was important to give the puppy the medication every day. Heartworms are spread from dog to dog by mosquitoes. When a mosquito bites a dog infected with heartworms, it can pick up and carry them to a dog not infected. Dogs can get heartworms at anytime during their life if they don't receive medication.

How can heartworm disease be controlled?
Think Critically: Why should the dosage of heartworm medication be increased as the puppy gains weight?

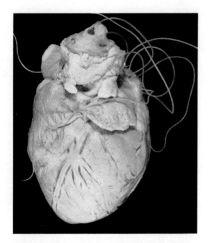

Figure 13-15. This heart of a dog is infected with heartworms.

Science and WRITING

Write a public service announcement for your local television station informing the community about heartworm disease in dogs. A veterinarian can probably provide much useful information.

walking barefoot over dirt or through fields. Hookworm eggs hatch in warm, moist soil. Wearing shoes is the best protection against hookworms.

Ascaris is found in the intestines of pigs, horses, and humans. Eggs enter the host's body in contaminated food or water. They travel to the intestines where they mature and mate. Masses of worms can block the intestines and cause death if left untreated.

Trichinella worms cause the disease trichinosis (trihk uh NOH sus). Humans become infected when they eat undercooked pork that has *Trichinella* cysts. A **cyst** is a young worm with a protective covering. Trichinosis can be prevented by thoroughly cooking pork.

The heartworms you treat your dog for enter the blood of a dog through a mosquito bite. They move to the heart, where they grow and reproduce. They can block the valves of the heart that lead to and from the lungs if the infection is left untreated. Medicine can be given to dogs to prevent heartworm disease.

The flatworms and roundworms are more complex than sponges and cnidarians. They have bilateral symmetry, three well-developed tissue layers, and organ systems. The roundworms have digestive systems with a mouth and an anus. Like sponges and cnidarians, these invertebrates probably evolved from the sea. They still live in water, a moist environment, or inside a living host in a watery environment.

SECTION REVIEW

1. Compare and contrast the body plans of flatworms and roundworms.
2. Give an example of a free-living flatworm and a parasitic flatworm.
3. What are three roundworms that cause diseases in humans? How can humans prevent becoming infected with each of these worms?
4. **Apply:** Which organism is more complex, a cnidarian or a flatworm? Explain.

Skill Builder

☑ **Outlining**

Make an outline of the material found in Section 13-4. If you need help, refer to Outlining in the **Skill Handbook** on page 681.

CHAPTER
REVIEW

13-1: What Is an Animal?

1. Animals are many-celled eukaryotic organisms that must find and digest their food.

2. Animals that have body parts arranged the same way on both sides of the body have bilateral symmetry. Animals with body parts in a circle around a central point are radially symmetrical.

3. Invertebrates are animals that don't have backbones. Animals with backbones are vertebrates.

13-2: Science and Society: Experiments Using Animals

1. Many lifesaving drugs and vaccines have been developed using animals for testing.

2. Many people feel animals have rights and should be treated humanely and with respect.

13-3: The Simplest Invertebrates

1. Sponges are considered the simplest animals in the animal kingdom. They are sessile and obtain food and oxygen by filtering water through pores. Sponges reproduce by egg and sperm and by budding or regeneration.

2. Cnidarians are hollow-bodied animals with radial symmetry. Most have tentacles with stinging cells to obtain food. Digestion takes place in a central cavity. Jellyfish, hydras, and corals are cnidarians.

13-4: The Simple Worms

1. Flatworms belong to the phylum Platyhelminthes. They have bilateral symmetry. There are both free-living and parasite forms. Planarians have one body opening. Tapeworms are parasitic forms of flatworms that have hooks and suckers to attach to a host. Roundworms belong to the phylum Nematoda. They have a tube within a tube body plan and bilateral symmetry. Roundworms have two body openings, a mouth and anus.

2. Free-living organisms don't depend on one particular organism for food or a place to live. Parasites depend on other organisms for food and a place to live.

3. Some parasitic roundworms that infect humans are hookworms, *Ascaris*, and *Trichinella*. Heartworms are roundworms that infect dogs.

KEY SCIENCE WORDS

a. **anus**
b. **bilateral symmetry**
c. **cnidarians**
d. **collar cells**
e. **cyst**
f. **filter feeders**
g. **free-living**
h. **hermaphrodite**
i. **invertebrates**
j. **larva**
k. **medusa**
l. **polyp**
m. **Porifera**
n. **radial symmetry**
o. **regeneration**
p. **sessile**
q. **tentacles**
r. **vertebrates**

UNDERSTANDING VOCABULARY

Match each phrase with the correct term from the list of Key Science Words.

1. body parts the same on each side
2. a young worm enclosed in a covering
3. a young organism different from the adult
4. opening for digestive wastes
5. attached, nonmoving animal
6. organisms with no backbones
7. animals that have backbones
8. cnidarian shaped like a tube or vase
9. an organism that makes both egg and sperm
10. used by cnidarians to capture food

CHAPTER REVIEW

Choose the word or phrase that completes the sentence.

1. Animal characteristics include _____.
   a. movement   c. eukaryotes
   b. heterotrophs   d. all of these
2. All of these belong to the same group except _____.
   a. fish   c. jellyfish
   b. clam   d. sponge
3. _____ is the opposite of dorsal.
   a. anterior   c. radial
   b. ventral   d. none of these
4. Sponges have _____.
   a. no symmetry   c. radial symmetry
   b. bilateral symmetry d. none of these
5. Sponges are members of Phylum _____.
   a. Cnidaria   c. Porifera
   b. Nematoda   d. Platyhelminthes
6. Sponges reproduce by _____.
   a. regeneration   c. budding
   b. egg and sperm d. all of these
7. The body plans of cnidarians are polyp and _____.
   a. larva   c. ventral
   b. medusa   d. buds
8. All are examples of cnidarians except _____.
   a. coral   c. planarian
   b. hydra   d. jellyfish
9. An example of a parasite is _____.
   a. sponge   c. tapeworm
   b. planarian d. jellyfish
10. Separate sexes are found in _____.
    a. *Ascaris* c. sponges
    b. planarian d. all of these

UNDERSTANDING CONCEPTS

Complete each sentence.

11. Most animals are _____, having no backbones.
12. _____ make up the bodies of some sponges.
13. All cnidarians have _____ symmetry.
14. _____ are used to paralyze prey.
15. The _____ is the bell-shaped body form of cnidarians.

THINK AND WRITE CRITICALLY

16. Using an example, explain the difference between bilateral and radial symmetry.
17. Explain the difference between budding and regeneration.
18. Describe how sponges and hydra obtain food.
19. Why do scientists feel that reforms and regulations in animal research may threaten the future of science?
20. Explain how the structure of a tapeworm and its life-style are related.

21. Compare the body organization of a sponge to that of a simple worm.

22. What is the advantage of having more than one means of reproduction to simple animals?

23. List the types of food sponges, hydras, and planarians eat. Explain why the size of the food particles is different in each organism.

24. Compare and contrast the medusa and polyp body forms of cnidarians.

25. What are some reasons why scientists believe the medusa stage was the first stage of the cnidarians?

MORE SKILL BUILDERS

If you need help, refer to the Skill Handbook.

1. Sequencing: Sequence the order of infection of a dog by heartworms.

2. Using Variables, Constants, and Controls: Design an experiment to test the sense of a planarian to touch.

3. Concept Mapping: Complete the concept map of classification in the animal kingdom.

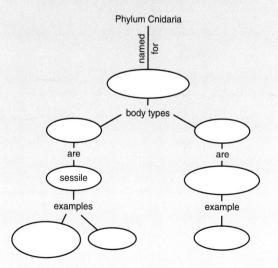

4. Hypothesizing: Make a hypothesis as to why cooking pork at high temperatures prevents worms from developing, if present in the uncooked meat.

5. Observing and Inferring: Observe the animals pictured in Activity 13-1. Use Figure 13-2 on page 303 to determine to which phylum each animal belongs.

PROJECTS

1. Make a map of the areas of the world where parasitic worms are problems to humans. What conditions cause the high rate of infection in people in these areas?

2. With your teacher, look in a stream on and under rocks for flatworms and roundworms. Observe under the microscope.

If you've ever walked along a beach, you've probably seen lots of seashells. Seashells come in many different colors, shapes, and sizes. Each shell is made of many rings or bands. Can you learn anything about the shell and the organism that made it by looking at the bands?

FIND OUT!

Do this simple activity to find out how many bands are on a clam shell and what they mean.

Use a hand lens to observe a clam shell. Count the number of rings or bands on the shell. Count the large top point called the crown as one ring. Are all of the bands the same width? The width of the bands tells you something about the year in the life of the clam. Compare your results with those of your classmates. Do all of the clams have the same number of bands? What do you think the bands represent? Why do you think some are wider than others?

Gearing Up

Previewing the Chapter

Use this outline to help you focus on important ideas in this chapter.

Section 14-1   Mollusks
▶ Features of Mollusks
▶ Classes of Mollusks
▶ Importance of Mollusks

Section 14-2   Segmented Worms
▶ Features of Segmented Worms
▶ Types of Segmented Worms
▶ Evolution of Segmented Worms and Mollusks

Section 14-3   Arthropods
▶ Features of Arthropods
▶ Classes of Arthropods

Section 14-4   Science and Society Pesticides
▶ Insect Pests?

Section 14-5   Echinoderms
▶ Features of Echinoderms
▶ Sea Stars

Previewing Science Skills

▶ In the **Skill Builders,** you will compare and contrast, interpret scientific illustrations, make a concept map, and observe and infer.
▶ In the **Activities,** you will observe, experiment, and collect and record data.
▶ In the **MINI-Labs,** you will experiment, observe, and record data.

What's next?

In this chapter you will study mollusks, segmented worms, arthropods, and echinoderms. You will learn about the lives of these organisms and about how these organisms are important to you and the environment.

New Science Words

mollusks
mantle
gills
open circulatory system
radula
closed circulatory system

Objectives

▶ Identify the features of mollusks.
▶ Name three classes of mollusks and identify a member of each.

Features of Mollusks

If you've collected shells on the beach, watched a snail crawl, or eaten oysters or squid, you are familiar with mollusks. The word *mollusk* comes from the Latin word meaning "soft" and describes the bodies of the organisms in the phylum Mollusca (mah LUS kuh). **Mollusks** are soft-bodied invertebrates that usually have shells. They are found on land, in fresh water, and in salt water. Like the simple worms, mollusks have bilateral symmetry. Unlike the simple worms, sponges, and cnidarians, mollusks have a fluid-filled body cavity that provides space for the body organs.

Mollusks come in many different sizes, shapes, and colors. They vary in size from the tiny aquarium snail to the giant squid that can reach a length of 18 m. Different as they are, all mollusks have the same basic body plan.

All mollusks have a soft body usually covered by a hard shell. Covering the soft body is the mantle. The **mantle** secretes the shell or protects the body if the mollusk does not have a shell. Between the soft body and the mantle is a space called the mantle cavity. In it are the **gills,** organs that exchange oxygen and carbon dioxide with the water. The body organs of mollusks are located together in an area called the visceral mass. The mantle covers the visceral mass. Finally, all mollusks have a muscular foot used for movement.

The circulatory system of most mollusks is an **open circulatory system.** In this type of system blood isn't completely contained in vessels the way your blood is. Blood bathes a mollusks organs in some areas of their bodies.

The classification of mollusks is based on whether or not a shell is present; if a shell is present, the kind of shell it is; and the kind of foot. In this section, you will learn about three classes of mollusks.

Figure 14-1. All mollusks have the same basic body plan: a shell, foot, mantle, and visceral mass.

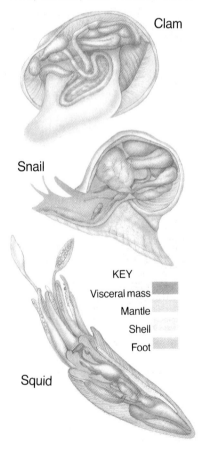

Clam

Snail

KEY
Visceral mass
Mantle
Shell
Foot

Squid

Classes of Mollusks

Univalves

The largest class of mollusks includes snails, slugs, abalones, whelks, sea slugs, and conches. Look at the organism in the top photograph of Figure 14-2. Can you see why these organisms are called one-shelled mollusks, or univalves? Except for slugs, they have a single spiral shell. Many have a pair of tentacles with eyes at the tips. They get their food with a structure called a radula. The **radula** is a tongue-like organ with rows of teeth that work like a file. It is used for scraping and tearing algae and other food materials.

Univalves are adapted for different ways of life. Slugs and many snails are adapted to life on land. They move by muscular contractions of the foot. Glands in the foot secrete a layer of mucus for the foot to slide along in. Slugs live where it is moist. They are protected by a layer of mucus.

Bivalves

Bivalves are two-shelled mollusks that have a two-part shell joined by a hinge. *Bivalve* means "two-shelled." Clams, oysters, and scallops are bivalve mollusks. These animals pull their shells closed with powerful muscles. To open their shells, they relax these muscles. The shell is made up of several layers made by the mantle. The smoothest layer is on the inside and protects the soft body.

Bivalves are very well adapted to living in water. For protection, clams burrow deep into the sand with their muscular foot. Mussels and oysters cement themselves to a solid surface or attach themselves with a strong thread. This keeps strong waves from washing them away. Scallops escape predators by rapidly opening and closing their shells. As the water pours out, its force moves them rapidly in the opposite direction.

Cephalopods

The class of mollusks with the most specialized and complex members are the cephalopods. The word *cephalopod* means "head-footed" and describes the body structure of these invertebrates. Squid, octopuses, and the chambered nautilus belong to this class. Cephalopods have a large, well-developed head. Their "foot" is divided into many tentacles with strong suckers for capturing prey.

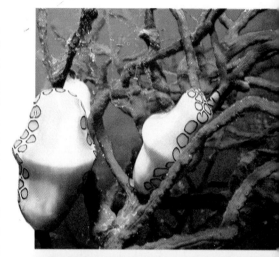

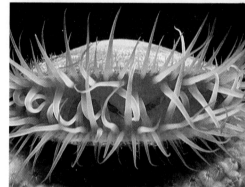

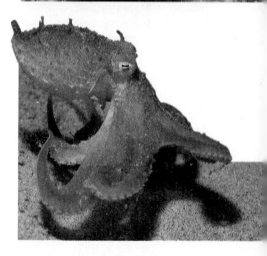

Figure 14-2. The organism in the top photo is a representative of the univalves. The scallop in the middle photo is a bivalve and the octopus in the bottom photo is a cephalopod.

Squid and octopuses have a well-developed nervous system and large eyes similar to human eyes. Unlike the other mollusks, in head-footed mollusks, blood containing food and oxygen is contained and transported in a series of vessels, in a **closed circulatory system.**

What is a closed circulatory system?

All cephalopods live in oceans and have bodies adapted for swimming. They move quickly by jet propulsion. When the space under the mantle is filled with water, they contract their mantle muscles and force the water from an opening near the head. The jet of water sends them backward. A squid can swim at more than 60 m per second this way. Although octopuses can swim by jet propulsion like squid can, they usually use their tentacles to creep more slowly over the ocean floor.

Importance of Mollusks

Mollusks provide food for fish, sea stars, and birds. Their empty shells provide homes for invertebrates such as hermit crabs. Clams, oysters, snails, and scallops are prized by humans for food. Humans also enjoy the pearls produced by many species of mollusks, especially the valuable ones made by the pearl oyster. Scientists are studying the nervous systems of the squid and octopus to help them understand how learning takes place and how memory works. Mollusks can also cause problems for humans. Snails and slugs feed on plants and damage crops. Certain species of snails are hosts of parasites that infect humans.

Figure 14-3. Pearls are formed in many bivalve mollusks. Smooth mother of pearl is secreted by the mantle in layers around a grain of sand or other particle trapped between the mantle and the shell.

SECTION REVIEW

1. What features are used to classify mollusks?
2. What is the function of the radula?
3. Name the three classes of mollusks and identify a member from each class.
4. How do head-footed mollusks move?
5. **Apply:** Why is the snail a good animal to have in an aquarium?

Skill Builder

☑ Comparing and Contrasting

Make a table that compares and contrasts the features of one-shelled mollusks, two-shelled mollusks, and head-footed mollusks. If you need help, refer to Comparing and Contrasting in the **Skill Handbook** on page 683.

Segmented Worms

Objectives

▶ Describe the traits of segmented worms.
▶ Describe the structures and digestive process of an earthworm.
▶ Identify the evolutionary relationship between segmented worms and mollusks.

New Science Words

setae
crop
gizzard

Features of Segmented Worms

The worms you see crawling across sidewalks and driveways after a hard rain and the night crawlers you dig up for fishing belong to the phylum Annelida (uh NEL ud uh). The phylum Annelida is made up of segmented worms. Their tube-shaped bodies are divided into many little sections, or segments. The word *annelid* means "little rings" and describes the bodies of these worms. Segmented worms are found in fresh water, salt water, and moist soil. Earthworms, leeches, and beautiful fan worms belong to this phylum.

Besides segments, members of this phylum have several other characteristics in common. Like mollusks, all segmented worms have a body cavity that holds their organs. On the outside of each segment they have bristle-like structures called **setae** (SEE tee) that help them move. Have you ever watched a bird try or tried yourself to pull an earthworm out of the ground? It's not that easy, is it? Segmented worms use their setae to hold on to the soil. Let's look more closely at two classes of segmented worms—earthworms and leeches.

Figure 14-4. Featherduster worms (top) and fireworms (bottom) are two types of segmented worms that live in the ocean.

Types of Segmented Worms

Earthworms

The tube-like body of an earthworm is divided into more than 100 segments. The segments aren't only on the outside; the body cavity is divided also. Each segment is identical except for those near the front and hind ends. Each body segment, except for the first and last, has two pairs of setae. Earthworms move by using their setae and two sets of muscles in the body wall.

To get food earthworms eat soil! While they burrow through the soil they are actually eating it. Earthworms get the energy they need to live from the bits of leaves and other plant and animal materials found in the soil. The digestive system of an earthworm is made up of a crop, gizzard, and intestine. The soil eaten by an earthworm moves to the **crop,** which is a sac used for storage. Behind the crop is a muscular structure, the **gizzard,** that grinds the soil. In the intestine, which follows, the food is broken down and absorbed by the blood. Undigested soil and waste materials leave the worm through the anus.

Look at the body structure of an earthworm in Figure 14-5. Earthworms have two blood vessels that run along the sides of the body and meet in the anterior, or front, end. The vessels meet here and form five pairs of structures, called aortic arches, that pump blood through the body. Smaller vessels go into each body segment. Because an earthworm's blood is all contained in tubes and vessels, it has a closed circulatory system. Wastes are removed from earthworms by small, coiled tubes found in each segment. Earthworms have small, simple brains in the anterior segment to control their bodies. Nerves in each segment join to form a main nerve cord that connects to the brain. Earthworms are sensitive to light, temperature, and moisture. Can you think of any times they show these sensitivities?

Earthworms don't have gills or lungs. They exchange oxygen and carbon dioxide through the skin. They have both male and female reproductive structures, but have to exchange sperm to reproduce. An individual worm can't fertilize its own eggs.

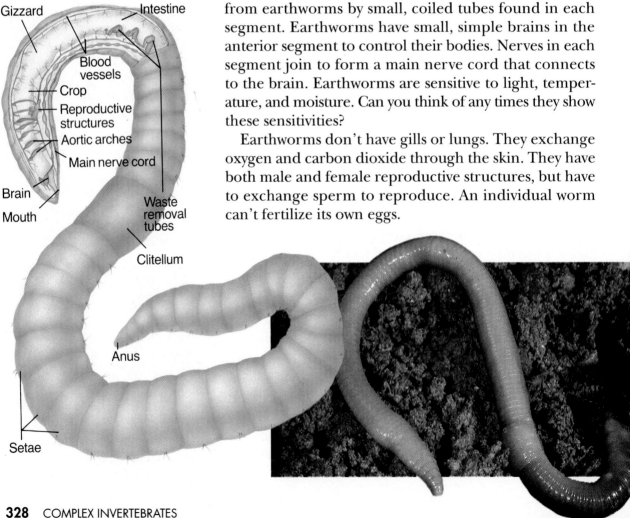

Figure 14-5. Segmented worms have circulatory, respiratory, excretory, digestive, muscular and reproductive systems.

Gizzard

Intestine

Blood vessels

Crop

Reproductive structures

Aortic arches

Main nerve cord

Brain

Mouth

Waste removal tubes

Clitellum

Anus

Setae

TECHNOLOGY

Leeches to the Rescue

No one likes to meet a leech by accident, but hospital pharmacies now stock leeches, in various sizes, for use in delicate microsurgery. In fact, a major leech farm ships 25 000 leeches each year to two dozen countries.

When doctors perform microsurgery to reattach small body parts like ears, fingers, and toes, they may have problems due to the tiny veins involved. These tend to become blocked and cut off the blood flow to the reattached tissue. Without a good blood flow, the tissue dies. To prevent this, surgeons attach leeches to the microsurgery site. The leeches suck some of the congested blood, and chemicals in their saliva keep the blood flowing for several hours.

Other chemicals in leeches' saliva may help humans. Scientists have found in leech saliva an anticlotting substance, an anesthetic, and a chemical that increases the size of veins.

Think Critically: How could these chemicals be useful for patients with circulatory problems?

Leeches

You or someone you know may have had to remove a leech from your body while swimming in a pond, lake, or river. Leeches belong to another class of segmented worms and are adapted to a life-style very different from earthworms. Their bodies are not as round or long as earthworms', and they don't have setae. Leeches feed on the blood of ducks, fish, and even humans. Two suckers, one at each end of the body, are used to attach to an animal. After the leech has attached itself, it cuts open a wound and sucks two to ten times its weight in blood. If you have had a leech attached to you, you know that when you pulled it off, the wound didn't stop bleeding for quite a long time. This is because the leech secretes a substance to keep your blood from clotting so it can feed more easily.

Figure 14-6. Leeches were once used to try to cure sick people.

Before the 1900s, physicians used leeches to drain blood from sick people. They thought that bleeding by leeches would drain away sickness and make the person well. The treatment usually caused patients to become weaker. Sometimes it even killed them.

Evolution of Segmented Worms and Mollusks

Scientists think that mollusks and segmented worms share a common ancestor. They were the first of the animal groups to have a body that provides space for the body organs. In both groups, the first stage of development is a structure that looks like a spinning top with cilia in the middle and at both ends. This structure, a larva, is shown in Figure 14-7. This larva is the best evidence that mollusks and segmented worms share a common ancestor.

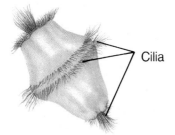

Cilia

Figure 14-7. Mollusks and segmented worms have the same type of larva.

SECTION REVIEW

1. What is the most noticeable feature of annelids?
2. Describe how an earthworm feeds and digests its food.
3. How are segmented worms related to mollusks?
4. How are leeches different from earthworms?
5. **Apply:** Farmers depend on the earthworms that live in the soil of their crop fields. Why are earthworms important to farmers?

Skill Builder

⊠ Interpreting Scientific Illustrations

Use the diagram in Figure 14-5 to list the body systems of an earthworm and organs in each system. If you need help, refer to Interpreting Scientific Illustrations in the **Skill Handbook** on page 693.

ACTIVITY 14-1
Observing a Segmented Worm

Problem: *How is an earthworm's structure related to its way of life?*

Materials

- live earthworm
- moist paper towels
- shallow pan
- water
- hand lens
- loose soil
- cotton swab
- vinegar

Procedure

1. Wet your hands and remove an earthworm from the container your teacher has provided. **CAUTION:** *Use care when working with live animals.* Keep your hands wet while working with the earthworm. Observe the body shape, especially at the ends.
2. Use a hand lens to observe the structure of the earthworm. Use the diagram on page 328 to help you locate the mouth, anus, and clitellum. Estimate the number of body segments.
3. Hold the worm gently between your thumb and forefinger. Observe its movements and record them in a data table like the one shown. Use the hand lens to observe the setae on the underside.
4. Touch the anterior and posterior areas of the body with a moist cotton swab. Record your observations.
5. Dip a cotton swab in vinegar. Draw a "line of vinegar" on the moist paper towel in front of the earthworm. Record your observations.
6. Place the earthworm on the surface of a thick layer of loose soil in a pan. Record the movements of the worm.
7. Return the earthworm to the place your teacher has provided. Wash your hands.

Data and Observations

Stimulus	Response
Moist paper towel	
Fingers	
Touch, anterior	
Touch, posterior	
Vinegar	
Soil	

Analyze

1. How many segments does the earthworm have?
2. How do the anterior and posterior differ?
3. Where are the setae located and how are they arranged on the body?
4. Does the earthworm have any visible sense organs?

Conclude and Apply

5. How does the earthworm's response to touch help it to live in soil?
6. How are the setae useful to living in soil?
7. How does the shape of the body help the earthworm to live in soil?
8. How is an earthworm's structure related to its way of life?

14-3   Arthropods

New Science Words

Arthropoda
appendages
exoskeleton
molting
spiracles
metamorphosis

Objectives

▶ Identify features used to classify arthropods.
▶ Relate the structure of the exoskeleton to its function.
▶ Distinguish between complete and incomplete metamorphosis.

Features of Arthropods

Have you ever swatted at a fly, been bitten by a mosquito, or been stung by a bee? If you have, you've been bugged by an arthropod (AR thruh pahd). The arthropods make up the largest phylum of animals in the animal kingdom. They have adapted to almost every environment on Earth. Insects, shrimp, spiders, and centipedes are all members of the phylum **Arthropoda.**

Arthropoda means "jointed foot" and describes the jointed appendages of arthropods. **Appendages** are structures that grow from the body. Your arms and legs are appendages. The jointed appendages of arthropods include legs, antennae, claws, and pinchers.

The bodies of arthropods are divided into segments like those of segmented worms. Because of this, scientists think that arthropods and segmented worms have a common ancestor. The bodies of some arthropods have many segments, whereas others have segments that are fused together to form body regions. Figure 14-8 shows three regions formed by fused segments: the head, the thorax, and the abdomen.

What are arthropods?

Figure 14-8. The segments of arthropods are fused together to form three regions: the head, the thorax, and the abdomen.

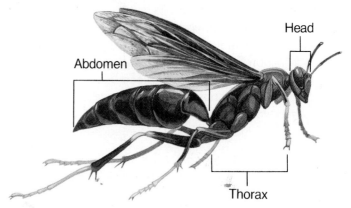

Head

Abdomen

Thorax

In addition to jointed appendages and segmented bodies, all arthropods have an external covering called the **exoskeleton.** The exoskeleton covers, supports, and protects the body. The lightweight exoskeleton is made of protein and a carbohydrate called chitin (KITE un). This covering also keeps the animal's body from drying out.

The exoskeleton is made of nonliving material, so it can't grow as the animal grows. From time to time, the old exoskeleton is shed and replaced by a new one in a process called **molting.** The new exoskeleton is soft and takes a while to harden. During this time the animal is not well protected from its predators. Many people enjoy eating soft-shelled crabs. The crab has just molted and its new shell hasn't hardened yet.

Arthropods have a body cavity and a digestive system with two openings, a mouth and an anus. They have a nervous system similar to that of annelids but with a larger brain. You will learn about five classes of arthropods in this section.

Figure 14-9. Arthropods molt several times as they grow.

Classes of Arthropods

Arachnids

Spiders, scorpions, mites, and ticks are arachnids (uh RAK nudz). Arachnids are arthropods with two body regions, a head-chest region called the cephalothorax and an abdomen, and four pairs of legs. You can tell an arachnid from other arthropods because it has eight legs. Other arthropods have only six legs. Arachnids are adapted to kill prey with poison glands, stingers, or fangs. Appendages near the mouth are used to hold food.

The spider in Figure 14-10 is a common arachnid. Spiders have eight simple eyes they use to sense light and darkness. A spider cannot chew food. Using a pair of fangs a spider injects poison into its prey; the poison paralyzes the prey and turns it into a liquid. The spider then sucks up the liquid. Oxygen and carbon dioxide are exchanged in structures called book lungs. They are called book lungs because they look like the pages of a book. Openings in the abdomen called **spiracles** allow oxygen and carbon dioxide to move into and out of the book lungs.

Figure 14-10. The external structures and book lungs of a common spider.

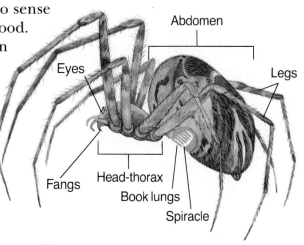

Abdomen

Legs

Eyes

Fangs

Head-thorax

Book lungs

Spiracle

Ticks and mites are arachnids that are parasites. Mites are very tiny. Housedust mites feed on dead skin cells found in the dust on floors and in bedding. There is even a type of mite that lives in the follicles of human eyelashes. Ticks attach to the skin of a host and feed on its blood. Some ticks spread diseases such as Rocky Mountain spotted fever and Lyme disease.

Scorpions have a sharp stinger at the end of their abdomen that contains poison. Scorpions grab their prey with their pinchers and inject venom to paralyze them. The sting of a scorpion is very painful to humans, but it usually is not fatal.

Figure 14-11. Scorpions (a) and housedust mites (b) are two arachnids very different in size.

PROBLEM SOLVING

Spinning Spiders

Have you ever looked closely at a spider web? Spiders make these interesting structures using three pairs of openings on the underside of the abdomen called spinnerets. A fluid protein is squeezed out of the spinnerets and hardens into a silk thread when exposed to air.

Some spiders use silk to construct webs to capture prey. Spiders spin two types of silk thread. One type of thread is very strong, whereas the other type is elastic and contains sticky droplets. Garden spiders spin the sticky thread along a spiral line that forms the trapping part of the web.

Spiders use the silk thread for other purposes. Some spiders use silk thread to change habitat. Maybe you've seen a spider glide through the air or lower itself from

a tree using a thread. Also, silk threads are used to make cocoons for fertilized eggs or a cozy nest in some species.

Think Critically: Imagine that an insect flies into a garden spider's web. Explain how the insect is captured by the silk, but the spider is able to walk to the prey.

Centipedes and Millipedes

Even though centipedes and millipedes look like worms, you know they are not because worms don't have legs. Centipedes and millipedes make up two classes of arthropods. They have long bodies with many segments, an exoskeleton, jointed legs, antennae, and simple eyes. They live on land in moist environments. Both reproduce sexually and make nests for their eggs. They stay with the eggs until they hatch.

Compare the centipede and millipede below. The centipede has one pair of jointed legs per segment, whereas the millipede has two pairs of legs per segment. Centipedes hunt for their food and have a pair of poison claws used to inject venom into their prey. Centipedes feed on snails, slugs, and worms. Their bites are very painful to humans. Millipedes don't move as quickly as centipedes and feed on plants.

Science and WRITING

Develop a plan for a new business involving one of the many animals in this chapter. Of course, your plan will describe an ethical and environmentally sound venture. Explain your business plan to your future investors—the class.

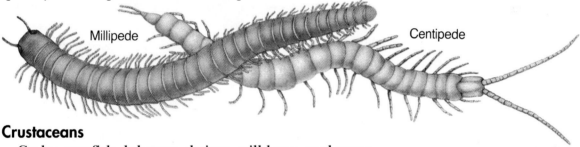

Millipede

Centipede

Crustaceans

Crabs, crayfish, lobsters, shrimp, pill bugs, and water fleas all belong to the Class Crustacea. Crustaceans are arthropods that have one or two antennae and jaws called mandibles used for crushing food. Most crustaceans live in water, but some, like pill bugs, live on land in moist environments. If you turn over a board or look under some leaves in your yard, you are sure to find a pill bug.

The crayfish in Figure 14-12 is a typical crustacean. Although some crustaceans have three body regions, the crayfish has a head and thorax joined to form one region.

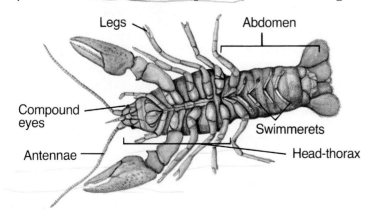

Legs

Abdomen

Compound eyes

Antennae

Swimmerets

Head-thorax

Figure 14-12. All crustaceans have body structures similar to those of a crayfish.

Crustaceans have many pairs of legs. The first pair of legs are claws that catch and hold food. The other four pairs are walking legs. The five pairs of appendages on the abdomen are swimmerets. They help the crustacean move and are used in reproduction. The swimmerets also force water over the feathery gills that crustaceans use for breathing. If a crustacean happens to lose an appendage, it can grow back, or regenerate, the lost part.

Barnacles are crustaceans very different in form from the others. They have a very hard, stony shell and spend their lives cemented to boats, piers, or animals such as whales.

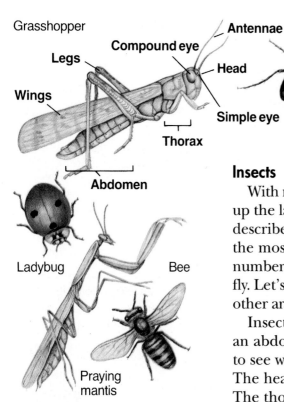

Figure 14-13. All insects have six legs, a head, a thorax, and an abdomen. They also have two pairs of wings, one pair of antennae, and a pair of compound eyes.

Insects

With more than 700 000 classified species, insects make up the largest group of complex invertebrates. Scientists describe thousands more each year. Actually insects are the most successful group of animals in both kinds and numbers. They are the only invertebrates that are able to fly. Let's look at the features that distinguish insects from other arthropods and find out why they are so successful.

Insects have three body regions: a head, a thorax, and an abdomen. With some insects it is almost impossible to see where one region stops and the next one begins. The head has one pair of antennae, eyes, and a mouth. The thorax has three pairs of jointed legs and, in many species, one or two pairs of wings. The abdomen is divided into 11 segments and has neither wings nor legs attached to it.

Most insects have one or two pairs of wings. Flies have one pair. Some insects such as silverfish and fleas don't have wings. Flying lets insects move to find new places to live, new food sources, and mates. It also helps them escape from their enemies.

The head of most insects has simple and compound eyes and a pair of antennae. Simple eyes are used to detect light and dark. Compound eyes contain many lenses and detect some colors and movement. The antennae are used for feel and smell.

Insects have open circulatory systems similar to that of mollusks. The open circulatory system carries digested food to cells and removes wastes. The almost colorless blood does not carry oxygen. As in arachnids, insects have spiracles on the abdomen and thorax that take in air and expel waste gases. You can see that insects have systems for digestion, reproduction, and removing wastes.

Insects reproduce sexually. Females lay thousands of eggs. Because there is no parental care, only a fraction of the offspring lives to be adults. Overproduction ensures the species will continue.

Many species of insects and other animals that hatch from fertilized eggs go through a series of changes in body form to become adults. This series of changes is called **metamorphosis.** Metamorphosis is controlled by chemicals secreted by the body of the animal. There are two kinds of metamorphosis—complete and incomplete.

Most insects, including butterflies, beetles, ants, bees, moths, and flies, develop through complete metamorphosis. The four stages of development are egg, larva, pupa, and adult. A fertilized egg hatches into a worm-like larva stage. Maggots and caterpillars are larvae. The larva spends its time eating and growing before forming a cocoon and going into a resting stage called the pupa. Inside the cocoon the larva changes and develops into an adult in a process that is little understood. The cocoon eventually opens and the adult comes out.

 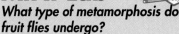
Did You Know?

The length of the thread in one silkworm cocoon would extend for ten football fields.

Figure 14-14. Butterflies and moths undergo complete metamorphosis. Crickets undergo incomplete metamorphosis.

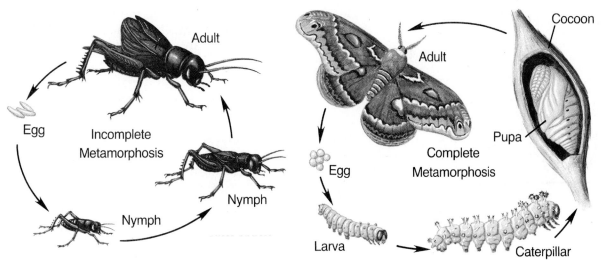

Grasshoppers, silverfish, lice, and crickets develop through incomplete metamorphosis. The three stages of development are egg, nymph, and adult. The fertilized egg hatches into a nymph that looks like a small adult, but without wings. A nymph molts several times before reaching the adult stage.

Adaptations such as an exoskeleton with wings and jointed appendages allow insects to live on land and to fly. Insects adapt to new environments rapidly because they have short life spans. Some can go through their whole life cycle in less than one month. Natural selection can take place more quickly than in organisms that take longer to reproduce. Small size allows them to live in a wide range of environments, use a small amount of food, and hide from their enemies. Many species of insect can live in the same area and not compete with one another for food.

Many people think the world would be better off without insects. They cause problems for people by eating crops, clothing, and wood in buildings. Some insects spread diseases. But it would be a serious mistake to think that we could live without them. They are also helpful to humans. They pollinate flowering plants, feed on decaying wood, and produce honey, silk, and other useful products.

SECTION REVIEW

1. What are three features of all arthropods?
2. What are the advantages and disadvantages of an exoskeleton?
3. Describe the stages in complete metamorphosis and the stages in incomplete metamorphosis.
4. **Apply:** Choose an insect you are familiar with and explain how it's adapted to its environment.

Skill Builder

☑ Concept Mapping

Make a concept map showing the events in the complete metamorphosis of an insect. Make another concept map showing the events in incomplete metamorphosis. If you need help, refer to Concept Mapping in the **Skill Handbook** on pages 688 and 689.

ACTIVITY 14-2
Observing a Crayfish

Problem: *How does a crayfish use its appendages?*

Materials

- crayfish in a small aquarium
- stirrer
- uncooked ground beef

Procedure

1. Your teacher will provide you with a crayfish in an aquarium. **CAUTION:** *Use care when working with live animals. Leave the crayfish in the aquarium while you do the activity.*
2. Touch the crayfish with the stirrer. How does the body feel?
3. Observe the crayfish move in the water. How many body regions does it have? Name the regions. Use the diagram on page 335 to help you. How many appendages does it have on each body region? What is the function of the appendages? Record your answers in a data table like the one shown.
4. Observe the compound eyes. On which body region are they located?
5. Drop a small piece of ground beef into the aquarium and observe how the crayfish eats.
6. Return the crayfish and aquarium to the place your teacher has assigned. Wash your hands.

Analyze

1. Describe the texture of the body of the crayfish.
2. How many body regions does it have?
3. How many appendages are located on each body region?
4. What structures does the crayfish use to get food?

Conclude and Apply

5. How does the location of the eyes permit the crayfish to look in different directions?
6. How does the structure of the claws aid in getting food?
7. How does the structure of the exoskeleton protect the crayfish?

Data and Observations

Body Region	Appendages	Function

14-4 Pesticides

New Science Words

pesticide
DDT

Objectives

▶ Describe the importance of pesticides in agriculture.
▶ Identify the impacts of pesticides on the environment.

Insect Pests?

What's your first reaction upon seeing an insect? Are you inclined to step on it? Most of us are! We typically view insects as pests that are better dead than walking around in our homes. Most insects are harmless. In fact, some, such as the praying mantis, are beneficial. These insects eat harmful insects. On the other hand, farmers and gardeners often find it necessary to destroy insects that damage crops and ornamental plants. In fact, many farmers could not be nearly as successful without the use of pesticides. **Pesticides** are chemicals that kill undesirable plants and insects. It is estimated that for every $3 million spent on pesticides, about $12 million is returned in additional crops. In addition, the price of pesticides has increased much more slowly than the price of other farm expenses. This makes pesticides a very smart investment for farmers.

Although pesticides are very beneficial to farmers, the environmental damage caused as a result of pesticides is believed to be about $1 billion per year! Studies show that little of the pesticide applied to crops actually reaches the target organism; often it's less than 0.01 percent! Instead, about 99 percent of the pesticide goes into the soil, water, or air. Here, it is not only the harmful insects that are killed, but most of our nation's 200 000 species of plants and animals are also affected. For example, animals that feed on the plant sap or tissue may come in contact with the pesticides. Some larger animals, including birds and mammals, may either come in direct contact with the pesticide or feed on plants and animals that have been contaminated. One study showed that the pesticide DDT accumulates in the environment and can contaminate organisms. **DDT** is a colorless, odorless pesticide that is toxic to many animals. DDT is no longer in use in the

Figure 14-15. The praying mantis is a beautiful and helpful insect.

United States. The study showed that in soil containing 10 parts per million of DDT, earthworms contained 141 parts per million of DDT, and robins that fed on those worms contained 444 parts per million in their brain tissues. It is estimated that there are about 45,000 human poisonings due to pesticides every year.

Pesticides that are sprayed over great distances, especially with airplanes, cause much pollution in the air. These vapors are easily inhaled by humans. The soil is the primary place for toxins to accumulate because pesticides often miss the target plant or drip off the plant into the soil. Although very little pesticide is applied directly to the water system, large amounts of pesticides ultimately reach rivers, lakes, and streams, due to the runoff of pesticides from agricultural fields. Human water supplies are very likely to be contaminated from such runoff.

EcoTip

Flea collars, sprays, dips, and powders often put poisons in the environment. Instead of using these items, comb your pet often with a flea comb and bathe it regularly with a nontoxic shampoo.

Figure 14-16. Planes are used to spray crops with pesticides.

SECTION REVIEW

1. Why are pesticides so important to our economy?
2. What are the current problems with pesticide application methods?

You Decide!

Our society has gained much from pesticides, but are we willing to pay for them with our health? Can some alternative solution be reached? Improved application methods may prevent some of the problem. Use of chemicals that break down easily with the help of sunlight, water, and biological action may also be an option. Even if these solutions are able to cut the current problem in half, should we still continue to use pesticides? Can we live without them?

SCIENCE & SOCIETY

14-5 Echinoderms

New Science Words

echinoderms
water-vascular system
tube feet

Objectives

▶ Identify the features of echinoderms.
▶ Describe how sea stars get and digest food.

Features of Echinoderms

Unless you live near the ocean, you may not have seen an echinoderm, but most of you know what a sea star is. Sea stars, sea urchins, sand dollars, and sea cucumbers are all echinoderms (ih KI nuh durmz). **Echinoderms** are spiny-skinned invertebrates that live on the ocean bottom. The name *echinoderm* means "spiny-skin." The spiny part refers to the spines that cover the outside of these animals. Their bodies are supported and protected by an internal skeleton made of calcium plates. The plates are covered by the thin, spiny skin.

A unique characteristic shared by all echinoderms is a water-vascular system. The **water-vascular system** is a network of water-filled canals. Thousands of tube feet are connected to this system. **Tube feet** act like strong suction cups and help the animal move, feed, get oxygen, and get rid of waste. Look at the tube feet shown in Figure 14-18. Another very obvious trait of echinoderms is their radial symmetry. The bodies of echinoderms can be divided into five sections all located around a central point. Let's look more closely at one of the most well known echinoderms, a sea star.

Figure 14-17. Sea stars and all other echinoderms have a water-vascular system that allows the animal to move, eat, get oxygen, and get rid of waste.

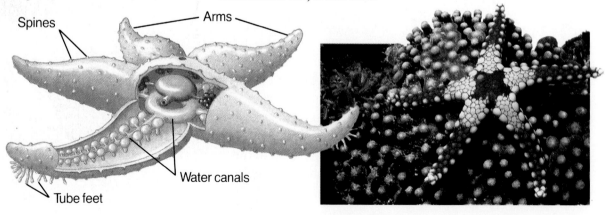

Spines
Arms
Water canals
Tube feet

Sea Stars

If you have ever pried open the shell of an oyster or a clam, you know it's not an easy job. Sea stars feed on these mollusks. Sea stars have five or more arms arranged around a central point. These arms are lined with thousands of tube feet. The sea star wraps its arms around a mollusk and uses the suction power of its tube feet to open the shell.

Figure 14-18 shows a sea star using its tube feet to open a clam. Once the shell is open slightly, the sea star turns its stomach inside out, pushes it through its mouth, and surrounds the body of the mollusk. The stomach secretes enzymes that digest the animal. Then when the meal is over, the sea star takes the stomach out of the clam shell and pulls it back inside its body.

Sea stars reproduce sexually by releasing eggs and sperm into the water. Females can produce 200 000 eggs in one season. They also reproduce asexually by regeneration. If a sea star loses an arm, it can grow a new one. If enough of the arm is lost, the arm itself can grow into a whole new sea star.

Figure 14-18. All echinoderms have tube feet.

Table 14-1

OTHER ECHINODERMS

Brittle Stars

Brittle stars are very secretive echinoderms. They live hidden under rocks or litter on the ocean floor. They move much more quickly than sea stars and drop their arms as defense when disturbed. The broken parts are quickly regrown.

Sea Urchins and Sand Dollars

Sea urchins and other sand dollars make up another class of echinoderms. Both have a skeleton made of calcium carbonate plates, and both are covered with spines. Sand dollars are very flat and covered with small, fine spines, whereas sea urchins are round and covered with longer spines.

Sea Cucumbers

Sea cucumbers are soft-bodied echinoderms with a leathery covering. They have tentacles around the mouth and rows of tube feet on the ventral, or bottom, side.

Brittle star

Sand dollar

Sea urchin

Sea cucumber

MINI-Lab

How do tube feet open clam shells?

Carry out this activity to show how sea stars can open clam shells that are held closed by muscles. Hold your arm straight out, palm up. Place a heavy book on your hand. Have your partner time how long you can hold your arm up with the book on it. If the book represents the sea star and your arm represents the clam, explain how this method of getting food works for the sea star.

Echinoderms are providing scientists with important information about how they regenerate lost parts. They are also important to the marine environment because they feed on dead organisms and help recycle materials. Many oyster and clam farmers don't find them as helpful. Sea stars feed on oysters and clams and destroy millions of dollars' worth of these organisms each year.

Scientists think that echinoderms are the most advanced group of invertebrates. They have radial symmetry like some of the less complex invertebrates, but they also have complex body systems. Another reason scientists view them as advanced is the way an echinoderm embryo develops. It develops the same way the embryos of chordates do, and not like the embryos of annelids, mollusks, and other less complex invertebrates. Humans belong to the chordate phylum which you will study in the next chapter.

Figure 14-19. A sea star using its tube feet to open an oyster.

SECTION REVIEW

1. Why are echinoderms called spiny-skinned animals?
2. What features do all echinoderms have in common?
3. How do echinoderms move and get their food?
4. **Apply:** Sea stars that wash onto the beach cannot crawl back into the water. Why?

Skill Builder

☑ Observing and Inferring

Observe the echinoderms pictured on page 343 and infer why they are slow moving and live on the ocean floor. If you need help, refer to Observing and Inferring in the **Skill Handbook** on page 682.

CHAPTER
REVIEW

14-1: Mollusks

1. Mollusks are soft-bodied invertebrates usually covered by a hard shell. Mollusks move by means of a muscular foot. All of a mollusk's body organs are located together in the visceral mass.
2. Mollusks with one shell, such as snails, are univalves. Bivalves are mollusks with two shells hinged together. Clams, and oysters are bivalves. Squid are cephalopods. A cephalopod has a foot divided into tentacles, and it has an internal shell.

14-2: Segmented Worms

1. Annelids are animals with segmented bodies. Annelids have a body cavity to hold internal organs. They have bristle-like structures called setae to help them move.
2. Earthworms have a digestive system made of a mouth, crop, gizzard, intestine, and anus. Earthworms burrow through soil, eating it as they go.
3. Both mollusks and annelid worms have a body cavity to hold body organs. They both develop from the same type of larva.

14-3: Arthropods

1. Arthropods are classified by number of body segments and appendages.

2. Arthropods are covered by an exoskeleton. The exoskeleton covers, protects, and supports the body.
3. Metamorphosis is a series of developmental stages. Complete metamorphosis has four stages: egg, larva, pupa, and adult. Incomplete metamorphosis has three stages: egg, nymph, and adult.

14-4: Science and Society: Pesticides

1. Pesticides control populations of insects that damage crops and ornamental plants. They allow farmers to produce greater amounts of crops.
2. Pesticides can build up in, and poison, animals that come in contact with them. Pesticides that are sprayed can be inhaled by humans. They can also accumulate in the soil and run off into water supplies and contaminate them.

14-5: Echinoderms

1. Echinoderms are spiny-skinned invertebrates. They all have a water-vascular system to help the animal move, feed, get oxygen, and get rid of wastes.
2. Sea stars use their tube feet to open the shells of mollusks. They push their stomach into the mollusk and use enzymes to digest the food.

KEY SCIENCE WORDS

a. **appendages**
b. **Arthropoda**
c. **closed circulatory system**
d. **crop**
e. **DDT**
f. **echinoderms**
g. **exoskeleton**
h. **gills**
i. **gizzard**
j. **mantle**
k. **metamorphosis**
l. **mollusks**
m. **molting**
n. **open circulatory system**
o. **pesticide**
p. **radula**
q. **setae**
r. **spiracles**
s. **tube feet**
t. **water-vascular system**

UNDERSTANDING VOCABULARY

Match each phrase with the correct term from the list of Key Science Words.

1. temporary food storage site
2. tongue-like organ in univalves
3. bristles earthworms use to hold on to soil
4. structure in earthworms that grinds soil
5. arms, legs, and antennae
6. outer covering made of chitin
7. shedding of the exoskeleton
8. spiny-skinned invertebrates
9. openings for air in some arthropods
10. structure that secretes the shell of mollusks

CHAPTER
REVIEW

CHECKING CONCEPTS

Choose the word or phrase that completes the sentence.

1. _____ holds the body organs of mollusks.
   a. gills   c. mantle
   b. foot   d. visceral mass

2. An example of an annelid is a(n) _____.
   a. snail   c. octopus
   b. slug   d. earthworm

3. The organism with a closed circulatory system is a(n) _____.
   a. earthworm   c. oyster
   b. snail   d. none of these

4. The largest phylum of animals are the _____.
   a. arthropods   c. annelids
   b. mollusks   d. none of these

5. Organisms with two body regions are _____.
   a. insects   c. arachnids
   b. mollusks   d. all of these

6. An example of an arthropod is _____.
   a. crab   c. scorpion
   b. fly   d. all of these

7. _____ are organisms with radial symmetry.
   a. Annelids   c. Echinoderms
   b. Mollusks   d. Arthropods

8. Echinoderms use tube feet to _____.
   a. open shells   c. get rid of wastes
   b. move   d. all of these

9. Regeneration is a means of reproduction in _____.
   a. sea stars   c. octopus
   b. snails   d. none of these

10. The most DDT would be found in _____.
    a. soil   c. a worm
    b. a bird   d. water

UNDERSTANDING CONCEPTS

Complete each sentence.

11. In mollusks, the muscular _____ is used for movement.

12. Squid and octopus are examples of _____ mollusks.

13. _____ is the main component of the exoskeleton.

14. Immature insects go through _____ to become adults.

15. Echinoderms have _____ that work like suction cups.

THINK AND WRITE CRITICALLY

16. Describe how each class of mollusks obtains food.

17. Compare the ability of clams, oysters, scallops, and squid to protect themselves.

18. Compare the life-styles of the earthworm and the leech.

19. Trace the path soil and food take through the earthworm's digestive system.

20. What evidence do scientists have that mollusks and annelids share a common ancestor?

APPLY

21. Describe the specialization of the spinnerets and swimmerets.
22. Why is it unwise to cut apart sea stars and throw the parts back into a water area which is already overpopulated with them?
23. What problems do arthropods have immediately after molting?
24. Compare the functions of simple and compound eyes of arthropods.
25. What structures do insects have that enable them to pollinate flowers?

MORE SKILL BUILDERS

If you need help, refer to the Skill Handbook.

1. **Classifying:** Group the following animals into arthropod classes: spider, pill bug, crayfish, grasshopper, crab, silverfish, cricket, sow bug, tick, scorpion, shrimp, barnacle, butterfly.
2. **Concept Mapping:** Copy and complete the map below that describes the characteristics of arthropods.

3. **Inferring:** Of what advantage is it to barnacles to live on a whale?
4. **Classifying:** The suffix *-ptera* means wings. Find out the meaning of the prefix of each insect class and give an example of a member of each group.
   DIPTERA   HOMOPTERA
   ORTHOPTERA   HEMIPTERA
   COLEOPTERA
5. **Graphing:** Make a pie graph of the species of arthropods.

Class of Arthropod	# of species
Arachnids	100 000
Crustaceans	25 000
Insects (known)	700 000

PROJECTS

1. Find out about the dance bees use to communicate to each other. Explain the dance to your class.
2. Begin an insect collection of your own. There are many good books at your local library

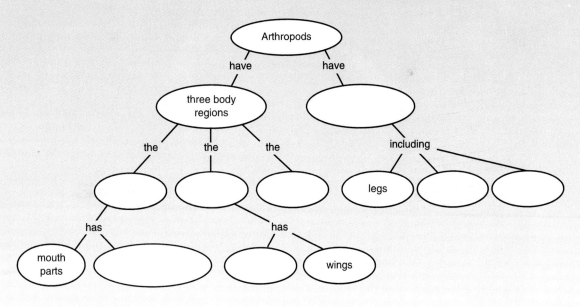

15 Cold-Blooded Vertebrates

Have you heard things about reptiles that made you wonder? For example, do snakes sting with their tongues? How can a snake swallow something as big as a rabbit? And, if snakes have no ears, how do they hear?

FIND OUT!

Do this simple activity to find out how snakes hear.

Hold a tuning fork by the stem and tap it on a wooden table. Then hold it next to your ear. What happens? Now tap it again and this time press the base of the stem hard against your chin. What do you observe? Snakes receive similar vibrations from their environment. How do you think snakes use these vibrations to find out about their environment?

Gearing Up

Previewing the Chapter

Use this outline to help you focus on important ideas in this chapter.

Section 15-1   Fish
- ▶ Vertebrate Characteristics
- ▶ What Is a Fish?
- ▶ Jawless Fish
- ▶ Cartilaginous Fish
- ▶ Bony Fish

Section 15-2   Amphibians
- ▶ What Is an Amphibian?
- ▶ Origin of Amphibians
- ▶ Frogs, Toads, and Salamanders

Section 15-3   Science and Society
Amphibian Population Decline
- ▶ Where Have All the Frogs Gone?

Section 15-4   Reptiles
- ▶ What Is a Reptile?
- ▶ Origin of Reptiles
- ▶ Modern Reptiles

Previewing Science Skills

- ▶ In the **Skill Builders,** you will outline, sequence, and make a concept map.
- ▶ In the **Activities,** you will observe, collect data, measure, infer and experiment.
- ▶ In the **MINI-Labs,** you will observe and infer, and research.

What's next?

In this chapter you will learn more about reptiles, including snakes. You will learn what they are and how they live. You will also learn about the other cold-blooded vertebrates, fish, and amphibians.

New Science Words

chordates *animals with vertabrits*
notochord *backbone*
dorsal nerve cord *bundled of nerves above*
gill slits *opening in throat behind mouth*
endoskeleton *inside skeleton*
cold-blooded *body warmth changes with environment*
warm-blooded *body temperature stays same*
fish *animals with vertabrit can live in water*
fins *fan like structures ticting octo the body used for steering*
scales *plates that cover & protect the fish*
cartilage *tough flexible tissue not bone*
predator *eats and kills another for prey*
prey *hunted by predator*

Objectives

▶ Identify the major characteristics of chordates.
▶ Explain the differences between cold-blooded animals and warm-blooded animals.
▶ Describe the characteristics that identify the three classes of fish.

Vertebrate Characteristics

Most of the groups of animals you've studied so far live in water. They are all invertebrates, and their bodies are well adapted to aquatic life. Animals with backbones, the vertebrates, can be found in almost every environment—oceans, fresh water, land, and air. How have these organisms become adapted to all these types of environments? To answer that question, let's look at some of the traits of vertebrates.

Vertebrate animals belong to the phylum Chordata (kor DAHT uh). The chordates are grouped into three subphyla, the largest being the vertebrates. The two small subphyla are made up of tunicates and lancelets, pictured in Figure 15-1. Tunicates, also called sea squirts, are sessile. They live a life very much like that of a clam or sponge. They are filter-feeders and live attached to objects in the sea. Lancelets also live in salt water and look a lot like fish. They can swim freely, but spend most of their time buried in the sand with only their heads sticking out. Lancelets are also filter-feeders.

What do sea squirts and lancelets have in common with vertebrates such as whales, bears, fish, and humans? Actually, three things: at sometime during their lives all **chordates** have a notochord, a dorsal hollow nerve cord, and gill slits. The **notochord** is a flexible, rodlike structure along the dorsal side, or back, of an animal. In vertebrates, the notochord is eventually replaced by bones that make up a backbone in the adult. A **dorsal nerve cord** is a bundle of nerves that lies above the notochord. In most vertebrates, it develops into a spinal cord

Figure 15-1. Tunicates, top, and lancelets, bottom, are both chordates.

with a brain at the front end. **Gill slits** are paired openings located in the throat behind the mouth. Gill slits develop into gills in fish. Traces of gills can be seen in human embryos.

Vertebrates are named for the column of bones called vertebrae that encloses the dorsal nerve cord. The vertebrae, skull, and the rest of the internal skeleton is called the **endoskeleton.** The endoskeleton supports and protects the internal organs and provides a place for muscles to attach.

There are seven classes of vertebrates. Five of the seven classes of vertebrates are cold-blooded. The body temperature of a **cold-blooded** animal changes with the temperature of its surroundings. **Warm-blooded** animals such as birds and mammals have a body temperature that stays the same in any environment. In this chapter, you will study the cold-blooded vertebrates—fish, amphibians, and reptiles.

What Is a Fish?

When you hear the word *fish*, the first thing that probably comes to mind is a pet goldfish, or a can of tuna in the kitchen cabinet. Actually, there are more than 30 000 different species of fish—more than all other species of vertebrates. What is a fish, and how is it adapted to its environment?

Fish are cold-blooded vertebrates that have three adaptations that allow them to live in water. These are gills, fins, and scales. All fish have gills for breathing. Gills are structures in the throat area that take oxygen from water as it passes over them. Carbon dioxide is given off to the water surrounding the gills. Second, most fish have **fins,** fanlike structures used for steering, balancing, and moving their streamlined bodies. The large tail fin moves back and forth to propel the fish through the water. Third, most fish have **scales,** hard, thin, overlapping plates that cover and protect a fish's body. Each scale grows larger as the fish grows. You can see the yearly growth rings in Figure 15-2. Like the age of some trees, the age of some fish can be estimated by counting growth rings.

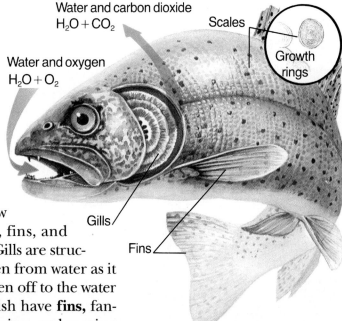

Water and carbon dioxide
$H_2O + CO_2$

Water and oxygen
$H_2O + O_2$

Scales

Growth rings

Gills

Fins

Figure 15-2. Fish have gills for taking in oxygen and scales for protection. Fins are used for steering, balancing, and moving.

Fish are divided into three classes, jawless fish, cartilaginous (kart uhl AJ uh nuhs) fish, and bony fish.

Jawless Fish

The lamprey in Figure 15-3 belongs to the class Agnatha. *Agnatha* is a Greek word that means "jawless." These jawless fish have round mouths and long tubelike bodies covered with slimy skin with no scales. Fish in this class have very flexible bodies made of cartilage. **Cartilage** is a tough, flexible tissue that is not as hard as bone. Feel your ears and the tip of your nose. These are also made of cartilage.

Hagfish live only in salt water, but many lampreys live in fresh water. Lampreys use their round mouths to attach to other fish by suction. They cut into the fish with toothlike structures and feed on its blood and body fluids. You can see the mouth of a lamprey in Figure 15-3.

Cartilaginous Fish

Sharks, skates, and rays are members of the class Chondrichthyes (kahn DRIHK thee eez). They have skeletons made of cartilage like jawless fish. Unlike jawless fish, chondrichthyes have movable jaws and scales. The scales resemble vertebrate teeth and cause their skin to feel like fine sandpaper.

The fact that sharks are predators gives them a reputation for being killers. A **predator** is an organism that kills and eats another for food. The organism that is killed and eaten is the **prey.** Unless they are provoked, few sharks will attack humans.

Shark eggs are fertilized inside the female's body. In most species, the fertilized eggs develop in the body and young are born alive.

Figure 15-3. Lampreys are jawless fish that feed on the blood and body fluids of other fish.

Did You Know?

The largest fish is the whale shark, which can be as large as 15-18 m long and weigh 15 tons.

Figure 15-4. Rays (left) and sharks (right) are members of the class Chondrichthyes.

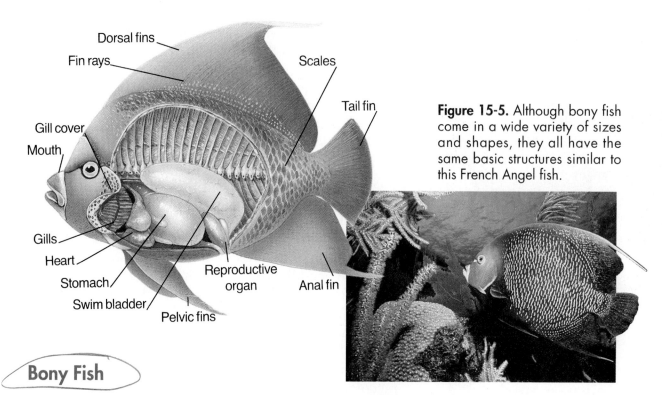

Dorsal fins

Fin rays

Scales

Tail fin

Gill cover

Mouth

Gills

Heart

Stomach

Swim bladder

Reproductive organ

Anal fin

Pelvic fins

Figure 15-5. Although bony fish come in a wide variety of sizes and shapes, they all have the same basic structures similar to this French Angel fish.

Bony Fish

Bony fish make up the class Osteichthyes (ahs tee IHK thee eez). The word *osteon* is Greek for bone, and *ichthyes* is Greek for fish. Fish that belong to this class have skeletons made of bone. About 95 percent of all species of fish belong to this class.

Floating is an important ability for fish. Most bony fish have adaptations for floating. Some float by trapping gases in a balloonlike structure called the swim bladder. By adjusting the amount of gas in the swim bladder, fish can stay at a particular depth in the water with little effort. Find the swim bladder in Figure 15-5.

The body structure of bony fish, a French angel fish, is shown in Figure 15-5. The gills are covered and protected by a bony flap called the gill cover. Gill covers aid the fish in breathing. They open and close, moving the water taken in through the mouth over the gills.

Most kinds of bony fish have separate males and females. The females release large numbers of eggs into the water in a behavior called spawning. Males then swim over the eggs and release sperm. The joining of egg and sperm cells outside the female body is called external fertilization.

Scientists who specialize in studying fish have divided the bony fish into three groups: lobe-finned fish, lungfish, and ray-finned fish. Most fish are ray-finned fish.

MINI-Lab

How does a fish adjust to depths?

Fill a balloon with air. Place it in a bowl of water. What happens? What structure does the balloon represent? Compare where in the water (surface, deep) a fish would be as this structure is being filled with air.

Figure 15-6. Fish are food for many animals.

Science and READING

Imagine you have just opened a fish market in your hometown. What different species will you offer, where will you get them, and what facts do you need to know about them?

Ray-finned fish have fins made of long, thin bones covered with skin. Yellow perch, tuna, salmon, swordfish, and eels are all ray-finned fish.

Lungfish have both gills and lungs for breathing. This adaptation allows many to live in shallow waters that dry up in summer. When the water evaporates, lungfish burrow into the mud and cover themselves with mucus until water returns. Lungfish are found in South America, Australia, and Africa.

The lobe-finned fish have fins that are lobe-like and fleshy. It was thought that these organisms had been extinct for more than 70 million years. But in 1938 one was caught in a net by some South African fishermen. Several living lobe-finned fish have been studied since. Scientists observed these fish using their lobed fins to swim in a way similar to the way land vertebrates walk. Lobe-finned fish are important because scientists think these fish are the ancestors of the first land vertebrates.

Fish are an important food source for animals such as raccoons, bears, and sea birds. They are also an important food source for humans. Some researchers think fish oils protect blood vessels from fat deposits that lead to heart disease. Because fish feed on insects such as mosquitoes, they help to control these populations that are pesty or dangerous. Some species of fish feed on plants that clog waterways. This helps keep them clear for boat traffic.

SECTION REVIEW

1. What are three characteristics of chordates?
2. What is the function of the endoskeleton in vertebrates?
3. Explain the differences between cold-blooded animals and warm-blooded animals.
4. What are the major characteristics of each of the three fish classes?
5. **Apply:** Female fish lay thousands of eggs. Why are the waters not overcrowded with fish?

Skill Builder

☑ Outlining

Outline the characteristics of chordates, vertebrates, and fish. If you need help, refer to Outlining in the **Skill Handbook** on page 681.

ACTIVITY 15-1
Effects of Water Temperature on Fish

Problem: *How does water temperature affect fish?*

Materials

- goldfish or guppy
- aquarium water
- small fishnet
- 600-mL beaker
- stirring rod
- thermometer
- container of ice water

Procedure

1. Fill the 600-mL beaker about one-half full of aquarium water.
2. Use the fishnet and transfer one fish from the aquarium to the beaker. **CAUTION:** *Use extreme care when handling live animals.*
3. With the thermometer, measure the temperature of the water in the beaker. Record the water temperature in the first column of your data table.
4. Locate the gill covers of the fish. Observe how the gill covers open and close. The breathing rate of a fish can be determined by counting the number of times the fish opens and closes its gill covers.
5. Observe how the fish moves in the beaker.
6. Count the number of times the fish opens its gill covers in one minute. Record this number in your data table.
7. Repeat Step 6 three more times recording your results as trials 2, 3, and 4.
8. Hypothesize how the breathing rate of the fish and the movements of the fish will be affected by cooling the temperature of the water. Record your hypothesis.
9. Place the beaker in a container of ice water. Allow the water in the beaker to cool to approximately 10°C. Use a stirring rod and gently stir the water in the beaker. **CAUTION:** *Stir with care so that you will not injure the fish.*
10. Record the water temperature in the second column of your data table.
11. Repeat Step 6 three more times and recording your results as trials 2, 3, and 4.
12. Return the fish to the aquarium.

Data and Observations

Trial	Water Temperature ____ °C Gill Openings	Water Temperature ____ °C Gill Openings
1		
2		
3		
4		
Total		
Average		
Fish Movements		

Analyze

1. Calculate the average number of times the gill covers open for each water temperature. Record the numbers in the data table.
2. Were there more or fewer gill openings in cold water?
3. What is the variable in this experiment?

Conclude and Apply

4. Predict what would happen if the water temperature increased.
5. Do the results of this experiment support your hypothesis? Explain.
6. How does water temperature affect the breathing rate of a fish and the movements of a fish?

15-2 Amphibians

New Science Words

amphibians *cold-blooded vertebrates live in water on land*
hibernation *sleeping all winter*
estivation *sleeping all summer*

Objectives

▶ Describe the adaptations that amphibians have for living in water and living on land.
▶ Identify the three kinds of amphibians and describe the characteristics of each.
▶ Describe the metamorphosis of a frog.

What Is an Amphibian?

The word *amphibian* comes from the Greek word *amphibios,* which means "double life." They are well named for **amphibians** are cold-blooded vertebrates that spend part of their life in water and part on land. Frogs, toads, and salamanders are amphibians. What adaptations do these animals have that allow them to live both on land and in water? Amphibians have moist, smooth, thin skin without scales. This allows them to breathe through their skin. Oxygen and carbon dioxide are exchanged through the skin and the lining of the mouth. Amphibians also have very small, simple, saclike lungs in the chest cavity to use for breathing.

Because amphibians are cold-blooded, their body temperatures change when the temperature of their surroundings changes. Did you ever wonder how frogs and toads survive cold winters in the northern states? Amphibians have adaptations that protect them from very cold and very warm temperatures. During the cold winter months they become inactive. They bury themselves in mud or leaves until the temperature warms up. The period of inactivity in the winter is called **hibernation.** Inactivity during the hot, dry summer months is called **estivation.**

Another adaptation amphibians have to life on land is a strong skeleton. Organisms living in water are supported by the water. However, on land a strong structure is needed to support the body.

Because their eggs lack shells and must be kept moist, most species of amphibians return to water to lay their eggs. The eggs hatch into larvae that live in water until they become adults and move to land.

Figure 15-7. Salamanders, top, and frogs, bottom, are both types of amphibians.

Origin of Amphibians

The fossil record shows that fish were the first vertebrates on Earth. For about 150 million years they were the only vertebrates. Then as competition for food and space increased, the lobe-finned fish may have easily traveled across land searching for deeper water. The lobe-finned fish had lungs and bony fins that could have supported their weight on land. Amphibians are thought to have evolved from the lobe-finned fish about 350 million years ago.

Evolution favored the development of amphibians because there wasn't much competition on land. Almost free of predators, land provided a great supply of food in the form of insects, spiders, and other invertebrates. Amphibians were able to reproduce in large numbers, and many new species evolved. For 100 million years or more, amphibians were the dominant land animals.

Frogs, Toads, and Salamanders

Frogs and toads are amphibians that have short, broad bodies with no neck, no tail, and four legs. The strong hind legs are longer than the front and are used for swimming and jumping. Bulging eyes and nostrils on top of the head let them see and breathe while almost totally submerged in water. On spring nights, they make their presence known with loud, distinctive sounds.

Figure 15-9 shows the external body structures of a frog. A frog's tongue is attached to the front of its mouth. When a frog sees an insect, it flips the loose end of its tongue out and the insect gets stuck in the sticky saliva on the tongue. Then the frog flips its catch back into its mouth. Frogs have round membranes called tympanic membranes on each side of the head just behind the eyes for hearing.

Toads live in drier environments than frogs. They have thick, rough skin that keeps them from drying out. Both frogs and toads return to the water to lay eggs.

Figure 15-8. The American Toad is a typical amphibian.

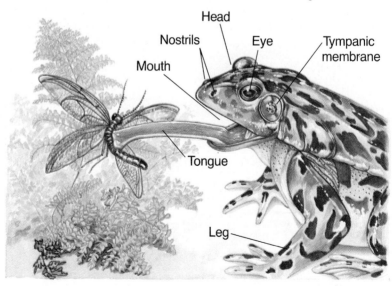

Figure 15-9. The external body structures of a frog.

Head

Nostrils

Eye

Tympanic membrane

Mouth

Tongue

Leg

MINI-Lab

How many types of amphibians are there?

Become an expert on amphibians. Research frogs, toads, or salamanders. Choose one species that interests you, and write a short report detailing all the organism's most unusual characteristics. Be sure to include color, habitat, size, and location. Present your report to the class.

Figure 15-10. Frogs undergo a series of changes from egg to adult.

Recall that metamorphosis is a series of changes that a larva goes through to become an adult. Most frogs and toads have a two-stage life cycle, a larva that lives in water and an adult that lives on land. Figure 15-10 shows the metamorphosis of a leopard frog.

The rate at which amphibians grow and the length of time they spend as larvae depend on the species, the water temperature, and the food available. The less food and the cooler the temperature, the longer it takes for metamorphosis. Bullfrogs may not go through metamorphosis for a year or more after hatching, whereas spadefoot toads change into adults in about two weeks.

Salamanders are amphibians often mistaken for lizards because of their long, slender bodies. They have smooth, moist skin and short legs. They rest under dead leaves and rocks during the day to avoid the drying heat of the sun. At night they come out and use their well-developed senses of smell and vision to feed on worms, crustaceans, and insects.

Amphibians are unique animals in many ways. Their adaptations allow them to live very successfully both on land and in water. The complete transition to life on land did not occur until the reptiles appeared. You will learn about reptiles in the next section.

Young legless tadpoles live off yolk stored in their bodies.

Fertilized eggs

Tadpoles with legs feed on plants in the water.

Young frog with structures needed for life on land.

Adult frog

PROBLEM SOLVING

Marsupial Frogs

Most frogs deposit their eggs in water where the eggs hatch into fishlike tadpoles. The tadpoles exchange gases and get nutrients in the water environment. Over a period of time, the tadpoles develop into adult frogs.

Researchers studying tree frogs in tropical rain forests have found that some species reproduce using a special pouch. Because of the pouch, they call these marsupial frogs.

The female marsupial frog lays eggs, and the male frog maneuvers the eggs one-by-one into a pouch on her back. The eggs are fertilized by sperm the male frog has deposited on the female's back.

The eggs are enclosed in a fluid-filled pouch lined with many blood vessels. In the pouch, the eggs undergo metamorphosis. The researchers think the tadpoles exchange gases, fluids, nutrients, and wastes with the female but get most of the nutrients they need from the yolk of the egg.

After development is complete, the female uses her toes to open the pouch and release the small frogs.

Think Critically: How is reproduction in marsupial frogs similar to that of other amphibians?

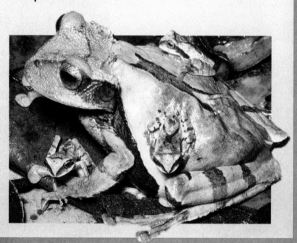

SECTION REVIEW

1. List three characteristics of amphibians for living in water and three characteristics for living on land.
2. Describe the three kinds of amphibians.
3. Describe how a tadpole is different from a frog.
4. **Apply:** Years ago many people thought that it rained frogs and toads because many appeared after a rain. What is a better explanation for the appearance of frogs and toads after a rain?

⊠ Sequencing

Sequence and describe each stage of frog metamorphosis. If you need help, refer to Sequencing in the **Skill Handbook** on page 680.

Skill Builder

15-3 Amphibian Population Decline

New Science Words

clear-cut *completly removed of trees*
biological indicators
species that reflect the condition of the environment

Objectives

▶ State three possible reasons for the recent decline in amphibian populations.
▶ Explain why amphibians are likely to be affected by pollution.

Where Have All the Frogs Gone?

Where have all the amphibians gone? That's what scientists all over the world are wondering. They have noticed a decline in the populations of toads, frogs, and salamanders in places like the United States, Costa Rica, Japan, and Australia. Yosemite toads, leopard frogs, and chorus frogs are a few of the many species of amphibians now in danger of becoming extinct.

What's causing this decline of amphibians? In 1990, a meeting of 40 scientists was called by the National Academy of Science to discuss the problem. A variety of possible factors was suggested.

Some scientists think that the changes people have made in our environment are responsible for this disappearing act. Destruction of native habitats is likely to be a contributing factor. Amphibians typically require moist habitats to breed. With the continual expansion of urban areas, drainage of wetlands, and with deforestation, suitable breeding areas for many types of amphibians are becoming very limited. In the northwestern United States where thousands of acres of forest have been **clear-cut,** completely removed of trees, scientists have reported noticeably fewer frogs than in unlogged areas.

Figure 15-11. Many amphibian habitats are being lost due to the clear-cutting of forests.

Industry and automobiles contribute to acid rain and snow, which can kill forests as well as salamander eggs. Other possible causes of amphibian extinction include pesticides and the introduction of amphibian-eating game fish to new locations. In addition, countries like Indonesia, India, and Malaysia provide huge amounts of frog legs to satisfy the appetites of many people. Although drought may be a natural cause of this loss of amphibians, people may be playing a major role.

Because of the way amphibians live, it makes sense that they would be very sensitive to pollutants in our environment. They live mostly in water or in damp soil. They have no scales or shells for protection. And because their skin absorbs oxygen, poisonous gases and chemicals can also be absorbed. For this reason amphibians are considered **biological indicators**—species that reflect the condition of the environment.

What can be done? Amphibians are the source of food for many birds mammals, fish, and reptiles. They also feed on many insects and other invertebrates. Will enough species be able to survive to prevent a disturbance in the world's food chain?

Pacific tree frog

Barred tiger salamander

Figure 15-12. Many species of frogs and salamanders are endangered by human activities.

SECTION REVIEW

1. What two current environmental problems may be contributing to the decline in amphibian populations?
2. Why are amphibians more likely to be affected by acid rain than reptiles, which also often live in the water?

You Decide!

SCIENCE & SOCIETY

Many environmentalists believe that the clear-cutting of forests in the northwestern United States is too destructive to be continued. Some scientists have found half the number of amphibians in logged areas as compared to unlogged areas. However, many people depend on logging to support their families. Without the logging industry, the economy of many areas would be ruined. What do you think the answer to this problem is?

ACTIVITY 15-2
Metamorphosis in Frogs

Problem: *How long does it take for a tadpole to develop into a frog?*

Materials

- 4-L aquarium or jar
- frog egg masses
- lake or pond water
- stereoscopic microscope
- watch glass
- small fishnet
- aquatic plants
- washed gravel
- boiled lettuce

Procedure

1. Collect a mass of frog eggs and 4 L of water from a lake or pond.
2. Prepare an aquarium with gravel, the pond water, and five or six aquatic plants.
3. Place the egg mass in the aquarium. Use the fishnet to obtain a few eggs and place the eggs in a watch glass. The eggs should have the dark side up and the white yolk down. **CAUTION:** *Handle the eggs with care.*
4. Observe the eggs and record your observations in the data table.
5. Examine the eggs twice each week and record any changes that you observe.
6. When the tadpoles hatch, observe the stages of development twice a week. Identify the fin on the back, mouth, eyes, gill cover, gills, nostrils, hind and front legs. Feed the tadpoles boiled lettuce. Observe how they feed.

Analyze

1. How long does it take for the eggs to hatch?
2. How long does it take for a tadpole to develop legs?
3. What organs do tadpoles have for breathing?
4. Which pair of legs appears first?

Conclude and Apply

5. What is the function of the jellylike coating around the eggs?
6. How do the eyes of the young tadpoles differ from the eyes of the older ones?
7. Why are plants needed in the aquarium?
8. Are tadpoles plant-eaters or meat-eaters?
9. How long does it take for a tadpole to develop into a frog?

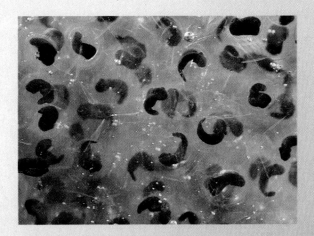

Data and Observations

Date	Observations

Reptiles

Objectives

▶ Identify the adaptations that enable reptiles to live on land.
▶ Infer why the early reptiles were so successful.
▶ Describe the characteristics of the modern reptiles.

New Science Words

reptile
amniote egg

What Is a Reptile?

The class Reptilia includes lizards, snakes, turtles, crocodiles, and alligators. They have many characteristics that are adaptations for life on land. A thick, dry, waterproof skin covered with scales prevents drying out and injury. With the exception of snakes, reptiles have four legs with claws that hold the body off the ground for moving quickly. The claws are used to dig, climb, and run.

Remember from the last section that even though amphibians live on land, they still need water for respiration and reproduction. Scientists hypothesize that, over time, some amphibians became less dependent on water and became the ancestors of reptiles. A **reptile** can be described as a cold-blooded vertebrate with a dry, scaly skin that lays eggs covered with a leathery shell.

Reptiles vary greatly in size, shape, and color. There are giant pythons longer than 10 meters that can swallow crocodiles whole. Some sea turtles have a mass of more than 0.9 metric tons and can swim faster than you can run. Three-horned lizards have movable eye sockets and tongues as long as their bodies. Reptiles live on every continent except Antarctica and in all the oceans except those in the polar regions.

Reptiles breathe with lungs. Even turtles that live in water must come to the surface to breathe air. A reptile's heart has three chambers. The lower chamber is partially divided. This keeps oxygen-rich blood coming from the lungs separated from the blood containing carbon dioxide returning from the body. This type of circulatory system provides a lot of oxygen to all parts of the body. Remember that oxygen is needed to produce energy by cell respiration.

Figure 15-13. A three-horned lizard, top, and an Eastern box turtle, bottom, are both reptiles.

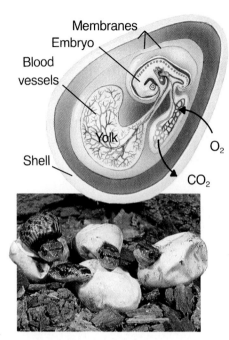

Membranes
Embryo
Blood vessels
Shell
Yolk
O_2
CO_2

Figure 15-14. The amniote egg, top, is one of the adaptations reptiles have for living on land. Young reptiles hatch from their eggs fully developed.

Science and WRITING

There is no one convincing answer that explains the disappearance of the dinosaurs from Earth. Research this subject and choose the theory you most agree with. Write a report explaining the theory and why you agree with it.

One of the most important adaptations of reptiles for living on land is the way they reproduce. Unlike the eggs of fish and amphibians, eggs of reptiles are fertilized internally, inside the body of the female. After fertilization, the female secretes a leathery shell around each egg, and then lays the eggs on land.

Figure 15-14 shows the structures in a reptile egg. The egg provides a complete environment for the embryo to develop in. This type of egg, called an **amniote egg,** contains membranes to protect and cushion the embryo, and to help it get rid of wastes. It also contains a large food supply, the yolk, for the embryo to use as it develops. Small holes in the shell, called pores, allow oxygen and carbon dioxide to be exchanged. By the time it hatches, a young reptile looks like a small adult.

Have you ever been hiking and seen the dry outer layer of skin a snake has left behind? Many snakes and other reptiles molt from time to time, depending on how fast they grow. The skin is a good source of protein so they often eat it after molting.

Origin of Reptiles

Reptiles evolved slowly over a period of millions of years, and during the Mesozoic Era they came to be rulers of Earth. The Mesozoic Era, which lasted over 160 million years, is known as the Age of the Reptiles. Many species emerged from the earliest reptiles called cotylosaurs (KAHD uh luh sahrs). As their numbers increased, some returned to the water to find a place to live. Others protected themselves with large, heavy, scale-like plates and speed. At least two species of flying reptiles developed.

The ancient reptiles were very successful. Why, then, did they die off? Scientists have developed many theories to explain their disappearance. One is that the climate cooled toward the end of the Cretaceous Period and it became too cold for the dinosaurs. They were too large to hibernate and had no body covering for protection. Another theory is that the explosion of a nearby star gave off dangerous radiation and caused cold, unfavorable weather for thousands of years. There are several other theories to explain the disappearance of dinosaurs. Many scientists suggest that no one theory completely explains why the dinosaurs died.

Modern Reptiles

Modern reptiles probably descended from similar amphibian ancestors. Today there are three orders of reptiles: turtles; crocodiles and alligators; lizards and snakes.

Table 15-1

ORDERS OF MODERN REPTILES

Turtles

Turtles make up a very successful order of animals. They can be found on almost every continent and in most of the world's oceans. The body of a turtle is covered by a hard shell on both top and bottom. Most turtles can withdraw into their shell for protection. Turtles have no teeth and use their beaks to feed on insects, worms, fish, and plants.

Painted Turtle

Green Turtle

Loggerhead Turtle

Johnston's Crocodile

American Alligator

Speckled Caiman

Crocodiles and Alligators

Crocodiles and alligators are among the world's largest living reptiles. They make up the order Crocodilia. Members of this order can be found in or near water in tropical climates. Crocodiles have long slender snouts and are very aggressive. They can attack animals as large as cattle. Alligators are less aggressive. They have broad snouts and feed on fish, turtles, and waterbirds.

Lizards and Snakes

Lizards and snakes make up the largest group of reptiles. Lizards have moveable eyelids, external ears, and legs with clawed toes on each foot. They feed on reptiles, insects, spiders, worms, and mammals. Snakes don't have legs, eyelids, or external ears. Snakes are meat-eaters. Some snakes wrap around and constrict their prey. Others inject their prey with poison venom. Many snakes feed on rodents and help control their populations.

Rough Green Snake

Land Iguana

Madagascar Day Gecko

Snake Oil Medicines

Scientists are finding potential medicines in unusual places. Ancrod, an ingredient in the venom of Malayan pit vipers, may help human stroke victims. Ancrod is a substance that stops blood from clotting. The victim of the pit viper dies from the large dose of ancrod it receives. In the correct doses, ancrod can prevent the damage of strokes caused by blood clots that block blood vessels in the brain of a human.

The snake venom is collected from the snakes by pressing their upper jaw against the top of a container. This causes the venom to drip from the snake's fangs.

Think Critically: About how long after a stroke would this treatment need to be tried to be successful?

SECTION REVIEW

1. What adaptations do reptiles have for living on land?
2. Describe the ancient reptiles.
3. How are turtles different from the other groups of reptiles?
4. Explain how snakes are different from lizards.
5. **Apply:** The poisonous coral snakes in the United States have bright red, yellow, and black colors. Some harmless snakes have similar colors. How is this an advantage to the nonpoisonous snakes?

Skill Builder

⊠ Concept Mapping

Make a concept map showing the major characteristics and orders of the reptile class. If you need help, refer to Concept Mapping in the **Skill Handbook** on pages 688 and 689.

SUMMARY

15-1: Fish

1. The phylum Chordata includes lancelets, tunicates, and vertebrates: all have a notochord, dorsal nerve cord, and gill slits.

2. Warm-blooded animals maintain a constant body temperature. The body temperature of a cold-blooded animal changes with its environment.

3. Classes of fish include jawless fish, cartilaginous fish, and bony fish.

15-2: Amphibians

1. Amphibians are cold-blooded vertebrates that live both in water and on land. The adaptations of amphibians include moist skin, mucus glands, and lungs.

2. Frogs live in wet areas, have jumping legs, and sensory organs. Toads live in drier areas and have hopping legs. Salamanders have smooth, moist skin and short legs.

3. Frogs go through metamorphosis from egg, to tadpole, to adult. Legs develop, lungs replace gills, and the tail is lost.

15-3: Science and Society: Amphibian Population Decline

1. Amphibian populations are declining due to habitat destruction, acid rain, pesticides, and predation.

2. Amphibians are sensitive to pollution because they have no scales or shells for protection. They also absorb materials through their skin, including pollutants.

15-4: Reptiles

1. Reptiles are true land animals having dry, scaly skin and lay amniote eggs with a leathery shell.

2. Early reptiles were successful because of their adaptations to living on land.

3. Reptile groups include turtles with tough shells, meat-eating crocodiles and alligators, and the largest group including snakes and lizards.

KEY SCIENCE WORDS

a. **amniote egg**
b. **amphibians**
c. **biological indicators**
d. **cartilage**
e. **chordates**
f. **clear-cut**
g. **cold-blooded**
h. **dorsal nerve cord**
i. **endoskeleton**
j. **estivation**
k. **fins**
l. **fish**
m. **gill slits**
n. **hibernation**
o. **notochord**
p. **predator**
q. **prey**
r. **reptile**
s. **scales**
t. **warm-blooded**

UNDERSTANDING VOCABULARY

Match each phrase with the correct term from the list of Key Science Words.

1. dorsal structure that becomes the backbone
2. cold-blooded land and water animals
3. the internal skeleton
4. tough, flexible tissue
5. organism that kills others for food
6. inactivity in winter
7. inactivity in summer
8. cold-blooded organisms with dry skin
9. fanlike steering structures in fish
10. area completely removed of trees

REVIEW

CHECKING CONCEPTS

Choose the word or phrase that completes the sentence.

1. Fish have _____.
   a. gills   c. scales
   b. fins   d. all of these
2. _____ fish do not have scales.
   a. bony   c. cartilaginous
   b. jawless   d. none of these
3. An example of a cartilaginous fish is a _____.
   a. hagfish   c. perch
   b. lamprey   d. shark
4. Most fish species belong to the _____ group.
   a. osteichthyes   c. cartilaginous
   b. jawless   d. chondrichthyes
5. A fish with both gills and lungs is a _____.
   a. shark   c. lungfish
   b. ray   d. perch
6. The group of vertebrates with lungs and moist skin is _____.
   a. amphibians   c. reptiles
   b. fish   d. all of these
7. A _____ is *not* a reptile.
   a. lizard   c. snake
   b. turtle   d. salamander
8. The largest group of reptiles includes lizards and _____.
   a. snakes   c. crocodiles
   b. turtles   d. alligators
9. Reptiles lay _____ eggs.
   a. amniote   c. jelly-like
   b. brown   d. hard-shelled
10. At some time in their lives, all chordates have a _____.
   a. notochord   c. gill slits
   b. dorsal nerve cord d. all of these

UNDERSTANDING CONCEPTS

Complete each sentence.

11. The _____ develops into the spinal cord in most vertebrates.
12. Animals whose body temperature is constant are _____.
13. Sharks and rays have skeletons made of _____.
14. The earliest reptiles were called _____.
15. A reptile's heart has _____ chambers.

THINK AND WRITE CRITICALLY

16. Describe the structural adaptations that allow fish to live in water.
17. Describe how lamprey and hagfish obtain food.
18. Describe three adaptations of amphibians to life on land.
19. Compare and contrast the adaptations of amphibians and reptiles to life on land.
20. Describe the life cycle of a frog.

APPLY

21. Why do you think there are fewer species of amphibians on Earth than any other type of vertebrate?
22. What is the advantage of the amniotic egg over the eggs laid by amphibians?
23. Why are amphibians considered biological indicators?
24. In what ways are tunicates similar to sponges?
25. What features are common to all vertebrates?

MORE SKILL BUILDERS

If you need help, refer to the Skill Handbook.

1. **Sequencing:** Sequence the order in which these structures appeared in evolutionary history and explain what type of organism had this adaptation and why: skin has mucus glands; skin has scales; fins used for movement; dry, scaly skin
2. **Concept Mapping:** Complete the concept map below describing the chordates.

3. **Comparing and Contrasting:** Make a chart comparing the features of fish, amphibians, and reptiles.
4. **Designing an Experiment:** Design an experiment to find out the effect of water temperature on frog egg development.
5. **Graphing:** Make a pie graph of the species of fish.

Classes of Fish	# of Species
Jawless Fish	45 species
Chondrichthyes	275 species
Osteichthyes	25 000 species

PROJECTS

1. Check the local library or nature center and find out what kinds of amphibians and reptiles are common in your area.
2. Study the tropical rain forests' amphibians. What special adaptations do they have for life there? Bring in pictures to share with the class.

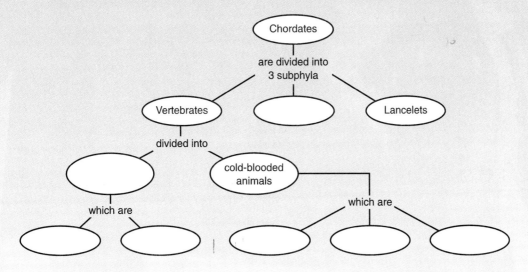

16 Warm-Blooded Animals

Have you ever watched birds eat from a feeder? If you have, you know that they eat one seed after another without stopping. Birds don't chew their food before swallowing, as you do. They don't have teeth, but they do have a muscular grinding sac called a gizzard. How does the gizzard work?

FIND OUT!

Do this simple activity to find out how a bird's gizzard works.

Place some cracked corn, birdseed, sunflower seeds, nuts, and some gravel in a mortar. Use a pestle to grind the seeds. What do the seeds look like now? A bird's gizzard works in much the same way. The gizzard has no teeth, but contains gravel to crush the food. How does the gizzard help in digestion?

Gearing Up

Previewing the Chapter

Use this outline to help you focus on important ideas in this chapter.

Section 16-1   Birds
- ▶ Characteristics of Birds
- ▶ Kinds of Birds
- ▶ Origin and Importance of Birds

Section 16-2   Mammals
- ▶ Characteristics of Mammals
- ▶ Kinds of Mammals
- ▶ Origin and Importance of Mammals

Section 16-3   Science and Society
Saving the Manatee
- ▶ "Sea Cows"?!
- ▶ The Future of Manatees

Previewing Science Skills
- ▶ In the **Skill Builders,** you will compare and contrast, and classify.
- ▶ In the **Activities,** you will observe, experiment, infer and classify.
- ▶ In the **MINI-Labs,** you will observe and infer.

What's next?

In this chapter, you'll learn more about birds. You'll learn how they've adapted for flight and how they live. You'll also learn about mammals, the class to which you belong. You will learn how mammals are classified and how they live.

16-1 Birds

New Science Words

incubate
contour feathers
down feathers
preening

Objectives

▶ Identify the characteristics of birds.
▶ Identify the adaptations birds have for flight.
▶ Explain how birds reproduce and develop.

Characteristics of Birds

There probably isn't a day that goes by in which you don't see a bird. Birds are found on rooftops, backyards, city streets, and in farmers' fields. What are the characteristics that make a bird a bird? First, unlike cold-blooded reptiles and amphibians, birds are warm-blooded. Warm-blooded organisms maintain a constant body temperature. A bird's body temperature is about 40°C. You are warm-blooded also and maintain a body temperature of 37°C.

Second, all birds are covered with feathers. They are the only members of the animal kingdom that have feathers. A third characteristic shared by all birds is they lay eggs enclosed in a hard shell. The parents keep the eggs warm, or **incubate** them, until they hatch. Fourth, the front legs of all birds are modified into wings. The two hind legs support the body and usually have claws.

People have always been fascinated by the ability of birds to fly. Now that you know the major characteristics of birds, let's look at the adaptations birds have for flight.

Adaptations for Flight

Flight requires a light, yet strong skeleton, wings, and feathers to help lift the bird off the ground. Keen senses, especially eyesight, and tremendous amounts of energy are also needed for flight.

A bird's body is covered with two types of feathers, contour feathers and down feathers. Strong, lightweight **contour feathers** give birds their coloring and smooth, sleek shape. These are the feathers birds use to fly. The long contour feathers on the wings and tail help the bird steer and keep from tipping over. Have you ever watched ducks swimming in a pond on a freezing cold day, and

Figure 16-1. Birds are the only organisms with feathers. Most birds incubate their eggs until they hatch.

Science and WRITING

Form a group in your class to develop a bird-feeding plan for your area of the country. Determine which species you should be feeding. What kind of feeders, locations, and food will these birds need?

wondered how they keep warm? Soft, fluffy **down feathers** provide an insulating layer next to the skin of adult birds and cover the bodies of young birds. Feathers help birds maintain their constant body temperature. They grow in much the same way as your hair grows. The base of each feather shaft is rooted in a tiny follicle and receives nutrients from the blood. When it is fully grown, the feather either falls off or is pushed out by a new feather. As you can see in Figure 16-2, the shaft of the feather has two vanes, each with many branches called barbs. Each barb has many cross braches that give the feather strength.

To care for its feathers, a bird has an oil gland located just above the base of its tail. Using its beak, the bird rubs oil from the gland over its feathers in a process called **preening.** The oil conditions the feathers and helps make them water repellent.

A bird sheds its feathers just as a reptile sheds its skin. Whereas a reptile sheds its skin all at once, a bird sheds and replaces its feathers a few at a time. The shedding of old feathers accompanied by the growth of new ones is called molting.

Flight requires that a bird have very sharp vision and hearing. Keen vision is necessary for taking off, landing, and hunting. For example, at night an owl can see a mouse on the forest floor from high in the branches of a tree. Acute hearing helps some species of bird locate prey, and it allows all birds to sense danger. Some of the adaptations birds have for flight can't be seen, because they are internal. One of these is a bird's skeleton. Many of the bones in a bird's skeleton are fused for extra strength and more stability for flight. To make a bird lighter, most of its bones

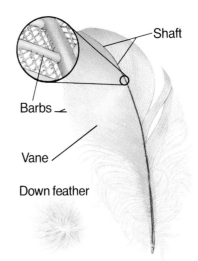

Shaft

Barbs

Vane

Down feather

Contour feather

Figure 16-2. Preening conditions feathers and helps make them waterproof.

Figure 16-3. Keen vision allows some birds to locate prey from a long distance.

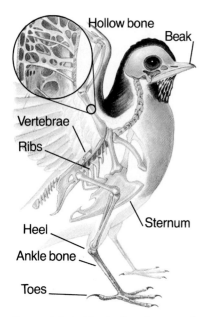

Hollow bone

Beak

Vertebrae

Ribs

Heel

Ankle bone

Toes

Sternum

Figure 16-4. The hollow bones of birds are an adaptation for flight.

are hollow with thin cross braces of bone inside for strength and support. The hollow spaces are filled with air. Why do you think it's important for a bird to have a light skeleton?

You can see the skeleton of a bird in Figure 16-4. Notice the sternum, or breastbone, supports the large chest muscles. The last bones of the spine support the tail feathers, which play an important part in steering and balancing during flight and landing.

Of course, one of the most important adaptations birds have for flight is wings. All birds have wings, even birds that don't fly such as ostriches and penguins. In flying birds, wings are attached to powerful chest muscles. Wings are curved on top and flat or slightly curved on the bottom. The shape gives the bird lift to get off the ground.

Wings also serve important functions for birds that don't fly. Penguins use their wings to swim under water. While running or walking, ostriches and rheas balance with their wings.

Figure 16-5. Flightless birds use their wings for other purposes. Ostriches (left) use their wings for balance, and penguins (right) use them for swimming.

Digestion and Respiration

Birds get the energy to fly from the food they eat. Because flying requires large amounts of energy, birds need to eat large amounts of food. An efficient digestive system breaks down the food quickly to supply birds with the energy they need. Whereas it takes us as long as a day to digest the food we eat, some birds can digest food in less than an hour.

You learned about part of a bird's digestive process in the Find Out activity at the beginning of this chapter. Food first passes from the mouth into the crop, where it is moistened and stored. From there, it moves into the first part of the stomach, where it is partially digested. Then it moves into the gizzard. Small stones and grit in the gizzard grind and crush seeds and other foods. Food then passes into the small intestine, where the rest of digestion occurs. Finally, nutrients are absorbed by the bloodstream.

Birds also need energy to maintain body temperature. Body heat is generated from the energy in food. Oxygen is needed to convert food to energy. To obtain oxygen, birds have an efficient respiratory system. As you can see in Figure 16-6, birds have two lungs with balloonlike air sacs attached to each one. The air sacs spread into different parts of the body, including the hollow bones. These air sacs increase the amount of oxygen a bird can take in. Having these air sacs spread throughout the body also makes a bird lighter.

Birds have a heart with four chambers. Blood with oxygen is kept separate from blood without oxygen. Blood is circulated very quickly because birds have a rapid heartbeat rate. The hearts of some birds can beat almost 1000 times in a minute.

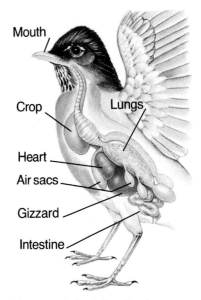

Figure 16-6. A bird's digestive system processes large amounts of food needed for energy. A bird's respiratory system allows a bird to take in a large quantities of oxygen.

Reproduction and Development

If you've ever cooked scrambled eggs, you are familiar with a bird's egg. Like reptiles, birds reproduce by laying an amniote egg with a shell. Remember that an amniote egg provides a complete environment for a developing embryo. Fertilization is internal, and the shell is formed around the fertilized egg. Bird eggs have the same membranes to protect and nourish the embryo as reptile eggs. Unlike a reptile's egg though, a bird's egg has a hard shell made of calcium carbonate, the same chemical that makes up seashells, limestone, and marble. Birds also usually stay with their eggs to incubate them, and they care for their young.

The female bird usually lays eggs in a nest. Most birds lay from two to eight eggs at one time. All the eggs laid at one time are called a clutch. The length of time the eggs must be incubated varies with the species and the size of the species.

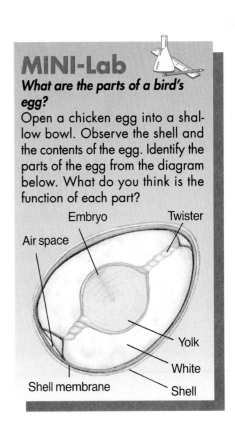

MINI-Lab

What are the parts of a bird's egg?

Open a chicken egg into a shallow bowl. Observe the shell and the contents of the egg. Identify the parts of the egg from the diagram below. What do you think is the function of each part?

Kinds of Birds

Almost 9000 species of birds belong to the Class Aves. Within this class, birds are classified into orders based on characteristic beaks, feet, feathers, and other physical features. The four most common orders of birds are: the flightless birds, water birds, birds of prey, and perching birds.

Figure 16-7. The four most common orders of birds are represented by the Emu (a), the Mandarin duck (b), the Barred Owl (c), Altamira oriole (d).

TECHNOLOGY

Healthier Eggs

Scientists and farmers are working to lower the amount of cholesterol in eggs. Two major tactics involve changes in feed and in the hen's environment. One way is to feed hens a diet high in fiber and natural vitamins and minerals. Another way is to use iodine-enriched feed, not to lower egg cholesterol, but to help people who eat the egg to process its cholesterol more quickly. Environmental changes have included removing dust from the air, providing artificial light similar to sunlight, treating water with ultraviolet rays, and reducing electro-magnetic radiation from machine motors.

Thinking Critically: How might changing a chicken's diet lower cholesterol in eggs?

Origin and Importance of Birds

Scientists have learned about the origins of birds by studying their fossils. Feathers and hollow bones decompose easily. As a result, there are few fossils to study. Those that do exist have convinced scientists that birds developed from reptiles millions of years ago. Today, birds still have some characteristics of reptiles. What are some of these characteristics?

The earliest bird fossils belong to the genus *Archaeopteryx* (ar kee AHP tuh rihks). Fossils of *Archaeopteryx* are about 150 million years old. The fossil image in Figure 16-8 shows that almost all the body had feathers. *Archaeopteryx* also had teeth, a reptilelike tail, solid bones, and three claws on each wing. It may have used its claws to climb trees. No one has been able to figure out if it could fly.

Birds play many very important roles in the environment. Birds eat insects and help control insect populations. Birds of prey control populations of rats and mice. Some birds, such as turkey vultures, feed on dead and decaying materials and in return help clean the environment. Hummingbirds pollinate nectar-producing flowers as they feed on the nectar.

Science and READING

Our endless demand for oil has led to an increased probability of oil spills. How do oil spills affect birds? What is being done to prevent these spills?

Figure 16-8. *Archaeopteryx* is considered a link between reptiles and birds.

SECTION REVIEW

1. List four characteristics shared by all birds.
2. Distinguish between contour and down feathers.
3. How are a bird's air sacs and skeleton adaptations for flight?
4. Describe reproduction in birds.
5. **Apply:** DDT, a pesticide, was once used in the United States to control populations of insect pests such as mosquitoes. Coming in contact with this pesticide caused eagles and other birds to lay eggs with very thin, brittle shells. What do you think was the effect on the populations of these birds? Explain.

☑ Comparing and Contrasting

Using the photographs in this chapter, compare and contrast the beaks and feet of flightless birds, water birds, birds of prey, and perching birds. If you need help, refer to Comparing and Contrasting in the **Skill Handbook** on page 683.

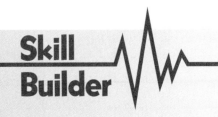

Skill Builder

ACTIVITY 16-1
Observing Contour and Down Feathers

Problem: *What is the structure of contour and down feathers?*

Materials

- contour feather
- down feather
- hand lens
- scissors
- balance

Procedure

1. Use a hand lens to examine a contour feather. Find the shaft, vanes, and barbs. Use Figure 16-2 on page 373 for help.
2. Hold the shaft by the thicker end and carefully bend the opposite end. Observe what happens when you release the bent end.
3. With the scissors, cut about 2 cm from the end of the shaft. Examine the cut end with the hand lens.
4. Separate the barbs near the center of the vanes. Use your fingers and gently rub the feather where you separated it. Observe what happens.
5. Draw the feather and label the shaft, vanes, and barbs.
6. Use a hand lens to observe a down feather.
7. Draw and label the structure of a down feather.
8. Use a balance to find out how many contour feathers have a mass of 1 g.

Data and Observations

Contour Feather	Down Feather

Analyze

1. What happens when you release the bent end of the contour feather?
2. Describe how the cut end of the shaft appears.
3. What happens to the separated barbs when you rub them with your fingers?
4. How many feathers have a mass of 1 g?

Conclude and Apply

5. Compare the shape, filaments (barbs), and shaft of the down feather with those of the contour feather.
6. How is the structure of a contour feather adapted for flight?
7. How is the structure of a down feather adapted for insulation?

Adelie Penguins, Antarctica

Mammals

Objectives

▶ Identify the characteristics of mammals and explain how they enable mammals to adapt to different environments.

▶ Distinguish among monotremes, marsupials, and placental mammals.

▶ Compare reproduction and development in the three kinds of mammals.

New Science Words

mammals
mammary glands
herbivores
carnivores
omnivores
placental mammals
gestation period
placenta
umbilical cord
marsupials
monotremes

Characteristics of Mammals

Cats, whales, moles, bats, horses, and people are all mammals. Mammals live almost everywhere, from tropical and arctic regions, to deserts, woodlands, and oceans. You may be wondering what you, a mole, and a whale have in common. Each species of mammal is adapted to its way of life, but all mammals share some characteristics. **Mammals** are warm-blooded vertebrates that have hair and produce milk to feed their young.

Nearly all mammals have hair on their bodies at some time during their lives. Many have thick fur that covers all or parts of their bodies to keep them warm. Others, such as whales and dolphins, have little hair. However, they do have a thick layer of fat that helps keep them warm. Elephants and rhinoceroses have little hair, but they live in warm climates. Porcupine quills and the spines of a hedgehog are modified hairs that protect them from their enemies. Sensory hairs, called whiskers, around the mouth of many mammals, such as cats, mice, and sea otters, help them keep in touch with their environment.

Skin covers and protects the bodies of all mammals. Hair, horns, claws, nails, and hooves are produced by the skin. The skin contains many different kinds of glands. **Mammary glands,** which are characteristic of all mammals, produce the milk female mammals use to feed their young. Oil glands produce oil to lubricate and condition the hair and skin, and sweat glands help mammals stay cool. Many mammals have scent glands that are used for self-defense and to recognize members of their own species.

Figure 16-9. Mammals care for their young after they are born. Mammary glands in the female secrete milk to feed the young.

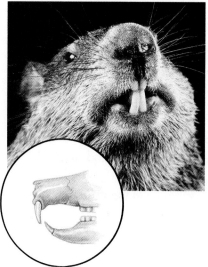

Figure 16-10. Mammals have teeth specialized for the food they eat.

What are herbivores, carnivores, and omnivores?

Look at the mammals in Figure 16-10. Can you tell anything about what these animals eat by looking at their teeth? Almost all mammals have specialized teeth. Front teeth, called incisors, bite and cut. Next to the incisors, pointed canine teeth grip and tear. Premolars and molars shred, grind, and crush. Rabbits use their large incisors to cut off blades of grass. Animals like the rabbit that eat plants are called **herbivores.** Many mammals are herbivores. **Carnivores,** such as tigers, are flesh-eating animals. Some animals, like yourself, eat both plants and animals and are called **omnivores.**

Mammals live very active lives. Think of all the things you do each day! The body systems of mammals allow them to be very active and to adapt to many environments. All mammals have a four-chambered heart and a network of blood vessels. This type of heart allows blood coming from the lungs, full of oxygen, to be pumped directly to the body. Mammals have well-developed lungs made up of millions of microscopic sacs that increase the surface area for exchange of carbon dioxide and oxygen.

The digestive system of mammals varies according to the kind of food the animal eats. Carnivores have a short digestive system compared to that of herbivores. Meat is more easily digested than plant material. Herbivores need a long digestive system to help them break down the carbohydrate called cellulose found in plants.

The nervous system is made up of a brain, spinal cord, and nerves. The brain in most mammals is larger than those of other animals the same size. Mammals are able to learn and remember more than other animals.

Reproduction and Development

All mammals reproduce sexually. Most mammals give birth to live young after a period of development inside a uterus. One or both parents care for the young after they are born.

Mammals are classified into three groups based on how the young develop. The three groups are: placental mammals, marsupials, and monotremes.

In **placental mammals,** embryos develop inside the female in an organ called the uterus. The time during which the embryo develops in the uterus is called the **gestation period.** Gestation periods range from 16 days in hamsters to 650 days in elephants. Placental mammals are named for the **placenta,** an organ developed by the growing embryo that attaches to the uterus. An **umbilical cord** attaches the embryo to the placenta. Several blood vessels make up the umbilical cord. The placenta absorbs oxygen and food from the mother's blood. The umbilical cord transports the food and oxygen to the embryo. The mother's blood never mixes with the blood of the embryo.

The kangaroo in Figure 16-12 is an example of a marsupial. **Marsupials** are pouched mammals that give birth to tiny, immature offspring. Young kangaroos are born only a few days after fertilization takes place and are about the size of a honeybee at birth. Immediately after birth, the young kangaroo crawls into the pouch on the female's abdomen and attaches to a nipple. It remains protected in the pouch while it develops more completely. After a few months, the young kangaroo, called a joey, is better developed and crawls out of the pouch. The joey returns to its mother's pouch for protection.

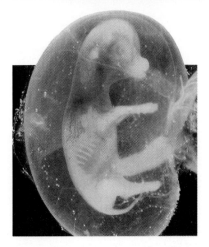

Figure 16-11. A mammal embryo develops inside a sac of fluid inside the uterus of a female.

Figure 16-12. Marsupials carry their developing young in a pouch outside their bodies. A kangaroo and baby (right) and an opossum with babies (left).

Figure 16-13. A duckbilled platypus is a monotreme. Monotremes are mammals that lay eggs.

The marsupials you are probably the most familiar with are kangaroos and opossums. Opossums are the only marsupials native to North America. Other marsupials are the koala, Tasmanian devil, and wallaby. Marsupials live primarily in Australia, Tasmania, and New Guinea.

Monotremes do not give birth to live young as placental mammals and marsupials do. Duckbilled platypuses are the most well-known monotreme. **Monotremes** are mammals that lay eggs with tough, leathery shells. The female incubates the eggs. Mammary glands of the monotremes do not have nipples. When the young hatch, they nurse by licking milk from the skin and hair surrounding the female's mammary glands.

Most placental mammals, as well as all marsupials and monotremes, are nearly helpless, and sometimes even blind, when they are born. They can't do much for themselves the first several days or even months. They just eat, sleep, and develop.

Mammal parents are very protective. They make homes in which their young can grow protected from predators and the weather. For some, such as bears and foxes, home is an underground burrow called a den. For chimpanzees and squirrels, home is a nest in the top of a tree. The young of some mammals, such as antelope, deer, elephants, whales, and dolphins, must be well developed at birth to be able to move with their constantly moving parents. Those that live on land can usually stand by the time they are a few minutes old. Marine mammals can swim as soon as they are born.

During the nursing period, young mammals learn skills they need to survive. Among most kinds of mammals, the mother raises the young alone. In some species, males help with nest building, finding food, and protecting the young.

Kinds of Mammals

There are 18 orders of modern mammals. Monotremes and marsupials make up one order each. Placental mammals make up the other orders. Each order has adaptations that help identify it. Characteristics and examples of several of the most common orders and examples are given in Table 16-1.

Table 16-2

Chiropterans
Bats
Front limbs adapted for flying; feed on fruit, insects or blood; active at night

Rodents
Mice, rats, squirrels and beavers
Pair of greatly enlarged incisors on upper and lower jaws; specialization for movements such as gliding, swimming, leaping, hopping, and running

Lagomorphs
Rabbits, hares, and pikas
Two pairs of upper incisors; bodies covered with soft fur; long legs adapted to jumping and running

Cetaceans
Whales, dolphins, and porpoises
Forelimbs are modified into flippers; breathe through one or two blowholes on top of their heads; little or no hair; largest animals on Earth

Perissodactyls
Horses, zebras, and rhinoceroses
Hooves made of a hard protein; odd number of toes; flat, grinding molars; large skeletons adapted for running

Artiodactyls
Deer, moose, camels, pigs, and cows
Hooves made of a protein called keratin; even number of toes; large, flat molars; complex stomachs and intestines

Carnivores
Cats, dogs, bears, and racoons
Long, sharp canine teeth; long, sharp claws; many hunt and kill prey

Proboscideans
Elephants
Elongated nose forms a trunk to eat and drink; pair of enlarged incisors forms tusks; leathery skin

Primates
Humans, apes, and monkeys
Long arms with grasping hands and five fingers; opposable thumb; eyes face forward; large brain

Bat

Mouse

Dolphin

Hare

Zebra

Camel

Raccoon

Elephant

Gorilla

What Colors Can Spot See?

What colors can dogs see? Most people believe that dogs are color-blind and see the world in black and white.

In 1969, scientists performed some experiments to determine if dogs were color-blind. The experiments indicated that dogs respond to color. But, because the experiments did not test whether the dogs were responding to color or differences in brightness, many scientists still believed dogs were color-blind.

A recent study indicates that dogs are not color-blind. The dogs in the experiments could tell the difference between white light and colored light and between colors at the opposite ends of the spectrum. The scientists were careful to control differences in brightness. Based on their investigation,

the scientists speculate that dogs can see blues, but they see greens, yellows, oranges, and reds as one shade.

Think Critically: Compare and contrast the 1969 experiment with the more recent investigation.

Origin and Importance of Mammals

About 65 million years ago, dinosaurs became extinct. This opened up new habitats for mammals, and they began to branch out into many different species. Eventually, they became the most numerous animals on Earth. Some species died out, but others gave rise to modern mammals. Today, there are more than 4000 species of mammals that evolved from tiny, shrewlike creatures that lived 200 million years ago.

Mammals are very important in maintaining a balance in the environment. Large carnivores such as lions help control populations of grazing animals. Bats help pollinate flowers, and some pick up plant seeds in their fur and distribute them.

Mammals are in trouble today. As millions of acres of wildlife habitat are developed for shopping centers, recreational areas, and housing, many mammals are left without food, shelter, and space to survive.

Figure 16-14. Large carnivores such as this cheetah help control populations of grazing animals.

Overhunting has threatened many mammal populations in the past, but most countries now have strict hunting regulations. However, these regulations don't keep people from killing and capturing wild mammals to sell. People use poisons to kill many mammals such as rats, prairie dogs, and rodents. Insect-eating mammals are affected by insecticides. Because of these problems, many people are working hard to protect mammals. You will learn more about measures being taken to protect endangered mammals and other species in Chapter 28.

Figure 16-15. Many elephants are killed by people for their ivory tusks.

SECTION REVIEW

1. Describe five characteristics of all mammals.
2. Differentiate among placental mammals, monotremes, and marsupials.
3. Give examples of six orders of mammals, and briefly list characteristics of each.
4. **Apply:** Suggest a reason why placental mammals are far more numerous than monotremes and marsupials.

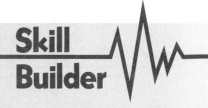

☑Classifying

Using Table 16-1, classify the following mammals into three groups: whales, echidnas, koalas, horses, elephants, opossums, kangaroos, rabbits, bats, bears, platypuses, monkeys. Compare and contrast their characteristics. If you need help, refer to Classifying in the **Skill Handbook** on page 680.

Skill Builder

16-3 Saving the Manatee

New Science Words

manatees
poaching

Objectives

▶ Identify the characteristics of manatees.
▶ Explain the major threats to manatees today.

"Sea Cows"?!

Have you ever thought about running into a cow in the water? Unless you live in Florida, you probably didn't

realize that "sea cows" exist. Sea cows, or **manatees,** are large mammals belonging to the order Sirenia that live in salt waters. Adults weigh about half a ton. They are known to live in the rivers, estuaries, and coasts in the tropical and subtropical regions. They cannot tolerate cold temperatures.

Unfortunately, manatees are now on the endangered species list. The slow, curious "sea cows" are not afraid to approach and investigate visiting humans, making them very easy to hunt. In the past, they were heavily hunted for their meat, oil, and hides.

Today, manatees are still dying. Manatees are in danger from barges and motorboats. They often collide with these boats and are injured or cut by propellers. In fact, collisions are so common with manatees that researchers are able to identify more than 900 individual manatees just by using their distinctive scars caused by these collisions. Manatees are herbivores and feed on aquatic plants that clog waterways. Many manatees are poisoned by herbicides used to kill these plants.

The Future of Manatees

Researchers are very concerned about the future of these huge, quiet mammals. Although the United States

EcoTip

Ask if your classroom can "adopt" an endangered animal at your local zoo. You will be helping to preserve wildlife.

protected them by law in 1983, the state of Florida cannot employ enough law enforcers to prevent illegal hunting called **poaching.** In 1988, 133 manatees were killed in Florida. By 1989 only about 1200 manatees were believed to be living in United States waters.

Manatees have a very slow rate of reproduction. Manatees that are killed by accident are not quickly replaced. Combine this steady decrease in population with the loss of habitat due to development (nearly 1000 people move to Florida each year) and extinction does not look to be very far away.

Figure 16-16. Warning signs are being placed in areas where manatees are found to help protect them from being injured.

What can be done to save the manatees? Some suggest developing more refuges where boats would not be allowed to travel. Because Florida real estate is very valuable, this is not likely to be popular with coastal landowners. Another option is to enforce a slower speed limit on the boats that travel in the Intracoastal Waterway where many manatees are injured.

Whatever the solution, manatees need more protection soon if we hope to save them from their current fate of extinction.

SECTION REVIEW

1. What are manatees and where do they live?
2. What two major factors account for the gradual decrease in the population?

You Decide!

In Miami, Florida, injured manatees are taken by a special ambulance to Miami's Seaquarium where they can be treated. Scientists are hoping to release the treated manatees and help the population become more stable. The estimated cost of treatment for one injured manatee is about $18 000. When returned to its environment, there is no guarantee that it will escape another, perhaps fatal, injury. Some people believe that it's not right to spend this much money on saving the manatees. What do you think?

ACTIVITY 16-2
Classifying Vertebrates

Problem: *How do scientists classify vertebrates?*

Materials

- paper
- pencil
- animals or pictures of animals

Procedure

1. Copy the four-column chart shown under Data and Observations.
2. Write the name of each animal you are studying in the first column.
3. Predict the class of the animal and write the predicted class in the second column.
4. Write the characteristics of the animal that helped you decide its class.
5. Use the key to find the class of each animal. Write the class name in the last column.

Data and Observations

Animal	Predicted class	Characteristics	Actual class

Analyze

1. How many of your predictions were correct?
2. What characteristics of each vertebrate class are used to identify the animals?

Conclude and Apply

3. How do scientists classify vertebrates?

1. Does the animal have a backbone?

YES   Go to 2.

NO   Invertebrate

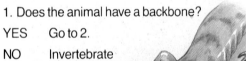

2. Does the animal have feathers?

YES   Class Aves

NO   Go to 3.

3. Does the animal have jaws?

YES   Go to 4.

NO   Class Agnatha

4. Does the animal have paired fins?

YES   Go to 5.

NO   Go to 6.

5. Does the animal have a bony skeleton?

YES   Osteichthyes

NO   Chondrichthyes

6. Does the animal have fur?

YES   Mammal

NO   Go to 7.

7. Does the animal have skin scales?

YES   Reptilia

NO   Amphibia

CHAPTER
REVIEW

SUMMARY

16-1: Birds

1. Birds are warm-blooded organisms that are covered with feathers and lay eggs. Their front legs are modified into wings.

2. The adaptations birds have for flight are: wings; feathers; a light, strong skeleton; and efficient body systems.

3. Birds lay eggs enclosed in hard shells. Most birds incubate their eggs until hatching.

16-2: Mammals

1. Mammals are warm-blooded vertebrates with hair that have mammary glands that produce milk.

2. There are three groups of mammals: Mammals that lay eggs are monotremes. Mammals that have pouches for the development of their embryos are marsupials. Mammals whose offspring develop within the uterus with a placenta are placental mammals.

16-3: Science and Society: Saving the Manatee

1. Manatees are large aquatic mammals that belong to the order Sirenia. Adults weigh about half a ton. Then live along the coasts in tropical and subtropical regions.

2. The major threats to manatees today are poachers, injury from boats, and habitat destruction.

KEY SCIENCE WORDS

a. **carnivores**
b. **contour feathers**
c. **down feathers**
d. **gestation period**
e. **herbivores**
f. **incubate**
g. **mammals**
h. **mammary glands**
i. **manatees**
j. **marsupials**
k. **monotremes**
l. **omnivores**
m. **placenta**
n. **placental mammals**
o. **poaching**
p. **preening**
q. **umbilical cord**

UNDERSTANDING VOCABULARY

Match each phrase with the correct term from the list of Key Science Words.

1. plant-eaters
2. process of keeping eggs warm
3. mammals whose embryos develop inside a uterus
4. feathers birds use for flying
5. animals that eat both plants and animals
6. glands that produce milk
7. feathers that help to insulate
8. activity of rubbing oil onto feathers
9. structure containing blood vessels that attaches embryo to the placenta
10. pouched mammals

CHAPTER
REVIEW

CHECKING CONCEPTS

Choose the word or phrase that completes the sentence.

1. Birds can fly because they have _____.
   a. feathers   c. keen vision
   b. wings   d. all of these

2. Wings of birds can be used for _____ .
   a. flying   c. balancing
   b. swimming   d. all of these

3. _____ are glands that produce milk.
   a. Oil glands   c. Mammary glands
   b. Sweat glands   d. None of these

4. Mammals that eat both plants and animals are called _____.
   a. herbivores   c. omnivores
   b. carnivores   d. none of these

5. A _____ is an example of a marsupial.
   a. cat   c. kangaroo
   b. human   d. all of these

6. Egg-laying mammals are called _____.
   a. marsupials   c. placental
   b. monotremes   d. all of these

7. _____ are mammals that have mammary glands with no nipples.
   a. marsupials   c. placental mammals
   b. monotremes   d. all of these

8. Teeth specialized for tearing are _____.
   a. canine   c. molars
   b. incisors   d. premolars

9. _____ is hunting animals illegally.
   a. placental   c. poaching
   b. incubate   d. omnivore

10. Humans and monkeys belong to the order _____.
    a. Primates   c. Edentates
    b. Carnivores   d. none of these

UNDERSTANDING CONCEPTS

Complete each sentence.

11. The _____ feathers help birds steer.

12. The two _____ with barbs add strength to feathers.

13. Birds shed feathers in a process called _____.

14. Eggs laid by one bird in a nest is called a(n) _____.

15. _____ are sensory hairs of mammals that can detect the environment.

THINK AND WRITE CRITICALLY

16. Why is it incorrect to tell someone who eats very little that he or she "eats like a bird"?

17. There are far more species of placental mammals than of marsupials or monotremes. Why do you think this is so?

18. Explain how the feet of birds are adapted to where they live.

19. Why is it difficult to study the origin of birds based on fossils?

20. What are the advantages of the lung structure of birds?

APPLY

21. Discuss the differences in reproduction between birds and reptiles.
22. Name a mammal group that probably doesn't have sweat glands and explain why it doesn't.
23. Which type of bird would have lighter wing bones—ducks or turkeys? Explain.
24. What features of birds allow them to be fully adapted to life on land?
25. Which mammal group has the best adaptations for the survival of its embryo? Why?

MORE SKILL BUILDERS

If you need help, refer to the Skill Handbook.

1. **Sequencing:** Sequence the order in which food passes through a bird's digestive system.
2. **Concept Mapping:** Complete the concept map describing the groups of mammals.

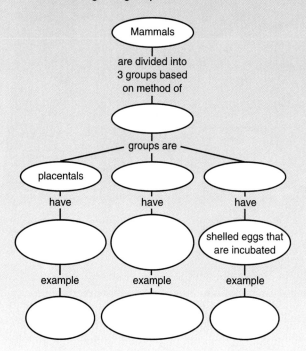

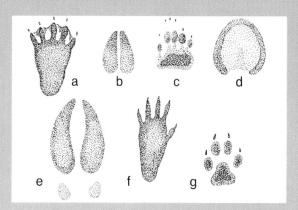

3. **Observing and Inferring:** Look at the diagrams of animals tracks. Decide which track belongs to which type of mammal by using Table 16-1. Fill in the chart. Describe how each animal's foot is adapted to its environment.

Animal	Track	Adaptation
Bear		
Beaver		
Cheetah		
Deer		
Horse		
Moose		
Raccoon		

4. **Comparing and Contrasting:** Compare and contrast the teeth of herbivores, carnivores, and omnivores. How is each tooth type adapted to the animal's diet?
5. **Classifying:** You discover three new species of mammals. The traits of each species is as follows: Mammal 1—swims and eats plants; Mammal 2—flies and eats fruit; Mammal 3—runs and hunts. Classify each mammal into its correct group.

PROJECTS

1. Research the birds in your area. Find out what they eat and the type of nests they build.
2. Write to the National Wildlife Federation about endangered birds and mammals. What is being done to save these animals?

17 Animal Behavior

Owls fluff up their feathers and spread their wings to appear larger when threatened. You quickly pull your hand away from a hot stove or iron, and blink your eyes when you see something rushing toward your face. Do organisms learn these actions, or do they occur naturally?

FIND OUT!

Do this simple activity to find out if some simple responses of organisms are learned or natural.

Obtain a piece of clear plexiglass and a wadded up sheet of paper from your teacher. Have a partner hold the plastic a few inches from his or her face. Stand three feet away and gently toss the wadded up paper toward your partner's face. What happened to his or her eyes? Toss the paper ball again. This time tell your partner not to blink. Was he or she successful? Do you think this behavior is learned, or does it occur naturally? Do you think it is good for some behaviors to occur naturally?

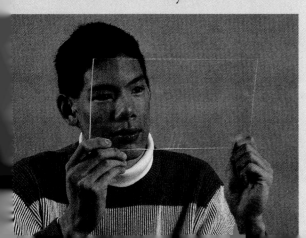

Gearing Up

Previewing the Chapter

Use this outline to help you focus on important ideas in this chapter.

Section 17-1   Types of Behavior
▶ Innate Behavior
▶ Learned Behavior

Section 17-2   Behavioral Adaptations
▶ Territorial Behavior
▶ Courtship Behavior
▶ Social Behavior
▶ Cyclic Behavior

Section 17-3   Science and Society
Rehabilitation of Wild Animals
▶ Saving Injured Animals
▶ Return to the Wild

Previewing Science Skills

▶ In the **Skill Builders,** you will make and use tables and use variables, constants and controls.
▶ In the **Activities,** you will experiment, observe, and collect and record data.
▶ In the **MINI-Labs,** you will hypothesize, experiment, and graph data.

What's next?

The Find Out activity demonstrated some of the things you do naturally and are not learned. In this chapter you will learn more about these types of behaviors and about behaviors that are learned. You will also learn how animals behave to be able to survive in their environments.

Types of Behavior

New Science Words

behavior
innate behavior
reflex
instinct
learning
imprinting
trial and error
motivation
conditioning
insight

Objectives

▶ Distinguish between innate and learned behavior.
▶ Recognize reflex and instinctive actions and explain how they help organisms survive.
▶ Describe and give examples of imprinting, trial and error, conditioning, and insight.

Innate Behavior

When you come home from school, does your dog run to meet you, barking and wagging his tail? After you play with him a while, does he sit at your feet and watch every move you make? Why does he do these things? Dogs are pack animals that generally follow a leader. They have been living with people for about 50 000 years, so it's easy for a dog to adopt a human as his leader.

If you have a cat, she doesn't jump up and lick your face when you come home, does she? Cats are domestic animals too. Even though cats are happy living with people, they keep some traits of wild cats. Living with people doesn't change some of the behaviors of cats and dogs.

Behavior is the way an organism acts toward its environment. Anything in the environment to which an organism reacts is called a stimulus. You are the stimulus that causes your dog to bark and wag his tail. Your dog's reaction to you is a response.

Dogs and cats are quite different from one another in their behavior. They were born with certain behaviors, and they have learned others. A behavior that an organism is born with is an **innate behavior.** Such behaviors are inherited and they do not have to be learned.

Innate behavior patterns are usually correct the first time an animal responds to a stimulus. Kittiwakes are sea birds that nest on narrow ledges. The chicks stand still as soon as they hatch. The chicks of a related bird, the herring gull, which nests on the ground, move around as soon as they can stand. A kittiwake chick can't do this because one step could mean instant death. They don't have time to learn.

Figure 17-1. Some behaviors an animal is born with are necessary for survival.

The lives of most insects are too short for the young to learn from the parents. In many cases, the parents have died by the time the young hatch. And yet, every insect reacts automatically to its environment. A moth will fly toward a light, and a cockroach will run away from it. Fleas are attracted to warm-blooded animals by the heat their bodies give off, and fruit flies are attracted to the odor of overripe fruit. They do not have to spend time learning what to do.

The simplest innate behaviors are reflex actions. A **reflex** is an automatic response that does not involve the brain. Sneezing, shivering, yawning, jerking your hand away from a hot surface, and blinking your eyes when something is thrown toward you are all reflex actions. All animals have reflexes. The fur on your cat's back stands on end when she is frightened. An octopus changes colors when it senses danger.

During a reflex, a message passes from a sense organ along the nerve to the spinal cord and back to the muscles. The message does not go to the brain. You are aware of the reaction only after it has happened. A reflex is not the result of conscious thinking.

An **instinct** is a complex pattern of innate behavior. Have you ever watched a spider spin a web? Spinning a web is very complicated, and yet spiders spin webs correctly on the first try. Unlike reflexes, instinctive behaviors may have several parts and take weeks to complete. Instinctive behavior begins when the animal recognizes a stimulus and continues until all parts of the behavior have been performed.

Figure 17-2. Spiders must automatically respond to their environment. There is no time for learning in their short life cycle.

Science and READING

What are some of the problems of using animals (or people) in behavioral studies?

Figure 17-3. When sea turtles hatch, they instinctively run to the ocean.

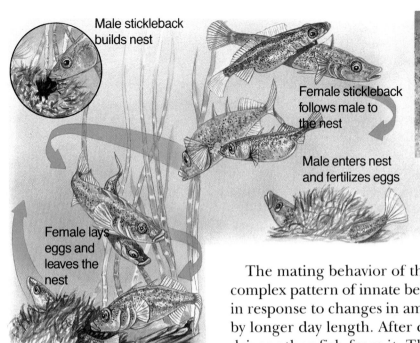

Male stickleback builds nest

Female stickleback follows male to the nest

Male enters nest and fertilizes eggs

Female lays eggs and leaves the nest

Male protects young after hatching

Figure 17-4. The male stickleback fish does not learn mating behavior. It is a complex innate behavior pattern.

Figure 17-5. Mammals have many more learned behaviors than other animals.

The mating behavior of the male stickleback fish is a complex pattern of innate behavior. The behavior begins in response to changes in amounts of hormones caused by longer day length. After choosing a mating area, he drives other fish from it. Then he collects plants and makes them into a small mound in which he creates a tunnel. The tunnel becomes his nest. Meanwhile, his normally dull, brown-colored body changes to bright red on the underside and bluish-white on top. When a female enters the mating area, he does a zigzag dance to lead her into the nest. She lays her eggs in the nest and swims away. The male fertilizes the eggs and stays with them. When the young hatch, he protects them until they are well developed. All male sticklebacks are born with this pattern of behavior. Even if young sticklebacks are not raised with other sticklebacks, they follow the same behavior pattern.

Learned Behavior

All animals have both innate and learned behaviors. **Learning** is a behavior that develops through experience. Instinct almost completely determines the behavior of insects, spiders, and other arthropods. These animals are able to learn very little, so their survival depends on innate behavior.

Fish, reptiles, amphibians, birds, and mammals can learn more than invertebrates. Fish behave more by instinct than birds. Birds show more instincts than mammals. In humans, babies suckle, smile, and grasp instinctively, but as they grow older, most of their behavior is learned.

Instincts can be modified by learning. Grouse and quail chicks leave their nest the day they hatch. They can run and find food, but they can't fly. When something moves above them, they crouch down and keep perfectly still until the danger is past. They will crouch without moving even if the falling object is only a leaf. Older birds have learned that leaves will not harm them, but they too freeze when a hawk moves overhead.

Imprinting

You have probably seen young ducks following their mother. This is an important behavior because the adult bird has had more experience in finding food, escaping predators, and getting along in the world. **Imprinting** is a type of learning in which an animal forms a social attachment to another organism within a specific time period after birth or hatching.

Konrad Lorenz, an Austrian naturalist, developed the concept of imprinting. Working with geese, he discovered that a gosling follows the first moving object it sees after hatching. It recognizes the moving object as its parent. It later recognizes similar objects as members of its own species. This behavior works well when the first moving object a young goose sees is an adult female goose. But, goslings hatched in an incubator may see a human first and may imprint on her. Animals that become imprinted toward animals of another species never learn to recognize members of their own species.

Figure 17-6. Young goslings may imprint on any object or organism present during hatching. Konrad Lorenz is shown here swimming with imprinted goslings.

Trial and Error

Can you remember when you learned to ride a bicycle? You probably fell many times before you learned to balance on the bicycle. But after a while you could ride without having to think about it. You have many skills that you have learned through trial and error. Skating and riding a bicycle are just a few.

Behavior that is modified by experience is called **trial and error** learning. Both invertebrates and vertebrates learn by trial and error. When baby chicks first learn to

Did You Know?

The archer fish, *Toxotes jaculatrix*, spits droplets of water onto insects sitting on twigs that overhang streams and ponds. The droplets of water knock the insects into the water, where they become easy prey for the fish.

Figure 17-7. Many pets become conditioned to be fed at certain times of the day.

feed themselves, they peck at many spots before they get any food. As a result of trial and error, they soon learn to peck only at grain.

A particular stimulus may cause a different response in the same animal at different times. When your cat sees food, she will eat it if she's hungry, but if she has just eaten, she will ignore the food. For a hungry rat, the motive to learn a maze may be the food at the end of the maze. **Motivation** is something inside an animal that causes the animal to act. It is necessary for learning to take place.

Conditioning

Animals often learn new behaviors by conditioning. In **conditioning,** behavior is modified so that a response previously associated with one stimulus becomes associated with another. Russian scientist Ivan P. Pavlov was the first person to study conditioning. He knew that the sight and smell of food made hungry dogs secrete saliva. Pavlov

PROBLEM SOLVING

The Disappearing Lizards

Julio's science class is studying vertebrate animals. His teacher asked each member of the class to choose a vertebrate animal, observe it for several days, and prepare a report.

Shortly after sunup, Julio went to a hot desert area near his home to observe lizards. Julio saw three lizards lying motionless on some rocks. He watched for a while, then went home for a cool drink. When he returned, the lizards seemed to have disappeared. The same thing happened on the next day.

One morning Julio stayed a little longer. One lizard left its rock and burrowed into the sandy soil. Soon, the other two lizards did the same thing. Then, on Saturday, Julio made more frequent visits to the rock. The

lizards stayed underground until sunset when they dug out and began hunting for food.

Was the lizards' behavior innate or learned?

Think Critically: Use what you learned about cold-blooded animals to explain the behavior of the lizards.

added another stimulus. He rang a bell when he gave the dogs food. The dogs began to connect the sound of the bell with food. Then Pavlov rang the bell without giving the dogs food. The dogs secreted saliva when the bell was rung even though he did not show them food. The dogs were conditioned to respond to the bell.

The American psychologist John B. Watson demonstrated that responses of humans can also be conditioned. In one experiment, he struck a metal object each time an infant touched a furry animal. The loud noise frightened the child. In time, the child became frightened by the furry animal when no sound was made.

Insight

When you solve a math problem, do you use what you have previously learned in math to solve the problem? **Insight** is a form of reasoning that enables animals to use past experiences to solve new problems. In Wolfgang Kohler's experiments with chimpanzees, a bunch of bananas was placed too high for the chimpanzees to reach. Chimpanzees piled up boxes found in the room, climbed up on them, and reached the bananas. Much of adult human learning is based on insight. Younger children learn by trial and error.

MINI-Lab

How does insight help you solve problems?

Obtain a chain of 15 safety pins. Count the safety pins on the chain to be sure there are 15. Make a hypothesis as to the *fewest* number of times you can open and close pins to break the chain into the following:

    5 pins attached
    4 pins attached
    3 pins attached
    2 pins attached, and
    1 alone

Each open-and-close counts as **one.** Test your hypothesis and compare with those of your classmates. (All pins must be closed at the end!)

SECTION REVIEW

1. Compare innate behavior with learned behavior.
2. Compare a reflex with an instinct.
3. Describe the four types of learned behavior.
4. How are trial and error and insight behaviors important to humans?
5. **Apply:** A family moves into a new home near an airport. They are awakened by the planes during the first few nights. Explain why after a week or two, they stop waking up even though the planes continue to fly.

☒ Making and Using Tables

Make a table that shows the kinds of innate and learned behaviors in this section. Include examples of each. If you need help, refer to Making and Using Tables in the **Skill Handbook** on page 690.

Skill Builder

ACTIVITY 17-1
Conditioning

Problem: *How can you demonstrate conditioning?*

Materials

- aquarium
- glass cover for aquarium
- thermometer
- washed coarse sand
- tap water aged three days
- metric ruler
- dish
- food for guppies
- fish net
- guppies
- snails
- water plants

Procedure

1. Wash and rinse the aquarium thoroughly. Place it on a flat surface where it will receive indirect sunlight or use an aquarium light.
2. Place 3 to 4 cm of sand on the bottom of the aquarium. Place a dish on the sand and pour aged tap water on the dish until the water level is about 5 cm above the sand.
3. Anchor plants near the back of the aquarium about 5 cm apart.
4. Add aged tap water slowly to fill the aquarium. Allow it to stand one day.
5. Add one guppy and one snail for each four liters of water. Cover the aquarium. Maintain a water temperature of about 24°C.
6. Feed the fish at the same time each day. Feed the same amount and the same kind of food. Before you feed the fish, tap gently on the side of the aquarium where you are going to place the food. Do this for two weeks.
7. After two weeks, at the normal feeding time, tap gently on the side of the aquarium where the food is usually placed. Do not put any food into the water. Observe the behavior of the fish. Feed the fish when you have finished observing.

Data and Observations

Date	Organism	Observations

Analyze

1. How do the fish move, breathe, and get food?
2. How are the movements of the snails different from those of the fish?
3. How do the snails keep the aquarium clean?
4. What happened when you tapped on the aquarium without putting in food?

Conclude and Apply

5. What is the role of the plants in the aquarium?
6. Why is the aquarium covered?
7. What was the cause of the behavior of the fish after the second week?
8. What is the relationship between tapping on the tank and feeding?
9. How did this experiment show conditioning?

Behavioral Adaptations 17-2

Objectives

▶ Recognize the importance of behavioral adaptations.
▶ Explain how courtship behavior increases the chances of reproductive success.
▶ Evaluate the importance of social behavior and cyclic behavior.

New Science Words

territory
aggression
courtship behavior
social behavior
society
communication
cyclic behaviors
circadian rhythm
migration

Territorial Behavior

Many animals set up territories for feeding, mating, and raising young. A **territory** is an area that an animal defends from other members of the same species. Ownership of a territory is set up in different ways. Songbirds sing to set up territories. Sea lions bellow and squirrels chatter. Other animals leave scent marks. Some patrol the area to warn intruders.

Pet dogs and cats have territories. A dog often barks and nips at other dogs around its home. Cats and dogs mark their territories with urine. A cat out hunting will sniff for scent marks of other cats. If the scent marks are fresh, the cat will take another path.

The size of a territory varies with the species. Song sparrows have territories that are as large as 3000 square meters where they feed, mate, and nest. Gulls, penguins, and other water birds nest in large groups, but each male and his mate have their own territory. Male sea lions defend small territories that are used only for mating. Squirrels have large territories for feeding. Female lizards defend feeding territories, and male lizards defend mating areas.

Have you ever watched a dog approach another dog eating a bone? What happens to the appearance of the dog with the bone? The hair stands up on its back, the lips curl, and the dog makes growling noises. This behavior is aggression. **Aggression** is a forceful act used to dominate or control another animal. Fighting and threatening are aggressive behaviors animals use to defend their territories, protect their young, or to get food.

Aggressive behaviors seen in birds include letting the wings droop below the tail feathers, taking another's

Figure 17-8. These puffins are defending their nesting territory.

perch, and thrusting the head forward in a pecking motion. These behaviors are intended to avoid physical contact. Fighting wastes valuable energy. And a missing feather or two can greatly reduce a bird's ability to fly.

Animals seldom fight to the death. They rarely use their teeth, beaks, claws, or horns to fight members of their own species. These structures are used for killing prey or for defense against members of another species. To avoid being killed, a defeated animal shows submission by lowering its posture or retreating.

Courtship Behavior

You have probably seen a male peacock spread the beautiful feathers on his lower back. The male frigate bird in Figure 17-9 has a bright red pouch on his throat that takes about 25 minutes to blow up. A male sage grouse fans his tail, fluffs his feathers, and blows up his two air sacs. These are examples of a behavior that both males and females of a species perform before mating. This type of behavior is called **courtship behavior.** Courtship behaviors allow male and female members of a species to recognize each other. They also allow males and females to be ready to mate at the same time. This helps provide reproductive success.

In most species, the males perform courtship displays to attract a mate. Songbirds sing. Other birds depend on bright colors and attention-getting movements or postures. Many species of birds move the head, wings, or other body parts. The response of the female may closely resemble the male's display, and so the two look as if they are dancing.

Some courtship behaviors allow males and females to find each other across distances. Male fireflies produce different

Figure 17-9. The male peacock (left) and the male frigate bird (right) are both trying to attract females with their displays.

patterns in their flashes of light. A female of the same species recognizes the pattern and flashes back. Female gypsy moths release chemical messengers called pheromones that attract males. Very small amounts of pheromone can attract male moths several kilometers away. Sound is another way males and females find each other. Insects such as crickets, grasshoppers, and locusts call to each other by sounds made by rubbing their legs or wings together. Frogs make sounds that can be heard hundreds of meters away.

Social Behavior

Do you know why geese fly in flocks and some fish swim in schools? Animals live together in groups for several reasons. One reason is that there is safety in large numbers. A wolf pack is less likely to attack a herd of musk oxen than an individual musk oxen. In some groups, large numbers of animals help keep each other warm. Penguins in Antarctica huddle together against the cold winds. Migrating animals in large groups are less likely to get lost than if they traveled alone.

Interactions among organisms of the same species are examples of **social behavior.** Social behaviors include courtship and mating, caring for the young, claiming territories, protecting each other, and getting food. These behaviors provide advantages for survival of the species.

Insects such as ants, bees, and termites live together in societies. A **society** is a group of animals of the same species living and working together in an organized way. Each member has a certain job. Usually there is a female that lays eggs, a male that fertilizes the eggs, and workers that do all the other jobs in the society.

Some societies are organized by dominance. Wolves usually live together in packs. In a wolf pack, there is a dominant female. The top female controls the mating of the other females. If there is plenty of food, she mates and allows the others to do so. If food is scarce, she allows less mating, and usually she is the only one to mate.

In all social behavior, communication is important. **Communication** is an exchange of information. How do you communicate with the people around you? Animals in a group communicate with sounds and actions. Alarm calls, pheromones, speech, courtship behavior, and aggression are all forms of communication.

Science and WRITING

Imagine you are a scientist who studies behavior. Write a proposal to study the behavior of an animal that interests you. Be sure to be specific about what behavior you want to study and why you think the study is important.

Figure 17-10. Wolves live together socially in packs. They hunt and raise their young together. Strong bonds are formed among members of the pack.

Cyclic Behavior

What determines when an owl sleeps and when it wakes up? Animals show regularly repeated behaviors such as feeding in the day and sleeping at night or the opposite. Many reproduce every spring and migrate every spring and fall.

Cyclic behaviors are innate behaviors that occur in a repeating pattern. They are often repeated in response to changes in the environment. Behavior that is based on a 24-hour cycle is called a **circadian rhythm.** Animals that are active during the day are *diurnal.* Animals that are active at night are *nocturnal.*

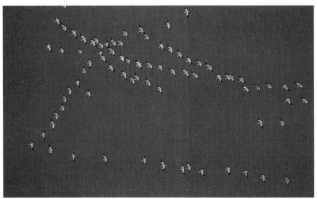

Figure 17-11. Migrating is a cyclic behavior.

Cyclic behaviors also occur over long periods of time. Hibernation is a cyclic response to cold temperatures and limited food supplies. During hiber-

T E C H N O L O G Y

Looking for a Sign

Young Loulis is learning language from his friends. This hardly seems unusual, except the language is American Sign Language (AMESLAN), and his friends are laboratory chimps.

Scientists have used many different techniques to study the language-learning abilities of nonhuman primates. Most have involved humans teaching apes language, but now some involve letting apes teach other apes. AMESLAN was originally used for studies because apes cannot produce certain human word sounds. AMESLAN is a complete, nonverbal language. Some scientists have made up new languages and have taught apes these.

Apes are using language, creating new words, and teaching these words to other apes. But ape language studies affect humans, too. Yerkish, a symbol language developed for apes, has allowed severely retarded humans to communicate with others for the first time.

Think Critically: What is the significance of apes, not humans, teaching other apes language?

nation, an animal's body temperature drops to near that of its surroundings, and its breathing rate is greatly reduced. An animal in hibernation survives on stored body fat. The animal remains inactive until the weather becomes warm in the spring. Some mammals and many amphibians and reptiles hibernate.

Have you ever seen large flocks of birds flying overhead in the fall or spring? Many birds and mammals move to new locations when the seasons change instead of hibernating. This instinctive seasonal movement of animals is called **migration.** Many species of birds fly hours or days without stopping. The blackpoll warbler flies non-stop a distance of more than 4000 km from North America to its winter home in South America. The trip takes nearly 90 hours. Arctic terns fly about 17 700 km from their breeding grounds in the Arctic to their winter home in the Antarctic. They return a few months later, traveling a distance of more than 35 000 km in less than a year. Gray whales swim from the cold Arctic waters to the waters off the coast of California. When the young are born, they make the return trip.

Animals have many different behaviors. Some behaviors are innate and some are learned. Many are a combination of innate and learned behaviors. Appropriate behaviors help animals survive, reproduce, and maintain the species.

MINI-Lab

How does an animal enter into hibernation?

Some animals respond to their cold environment by lowering the thermostat of their body. Use the data of a ground squirrel to graph this reaction.

Temperature	Hours
37°C	1
25°C	2
30°C	3
15°C	4
14°C	5
13°C	6
10°C	7

Body temperature is maintained between 5°C and 10°C. If the temperature drops below this level, the animal becomes active. How is this helpful?

SECTION REVIEW

1. How do animals communicate?
2. What are some examples of courtship behavior?
3. Give three reasons why animals live in groups.
4. How are cyclic behaviors a response to stimuli in the environment?
5. **Apply:** What behaviors do pet dogs have that indicate they are related to wolves?

✉ Using Variables, Constants, and Controls

Skill Builder

Design an experiment to show that ants leave chemical trails to show other ants where food can be found. If you need help, refer to Using Variables, Constants, and Controls in the **Skill Handbook** on page 686.

SCIENCE
&
SOCIETY

17-3 Rehabilitation of Wild Animals

New Science Words

carrying capacity

Objectives

▶ Explain some of the effects of human development on wildlife.
▶ Describe the disadvantages of releasing rehabilitated animals into the wild.

Saving Injured Animals

Each year, millions of animals are killed due to the movement of humans into animal territories. Thousands of birds are killed each year after they fly into electrical towers during their night migration. You might have seen

wild animals lying along the road after being hit by a car. Thousands of large birds like hawks, owls, and eagle, which prey on other animals, are electrocuted each year while perching on a telephone pole or electric wire.

Many volunteers around the country are working day and night to save animals that have been injured due to human presence. Nursing wild animals back to health is becoming very popular in the United States.

These wild animal rehabilitation programs can be very difficult to conduct. Wild animals are often very uncomfortable out of their natural environment. They require special conditions in order for them to heal and to prevent them from becoming too familiar with their human caretakers. In many rehabilitation programs for birds of prey, the young owls, hawks, or eagles never see their human caretakers. Instead, they are fed by puppets that look very much like their natural parents. By using such puppets to feed them their natural food source, these young have a better chance of surviving on their own in the wild.

Return to the Wild

Although injured wild animals are often nursed back to good health, some scientists argue that although the individual animal is saved, wild populations do not benefit from releasing rehabilitated animals. We may actually be hurting wild populations by returning these animals back into the wild. Through natural selection, the genes of weak individuals are removed from the population to ensure the good health of future generations. Although saving these animals appears to be a very humane venture, the consequences of rehabilitation must be carefully considered. A great deal of research is needed to study the effects of a released animal on its new environment and the effects of the new environment on the animal. Many animals are very territorial. Each territory is designed to hold a certain number of organisms. The number of animals that the environment can support with food and shelter in a given area is called the **carrying capacity.** For example, if an owl was released in a forest that provided only enough resources for the one owl that already lived there, the newly released owl would not survive. Similarly, if the new owl established itself in the forest, the established owl may be forced to leave. In each case, one animal is likely to die due to a lack of resources.

Although rehabilitation appears to be very kind and noble, we must think carefully about its consequences. We must try to reach a balance between our humane instincts and the reality of the biology of the natural world.

SECTION REVIEW

1. Name three ways in which humans cause injury or death to wild animals.
2. Name two dangers in releasing wild animals into new environments.

You Decide!

SCIENCE & SOCIETY

Often during the spring months newly hatched birds are found on the ground after falling out of their nests. Our first tendency may be to help the young bird by bringing it inside and trying to nurse it back to health. Some people might argue that the young bird will serve as food for another animal or for insects. Is it wrong to let nature take its course?

ACTIVITY 17-2
Observing Social Behavior in Ants

Problem: *How do ants live?*

Materials

- 20 ants
- large jar with screen wire cover
- soil
- black paper
- small moist sponge
- water
- food—honey, sugar, bread crumbs
- small can with lid
- spoon or trowel
- hand lens

Procedure

1. Fill the large jar 3/4 full with moistened loose soil. Place the damp sponge in the jar on top of the soil.
2. Find an ant hill. Use the spoon or trowel to place loose soil from the nest into the small can. Look for ants, small white eggs, cocoons, and larvae. Try to find a queen. The queen will be larger than the other ants. Cover. Place the ants in the refrigerator for a few minutes to slow their movements.
3. Gently place the ants in the jar. Add a small amount of each of the types of food. Place the screen wire cover on the jar.
4. Tape the black paper around the jar. Leave about 2 cm at the top uncovered.
5. Take the paper off for a short period of time each day and observe the ants at work. Use a hand lens to observe individual ants.
6. Keep the sponge moistened and add food each day. Record your observations each day.

Data and Observations

Date	Number of ants visible	Other observations

Analyze

1. How long did it take for the ants to build tunnels after they were placed in the jar?
2. What did you observe that indicated the ants were working together?
3. What kinds of foods do ants prefer?
4. How do the ants in the jar differ?

Conclude and Apply

5. What is a society?
6. What evidence do you have that ants are social insects?

CHAPTER
REVIEW

SUMMARY

17-1: Types of Behavior

1. Behavior that an animal is born with is innate behavior. Some animal behaviors are learned. These behaviors are formed through experience.

2. Reflexes are the simplest innate behaviors. An instinct is a complex pattern of innate behavior. A spider spins a web by instinct. Birds build their nests by instinct.

3. Imprinting is a learned behavior in which an animal forms a social attachment to another organism soon after birth. Behavior that is modified by experience is learning by trial and error. Conditioning occurs when a response previously associated with one stimulus becomes associated with another. Insight is a form of reasoning that uses past experiences to solve new problems.

17-2: Behavioral Adaptations

1. Behavioral adaptations such as defense of territory, courtship behavior, and social behavior help species of animals survive and reproduce.

2. Courtship behaviors allow males and females to recognize each other. Courtship behaviors help provide for reproductive success.

3. Interactions among members of the same species are social behaviors. Cyclic behaviors are behaviors that occur in repeating patterns. Cyclic behaviors such as hibernation, estivation, and migration help animals survive harsh environmental conditions.

17-3: Science and Society: Rehabilitation of Wild Animals

1. Millions of animals are killed or injured each year due to the movement of humans into animal territories. Many animals are hit by cars. Some animals fly into electrical towers, and others are electrocuted while perching on telephone poles or on electric wires.

2. Rehabilitated animals released back into the wild may not be able to find food on their own. The carrying capacity of the environment may also be disturbed by adding these additional animals.

KEY SCIENCE WORDS

a. **aggression**
b. **behavior**
c. **carrying capacity**
d. **circadian rhythm**
e. **communication**
f. **conditioning**
g. **courtship behavior**
h. **cyclic behaviors**
i. **imprinting**
j. **innate behavior**
k. **insight**
l. **instinct**
m. **learning**
n. **migration**
o. **motivation**
p. **reflex**
q. **social behavior**
r. **society**
s. **territory**
t. **trial and error**

UNDERSTANDING VOCABULARY

Match each phrase with the correct term from the list of Key Science Words.

1. an inherited, not learned behavior

2. automatic response to a stimulus

3. forming a social bond to another organism after birth

4. the way an organism behaves toward its environment

5. change in behavioral response to a given stimulus

6. a defended area

7. using reasoning to solve a problem

8. an organized group of animals in a species

9. behaviors before mating

10. instinctive seasonal movement

CHAPTER
REVIEW

CHECKING CONCEPTS

Choose the word or phrase that completes the sentence.

1. An example of a reflex is _____.
   a. writing   c. sneezing
   b. talking   d. none of these
2. An instinct is an example of _____.
   a. innate behavior   c. imprinting
   b. learned behavior   d. conditioning
3. _____ is an example of an instinct.
   a. Nest building   c. Web spinning
   b. Mating behavior d. All of these
4. The animals that depend least on instinct and more on learning are _____.
   a. birds   c. mammals
   b. fish   d. amphibians
5. _____ involves using reasoning to solve problems.
   a. Insight   c. Conditioning
   b. Imprinting d. All of these
6. Animals defend territories for _____.
   a. feeding   c. protection
   b. mating   d. all of these
7. Teeth, beaks, and claws are used for _____.
   a. killing prey c. hurting other birds
   b. fighting   d. none of these
8. All are examples of courtship behavior except _____.
   a. fluffing feathers
   b. taking over a perch
   c. singing songs
   d. releasing pheromones
9. An organized group of animals working specific jobs is a _____.
   a. community   c. society
   b. territory   d. all of these

10. The response of inactivity and slowed metabolism that occurs during hot conditions is _____.
    a. hibernation   c. migration
    b. estivation   d. circadian rhythm

UNDERSTANDING CONCEPTS

Complete each sentence.

11. A social attachment formed after hatching is _____.
12. _____ is what causes an organism to learn.
13. Learning by associating stimuli and responses is called _____.
14. Domination through force or _____ allows one organism control over another.
15. Caring for young is an example of _____ behavior.

THINK AND WRITE CRITICALLY

16. What is the advantage of living in a group?
17. What are the advantages of reflex behaviors?
18. Give an example of something you learned by trial and error.
19. Describe the ways territoriality is expressed to other members of the species.
20. Distinguish between conditioning, trial and error, and imprinting by using an example of each.

21. Explain the type of behavior involved when the bell rings at the end of class.
22. Discuss the advantages and disadvantages of migration as a means of survival.
23. Explain how a habit, such as tying your shoes, is different from a reflex.
24. Use one example to explain how behavior increases an animal's chance for survival.
25. Hens lay more eggs in the spring when day length increases. How can farmers use this knowledge of behavior to their advantage?

MORE SKILL BUILDERS

If you need help, refer to the Skill Handbook.

1. **Classifying:** Make a list of 25 things that you do regularly. Classify each as an innate or learned behavior. Which behaviors do you have more of?
2. **Concept Mapping:** Complete the following concept map outlining the types of behavior.

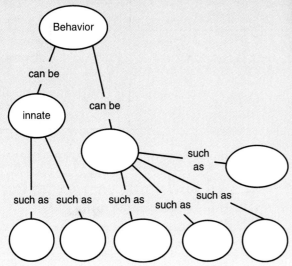

3. **Observing:** Make observations of a dog, cat, or bird for a week. Record what you see. How did the animal communicate with other animals and with you?
4. **Using Variables, Constants, and Controls:** Design an experiment to get a specific response to a stimulus by an animal.
5. **Hypothesizing:** Make a hypothesis about how frogs commmunicate with each other. How could you test your hypothesis?

PROJECTS

1. View the film *Never Cry Wolf* (Disney). Write a summary of the behaviors of the wolves.
2. Draw a map showing the migration route of caribou, the gray whale, or arctic wolf.

GLOBAL CONNECTIONS

Animals

In this unit, you have studied a variety of animals. Now find out how animals are connected to other subjects in different parts of the world.

120° 60°

OCEANOGRAPHY

AN INVASION OF THE U.S. MAINLAND
Lake St. Clair, Michigan

They look insignificant, but zebra mollusks are threatening city water systems and beaches along the Great Lakes. They have few natural predators. Why have zebra mollusks become so abundant? Suggest some ways that zebra mollusks might be controlled.

30°

60°

GEOGRAPHY

ADVENTURES WITH BLACK EAGLES
Pretoria, South Africa

Largest of all the eagles, black eagles inhabit the wild highlands of Southeast Africa. Their enemies are fire, drought, and sheep farmers. Why would fire and drought be a problem for the eagles?

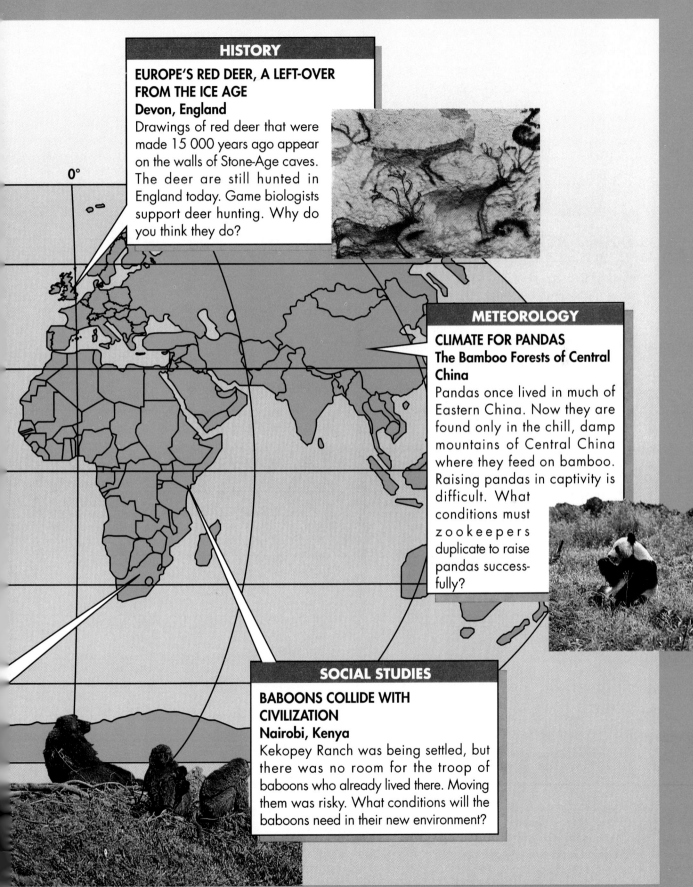

HISTORY

EUROPE'S RED DEER, A LEFT-OVER FROM THE ICE AGE
Devon, England
Drawings of red deer that were made 15 000 years ago appear on the walls of Stone-Age caves. The deer are still hunted in England today. Game biologists support deer hunting. Why do you think they do?

0°

METEOROLOGY

CLIMATE FOR PANDAS
The Bamboo Forests of Central China
Pandas once lived in much of Eastern China. Now they are found only in the chill, damp mountains of Central China where they feed on bamboo. Raising pandas in captivity is difficult. What conditions must zookeepers duplicate to raise pandas successfully?

SOCIAL STUDIES

BABOONS COLLIDE WITH CIVILIZATION
Nairobi, Kenya
Kekopey Ranch was being settled, but there was no room for the troop of baboons who already lived there. Moving them was risky. What conditions will the baboons need in their new environment?

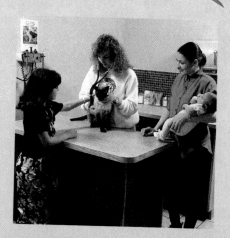

ZOOLOGIST

A *zoologist* is a scientist who studies animals. These scientists are interested in the animal's habitat, behavior, diseases, and life processes. Zoologists who study birds are called ornithologists. Those who study reptiles are called herpetologists. Mammalogists study mammals and ichthyologists study fish.

A person who wants to become a zoologist should like working with animals and be willing to spend long and irregular hours with them. Zoologists need a background in science, particularly biology, zoology, and animal behavior. A trained zoologist will need to have a bachelor of science degree for non-research work. If they plan to do research, they will need to have a master's degree.

For Additional Information

Contact the American Society of Zoologists, 104 Sirius Circle, Thousand Oaks, CA 91360.

VETERINARIAN'S TECHNICIAN

A *veterinarian's technician* likes animals and enjoys working with them. He or she should be calm and reliable, as well as willing to work hard. Some of the work that veterinarian's technicians do is not easy. Cages have to be cleaned, animals groomed, and excited animals must be calmed. Most veterinary technicians are trained on the job. It is possible to start as a part-time animal attendant and advance to technician. Experienced technicians may also find work in kennels, small zoos, pet stores, as assistant laboratory animal technicians, or with the Humane Society.

Some veterinarian technicians want to open their own kennels and raise, groom, or board small animals.

For Additional Information

Contact Animal Caretakers Information, The Humane Society of the U.S., Companion Animals Division, Suite 100, 5430 Grosvenor Lane, Bethesda, MD 20814.

UNIT READINGS

▶"Zebras Are Coming." *Popular Mechanics*, February 1991.
▶Schaller, George G. "Pandas in the Wild." *National Geographic*, December 1981.
▶Clutton-Brock, T.H., "Red Deer and Man." *National Geographic*, October 1986.

John James Audubon
The American Bison

Many people know of Audubon's beautiful bird paintings. In fact, Audubon's birds are what he is best known for today. But Audubon painted other animals, or quadrupeds, as he called them. This painting of the American bison was done in 1845 during a trip Audubon made to the Dakota Prairies.

Audubon did this painting of a male bison. As you study it, you will notice that the painting is so carefully done, it seems almost like a photograph. All attempts were made to be true to nature. Audubon had a dead bison measured and weighed, and made careful notes of the measurements. The painting was one seventh the original size of the animal.

Drawing birds and wild animals was the only thing that made Audubon really happy. Born in Haiti, he spent his early years in France before going to America at 18. His father, a wealthy French planter, tried to set him up in business, but Audubon failed miserably because he was, as a business partner said, continually in the forest. To develop detailed paintings of birds, he used dead birds in their natural settings as his models. In 1826, he began to publish volumes of his works on North American birds. By 1845, Audubon had sold a series of subscriptions for his bird paintings throughout Europe and America. The work had taken him over twenty years to produce.

Now he wanted to complete a series of quadrupeds as well. But he was 53 years old and losing his memory. Only 150 prints of animals were ever completed. Audubon was deeply saddened by the killing of bison and wrote of a hunt he had seen, "What a terrible destruction of life, as it were for nothing, or next to nothing....."

In Your Own Words

▶ Investigate an extinct or endangered species of North American animal. Describe the animal and how it became endangered or extinct. Illustrate the animal in some way.

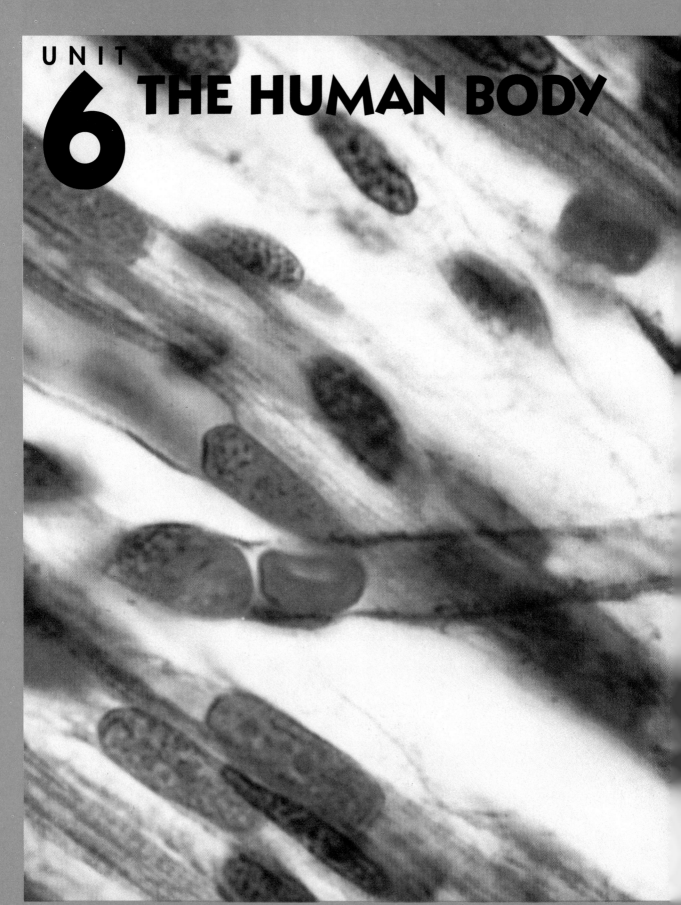

UNIT

6 THE HUMAN BODY

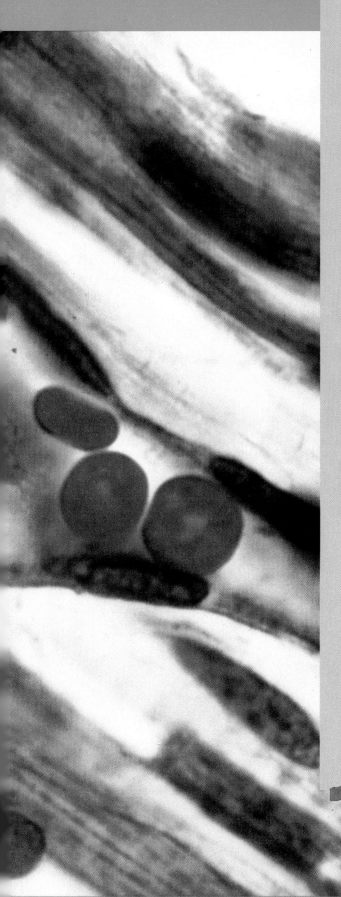

What's Happening Here?

Blood surges through your blood vessels with every beat of your heart. Red blood cells carrying oxygen bend and contort as they are pushed through narrow capillaries. White blood cells tumble past in the river of plasma, on their way to the day-to-day work of keeping you healthy. A ride through a water slide may give you an idea of what it is like to be a blood cell on this journey. In this unit, you will learn about your circulatory system. You will also learn about the other body systems on which your life depends.

UNIT CONTENTS

Chapter 18   Bones, Muscles, and Skin
Chapter 19   Nutrients and Digestion
Chapter 20   Your Circulatory System
Chapter 21   Respiration and Excretion
Chapter 22   Body Regulation
Chapter 23   Reproduction and Growth

CHAPTER

18 Bones, Muscles, and Skin

Like the speed skater on the left, you might have experienced tired muscles after gym class or a soccer game. Although large muscles are the ones that you notice when they tire, your body has many small muscles that can tire after just a little bit of work.

FIND OUT!

Do this activity to find out about some of your small muscles.

Hold a snap-type clothespin between the thumb and forefinger of your writing hand. Rapidly pinch the clothespin open and shut. Count the number of times you can pinch the clothespin before the fingers in your hand become tired. Record the number. Use the thumb and forefinger of your other hand. How do they compare? Do small muscles that are exercised more (your writing hand) tire faster or slower than those in the hand that gets less exercise?

Gearing Up

Previewing the Chapter

Use this outline to help you focus on important ideas in this chapter.

Section 18-1   The Skeletal System
▶ What Is a Skeletal System?
▶ Bone
▶ Bone Development
▶ Fractures
▶ Joints

Section 18-2   The Muscular System
▶ The Muscular System
▶ Three Types of Muscle Tissue
▶ Muscles at Work

Section 18-3   Science and Society
Drugs for Fitness?
▶ Do Steroids Give a "Winning Edge"?

Section 18-4   Skin
▶ The Body's Largest Organ
▶ Skin at Work

Previewing Science Skills

▶ In the **Skill Builders**, you will outline, sequence, and make a concept map.
▶ In the **Activities**, you will observe, collect data, hypothesize, and experiment.
▶ In the **MINI-Labs**, you will observe and experiment.

What's next?

Throughout the day, hundreds of muscles, both large and small, work to move your body. In this chapter, you'll learn how muscles and bones provide the body with a working structure. You'll also learn about skin, your body's largest organ, and its many functions.

18-1   The Skeletal System

New Science Words

skeletal system
periosteum
marrow
cartilage
fracture
joint
ligament
immovable joint
movable joint

Objectives

▶ Identify the five major functions of the skeletal system.
▶ Describe how a fracture heals.
▶ Compare and contrast movable and immovable joints.

What Is a Skeletal System?

Have you ever gone to a museum and seen an exhibit of bones from an ancient burial site? If you have, you might have the impression that all bones are dead structures made of dry, rocklike material. Although the museum bones are no longer living, the bones in your body are very much alive. Each bone within your body is a living organ. Cells in these bones take in food and expend energy. They have the same requirements as other cells throughout your body.

Because you have a skeleton, you stand, walk, run, and breathe. All the bones together make up your **skeletal system,** which is the framework of your body. The human skeletal system has five major functions. First, it gives shape and support to your body, much like the framework of a building. Second, bones protect your internal organs. In the skeleton shown in Figure 18-1, ribs surround the heart and lungs with a bony cage, and a hard skull encloses the brain. Third, major muscles of the body are attached to bone. Muscles move bones. Fourth, blood cells are formed in the marrow of some bones. Bone marrow is a soft, spongy tissue in the center of the many bones. Finally, the skeleton is the place where the minerals calcium and phosphorus are stored in the body. Calcium and phosphorus make bone hard.

Figure 18-1. The Human Skeletal System

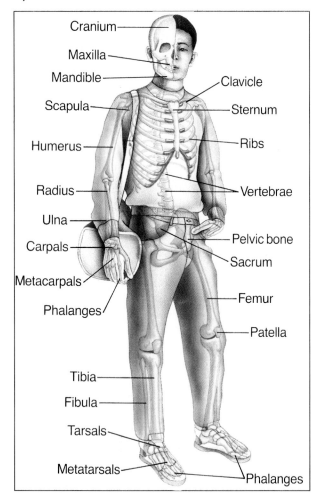

Cranium
Maxilla
Mandible
Scapula
Humerus
Radius
Ulna
Carpals
Metacarpals
Phalanges
Clavicle
Sternum
Ribs
Vertebrae
Pelvic bone
Sacrum
Femur
Patella
Tibia
Fibula
Tarsals
Metatarsals
Phalanges

Bone

Pick up a bone and you'll find that it isn't all smooth. There are bumps, edges, round ends, rough spots, and many pits and holes. Each of these marks has a purpose. Muscles attach to some of the bumps and pits. Blood vessels and nerves enter and leave through the holes.

Your skeleton has 206 bones of various sizes and shapes. Bones are frequently classified according to shape. Figure 18-2 shows bones that are long, short, flat, or irregular. Their shapes are genetically controlled and modified by the work of muscles attached to them.

Many internal and external characteristics of bone are easily seen in the humerus shown in Figure 18-3. The humerus is a long bone in your upper arm. The surface of the long portion of the bone is covered with a tough, tight-fitting membrane called **periosteum** (per ee AHS tee um). Small blood vessels in the periosteum carry nutrients into the bone. This membrane is also important in the growth and repair of bone. Under the periosteum is compact bone, a hard, strong layer of bone. Compact bone contains bone cells, blood vessels, the minerals calcium and phosphorus, and elastic fibers. Rickets and osteoporosis are two diseases that result from lack of minerals in bone. Elastic fibers keep bone from being too rigid and brittle or easily broken.

Spongy bone in a long bone is found toward the ends of the bone. Spongy bone is much less compact and has many small open spaces that make the bone lightweight. If all your bones were completely solid, you'd have a much greater mass. Long bones have large openings, or cavities. The cavities in the center of long bones and the

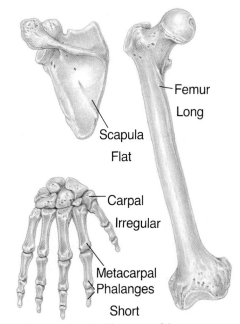

Figure 18-2. Shapes of human bones show something about their functions.

Did You Know?

An adult male is 3.84 times as tall as the length of his thigh bone.

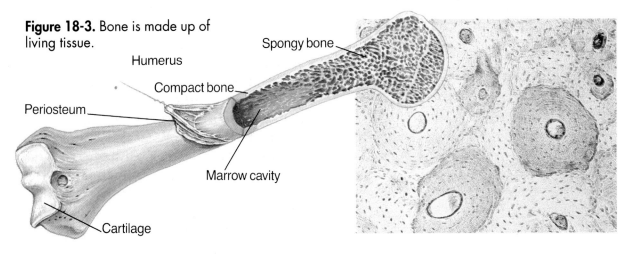

Figure 18-3. Bone is made up of living tissue.

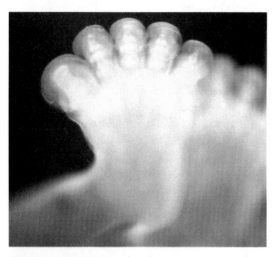

Figure 18-4. During development before birth, the skeleton is first made up of cartilage, which is then gradually replaced by bone.

How is bone formed and reformed?

Figure 18-5. For a fracture to heal, the broken ends of the bone have to be brought together.

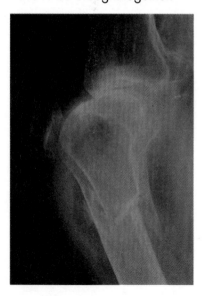

spaces in spongy bone are filled with a fatty tissue called **marrow.** In a healthy person, marrow produces red blood cells at an incredible rate of between two and three billion cells per second. White blood cells are also produced in bone marrow, but in lesser amounts.

Unless you have a condition called arthritis, you move about fairly comfortably. This is because the ends of your bones are covered with a thick, smooth layer of tissue called **cartilage.** Cartilage does not contain blood vessels or minerals. It is flexible and is important at joints, where it absorbs shock and makes movement easier.

Bone Development

Before you were born, your skeleton was first made in the form of cartilage. Gradually the cartilage was broken down and replaced by bone-forming cells called osteoblasts (AHS tee oh blastz). These cells deposit calcium and phosphorus that make bone tissue hard. At birth, your skeleton was made up of more than the 206 bones you now have. As you developed, some bones fused, or grew together.

Healthy bone tissue is dynamic. It is always being formed and reformed by the cells it contains. A second type of bone cell, an osteoclast, breaks down bone tissue. This is a normal process in a healthy person. Osteoclasts break down bone and release calcium and phosphorus. This process keeps the calcium and phosphorus in your bloodstream at about the same level.

Fractures

Although bones are strong and flexible, they can break. A break in a bone is a **fracture.** A simple fracture occurs when a bone has broken but the broken ends do not break through the skin. In a compound fracture, the broken ends of the bone stick out through the skin.

To heal, the broken ends of the bone have to be brought in contact with each another. The periosteum starts to make new bone cells. A thick band of new bone forms around the break, acting like a built-in splint. Over time, the thickened band disappears as bone is reshaped with the help of osteoclasts. Breaks are usually held immobile with a cast.

Joints

Think of all the different actions you performed this morning getting ready for school. You opened your mouth to yawn, chewed your breakfast, reached for a toothbrush, and stretched out your arm to turn the doorknob as you walked out the door. All these motions were possible because your skeleton has joints.

Any place where two or more bones meet is a **joint.** Sometimes a model of a joint is made from two cardboard tubes and some rubber bands. The tubes represent bones, and the rubber bands represent ligaments. A **ligament** is a tough band of tissue that holds bones together at joints. Many joints, such as your knee, are held together by more than one ligament.

Joints are classified as immovable or movable depending on how much movement takes place. An **immovable joint** allows little or no movement. The joints of the bones of your skull and pelvis are classified as immovable. A **movable joint** allows the body to make a wide range of movements. Shooting baskets or working the controls of a video game require movable joints. There are several types of movable joints: pivot, ball-and-socket, hinge, and

Science and READING

You may have heard of someone, perhaps an athlete, who has had arthroscopic surgery. Find out about this procedure and the part of the body involved. How is this surgery different from other types of surgery?

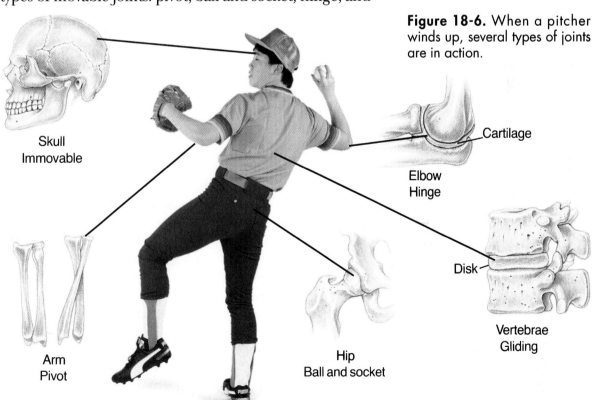

Figure 18-6. When a pitcher winds up, several types of joints are in action.

Skull
Immovable

Cartilage

Elbow
Hinge

Arm
Pivot

Hip
Ball and socket

Disk

Vertebrae
Gliding

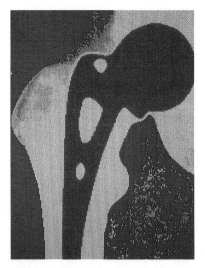

Figure 18-7. Certain joints, especially those in the hip, knee, and elbow, have been successfully replaced by artificial joints.

Where is cartilage found?

gliding joints. In a pivot joint, one bone rotates in a ring of another bone. Turning your head is an example of a pivot movement. In a ball-and-socket joint, one bone has a rounded end that fits into a cuplike cavity on another bone.

A third type of joint is a hinge joint. This joint has a back and forth movement like that of hinges on a door. Elbows, knees, and fingers have hinge joints. A fourth type of joint is a gliding joint where one part of a bone glides over another bone. Gliding joints are found in your wrists and ankles and between vertebrae. Gliding joints are the most frequently used joints in your body. You can't write a word, pick up a sock, or take a step without using a gliding joint.

Cartilage helps make body movements easier. It covers the ends of bones in movable joints. Pads of cartilage called disks are also found between the vertebrae. Here, cartilage also acts as a cushion and prevents injury to your spinal cord. Your outer ear and the end of your nose are also made of cartilage.

Your body contains a living framework in the form of bones. Bones not only support the body but also supply it with minerals and blood cells. Joints are places between bones that enable the framework to be flexible and to be more than just a storehouse for minerals.

SECTION REVIEW

1. What are the five major functions of a skeleton?
2. What are two jobs of the periosteum?
3. Name and gave an example of one kind of movable joint.
4. What are the functions of cartilage?
5. **Apply:** The thick band of bone that forms around a healing broken bone is called a callus. In time it disappears. What is there in bone that enables this extra amount of bone to disappear?

Skill Builder

☑ **Outlining**

Outline the major functions of bone and give an example of each. If you need help, refer to Outlining in the **Skill Handbook** on page 681.

ACTIVITY 18-1
Observing Bones

Problem: *What are the parts of a long bone?*

Materials

- beef bone
- hand lens
- scalpel
- microscope slide
- microscope
- coverslip
- dropper
- water

Procedure

1. Make a table like the one shown.
2. Obtain a beef bone that has been cut in half along the length and width.
3. Observe the bone with a hand lens. Identify the periosteum, compact bone, spongy bone, and any marrow that is present.
4. Draw a diagram of the bone and label the parts you have been able to recognize. In the table, describe each part.
5. Use a scalpel to carefully remove a very small piece of red bone marrow. **CAUTION:** *Always use extreme care when using sharp instruments.*
6. Make a temporary wet mount slide of the marrow. Examine it under low power. Describe and draw what you see.

Data and Observations

FEATURES OF BONE	
Part	**Description**
Periosteum	
Compact bone	
Spongy bone	
Marrow	

Analyze

1. What parts of the bone were you able to identify?
2. Describe the portions of the bone that contain marrow.
3. What differences did you observe in the overall shape of the bone?

Conclude and Apply

4. How might the function of the spongy bone area and the compact bone areas be related to the shape of the areas in which they are found?
5. From your observations, where would you say that most calcium is stored in a long bone?

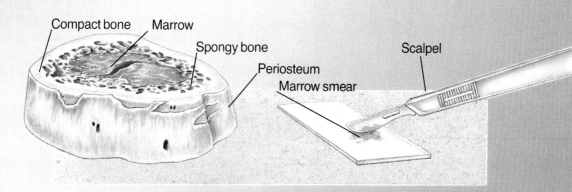

Compact bone Marrow Spongy bone Periosteum Marrow smear Scalpel

The Muscular System

New Science Words

muscle
voluntary muscles
involuntary muscles
skeletal muscles
tendons
smooth muscles
cardiac muscle

Objectives

▶ Describe the major function of muscles.
▶ Compare and contrast three types of muscles.
▶ Explain how muscle action results in movement of body parts.

The Muscular System

Bones and joints together are somewhat like simple machines, but on their own they have no power to move. Muscles are the motors that move body parts. There are more than 600 muscles in your body. This means that nearly 35 to 40 percent of your body mass is muscle tissue. No matter how still you might try to be, there is always movement taking place in your body. Every system in your body contains some type of muscle tissue as a part of that system. As a result, every part of your body is moved at some time during your life, if not every day. A **muscle** is an organ that contracts and gets shorter. As a result, body parts move. Energy is used, and work is done.

Voluntary muscles are muscles that you control. Your arm and leg muscles are voluntary. So are the muscles of your hands and face. You can choose to move them or not to move them. In contrast, **involuntary muscles** are muscles you can't consciously control. You don't have to decide to make these muscles work. They just go on working all day long, all your life. Blood gets pumped through blood vessels, and food is moved through your digestive system by the action of involuntary muscles. You can sleep at night without having to think about how to keep these muscles working.

Figure 18-8. Muscles of the Human Body

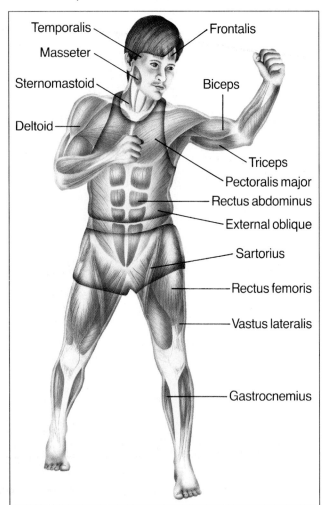

Temporalis
Frontalis
Masseter
Sternomastoid
Biceps
Deltoid
Triceps
Pectoralis major
Rectus abdominus
External oblique
Sartorius
Rectus femoris
Vastus lateralis
Gastrocnemius

Table 18-1

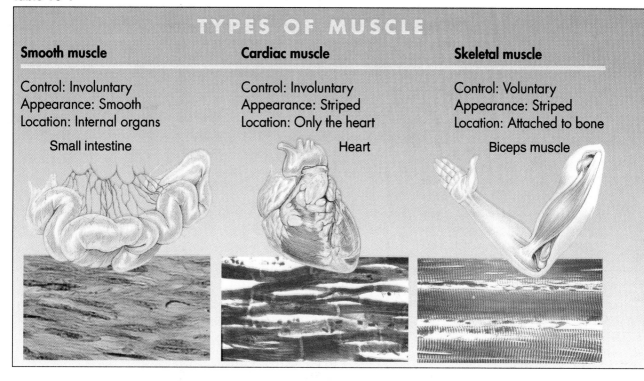

TYPES OF MUSCLE

Smooth muscle	Cardiac muscle	Skeletal muscle
Control: Involuntary Appearance: Smooth Location: Internal organs	Control: Involuntary Appearance: Striped Location: Only the heart	Control: Voluntary Appearance: Striped Location: Attached to bone
Small intestine	Heart	Biceps muscle

Three Types of Muscle Tissue

There are three types of muscle tissue in your body: skeletal, smooth, and cardiac. Skeletal muscles are the most numerous muscles in the body. Under a microscope, skeletal muscle cells look striped, or striated. **Skeletal muscles** are attached to bones by tendons. **Tendons** are thick bands that pull on the bone as the muscle contracts. These muscles are voluntary muscles. You control their use when you choose to walk or not to walk. Skeletal muscles tend to contract quickly and tire easily.

Smooth muscles are involuntary. The walls of the stomach, intestine, uterus, bladder, penis, and blood vessels are some of the places where one or more layers of smooth muscle are found. Smooth muscles contract and relax slowly. They have no striations.

The third type of muscle, **cardiac muscle,** is found only in the heart. Cardiac muscle is also involuntary. As you can see from Table 18-1, cardiac muscle has striations like skeletal muscle. However, cardiac muscle is like smooth muscle in that it is involuntary. Cardiac muscle contracts about 70 times per minute every day of your life. You know each contraction as a heartbeat, but it isn't something you can control.

Science and MATH

Because of regular exercise during the track season, Hope was able to reduce her at-rest pulse rate from 76 beats per minute to 66. Estimate how many beats Hope is saving her heart muscle per day.

Muscles at Work

Skeletal muscle movements are the result of pairs of muscles working together. When one muscle of a pair contracts, the other muscle relaxes, or returns to its original length. Sit up straight in a chair with your feet on the floor as in Figure 18-9a. Slowly bring your right leg up so that your leg is straight out. Now slowly bring the leg down so that your right foot is on the floor again. When you straighten your leg at the knee, one set of muscles in the upper part of your leg contracts. This causes the bones of your lower leg to be pulled straight up. Muscles always pull; they never push. When your leg moves down, muscles on the back of your upper leg contract to pull the leg downward.

When you straightened your leg, your muscles used energy. Muscles use chemical energy in the form of glucose. As the bonds in glucose break, chemical energy changes to mechanical energy and the muscle contracts. When the supply of glucose in a muscle gets used up, it becomes tired and needs to rest. Muscles also produce thermal energy when they contract. The heat produced by muscle contraction helps to keep your body temperature constant.

Over a period of time, muscles become larger or smaller, depending on how much work they do. Skeletal muscles that do a lot of work, such as those in your writing hand or in the arms of a brick layer, become large and strong. In contrast, if you just sit and watch TV all day, your muscles will become soft and flabby, and will lack strength. Muscles that aren't exercised become smaller in size.

Figure 18-9. Skeletal muscles work in pairs. When one muscle in a pair contracts, the other is relaxed.

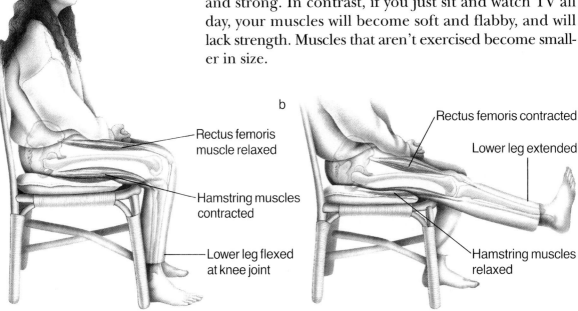

a

Rectus femoris muscle relaxed

Hamstring muscles contracted

Lower leg flexed at knee joint

b

Rectus femoris contracted

Lower leg extended

Hamstring muscles relaxed

PROBLEM SOLVING

The Case of the Skinny Arm

Kristin was a co-captain of the seventh-grade volleyball team. She was great, so everyone on the team was a little upset when she came to school one morning with a cast on her arm. She had broken it while playing with her dog in the backyard. The doctor told her she would have to wear the cast for six weeks. Her arm itched constantly inside the cast.

When the doctor cut the cast off, Kristin looked at her arm and groaned. It was pale and shriveled, and it still itched. Not only that, but "Mom," she wailed, "it's so skinny. Is it always going to look so gross?" Why did Kristin's arm become skinny?

Think Critically: What directions will the doctor give Kristin so she can play volleyball again?

Could you lift and lower your leg all day? What would it feel like after one minute? After five minutes? Your leg would probably feel tired and achy after five minutes of flexing, don't you think? Large and small muscles need to rest from time to time to be resupplied with glucose.

SECTION REVIEW

1. What is the function of the muscular system?
2. Compare and contrast the three types of muscle.
3. What attaches a muscle to a bone?
4. What three forms of energy are involved in a muscle contraction?
5. **Apply:** What happens to your muscles when you bend your arm at the elbow?

☑ Sequencing

Sequence the activities that take place when you bend your leg at the knee. If you need help, refer to Sequencing in the **Skill Handbook** on page 680.

Skill Builder

18-3 Drugs for Fitness?

New Science Words

anabolic steroids

Objectives

▶ List side effects of anabolic steroid use.
▶ Discuss the use of anabolic steroids among athletes.

Do Steroids Give a "Winning Edge"?

Have you stood in front of the mirror flexing your muscles, wishing you looked like the bodybuilders you've seen on TV or in magazines? In our society, a well-built body is often admired. Athletes from junior high school students to the top professionals feel the desire to be bigger, better, or faster. They spend hours each week training and building their muscles. But some athletes feel that they aren't getting big enough fast enough. Some even turn to misuse of drugs called anabolic steroids.

Anabolic steroids are drugs that contain a variation of the hormone testosterone. Testosterone occurs naturally in both men and women, but it reaches much higher levels in males. It produces male characteristics such as a deep voice. Anabolic steroids were originally developed in the 1930s to help sick people build muscle tissue.

Figure 18-10. Abuse of anabolic steroids among high school athletes causes health problems.

Many athletes feel that if normal amounts of testosterone are good for muscle building, then increased amounts are even better. But is this true?

Athletes who use anabolic steroids may endanger their health. When women use steroids, they grow excessive facial hair, their voices may deepen, and their breasts may shrink. In males, steroid use may cause testicles to shrink and small lumps of breast tissue to develop. Both males and females who use anabolic steroids may develop hypertension and emotional swings. When taken in abusive amounts, some athletes have become extremely aggressive, retain excess water, and show excessive acne. When adolescents use steroids, their growth can be stunted, and that growth can't be made up in later life.

Is steroid use worth it? Does it give an athlete the "winning edge"?

In 1988, Canadian athlete Ben Johnson won a gold medal at the Olympic games in Seoul, Korea. He ran the 100-meter race in 9.79 seconds, a world record. Three days later Ben Johnson's gold medal and world record were taken from him. Olympic officials had found anabolic steroids in his urine sample. Like most major amateur sporting events, the Olympics ban the use of steroids and other drugs. Johnson has since said that he had used steroids for about seven years.

Some college and professional athletes are known to use anabolic steroids. Some feel strongly that when taken in prescribed doses, these drugs are safe, heal damaged tissues, and enhance athletic ability. The greater concern comes from the use of these drugs by developing adolescents who may think more is better and who misuse the drugs.

An additional problem becomes clear. If athletes use drugs such as anabolic steroids, is real athletic ability being demonstrated? How fair is the high school track meet if some athletes use the drugs and some don't? And what price do students pay? One researcher has warned that the drugs are too powerful not to have some damaging effects if used over a long period.

Figure 18-11. In 1984, the International Olympic Committee banned the use of anabolic steroids to maintain fairness in the events.

SECTION REVIEW

1. Why were anabolic steroids originally developed?
2. What are some of the side effects of anabolic steroid use?

You Decide!

Tests have been developed to detect the presence of anabolic steroids in blood and urine. Should professional and college athletes be allowed to use these drugs? What about younger athletes? Steroid abuse has been found in junior high and high school students. Should school athletes be allowed to use these drugs, even if prescribed?

18-4 Skin

New Science Words

epidermis
melanin
dermis

Objectives

▶ Compare and contrast the epidermis and dermis of the skin.
▶ List the functions of the skin.
▶ Discuss how skin protects the body from disease and how it heals itself.

Did You Know?

Goose bumps result when small smooth muscles at the base of each hair in your skin contract. Each hair stands on end as the muscle pulls on the hair.

Figure 18-12. Skin is made up of two layers, the epidermis and the dermis. The dermis contains blood vessels, glands, and nerves.

The Body's Largest Organ

Your skin, hair, nails, and millions of sweat and oil glands are part of your body's largest system, the integumentary (ihn teg yuh MENT uh ree) system.

Skin is the largest organ of your body. It is the one organ you are most familiar with, yet you may know less about your skin than about your muscles. Much of the information you receive about your environment comes through your skin. Although only a few millimeters thick in most places, skin is made up of two layers of tissue, the epidermis and the dermis. The **epidermis** is the surface layer of your skin. The cells on the top of the epidermis are dead. Thousands of these cells rub off every time you take a shower, shake hands, blow your nose, or scratch your elbow. New cells are constantly produced at the bot-

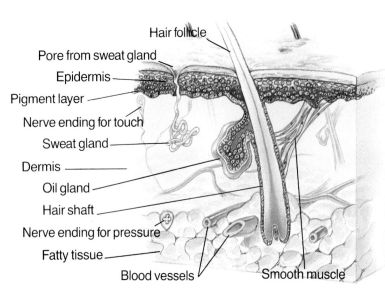

Hair follicle
Pore from sweat gland
Epidermis
Pigment layer
Nerve ending for touch
Sweat gland
Dermis
Oil gland
Hair shaft
Nerve ending for pressure
Fatty tissue
Blood vessels
Smooth muscle

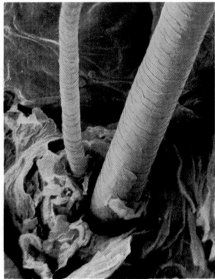

tom of the epidermis to replace the ones that are rubbed off. Cells in the epidermis produce the chemical melanin (MEL uh nun). **Melanin** is a pigment that gives your skin color. The more melanin, the darker the color of the skin. Melanin increases when your skin is exposed to the ultraviolet rays of the sun. If someone has very few melanin-producing cells, very little color gets deposited. These people have less protection from the sun. They burn more easily and may develop skin cancer more easily.

The **dermis** is the layer of tissue under the epidermis. This layer is thicker than the epidermis and contains many blood vessels, nerves, and oil and sweat glands. Notice in Figure 18-12 that under the dermis there are fat cells. This fatty tissue insulates the body. When a person gains too much weight, this is also where much of the extra fat is deposited.

The epidermis may be very thin, but injury to large areas of the skin can cause death. If the epidermis is burned away in a third degree burn, there are no cells left that can divide to replace this lost layer. As a result, nerve endings and blood vessels in the dermis are exposed. Water is lost rapidly from the dermis and muscle tissues. Body tissues are exposed to bacteria and to potential infection, shock, and death.

If injury to the epidermis is slight, a scab forms as in Figure 18-14. In scab formation, cells of the deepest layer of the epidermis can reproduce to cover the injured dermis. Later, the scab falls off on its own.

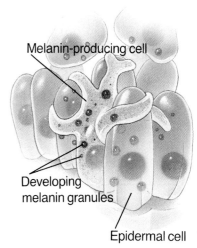

Figure 18-13. Pigment cells release melanin, which moves into other cells in the skin.

Figure 18-14. Within minutes of an injury, a loose blood clot forms (a). In a few days, new cells from the epidermis grow under the hardening clot (b). In a week, the hardened scab is ready to be pushed off (c).

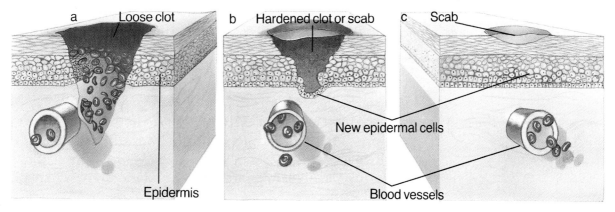

Robot Skin

Industrial robots are programmed to use a specific force to pick up an object. So long as they are built to handle a specific type of object, this works well. But, what if a robot had sense organs? Then it could adjust itself to doing different tasks.

Scientists are developing an artificial skin for robots that can sense the difference between a rock and a tomato and handle each correctly. The artificial skin is modeled after human skin. The outer layer is made of electrode sheets with gel between them. This layer reads the amount of pressure placed on an object. The inner layer consists of a layer of sensors between two rubber sheets. These sensors can detect very fine textures and friction.

Right now, scientists are looking for a way to make the artificial skin without making it too thick.

Think Critically: How does artificial skin resemble human skin?

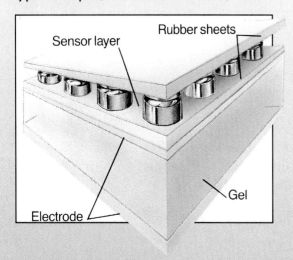

Sensor layer
Rubber sheets
Gel
Electrode

EcoTip

Persons who burn easily should avoid excessive exposure to ultraviolet light—both out in the sun and in a tanning bed.

Skin at Work

Your skin has five major functions. First, it forms a protective covering over the body. As a covering, it prevents injury and disease. Its large bacterial population works to destroy invading harmful pathogens. Skin prevents water loss from body tissues.

Second, skin has an important homeostasis function because it helps regulate body temperature. Humans, unlike most fur-bearing animals, have very little hair to help them regulate body temperature. Hair is an adaptation that usually helps control body temperature. Instead, sweating cools the body. Blood vessels in the skin can help hold or release heat.

There are about three million sweat glands in the dermis. These glands help rid the body of wastes and are part of the body's method of keeping body temperature constant. When the body gets hot, blood vessels expand or dilate. Pores leading to the sweat glands in the skin

open. Perspiration, or sweat, moves out onto the skin. The body then cools as sweat evaporates. This system balances heat produced by muscle contractions.

A third function of the skin is to excrete wastes. Sweat glands release water, sodium chloride, and a protein product called urea. Fourth, skin serves as a sensory organ. Nerve endings in skin funnel information about temperature, touch, and pressure. The fifth function is the formation of vitamin D. Small amounts of this vitamin are produced in the epidermis in the presence of sunlight. Vitamin D is needed to absorb calcium.

Your skin is a remarkable organ. It is your first contact with the environment. Skin protects the body from harmful outside substances and preserves the tissues within it.

MINI-Lab

Is there water in sweat?
Note the color of a piece of cobalt chloride paper; record. With a medicine dropper, add a drop of water. Observe and record the color now. Do vigorous jumping jacks for three minutes, being sure to clap your hands. Then hold the cobalt chloride paper in your hand. What color is it now? What can you conclude about the distribution of sweat glands on your hands?

SECTION REVIEW

1. Compare and contrast the epidermis and dermis.
2. Describe the five functions of the skin.
3. How does skin help prevent disease in the body?
4. Explain how a scab forms.
5. **Apply:** Why is a person who has been severely burned in danger of death from loss of water?

☑ Concept Mapping

Make an events chain concept map to show how skin helps keep body temperature constant. If you need help, refer to Concept Mapping in the **Skill Handbook** on pages 688 and 689.

Skill Builder

ACTIVITY 18-2
Observing Muscle

Problem: *What do different types of muscle look like?*

Materials
- prepared slides of smooth, skeletal, and cardiac muscles
- microscope
- cooked turkey leg
- dissecting pan or cutting board
- dissecting probes (2)
- hand lens

Procedure
Part A
1. Using the microscope, first on low power, and then on high power, observe three different types of muscle.
2. On a sheet of paper, draw and label each type of muscle that you observe.

Part B
3. Muscle tissue is made up of groups of cells held together in fibers, usually by a transparent covering called connective tissue. Obtain a piece of cooked turkey leg from your teacher. On the cutting board, use the two probes to tease the muscle fibers apart.
4. Use a hand lens to examine the muscle fibers and any connective tissue you see from the turkey leg.
5. Draw and measure five turkey leg fibers and describe the shape of these muscle fibers.

Data and Observations

Skeletal	Cardiac	Smooth
Length of fibers		

Analyze
1. Which muscles on the slides have stripes, or striations?
2. How long are the muscle fibers in the turkey leg?
3. What type of muscles are there in a turkey leg?
4. How are muscle fibers arranged in the slides and in the turkey leg?

Conclude and Apply
5. How might the shape of a muscle fiber be related to its function?
6. Can you conclude that striations have anything to do with whether a muscle is voluntary or involuntary?

SUMMARY

18-1: The Skeletal System

1. Bones are living structures that protect, support, make blood, store minerals, and provide for muscle attachment.

2. Broken bones heal when the broken ends contact and a thick band of cells produced by the periosteum forms.

3. Movable joints move freely and are pivot, hinge, ball-and-socket, or gliding in type. The skull and pelvic joints in adults do not move and are classified as immovable.

18-2: The Muscular System

1. Muscle contracts to move bones and body parts.

2. Skeletal muscle is voluntary and moves bones. Smooth muscle is involuntary and controls movement in internal organs. Cardiac muscle is involuntary and located only in the heart.

3. Muscles contract to move body parts. Muscles pull, never push, body parts. Skeletal muscles work in pairs. When one contracts, the other relaxes.

18-3: Science and Society: Drugs for Fitness?

1. Anabolic steroids build muscle, but the effects of abuse may be threatening to health.

2. Use of anabolic steroids is controversial.

18-4: Skin

1. The epidermis is the outer layer with dead cells on the surface. Bottom layers of epidermis give rise to new skin cells. Melanin is found in the inner layers. The dermis is the inner layer with hair follicles, nails, nerves, sweat and oil glands, and blood vessels.

2. Protection, water retention, storage of vitamin D, and helping with body temperature are the skin's jobs.

3. Undamaged epidermis destroys bacteria and can form protective scabs.

KEY SCIENCE WORDS

a. **cardiac muscle**
b. **cartilage**
c. **dermis**
d. **epidermis**
e. **fracture**
f. **immovable joint**
g. **involuntary muscles**
h. **joint**
i. **ligament**
j. **marrow**
k. **melanin**
l. **movable joint**
m. **muscle**
n. **periosteum**
o. **skeletal muscles**
p. **skeletal system**
q. **smooth muscles**
r. **anabolic steroids**
s. **tendons**
t. **voluntary muscles**

UNDERSTANDING VOCABULARY

Match each phrase with the correct term from the list of Key Science Words.

1. tough outer covering of bone
2. our inside body framework
3. tissue or organ that contracts
4. a broken bone
5. muscles you can control
6. involuntary heart muscle
7. outer layer of skin
8. skin pigment
9. holds bones together
10. attach muscles to bones

CHAPTER
REVIEW

Choose the word or phrase that completes the sentence.

1. _____ bone is the most solid form of bone.
   - **a.** Compact
   - **b.** Periosteum
   - **c.** Spongy
   - **d.** Marrow

2. Blood cells are made in the _____.
   - **a.** compact bone
   - **b.** periosteum
   - **c.** spongy bone
   - **d.** marrow

3. Minerals are stored in _____.
   - **a.** bone
   - **b.** skin
   - **c.** muscle
   - **d.** all of these

4. _____ covers the ends of bones.
   - **a.** Cartilage
   - **b.** Tendons
   - **c.** Ligaments
   - **d.** None of these

5. Immovable joints are found _____.
   - **a.** at the elbow
   - **b.** at the neck
   - **c.** in the wrist
   - **d.** in the skull

6. The knees and fingers are examples of a _____ joint.
   - **a.** pivot
   - **b.** hinge
   - **c.** gliding
   - **d.** ball-and-joint

7. Vitamin _____ is made in the skin.
   - **a.** K
   - **b.** B
   - **c.** D
   - **d.** none of these

8. Dead cells are found on the _____.
   - **a.** dermis
   - **b.** marrow
   - **c.** epidermis
   - **d.** periosteum

9. Anabolic steroids promote _____.
   - **a.** strength
   - **b.** muscle growth
   - **c.** speed
   - **d.** all of these

10. _____ helps retain fluids in the body.
    - **a.** Bone
    - **b.** Muscle
    - **c.** Skin
    - **d.** A steroid

UNDERSTANDING CONCEPTS

Complete each sentence.

11. Osteoblasts are cells that _____ bone.
12. Involuntary _____ muscles line the stomach.
13. Cardiac and smooth muscles are both _____ in action.
14. The _____ is the body's largest organ.
15. The _____ is the layer of skin where sweat glands are found.

THINK AND WRITE CRITICALLY

16. Distinguish between the functions of ligaments and tendons.
17. What would result if a person had a disease of the periosteum?
18. In arthritis, cartilage is frequently damaged. Why does movement then become painful?
19. From a coach's point of view, why are there advantages and disadvantages to use of anabolic steroids?
20. What would happen if a person's sweat glands didn't produce sweat?

21. When might skin not be able to produce enough vitamin D?
22. What effects do sunblocks have on melanin?
23. What would lack of calcium do to bones?
24. How could you distinguish among the three muscle types under the microscope?
25. What function of skin in your lower lip changes when a dentist gives you novocaine for a filling in your bottom teeth? Why?

MORE SKILL BUILDERS

If you need help, refer to the Skill Handbook.

1. **Hypothesizing:** Make a hypothesis to explain why a person who "slips a disc" is in pain.
2. **Designing an Experiment:** Design an experiment to compare the heartbeat of athletes and nonathletes in your class.
3. **Hypothesizing:** Make a hypothesis about the distribution of sweat glands throughout the body. Are they evenly distributed?
4. **Concept Mapping:** Complete the events chain concept map to describe scab formation.

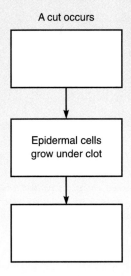

A cut occurs

↓

Epidermal cells grow under clot

↓

5. **Observing and Inferring:** The joints in the skull of a newborn baby are soft, whereas those of a 17-year-old are tightly grown together. Infer why the infant's skull joints are soft.

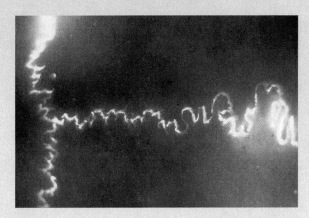

PROJECTS

1. Find out the differences among first, second, and third degree burns. A local hospital's burn unit or fire department are sources of information on burns.
2. How do tanning booths give you a suntan? Research the safety of these booths.

19 Nutrients and Digestion

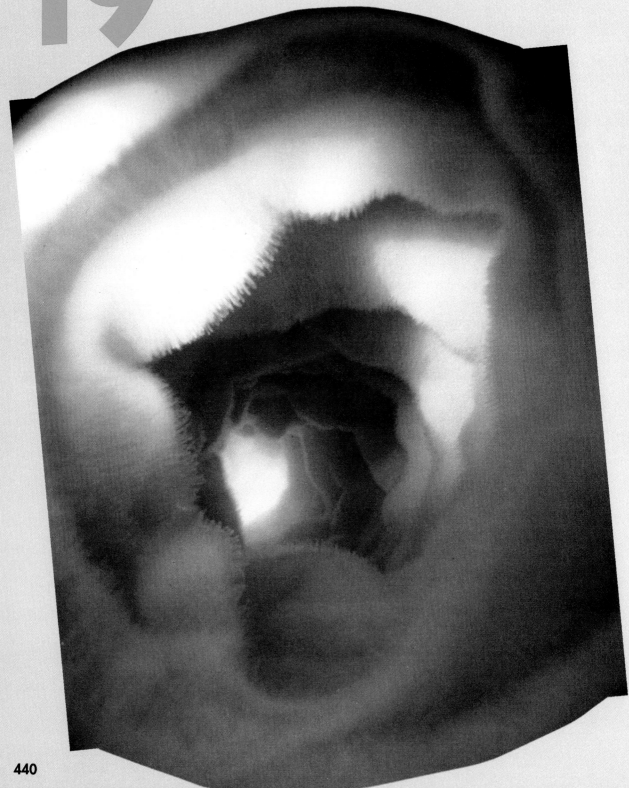

Food that you eat is broken down and absorbed in the soft tissues of your small intestine as shown in the photograph on page 440. Energy from this food is measured in kilocalories. You know these simply as calories. How many calories do you use each day?

FIND OUT!

Calculate the rate at which your body uses energy.

Males use about 1.0 calorie per kilogram (kg) of body mass per hour. Females burn 0.9 calorie per kg of body mass per hour.

1. Convert your mass in pounds to kilograms.
   Pounds × 0.4536 = kg
2. Multiply your mass by either 1.0 or 0.9 based on your sex. Your answer is how much energy (cal) you use per hour.
3. Multiply the calories used in one hour by 24 (hours per day). Your answer is the amount of energy you burn per day.

Gearing Up
Previewing the Chapter
Use this outline to help you focus on important ideas in this chapter.

Section 19-1   Nutrition
▶ Why Do You Eat?
▶ Food Groups

Section 19-2   Your Digestive System
▶ Processing Food
▶ In Your Mouth
▶ In Your Stomach
▶ In Your Small Intestine
▶ In Your Large Intestine

Section 19-3   Science and Society
Eating Disorders
▶ Are Looks That Important?
▶ Eating Disorders
▶ What Can You Do?

Previewing Science Skills
▶ In the **Skill Builders**, you will make and use tables and observe and infer.
▶ In the **Activities**, you will hypothesize, experiment, and collect data.
▶ In the **MINI-Labs**, you will measure in SI and make models.

What's next?

Food that you eat each day gives you the energy you need to live. Find out how your body processes food that supplies you with this energy.

New Science Words

nutrients
carbohydrates
proteins
amino acids
fats
vitamins
minerals
food group

Objectives

▶ List the six classes of nutrients.
▶ Describe the importance of each type of nutrient.
▶ Explain the relationship between diet and health.

Why Do You Eat?

While eating cereal for breakfast, you've probably read all the ads and offers on the box. You may also have noticed the list of nutrients on the side panel. By law, the amount of each nutrient in the cereal has to be listed for you on the label. You think you're eating toasted corn with raisins, but you're really taking in nutrients. **Nutrients** are substances in foods that provide energy and materials for cell development, growth, and repair.

There are six kinds of nutrients available in food: carbohydrates, proteins, fats, vitamins, minerals, and water. Carbohydrates, proteins, vitamins, and fats are all organic nutrients. In contrast, minerals and water are inorganic. They do not contain carbon. Foods containing carbohydrates, fats, and proteins are usually too complex to be absorbed right away by your body. These substances need to be broken down into simpler molecules before the body can make use of them. In contrast, minerals and water can be absorbed directly into your bloodstream. They don't require digestion or breakdown.

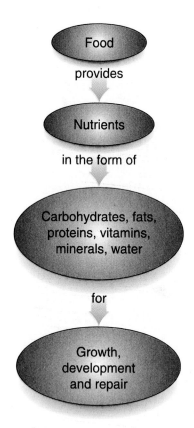

Figure 19-1. Food from a variety of sources provides your body with six types of nutrients.

Carbohydrates

If you look at the panels on several boxes of cereal, you'll notice that carbohydrates are frequently listed first. That means that most of the nutrient in that particular cereal is in carbohydrate form. **Carbohydrates** are the main sources of energy for your body. They contain carbon, hydrogen, and oxygen atoms. During respiration, energy is released when molecules of carbohydrate break down in your cells. Starch, cellulose, and sugar are three types of carbohydrates. Starch and cellulose are complex carbohydrates. Starch is in foods such as potatoes and those made from grains such as pasta. Cellulose occurs in plant cell walls. There are many types of sugars. You're probably most familiar with one called table sugar. Table sugar is an example of a simple carbohydrate. Fruits, honey, and milk are sources of sugar. Your cells use sugar in the form of glucose.

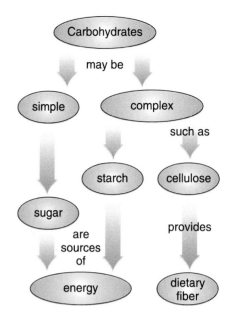

Figure 19-2. Sugar, starch, and cellulose are three carbohydrates found in foods.

Figure 19-3. Grains and fish are good sources of protein. The grain shown here is amaranth, grown in the tropics.

Proteins

Proteins are nutrients needed throughout your body for growth, as enzymes, and in the replacement and repair of body cells. Proteins are large molecules that contain carbon, hydrogen, oxygen, and nitrogen. A molecule of protein is made up of a large number of subunits or building blocks called **amino acids.** In Chapter 4 you learned that proteins are made according to directions supplied by genes that you inherit. Your body needs 22 different amino acids to be able to construct the proteins needed in your cells. Fourteen of these amino acids can be made in your cells. The eight remaining amino acids are called *essential* amino acids. Your body doesn't have genetic instructions to con-

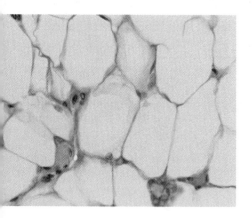

Figure 19-4. Certain cells in your body become filled with fat. The cytoplasm and nucleus get pushed to the edge of the cell.

Figure 19-5. In your digestive system, a single molecule of fat breaks down into fatty acids and glycerol.

struct them in your cells. Therefore, they have to be supplied through food in your diet. Eggs, milk, and cheese contain all the essential amino acids. Beef, pork, fish, chicken, and nuts supply only some of them. You might be surprised to know that whole grains such as wheat, rice, and soybeans supply many needed amino acids in addition to carbohydrates.

Fats

Fats are nutrients that provide energy and help your body store some vitamins. For good health, your diet should be no more than 30 percent fat. Fats are stored in your body in the form of fat tissue that cushions your internal organs. Carbohydrates supply most people with most of the energy they need, because people eat a lot of carbohydrates. However, a molecule of fat releases more energy than a molecule of carbohydrate. A single molecule of fat breaks down into smaller molecules called fatty acids and glycerol.

There are two types of fats: unsaturated and saturated fats. Plants supply unsaturated fats. Corn, safflower, and soybean oils are all unsaturated fats. Some unsaturated fats are also found in poultry, fish, and nuts. Saturated fats are found in red meats. Saturated fats have been associated with high levels of blood cholesterol that contribute to heart disease. A lot has been written about the bad effects of cholesterol. However, cholesterol does occur normally in all your cell membranes. But, too much cholesterol in your diet causes fat deposits to form on the walls of blood vessels, resulting in a cutoff of blood supply to organs and an increase in blood pressure. Figure 19-4 shows the kind of fat tissue that builds up under the skin.

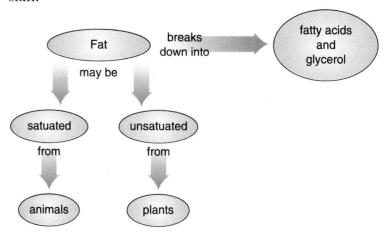

TECHNOLOGY

Fake Fat

Americans obtain an average of 37 percent of their daily calorie intake from fat. Fats and sodium often make the food taste great. Various companies are experimenting with fat substitutes so that people can eat rich-tasting foods, without gaining weight.

Foods using fat substitutes or fake fats have to be lower in calories than real fat and still try to maintain the taste of fat-rich foods. Some fake fats are useful in frozen products, but can't be used to cook with because they break down when heated. Many fail taste tests.

One fat substitute, however, is waiting approval by the Food and Drug Administration. It is composed of table sugar molecules attached to fatty acid molecules. It looks like fat and tastes like it, too. This product passes through the digestive system without being absorbed. In addition, it can be used in cooking and has no calories.

Think Critically: What are the possible disadvantages of using fake fat in your diet?

Vitamins

Vitamins are essential, organic nutrients needed in small quantities to help your body use other nutrients. For instance, vitamin D is needed for bone cells to use the mineral calcium. In general, vitamins promote growth and regulate many body functions.

Most foods supply some vitamins, but no one food has them all. Eating a variety of foods usually supplies all the vitamins the body needs. Some vitamins dissolve easily in water and are called water-soluble vitamins. Others dissolve only in fat and are called fat-soluble vitamins. Although some people feel that taking extra vitamins is helpful, normally eating a balanced diet is sufficient to give your body all the vitamins it needs. Vitamins are found in a variety of meats and vegetables. Your body makes vitamin D when your skin is exposed to sunlight. Some vitamin K is made with the help of bacteria that live in your large intestine. Table 19-1, on the next page, lists major vitamins, their effects on your health, and some of the foods that provide them.

What are two types of vitamins?

Table 19-1

VITAMINS		
Vitamin	**Health Effect**	**Food Sources**
A	growth, good eyesight, healthy skin	green/yellow vegetables, liver and fish liver oils, milk, yellow fruit
B (thiamine, riboflavin, niacin, B_6, B_{12})	growth, healthy nervous system, use of carbohydrates, red blood cell production	meat, eggs, milk, cereal grains, green vegetables
C	growth, healthy bones and teeth, wound healing	citrus fruits, tomatoes, green leafy vegetables
D	absorption of calcium and phosphorus by bones and teeth	milk, eggs, fish
E	formation of cell membranes	vegetable oils, eggs, grains
K	blood clotting, wound healing	green leafy vegetables, egg yolks, tomatoes

Science and WRITING

How's your diet? Using the sides of food packages and books that list the amount of fat, cholesterol, and sodium, chart your weekly intake of these substances. Consult a nutrition text for the Recommended Dietary Allowances of nutrients for a person your age. Does your diet provide the recommended amounts?

Minerals

Minerals are inorganic nutrients that regulate many chemical reactions in your body. Minerals are chemical elements such as phosphorus. About 14 elements are used by your body for building cells for chemical reactions in cells, for sending nerve impulses throughout your body, and for carrying oxygen to body cells. Minerals used in the largest amounts in your body are given in Table 19-2. These include calcium, phosphorus, potassium, and sodium. Some minerals, called trace minerals, are required in only very small amounts. Trace minerals include iron, copper, and iodine.

Figure 19-6. Minerals are needed for healthy bones and muscle contraction.

Water

You don't have to be lost in a desert to know how important water is for your body. Next to oxygen, water is the most vital factor for survival. You could live a few weeks without food, but only a few days without water. Most of the nutrients you have studied in this chapter can't be used by your body unless they are carried in a solution. This means that they have to be dissolved in water. Water enables chemical reactions to take place in cells.

Your body is about 60 percent water. This water is found in and around cells and in plasma and lymph. Water removes waste products from cells. Wastes dissolved in water leave your body as urine or perspiration. To balance water lost each day, you need to drink about two liters of liquids. But don't think that you have to drink just water to keep your cells supplied. Most foods have more water in them than you realize. An apple is about 80 percent water and many meats are as much as 90 percent water.

Where is water found in the body?

MINI-Lab

How much water?
Using a pan balance, find the mass of an empty 200 mL beaker. Fill the beaker with sliced celery or sliced carrots and find the mass of the filled beaker. Obtain permission to dry the vegetable pieces overnight in an oven on a flat tray at very low heat. Use an oven mitt to remove the tray. Allow the tray and vegetables to cool. Then determine the mass of the dried vegetables. How much water was in the fresh vegetables?

Table 19-2

MINERALS		
Mineral	**Health Effect**	**Food Sources**
Calcium	strong bones and teeth, blood clotting, muscle and nerve activity	milk, eggs, green leafy vegetables
Phosphorus	strong bones and teeth, muscle contraction, stores energy	cheese, meat, cereal
Potassium	balance of water in cells, nerve impulse conduction	bananas, potatoes, nuts, meat
Sodium	fluid balance in tissues, nerve impulse conduction	meat, milk, cheese, salt, beets, carrots
Iron	carries oxygen in hemoglobin in red blood cells	raisins, beans, spinach, eggs
Iodine	thyroid activity, stimulates metabolism	seafood, iodized salt

Table 19-3

WATER LOSS	
Through	**Amount (mL/day)**
Exhaled air	350
Feces	150
Skin (mostly as sweat)	500
Excretory system	1800

Your body also loses about two liters of water every day through excretion, perspiration, and respiration. Table 19-3 shows how water is lost from the body. The body is equipped to maintain its fluid content, however. When your body needs water, it sends messages to your brain. A feeling of thirst develops. Drinking a glass of water usually restores the body's homeostasis, and the signal to the brain stops.

Food Groups

Because no one food has all the nutrients, you need to eat a variety of foods. Nutritionists have developed a simple system to help people plan meals that include all the nutrients required for good health. This system involves making choices from foods that have been classified according to the major nutrients they contain.

Foods that contain the same nutrients belong to a **food group.** Figure 19-7 shows the four basic food groups with the serving suggestions for maintaining health. The groups are: the milk group, the fruit and vegetable group, the grain group, and the meat group. Eating a certain amount from each food group will supply your body with the nutrients it needs for energy and growth. Of course, most people eat from these food groups in a combined form. Combinations of food contain ingredients from

Figure 19-7. Selections made from food groups will provide needed nutrients.

Milk group
Supplies:
calcium
riboflavin (B$_2$)
protein
for strong bones and
teeth, healthy skin,
and good vision
Eat 4 servings
per day

Meat group
Supplies:
protein
fats
niacin (B$_{12}$)
iron
thiamin (B$_1$)
for muscle, bone, and
blood cells and
healthy skin
and nerves
Eat 2 servings
per day

Fruit-vegetable group
Supplies:
vitamin A
vitamin C
for night vision and to
help resist infections
and heal wounds
Eat 4 servings
per day

Grain group
Supplies:
carbohydrate
thiamin (B$_1$)
iron
niacin (B$_{12}$)
for energy and a
healthy nervous
system
Eat 4 servings
per day

PROBLEM SOLVING

The Big Race

Jerry is a long-distance runner. He plans to run the Boston Marathon on Patriots' Day. This world-famous race is more than 42 kilometers. His mother asked him to choose one of the following menus for dinner the night before the big race.

a) hamburger, french fries, chocolate cake, a large glass of cola
b) spaghetti with tomato sauce, fresh vegetable salad, whole wheat roll, fresh fruit, a large glass of water
c) fried chicken, mashed potatoes and gravy, broccoli with cheese sauce, roll and butter, and ice cream.

Jerry wants a meal with a lot of complex carbohydrates. Which menu should Jerry choose for dinner?
Think Critically: Why does Jerry want to eat carbohydrates before the big race?

more than one food group and supply the same nutrients as the foods they contain. Examples of food group combinations include pizza, stew, macaroni and cheese, rice and beans, and banana milk shakes.

EcoTip
Eat lower on the food chain by consuming more vegetables and fruits.

SECTION REVIEW

1. List six classes of nutrients and give one example of a food source for each.
2. Describe a major function of each class of nutrients.
3. Discuss the relationship between your diet and your health.
4. Explain the importance of water in the body.
5. **Apply:** What foods from each food group would provide a balanced breakfast? Explain your choices.

☑ Making and Using Tables

Skill Builder

Use the information in Table 19-1 and Table 19-2 to determine the vitamins and minerals needed for healthy bones. If you need help, refer to Making and Using Tables in the **Skill Handbook** on page 690.

ACTIVITY 19-1
Identifying Vitamin C Content

Problem: *Which juices contain vitamin C?*

Materials

- indophenol solution
- graduated cylinder
- glass marking pencil
- 10 test tubes
- test-tube rack
- 10 dropping bottles containing water, orange juice, pineapple juice, apple juice, lemon juice, tomato juice, cranberry juice, carrot juice, lime juice, mixed vegetable juice

Procedure

1. Make a data table like the one shown to record your observations.
2. Label the test tubes 1 through 10.
3. Hypothesize which juices contain vitamin C. Record your hypotheses on a separate sheet of paper.
4. Measure 5 mL of indophenol into each of the 10 test tubes. **CAUTION:** *Wear your goggles and apron.* Indophenol is a blue liquid that turns colorless when vitamin C is present. The more vitamin C in a juice, the less juice it takes to turn indophenol colorless.
5. Add 20 drops of water to test tube 1. Record your observations.
6. Begin adding orange juice, one drop at a time, to test tube 2.
7. Record the number of drops needed to turn indophenol colorless.
8. Use Steps 6 and 7 to test the other juices.

Data and Observations

Test tube	Juice	Prediction (yes or no)	Number of drops
1	water		
2	orange		
3	pineapple		
4	apple		
5	lemon		
6	tomato		
7	cranberry		
8	carrot		
9	lime		
10	vegetable		

Analyze

1. What was the purpose of test tube 1?
2. Which juice did not contain vitamin C?
3. Does the amount of vitamin C vary in fruit juices?

Conclude and Apply

4. What is the best way to take in vitamins?
5. Why is scurvy uncommon today?

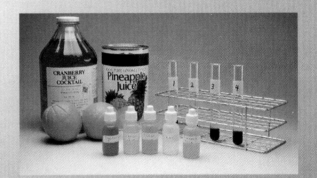

Your Digestive System 19-2

Objectives

▶ Distinguish between mechanical and chemical digestion.
▶ Name the organs of the digestive system and describe what takes place in each.
▶ Explain how homeostasis is maintained in digestion.

New Science Words

digestion
mechanical digestion
chemical digestion
saliva
peristalsis
chyme
villi

Processing Food

Like the other animals you have studied so far, you are a consumer. The energy you need for life comes from food sources outside yourself. To keep the cells in your body alive, you take in food every day. Food is processed in your body in four phases: ingestion, digestion, absorption, and elimination. Whether it is a fast-food burger or a home-cooked meal, all the food you eat is treated to the same processes in your body. As soon as it enters your mouth, or is ingested, food begins to be broken down. **Digestion** is the process that breaks food down into small molecules so they can be absorbed, or taken into the cells of your body. Food molecules then move into cells during the process of absorption. Molecules that aren't absorbed are eliminated and pass out of your body as wastes.

Figure 19-8 shows the major organs of your digestive tract: mouth, esophagus (i SAH fuh guhs), stomach, small intestine, large intestine, rectum, and anus. Food passes *through* all of these organs. However, food *doesn't* pass through your liver, pancreas, or gall bladder. These three organs produce or store enzymes and chemicals that help break down food as it passes through the digestive tract.

Digestion is both mechanical and chemical. **Mechanical digestion** takes place when food is chewed and mixed in the mouth, churned in your stomach, and acted on by bile. **Chemical digestion** breaks down large molecules of food into smaller molecules that can be absorbed by cells. Chemical digestion takes place in your mouth, stomach, and small intestine.

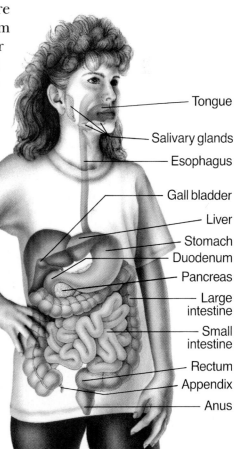

Tongue
Salivary glands
Esophagus
Gall bladder
Liver
Stomach
Duodenum
Pancreas
Large intestine
Small intestine
Rectum
Appendix
Anus

Figure 19-8. The Major Organs for Digestion

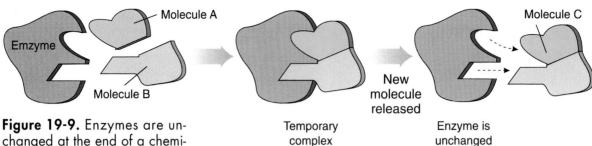

Figure 19-9. Enzymes are unchanged at the end of a chemical reaction.

Temporary complex forms

New molecule released

Enzyme is unchanged

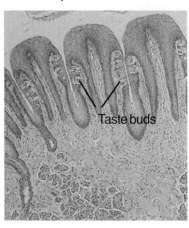

Figure 19-10. Taste buds help you to figure out whether you like the taste of a particular food.

Taste buds

Enzymes are proteins that are vital in chemical digestion. An enzyme enters a reaction and helps to join or break up two substances. The enzyme then leaves the reaction without being changed itself. You could say that enzymes are regulators. Some enzymes speed up reactions. Others enable a large molecule to break up without releasing a lot of excess heat energy in the cell. Thousands of enzyme-assisted reactions are taking place in your cells right now. But you aren't at all aware of this activity.

In Your Mouth

The process of digestion begins in your mouth. There, your tongue and teeth mechanically break food up into small pieces. Humans are adapted with several kinds of teeth for cutting, grinding, tearing, and crushing.

Some chemical digestion also starts in your mouth. As you chew, your tongue moves food around and mixes it with a watery substance called **saliva.** Saliva is produced by three types of glands in your mouth that are shown in Figure 19-8. Saliva is made up mostly of water, but it also contains mucus and an enzyme called amylase. Amylase starts the breakdown of starch to sugar in your mouth. Food that is mixed with saliva becomes a soft mass. The food mass is moved to the back of your tongue where it is swallowed and passes into your esophagus. Now the process of ingestion is complete, and the process of digestion has begun.

Your esophagus is a muscular tube about 25 cm long. Through it, food passes to your stomach in about four to eight seconds. No digestion takes place there. Smooth muscles in the walls of the esophagus move food downward by a squeezing action. These waves or contractions, called **peristalsis** (pe ruh STAHL sis), move food along throughout the digestive system. Figure 19-11 shows how peristalsis works.

In Your Stomach

Your stomach is a muscular bag. When it is empty, it is somewhat sausage-shaped with folds on the inside. As food enters from the esophagus, the stomach expands and the folds smooth out. Both mechanical and chemical digestion take place in the stomach. Mechanically, food is mixed by the muscular walls of the stomach and by peristalsis. Food is also mixed with strong digestive juices. Hydrochloric acid and enzymes are made by cells in the walls of the stomach. The stomach also produces mucus that lubricates the food, making it more slick. Mucus also protects the stomach itself from the strong digestive juices. Food moves through your stomach in about four hours. At the end of this time, it doesn't look like food anymore, but has been changed to a thin, watery liquid called **chyme**. Little by little, chyme moves out of your stomach and into your small intestine.

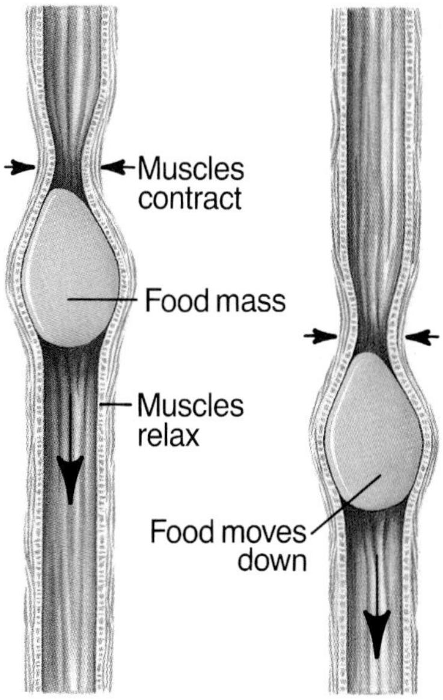

Figure 19-11. During peristalsis, muscles behind the food contract and push the food forward. Muscles in front of the food relax.

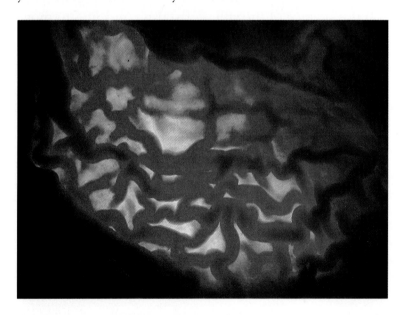

Figure 19-12. Wrinkles in the stomach wall smooth out as it fills with food.

In Your Small Intestine

Your small intestine is small in diameter, but it is nearly seven meters in length. As chyme leaves your stomach, it enters the first part of your small intestine, called the duodenum. The major portion of all digestion takes place in your duodenum. A lot of different things take place here at the same time. Here, digestive juices from the liver and pancreas are added to the mixture. Your liver produces a greenish fluid called bile, which it stores in a

Where does most digestion take place?

Figure 19-13. The liver, gall bladder, and pancreas are at the beginning of the small intestine.

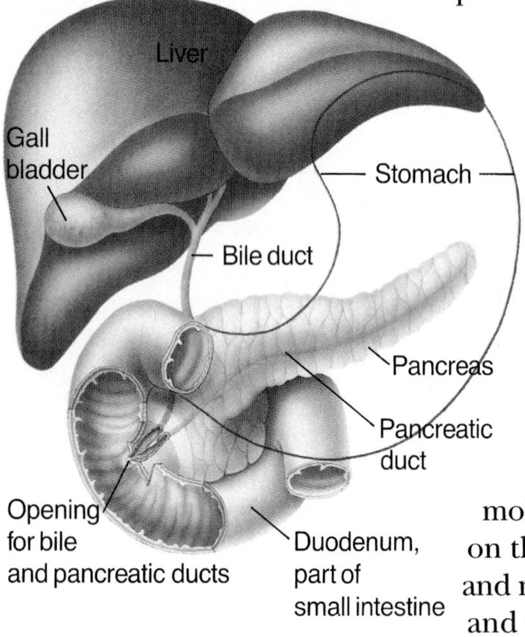

Liver

Gall bladder

Stomach

Bile duct

Pancreas

Pancreatic duct

Opening for bile and pancreatic ducts

Duodenum, part of small intestine

Where are nutrients absorbed?

small sac called the gall bladder. The acid from the stomach makes large fat particles float to the top of the liquid. Bile physically breaks up these particles into smaller pieces, the way detergent acts on grease on dishes.

Your pancreas makes insulin and substances that stop the action of stomach acid. It also produces enzymes that break down carbohydrates, fats, and proteins still further.

The walls of your small intestine are not smooth like the inside of a garden hose. Rather, they have many ridges and folds. These folds are covered with tiny, fingerlike projections called **villi.** Villi make the surface of the small intestine larger so that there are more places for food to be absorbed. Villi are shown in Figure 19-14.

By this time, chyme has become a soup of molecules that is ready to be absorbed through the cells on the surface of the villi. Peristalsis continues to move and mix the chyme. In addition, the villi themselves move and are bathed in the soupy liquid. Molecules of nutrients pass by diffusion, osmosis, or active transport into blood vessels in each villus. From there, blood transports the nutrients to all the cells of the body. Peristalsis continues to slowly force the remaining materials that are not absorbed along into the large intestine.

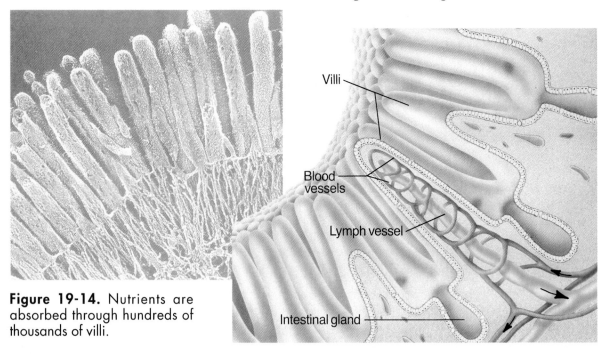

Figure 19-14. Nutrients are absorbed through hundreds of thousands of villi.

Villi

Blood vessels

Lymph vessel

Intestinal gland

In Your Large Intestine

As chyme enters the large intestine, it is still a thin, watery mixture. The main job of the large intestine is to absorb this water from the undigested mass. In doing so, large amounts of water are returned to the body and homeostasis is maintained. Peristalsis slows down somewhat in the large intestine. As a result, chyme may stay in the large intestine as much as three days. During this time, excess water and sodium are absorbed back into the bloodstream. The remaining materials, consisting of undigested cellulose and bacteria, become more solid. Bacteria that live in your large intestine feed on undigested materials like cellulose. This is a symbiotic relationship. The bacteria feed on cellulose and in return they produce several vitamins that you need. Muscles in the rectum and anus control the release of solidified wastes from the body in the form of feces.

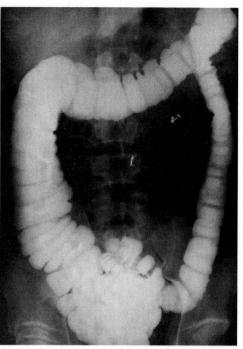

Figure 19-15. The large white area in this X ray is the large intestine.

Food is processed in your digestive system for the purpose of supplying your body with raw materials for metabolism. These raw materials are in the form of nutrients. Those that are not digested and absorbed are eliminated.

SECTION REVIEW

1. Name in order the organs through which food passes as it moves through the digestive system.
2. What is the difference between mechanical and chemical digestion?
3. How are the liver, pancreas, and gall bladder related to digestion?
4. How do activities in the large intestine help maintain homeostasis?
5. **Apply:** Crackers contain starch. Explain why a soda cracker held in your mouth for five minutes might begin to taste sweet.

☒ Observing and Inferring

What would happen to food if the pancreas did not secrete its juices into the small intestine? If you need help, refer to Observing and Inferring in the **Skill Handbook** on page 682.

Skill Builder

19-3 Eating Disorders

New Science Words

anorexia nervosa
bulimia

Objectives

▶ Name and describe two types of eating disorders.
▶ Infer the consequences of improper diets associated with eating disorders.

Are Looks That Important?

Have you ever tried on a bathing suit or a pair of jeans in the store only to be disappointed by the fact that they just didn't fit? Do you feel bad when someone comments on your weight? American culture is so fashion conscious that a person's self-worth sometimes becomes dependent on looks. This can be quite a problem because people often rely on food. Sometimes the thought of looking fit and trim is so important that people become obsessed with loosing extra mass as quickly as possible. But often people begin a diet or exercise program, and then return to old eating habits after just a few days.

Eating Disorders

Anorexia nervosa and bulimia are two eating disorders that are very dangerous. Although these disorders are more common in adolescent girls, a small percentage of boys have been known to have problems as well.

Anorexia nervosa is an eating disorder that involves extreme weight loss to the point of damaging vital organs and even death. It is characterized by preoccupation with eating as little food as possible due to the fear of gaining mass. The goal is to become more attractive, but the opposite effect often results. The extreme lack of food results in starvation-like symptoms, including dry skin and hair, cold hands and feet, and general weakness. There is also a tendency toward increased infections, stress fractures in bones, and weakness of the heart muscle that has resulted in death in some cases.

Bulimia is an eating disorder that involves binging, or eating huge amounts of food in a short period of time, fol-

Science and READING

The United States Department of Agriculture has composed a list of seven diet goals for improving and maintaining health. Find out what the seven diet goals are. How do people with eating disorders fall short of these goals?

lowed by self-induced vomiting, for the purpose of not adding mass to the body. Bulimics also fast and abuse laxatives to move food through their intestines quickly. As a result, the small intestine does not absorb vital nutrients. They sometimes exercise fanatically. Severe dental problems result from exposing the teeth to stomach enzymes and acid during vomiting. Painful ulcers may develop in the mouth and stomach and muscle weakness (the heart is a muscle too) may also develop. In both cases, basic nutritional needs of the body are not satisfied. Over a period of time, the body is starved to death.

Some people may turn and look in admiration at a very thin person. Everyone likes to receive positive comments on his or her appearance. However, the consequences of extreme weight loss or self-induced vomiting make a person look much less attractive. By talking and learning about the problem, victims of eating disorders will come to feel better about themselves and restore themselves to health.

Figure 19-16. Persons with eating disorders may have difficulties with their self-esteem.

What Can You Do?

Do you or does someone that you know have an eating disorder? If so, what can you do? It is often impossible to deal with an eating disorder alone. However, many people are willing to help. Through treatment, the problem can be controlled. The school guidance counselor and nurse are specially trained to help with these problems. Programs have been specifically developed to control these disorders.

SECTION REVIEW

1. Describe two types of eating disorders.
2. What are the effects of eating disorders?

You Decide!

SCIENCE & SOCIETY

Individuals with eating disorders are usually very unwilling to talk about their problems with friends. Maybe they're embarrassed about the condition, or afraid that their families may eventually find out. If you think a friend has an eating disorder, would it be right for you to mention this to the school nurse or guidance counselor? Would you be a caring friend if you chose not to seek help for that person?

ACTIVITY 19-2
Protein Digestion

Problem: *What conditions are necessary for the digestion of protein by pepsin?*

Materials
- unflavored gelatin
- dropper
- two test tubes in rack
- drinking glass
- pepsin powder
- cold water
- graduate cylinder
- marking pen
- dilute hydrochloric acid

Procedure
1. Prepare a data table like the one shown.
2. Prepare the gelatin according to the directions on the package.
3. Pour 10 mL of the gelatin into each of the 2 test tubes. Place the test tubes in a rack and do not disturb them while the gelatin sets.
4. Label one test tube "pepsin with acid," and the other one "pepsin without acid."
5. When the gelatin has set, add 10 drops of the dilute acid to the test tube labeled "pepsin with acid." **CAUTION:** *Always use care when working with acid. Wash your hands thoroughly after pouring the acid.*
6. Sprinkle enough pepsin powder to cover the surface of the gelatin in *both* test tubes.
7. Place the 2 test tubes upright into a drinking glass containing cold water.
8. Observe the gelatin every 10 minutes, and record your results in the data table after each observation.

Analyze
1. What did you observe in the test tubes?
2. Was there a difference?
3. Why were the test tubes kept in cold water?
4. What are the constants in this experiment?

Data and Observations

Time minutes	Pepsin with acid	Pepsin without acid
10		
20		
30		
40		
50		

Conclude and Apply
5. Did the acid have any effect on the activity of the pepsin?
6. How is this related to the activity of this enzyme in the stomach?
7. Infer why the activity of pepsin stops in the small intestine.

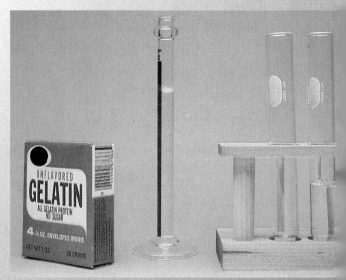

REVIEW

19-1: Nutrition

1. Carbohydrates, fats, proteins, minerals, vitamins, and water are the six nutrients found in food.

2. Carbohydrates provide energy; proteins are needed for growth and repair; fats store energy and cushion organs. Vitamins and minerals regulate functions. Water makes up about 60 percent of body mass and is used for a variety of homeostatic functions.

3. Health is affected by the combination of foods that make up a diet.

19-2: Your Digestive System

1. The digestive system breaks food down mechanically by chewing and churning, and chemically, with the help of enzymes, to substances that cells can absorb and use.

2. Food passes through the mouth, esophagus, stomach, small intestine, large intestine, rectum, and out the anus.

3. Homeostasis is maintained by absorption of water in the large intestine.

19-3: Science and Society: Eating Disorders

1. Anorexia nervosa and bulimia are two eating disorders that involve the use of starvation and extreme behaviors to control body mass.

2. Eating disorders result in damage to organs and even death.

KEY SCIENCE WORDS

a. **amino acids**
b. **anorexia nervosa**
c. **bulimia**
d. **carbohydrates**
e. **chemical digestion**
f. **chyme**
g. **digestion**
h. **fats**
i. **food group**
j. **mechanical digestion**
k. **minerals**
l. **nutrients**
m. **peristalsis**
n. **proteins**
o. **saliva**
p. **villi**
q. **vitamins**

UNDERSTANDING VOCABULARY

Match each phrase with the correct term from the list of Key Science Words.

1. process of breaking down food
2. muscular contractions that move food
3. enzyme-containing fluid in the mouth
4. fingerlike projections in small intestine
5. starch and sugars
6. nutrients that form a cushioning tissue
7. physical breakdown of food
8. inorganic nutrients
9. subunits of proteins
10. eating disorder with induced vomiting

CHAPTER
REVIEW

Choose the word or phrase that completes the sentence.

1. Most digestion occurs in the_____.
   a. duodenum   c. liver
   b. stomach   d. large intestine

2. The _____ makes bile, which acts on fats.
   a. gall bladder   c. stomach
   b. liver   d. small intestine

3. Water is absorbed in the _____.
   a. liver   c. esophagus
   b. small intestine   d. large intestine

4. Food does not pass through the _____.
   a. mouth   c. small intestine
   b. stomach   d. liver

5. Nutrients that store vitamins are _____.
   a. fats   c. carbohydrates
   b. proteins   d. minerals

6. The vitamin not used for growth is _____.
   a. A   c. C
   b. B   d. K

7. In the _____, hydrochloric acid is added to the food mass.
   a. mouth   c. small intestine
   b. stomach   d. large intestine

8. The _____ produces enzymes that digest proteins, fats, and carbohydrates.
   a. mouth   c. large intestine
   b. pancreas   d. gall bladder

9. The food group containing yogurt and cheese is _____.
   a. milk   c. meat
   b. grain   d. fruit

10. Carbohydrates are best obtained from _____.
    a. milk   c. meat
    b. grains   d. eggs

UNDERSTANDING CONCEPTS

Complete each sentence.

11. _____ is made by the skin using sunlight.

12. _____ is necessary to dissolve nutrients.

13. _____ involves vomiting to control weight.

14. The _____ connects the mouth with the stomach.

15. Undigested materials exit the body through the _____.

THINK AND WRITE CRITICALLY

16. What do chewing and the action of bile have in common in the digestive system?

17. Describe the differences among ingestion, digestion, absorption, and elimination.

18. Explain why it isn't really necessary to have food prepared using elaborate recipes. Why do people go to the trouble of cooking meals?

19. List the structures that add enzymes to chyme in the small intestine.

20. Why is a balanced diet important to maintaining homeostasis?

APPLY

21. What types of food would a person whose gall bladder has been removed need to limit in his or her diet? Explain your choice.

22. In what part of the digestive system do antacids work? Explain your choice.

23. Bile's action is similar to soap. Use this information to explain bile working on fats.

24. Vitamins are in two groups: water- or fat-soluble. Which of these might your body retain? Explain your answer.

25. Based on your knowledge of food groups and nutrients, discuss the meaning of the familiar statement: "You are what you eat."

If you need help, refer to the Skill Handbook.

1. Making and Using Graphs: Recommended Dietary Allowances (RDA) are made for the amounts of nutrients people should take in to maintain health. Prepare a bar graph of the percent of RDA of each nutrient from the breakfast product information listed below.

Nutrient	Precent US RDA
Protein	2
Vitamin A	20
Vitamin C	25
Vitamin D	15
Calcium (Ca)	less than 2
Iron (Fe)	25
Zinc (Zn)	15

Which nutrients are given the greatest percent of the Recommended Dietary Allowance? Could a person on a fat-restricted diet eat this product? Explain.

2. Sequencing: In a table, sequence the order of organs through which food passes in the digestive system. Indicate whether ingestion, digestion, absorption, or elimination takes place in the individual organs.

3. Comparing and Contrasting: Compare and contrast the location, size and functions of the esophagus, stomach, small intestine, and large intestine.

4. Sequencing: Sequence the digestion of a starch, a fat, and a protein, listing where it occurs, what happens, the enzymes used, and the end product of this digestion.

5. Interpreting Data: Use a label from a food, list the nutrients and food groups to which each belongs. How many calories are provided by each type?

1. Research the ingredients of products used in diarrhea and laxatives. Where in the digestive system do these products act and how?

2. Research diet fads that emphasize taking in only one type of food such as all fruit or all rice. In a written report, discuss whether these diets are healthful or not and why.

Strenuous swimming could tire you out, but because your heart constantly pumps blood throughout your body you can continue to swim and play. How do you know that your heart is pumping? Why does it pump faster at certain times?

FIND OUT!

Do this activity to find out about the pumping activity of your heart.

Place your middle and index fingers over one of the carotid arteries in your neck. These arteries are on either side of your trachea. Don't press too hard. You should feel movement as blood is pumped through this artery. This movement is a pulse. Count your carotid pulse rate for 15 seconds, then multiply it by four. This number is your resting heartbeat rate. Now, jog in place for one minute. Take your pulse again. Is there a difference from your resting heart rate? Why do you think exercise causes a difference in pulse rate?

Gearing Up
Previewing the Chapter

Use this outline to help you focus on important ideas in this chapter.

Section 20-1   Circulation
► Your Cardiovascular System
► Your Heart
► Pathways of Circulation
► Blood Pressure
► Diseases and Disorders of the Heart

Section 20-2   Blood
► Functions of Blood
► Parts of Blood
► Blood Clotting
► Blood Types
► Diseases and Disorders of Blood

Section 20-3   Science and Society
Autologous Blood Transfusions
► Saving Your Own Blood

Section 20-4   Your Lymphatic System
► Functions of Your Lymphatic System
► Lymphatic Organs
► A Disease of the Lymphatic System

Previewing Science Skills

► In the Skill Builders, you will make a concept map, interpret data, and compare and contrast.
► In the Activities, you will observe, experiment, and collect data.
► In the MINI-Labs, you will diagram and observe and interpret.

What's next?

You've just learned that your pulse can tell you something about your heartbeat rate. In this chapter, you will learn about your heart and your blood and your lymphatic system.

Circulation

New Science Words

atria
ventricles
pulmonary circulation
arteries
veins
capillaries
systemic circulation
coronary circulation
blood pressure
atherosclerosis
hypertension

Objectives

▶ Compare arteries, veins, and capillaries.
▶ Trace the pathway of blood through the chambers of the heart.
▶ Describe pulmonary and systemic circulation.

Your Cardiovascular System

With a body made up of trillions of cells, you're quite different from a one-celled amoeba living in a puddle of water. But are you really that different? Even though your body is larger and made up of complex systems, the cells in your body have the same needs as the smaller life-form. Both of you need a continuous supply of oxygen and nutrients and a way to remove cell wastes.

An amoeba takes oxygen directly from its watery environment. Nutrients are distributed throughout its single cell by cytoplasmic streaming. In your body, a cardiovascular system moves oxygen and nutrients to cells and removes carbon dioxide and other wastes. *Cardio-* means heart and *vascular* means vessel. This system includes your heart, blood, and kilometers of vessels that carry blood to every part of your body. It is a closed system because blood moves within vessels. How do the parts of this system work?

Your Heart

Your heart is a muscular organ about the size of a closed fist. It is located behind your sternum and between your lungs. Your heart has four cavities called chambers. The two upper chambers are the right and left **atria** (AY tree uh) (*singular* atrium). The two lower chambers are the right and left **ventricles** (VEN trih kulz). During a single heartbeat, both atria contract at the same time. Then both ventricles contract at the same time. A valve separates each atrium from the ventricle below it, so that blood flows only from an atrium to a ventricle.

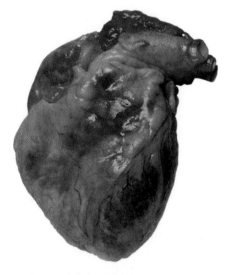

Figure 20-1. A Human Heart

Pathways of Circulation

Three major pathways for blood movement through your circulatory system are called pulmonary (PUL mo ner ee), systemic (sihs TEM ihk), and coronary circulations.

Pulmonary Circulation

Pulmonary circulation is the flow of blood through the heart, to the lungs, and back to the heart. Blood from body cells is high in carbon dioxide and enters the right atrium of the heart through a large vein called the superior vena cava. When the right atrium contracts, this blood is forced into the right ventricle. The right ventricle then contracts, and blood leaves the heart through the pulmonary arteries to go to the lungs. As blood circulates through the lungs, carbon dioxide is exchanged for oxygen. Oxygen-rich blood then returns to the heart through the pulmonary vein and fills up the left atrium. This is the only vein in the body that carries oxygen-rich blood. When the left atrium is full of oxygen-rich blood, it contracts and forces blood into the left ventricle. The final step of this path through the heart occurs when the left ventricle contracts and forces blood up and out of the heart into the largest artery of the body, called the aorta. The aorta carries blood away from the heart to many branching arteries that distribute it to all

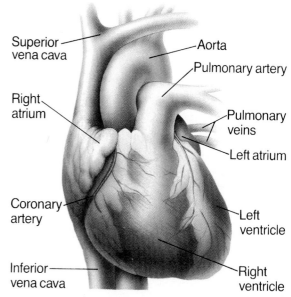

Figure 20-2. In mammals, the heart is a two-pump organ. The right ventricle pumps oxygen-poor blood to the lungs, and the left ventricle pumps oxygen-rich blood to body tissues.

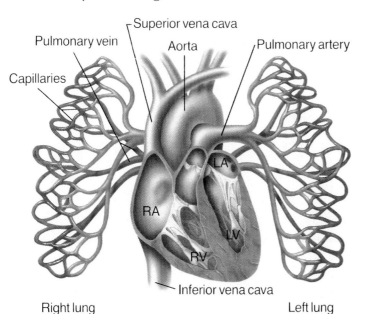

Figure 20-3. Pulmonary circulation moves blood between the heart and lungs.

Direction of blood flow

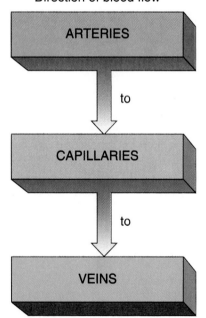

Figure 20-4. Blood flows from arteries to capillaries to veins. Valves in veins and muscles to the right help blood flow back toward the heart.

body parts. Use Figure 20-3 to trace the pathway of blood through the heart, to the lungs, and back to the heart again.

Blood Vessels

Until the work of William Harvey was published in 1628, many people believed that blood moved back and forth in the body like an ocean tide. His work showed that blood circulates only in one direction and that it is moved by the pumping action of the heart. He found that blood flows from arteries to veins. But he couldn't figure out how blood got from arteries to veins. It wasn't until the invention of the microscope that capillaries, the tiniest vessels of the cardiovascular system, were seen.

When blood is pushed out of your heart, it begins a journey through your arteries, capillaries, and veins. **Arteries** are blood vessels that move blood *away* from your heart. Arteries have thick elastic walls that are lined with smooth muscle. Each ventricle of the heart is connected to an artery, so with each contraction blood is moved from the heart into arteries.

Veins are blood vessels that move blood *to* the heart. Veins have one-way valves to keep blood moving toward the heart. If there is a backward movement of the blood, the pressure of the blood closes the valves. The greatest number of valves are in veins in the legs. Why do you think this is so? Veins that are near skeletal muscles are squeezed when these muscles contract. This action also helps blood move toward the heart. Blood in veins carries waste materials from cells and is therefore low in oxygen.

Capillaries are microscopic blood vessels that connect arteries and veins. The walls of capillaries are only one

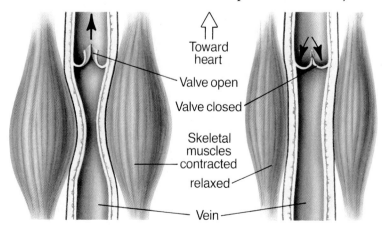

Toward heart

Valve open

Valve closed

Skeletal muscles contracted

relaxed

Vein

cell thick. Food and oxygen diffuse to body cells through the small capillary walls. Waste materials move from body cells into the capillaries to be carried back to the heart.

Systemic circulation moves blood to all body tissues except the lungs and heart. This is the longest of the three pathways. It carries oxygen-rich blood from the left ventricle through the aorta to arteries and capillaries in all the organs and tissues of the body. Nutrients and oxygen are exchanged for carbon dioxide and wastes. Blood returns to the heart in veins from the head and neck through the superior vena cava. Blood returns from your abdomen and the lower parts of your body through the inferior vena cava to the right atrium. Then, oxygen-poor blood is sent to the lungs.

Your heart has its own blood vessels that supply it with nutrients and oxygen and remove wastes. These blood vessels are the coronary arteries and veins. It is on these blood vessels that coronary by-pass surgery is performed. **Coronary circulation** is the flow of blood to the tissues of the heart.

Blood Pressure

When you pump up a bicycle tire, you can feel the pressure of the air on the walls of the tire. In the same way, when the heart pumps blood through the cardiovascular system, blood exerts a force called **blood pressure** on the walls of the vessels. This pressure is highest in arteries.

As the wave of pressure rises and falls in your arteries, it is felt throughout your body as a pulse. Normal pulse rates are between 65 and 80 beats per minute. There is less pressure in capillaries and even less in veins.

Blood pressure is measured in large arteries and is expressed by two numbers, such as 120 over 80. The first number is a measure of the pressure caused when the ventricles contract and blood is pushed out of the heart. Then blood pressure suddenly drops as the ventricles relax. The lower number is a measure of the pressure when the ventricles are filling up, just before they contract again.

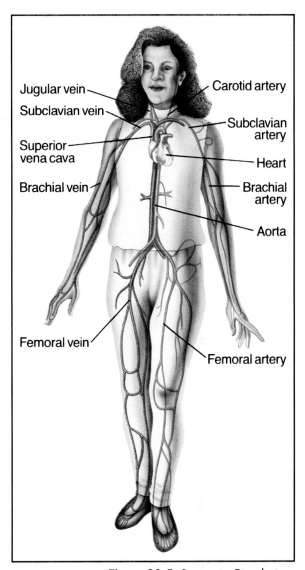

Figure 20-5. Systemic Circulation

Did You Know?

Your capillaries expand while you sleep. As a result, your blood pressure becomes lower.

Diseases and Disorders of the Heart

Any disease or disorder that affects the cardiovascular system can be serious to a person's health. The term *heart disease* is often used to describe any of the health problems that affect the heart. Heart disease is the major cause of death in the United States.

One leading cause of heart disease is **atherosclerosis** (ath uh roh skluh ROH sus), a condition of fatty deposits on arterial walls. Eating too many foods that contain cholesterol can cause these deposits. The fat can build up and form a hard mass that clogs the inside of the vessel. As a result, less blood flows through the artery. If the artery is clogged completely, blood is not able to flow through. When this occurs in a coronary artery, it can cause a heart attack. If an artery in the brain is clogged, a stroke can occur.

Another common disorder of the cardiovascular system is high blood pressure, or **hypertension** (hi pur TEN chun). One cause of hypertension is the condition described above. A clogged artery can cause the pressure within the vessel to increase. This can cause the walls to lose their ability to contract. There also is extra strain on the heart to work harder to keep blood flowing. Being overweight as well as eating foods with too much salt and fat may contribute to hypertension. Smoking and stress also can increase blood pressure.

Your cardiovascular system efficiently provides your body cells with nutrients and oxygen and removes cell wastes. A well-functioning cardiovascular system is important for good health. You can promote a healthy heart! Choose to eat a healthful diet and exercise regularly.

MINI-Lab

What are the parts of the heart?
Draw and label a diagram of the heart. Color the oxygen-rich parts red and the carbon-dioxide parts blue. What purpose is served by the thick septum or wall of muscle between the left and right sides of the heart?

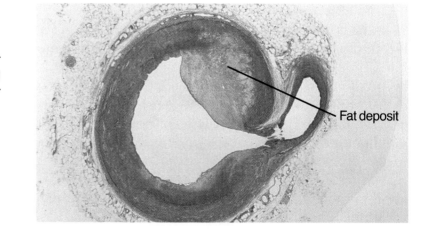

Figure 20-6. Atherosclerosis interferes with blood flow by blocking blood vessels with fatty substances.

Fat deposit

TECHNOLOGY

An Assist for the Heart

Some patients need temporary help until a damaged or transplanted heart is able to function properly. Miniature heart pumps, like the Hemopump, may be the answer.

The Hemopump is the size of the eraser of a number 2 pencil. When a transplanted heart shows signs of being rejected, the Hemopump can take over, pumping blood for several days until antirejection drugs allow the patient's new heart to function.

The Hemopump is inserted into an artery in the upper part of the leg. From here it is carefully pushed up through the blood vessels into the left ventricle. A tiny blade, making 25 000 revolutions per minute, draws the blood through the tube and spills it into the aorta. The pump is connected to a motor outside the patient's body by a thin

cable. The operation to insert the pump takes 20 minutes.

Think Critically: How could the Hemopump be used to help victims of heart attack?

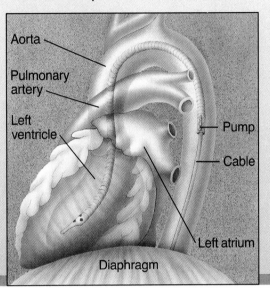

SECTION REVIEW

1. Describe differences among the three types of blood vessels.
2. Explain the pathway of blood through the four chambers of the heart.
3. Explain the difference between pulmonary and systemic circulation.
4. **Apply:** Your heart, like any muscle, needs exercise. What exercises should you do to give your heart a workout?

☒ Concept Mapping

Make an events chain concept map to show pulmonary circulation beginning at the right atrium and ending at the aorta. If you need help, refer to Concept Mapping in the **Skill Handbook** on pages 688 and 689.

Skill Builder

ACTIVITY 20-1
Taking Blood Pressure

Problem: *How can you measure arterial pressure?*

Materials

- sphygmomanometer
- stethoscope
- table
- chairs (2)
- alcohol
- cottonballs

Procedure

1. Your partner should sit down on a chair with his or her arm on the table. One hand should face up as in the photo.
2. Sit and face your partner. Place the cuff of the sphygmomanometer on your partner's arm above the elbow. Align the arrows on the cuff. Close the cuff snugly.
3. Close the valve on the pump. Place the ear pieces of the stethoscope in your ears. Place the round stethoscope head on your partner's brachial artery. Squeeze the pump until the needle reaches 160 on the gauge. No blood will flow through this constricted area.
4. *Slowly* open the valve of the pump. *Do not open the valve quickly.* Watch the gauge. The needle will drop at a constant rate. Note the number on the gauge when you first hear the heart beat. This is the top, or systolic, number.
5. Keep listening for a heartbeat. Watch the needle on the gauge. Note the number on the gauge when you no longer hear the heart beating. This is the bottom, or diastolic, number. At this point, blood pressure has dropped; blood flow has returned to normal.
6. Take the cuff off your partner's arm. Record your partner's blood pressure. Clean ear pieces with alcohol. Trade places with your partner. **CAUTION:** *Do not do this activity on the same person more than one time per class period.*
7. Make and fill in a table like the one shown.

Analyze

1. Describe what happened in your brachial artery during this activity.
2. As you listened to your partner's blood pressure, what did you notice about the needle on the gauge when you first heard the heartbeat rate and later when it stopped?

Conclude and Apply

3. How was your blood pressure different from your partner's?
4. What can you conclude about a person who has low blood pressure?

Data and Observations

Blood Pressure	Example	Yours	Partner's
Systolic	120		
Diastolic	80		

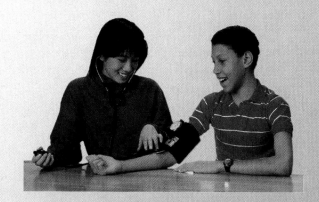

Blood

Objectives

▶ Describe the characteristics and functions of the parts of blood.
▶ Explain the importance of checking blood types before a transfusion is given.
▶ Describe a disease and a disorder of blood.

New Science Words

plasma
hemoglobin
platelets

Functions of Blood

Blood makes up about eight percent of your body's total mass. If you weigh 45 kg, you have about 3.6 kg of blood moving through your body. The amount of blood you have in your body would fill five one-liter bottles. If this volume falls, the body is sent into shock as blood pressure falls rapidly.

Blood is a tissue consisting of cells, cell fragments, and liquid. Blood has many important functions. It plays a part in every major activity of your body. First, blood carries oxygen from your lungs to all body cells. It also removes carbon dioxide from your body cells and carries it to the lungs to be exhaled. Second, it carries waste products of cell activity to your kidneys to be removed. Third, blood transports nutrients from the digestive system to body cells. Fourth, materials in blood fight infections and help heal wounds. Anything that disrupts or changes any of these functions affects all the tissues of the body.

Parts of Blood

If you've ever taken a ride in a water slide at an amusement park, you have some idea of the twisting and turning travels of a blood cell inside a blood vessel. Surrounded by water, you travel rapidly through a narrow watery passageway, much like a red blood cell moves in the plasma of blood.

Figure 20-7. Donated blood is measured in units. The units pictured show how much blood is in your body.

Science and READING

CPR is a life-saving technique every-one should know. What does it stand for? Find out where you can learn more.

If you examine blood closely, you would see that is it not just a red-colored liquid. Blood is a tissue made of red and white blood cells, platelets, and plasma. **Plasma** is the liquid part of blood and consists mostly of water. Plasma makes up more than half the volume of blood. Nutrients, minerals, and oxygen are dissolved in plasma.

A cubic millimeter of blood has more than five million red blood cells. These disk-shaped blood cells contain **hemoglobin,** a chemical that can carry oxygen and carbon dioxide. Hemoglobin carries oxygen from your lungs to body cells. Red blood cells also carry carbon dioxide from body cells to your lungs. Red blood cells have a life span of about 120 days. They are formed in the marrow of long bones at a rate of two to three million per second and contain no nuclei. About an equal number of old ones wear out and are destroyed in the same time period.

In contrast to red blood cells, there are only about five to ten thousand white blood cells in a cubic millimeter of blood. White blood cells fight bacteria, viruses, and other foreign substances that constantly try to invade your body. Your body reacts to infection by increasing its number of white blood cells. White blood cells slip between the cells of capillary walls and out around the tissues that have been invaded. Here, they ingest foreign substances and dead cells. The life span of a white blood cell is about 30 days.

Platelets are irregularly shaped cell fragments that help clot blood. A cubic millimeter of blood may contain as many as 400 thousand platelets. Platelets have a life span of five to nine days. Table 20-1 summarizes the solid parts of blood and their functions.

Figure 20-8. A cut vessel below shows an escaping red blood cell. Blood contains red blood cells, several types of white cells, platelets, and plasma as shown to the right.

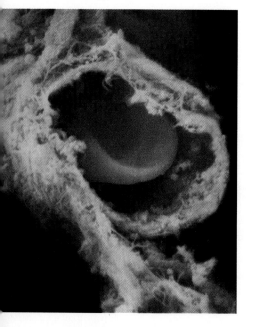

Table 20-1

TYPES OF BLOOD CELLS			
Name	**Nucleus**	**Function**	**Where Formed**
Red blood cells	no	carry oxygen and carbon dioxide	red bone marrow
White blood cells	yes	destroy bacteria, foreign substances	red bone marrow, some move to lymph tissue to produce more white blood cells
Platelets	no	help form blood clots	red bone marrow (fragments of another type of blood cell)

Blood Clotting

It would be serious if you got a paper cut that would not stop bleeding. Platelets in your blood help prevent loss of blood by making a blood clot. A blood clot is somewhat like a bandage. When you cut yourself, a series of chemical reactions cause threadlike fibers called fibrin to form a sticky net that traps escaping blood cells and plasma. This forms a clot and helps prevent further loss of blood. Blood clots are important for homeostasis. Figure 20-9 shows blood clotting after a cut.

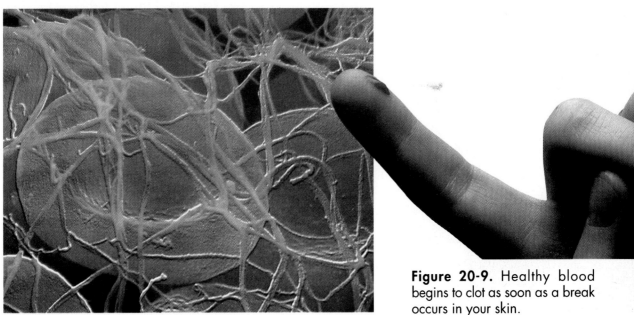

Figure 20-9. Healthy blood begins to clot as soon as a break occurs in your skin.

MINI-Lab

How does a stethoscope work?
Listen to your heart through a stethoscope. What is causing the sounds you hear? Describe the two sounds.

Blood Types

Sometimes, after an accident or during surgery, a person loses a lot of blood. This person may receive blood from another person through a blood transfusion. During a blood transfusion, a person receives blood or parts of blood. In the past, transfusions could cause red blood cells to clump together. Clots would form in blood vessels and result in death. Then, in the early 1900s, Dr. Karl Landsteiner, an Austrian-American scientist, discovered that there are four different types of blood. He called the four types A, B, AB, and O. Landsteiner found that each type has a chemical identification tag called an antigen on its red blood cells. Type A blood has A antigens. Type B has B antigens. Type AB has both A and B antigens on each blood cell. Type O has no antigens.

Each type also has specific antibodies in the plasma of that blood. The antibodies prevent it from mixing with most of the other blood types. Type A blood has antibodies against type B. If you mix type A blood with type B blood, type A red blood cells react to type B blood as if it were a foreign substance. The antibodies in type A respond by clumping the type B blood. Type B blood has antibodies against type A. Type AB has no antibodies, so it can receive blood from A, B, and AB. Type O has both A and B antibodies. Table 20-2 lists the four blood types, what they can receive, and what types they can donate to.

If you have already studied the chapter on genetics in this textbook, then you know that blood type is inherited. You cannot change your blood type.

Table 20-2

American Red Cross
Blood Services
Central Ohio Region
995 E. Broad Street
Columbus, Ohio 43205
1-614-253-7981

301 32 4706 16
BUCHHOLZ BARBARA A

012138 F
0 POS

BLOOD TRANSFUSION POSSIBILITIES

Type	Can receive	Can donate to
A	O, A	A, AB
B	O, B	B, AB
AB	all	AB
O	O	all

PROBLEM SOLVING

The Blood Type Mystery

Detective Johnson was on to something. He had been assigned to a confusing robbery case. He had received conflicting testimony from the people involved. Now he had the last piece of evidence he needed to solve the crime.

A person had come home to find someone he knew robbing his apartment. The victim struggled with the robber. He broke a vase over the robber's head. The victim later identified the robber in a police line-up, but the robber said he had an alibi.

While investigating, Detective Johnson found blood on the vase and carpet. He sent the blood to a lab to be analyzed. The blood of the victim and robber also were analyzed, even though the robber offered proof that he had just received a blood transfusion with type O blood.

When Detective Johnson received the blood analysis report, the blood on the vase and carpet was found to be type A. The victim's blood type was B. The robber's blood type was A. The robber was found guilty. The case was solved.

Think Critically: What did the robber know about the blood he received?

The Rh factor is another inherited substance in blood. If present in a person's blood, the person has Rh-positive (Rh+) blood. If it is not present, the person is said to be Rh-negative (Rh−). An Rh− person receiving blood from an Rh+ person will produce antibodies against the Rh+ factor. Antibodies are proteins that destroy or neutralize foreign substances, such as pathogens, in your body.

A problem also occurs when an Rh− mother carries an Rh+ baby. Close to the time when the baby is about to be born, antibodies from the mother can cross the placenta and destroy the baby's red blood cells. If this happens, the baby can receive a blood transfusion before or right after birth. At 28 weeks and immediately after the birth, the mother can receive an injection that destroys any Rh+ antibodies she has made. Thanks to the work of Dr. Landsteiner, blood groups and Rh factor now are checked before transfusions and during pregnancies.

Did You Know?

Rh, or Rhesus, factor was first discovered in the rhesus monkey in 1940. From 85 to 90 percent of the people in the United States have this antigen.

Diseases and Disorders of Blood

Blood, like any other tissue in your body, is subject to illness. Because blood circulates to all parts of the body and performs so many vital functions, any illness related to blood or circulation is cause for concern. Anemia is a disorder in which there are too few red blood cells, or too little hemoglobin in the red blood cells. Because of this, body tissues do not receive enough oxygen. They are unable to carry on their usual activities. Sometimes the loss of great amounts of blood or improper diet will cause anemia. Anemia can also result from the effects of a disease or side effects of treatment for a disease.

Leukemia is a disease in which one or more types of white blood cells are produced in increased numbers. However, these cells are immature and do not effectively fight infections. Blood transfusions and bone marrow transplants are used to treat this disease, but they are not always successful.

Blood has many functions. It transports oxygen and nutrients to body cells. Blood takes wastes from these cells to organs for removal. Cells in blood help fight infection and heal wounds. You can understand why blood is sometimes called the tissue of life.

Figure 20-10. A sample of blood from a person with leukemia shows red blood cells and immature white blood cells.

SECTION REVIEW

1. What are the four functions of blood in the body?
2. What are the characteristics and function of blood cells, plasma, and platelets?
3. Why must a person's blood type be checked before he or she is given a transfusion?
4. Describe a disease and a disorder of blood.
5. **Apply:** Think about the main job of your red blood cells. If red blood cells couldn't pick up carbon dioxide and wastes from your cells, what would be the condition of your tissues?

Skill Builder

☒ Making and Using Tables

Look at the data in Table 20-2 on page 474 about blood group interactions. To which group(s) can type AB donate blood? If you need help, refer to Making and Using Tables in the **Skill Handbook** on page 690.

ACTIVITY 20-2
Comparing Blood Cells

Problem: *How do human blood cells compare with those of other vertebrates?*

Materials
- prepared slides of human blood and blood of two other vertebrates (fish, frog, reptile, bird)
- microscope

Procedure
1. Under low power, examine the prepared slide of human blood. Locate the red blood cells.
2. Examine the red blood cells under high power.
3. In a table like the one shown, draw, count, and describe the red blood cells.
4. Move the slide to another position. Find one or two white blood cells. They will be blue or purple due to the stain.
5. Draw, count, and describe the white cells in the space provided in the table.
6. Still using high power, examine the slide for very small fragments that appear blue. These are platelets.
7. Draw, count, and describe the platelets in the table.

8. Follow Steps 1 to 7 for each of the two other slides of vertebrate blood.

Analyze
1. Which type of blood cells are present in the greatest number?
2. How are the red blood cells of the other vertebrates alike or different from the human cells?
3. How are the white blood cells alike or different among vertebrates?
4. Are the platelets all alike?

Conclude and Apply
5. Does each vertebrate studied have all three cell types?
6. What might you infer about the ability of the different red blood cells to carry oxygen?
7. What is the function of each of the three types of blood cells?

Data and Observations

Vertebrate type	Blood cell type	Description	Number in field	Drawing
Human	Red			
	White			
	Platelets			
Bird	Red			
	White			
	Platelets			
Frog	Red			
	White			
	Platelets			

20-3 Autologous Blood Transfusions

New Science Words

homologous blood transfer
autologous blood transfer

Objectives

▶ Explain the advantages of an autologous blood transfusion.
▶ Name one problem with saving one's own blood.

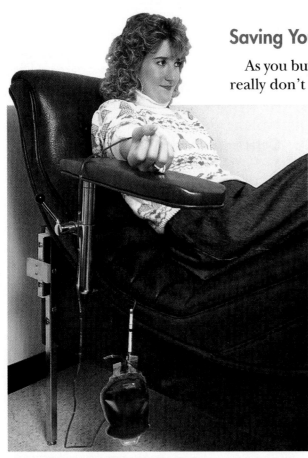

Figure 20-11. Autologous blood transfer involves giving and storing your own blood for your own future use.

Saving Your Own Blood

As you buy a snack, new T-shirt, or magazine (that you really don't need), you might feel a bit guilty about not saving that money away somewhere so it will be safe until you really need it. Today, doctors are suggesting that money isn't the only thing that people should be putting in the bank. Have you ever read about someone storing his or her own blood just in case it is needed?

Because new blood cells are constantly being produced in your body, lost blood is replaced quickly in a healthy person. You probably know that the Red Cross Blood Mobile collects units of blood from individuals willing to donate to others who might need blood. A **homologous blood transfer** is blood taken from one person and given to another. Some people store their own blood if they are anticipating surgery. **Autologous** (aw TAHL uh gus) **blood transfer** is the use of one's own blood for transfusion. This blood is collected prior to surgery.

Unfortunately, there are several drawbacks to this technology. The biggest problem lies in the expense of storing blood. Doctors estimate that it costs about $200 per year to safely store blood. In addition, the patient may be hundreds or thousands of miles away from his or her blood bank when the blood is needed.

However, in response to people who are interested in this procedure, doctors at Northwestern Memorial

Hospital in Chicago have developed two forms of autologous blood transfusion. Blood lost during surgery is collected with suction devices. This blood may be put back into the patient's body after it has been cleansed. Lost blood also can be collected with sponges and squeezed out into a bowl of saline, a type of salt solution. Within 15 minutes, it is processed and put back into the patient's circulation. By using both methods, doctors believe that they can recover up to 90 percent of blood that would otherwise be lost.

How can lost blood be returned to a patient?

Still, in some situations, it is very difficult to collect blood from a patient if much of it is lost before medical help is available. To solve this problem, doctors are working on ways to develop artificial hemoglobin that would temporarily transport oxygen and carbon dioxide throughout the body. Another idea being researched is the reproduction of a hormone that causes the body to produce blood cells much more quickly than it normally does. This would allow the body to replace much of its own blood rather than having to receive new blood. One last idea includes doctors using lasers, rather than scalpals, to perform surgery. Lasers cause much less damage to body tissue, thus preventing blood loss due to the use of a scalpal.

Researchers are working hard to develop new techniques to protect people from blood contaminated by disease. Saving one's own blood for later use appears to be a very good idea. What do you think?

EcoTip

Keep your heart healthy. Toxic materials often accumulate in fat tissue. Trim excess fats from meats.

SECTION REVIEW

1. What is the difference between an autologous and a homologous blood transfer?
2. What are two problems with autologous blood banks?

You Decide!

When the American Red Cross collects blood from volunteer donors, the blood is screened for the AIDS virus. If a donor is found to have the virus, it is the policy of the Red Cross that that individual is notified. Why would the Red Cross have such a policy? Do you think this policy is a good one?

SCIENCE & SOCIETY

Your Lymphatic System

New Science Words

lymphatic system
lymph
lymphocytes
lymph nodes

Objectives

▶ Describe the functions of the lymphatic system.
▶ Explain where lymph comes from.
▶ Explain the role of lymph organs in fighting infections.

Functions of Your Lymphatic System

You have learned that blood carries nutrients and oxygen to cells. Molecules of these substances pass through capillary walls to be absorbed by nearby cells. Some of the water and dissolved substances around cells becomes part of tissue fluid between cells. What would happen if this fluid kept collecting in the spaces? The tissue would swell and eventually burst. Obviously, this does not happen. Your **lymphatic** (lihm FAT ihk) **system** collects fluid from body tissue spaces and returns it to the blood through lymph capillaries and larger lymph vessels. This system also contains cells that help your body defend itself against pathogens.

What is the function of your lymphatic system?

Lymphatic Organs

The lymphatic system carries fluid away from tissues into the lymphatic capillaries found in most tissues. This fluid is known as **lymph** (LIHMF). Lymph enters the cap-

Figure 20-12. Lymph is fluid that has moved from around cells into lymph vessels.

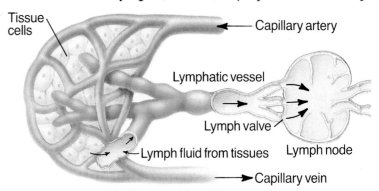

Tissue cells
Capillary artery
Lymphatic vessel
Lymph valve
Lymph fluid from tissues
Lymph node
Capillary vein

illaries by absorption and diffusion. Lymph consists mostly of water, dissolved substances, and **lymphocytes** (LIHM fuh sites), a type of white blood cell. The lymphatic capillaries join with larger vessels that eventually drain the lymph into large veins near the heart. There is no heartlike structure to pump the lymph through the lymphatic system. The movement of lymph is due to contraction of skeletal muscles and the smooth muscles in lymph vessels. Like veins, the lymphatic vessels have valves that prevent the backward flow of lymph.

Before lymph enters blood, it passes through bean-shaped structures throughout the body known as **lymph nodes.** Lymph nodes filter out microorganisms and foreign materials that have been engulfed by lymphocytes. Sometimes an infection takes over a lymph node. It becomes inflamed and tender to the touch. You have felt an enlarged lymph node in your neck when you've had a cold.

Larger groups of lymph nodes are the tonsils, thymus, and spleen. Tonsils are in the back of the throat. They provide protection to the mouth and nose against pathogens. The thymus is a soft mass of tissue located behind the sternum. The thymus produces lymphocytes that travel to other lymph organs. The spleen is the largest organ of the lymphatic system and is located behind the upper left part of the stomach. Blood flowing through the spleen gets filtered. Here, old, worn out, and damaged red blood cells are broken down. Large, specialized cells in the spleen engulf and destroy bacteria and other foreign substances.

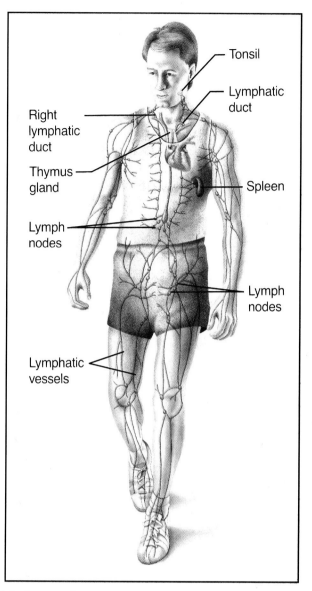

Figure 20-13. The Human Lymphatic System

What is the function of a lymph node?

A Disease of the Lymphatic System

As you read in Chapter 8, the AIDS virus is deadly. When the AIDS virus enters a person's body, it attacks and destroys a particular kind of lymphocyte called helper T cells. Normally, helper T cells help produce antibodies to fight infections. With fewer numbers of helper

Figure 20-14. Ryan White was infected with the AIDS virus after receiving blood transfusions before donated blood was tested for the AIDS virus. Here Ryan (right) is shown with Lukas Haas, who played Ryan in a movie about his life.

T cells, a person is less able to fight pathogens. A person infected with the AIDS virus may develop infections that a healthy person would be able to fight. These infections become difficult to treat and often result in death.

Your lymphatic system collects extra fluid from body tissue spaces. It also produces lymphocytes that fight infections from microorganisms and foreign material that enter the body. This system works hard to helps keep your body healthy.

SECTION REVIEW

1. Describe the role of your lymphatic system.
2. Where does lymph come from and how does it get into the lymphatic capillaries?
3. What happens when the AIDS virus enters the body?
4. **Apply:** How do your lymphatic vessels differ from your arteries?

Skill Builder

☑ Comparing and Contrasting

Compare and contrast your lymphatic system and your cardiovascular system. If you need help, refer to Comparing and Contrasting in the **Skill Handbook** on page 683.

CHAPTER
REVIEW

20-1: Circulation

1. Arteries carry blood from the heart; capillaries exchange food and oxygen and wastes in cells; veins bring blood back to the heart.

2. Blood enters the right atrium of the heart through veins, moves to the right ventricle, to the lungs by the pulmonary artery. Blood rich in oxygen returns to the left atrium, moves into the left ventricle, and then out through the aorta to the body.

3. Pulmonary circulation is the path of blood to and from the heart and lungs. Circulation through the rest of the body is systematic circulation.

20-2: Blood

1. Red blood cells carry oxygen; platelets form clots; white blood cells fight infection.

2. A, B, AB, and O blood types are determined by the presence or absence of antigens. Correct type transfusion is necessary for survival.

3. In anemia, too little oxygen reaches tissues because of too few red blood cells or too little hemoglobin. In leukemia, larger numbers of white blood cells are produced, none of which can fight disease.

20-3: Science and Society: Autologous Blood Transfusions

1. Autologous blood transfusion is the use of one's own blood for transfusion.

2. Cost of storage and having the blood easily available are problems.

20-4: Your Lymphatic System

1. Lymphatic vessels return fluid to the circulatory system and fight disease.

2. Lymph is fluid between cells.

3. Lymph structures filter blood, produce certain white blood cells that destroy bacteria, and destroy worn-out red and white blood cells.

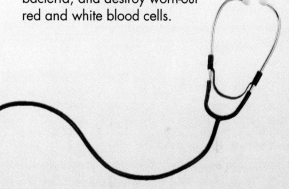

KEY SCIENCE WORDS

a. **arteries**
b. **atherosclerosis**
c. **atria**
d. **autologous blood transfer**
e. **blood pressure**
f. **capillaries**
g. **coronary circulation**
h. **hemoglobin**
i. **homologous blood transfer**
j. **hypertension**
k. **lymph**
l. **lymphatic system**
m. **lymph nodes**
n. **lymphocytes**
o. **plasma**
p. **platelets**
q. **pulmonary circulation**
r. **systemic circulation**
s. **veins**
t. **ventricles**

UNDERSTANDING VOCABULARY

Match each phrase with the correct term from the list of Key Science Words.

1. filters microorganisms
2. upper heart chambers
3. vessels connected to the heart ventricles
4. path of blood between heart and lungs
5. path of blood to the heart tissue
6. fatty deposit on artery walls
7. high blood pressure
8. liquid portion of the blood
9. blood vessels that connect arteries to veins
10. active in blood clot formation

CHAPTER
REVIEW

CHECKING CONCEPTS

Choose the word or phrase that completes the sentence.

1. Exchange of food, oxygen, and wastes occurs through the _____.
   - **a.** arteries
   - **b.** capillaries
   - **c.** veins
   - **d.** all of these

2. Oxygen-rich blood first enters the _____.
   - **a.** right atrium
   - **b.** left atrium
   - **c.** left ventricle
   - **d.** right ventricle

3. Circulation to all body organs is _____.
   - **a.** coronary
   - **b.** pulmonary
   - **c.** systemic
   - **d.** none of these

4. Blood is under great pressure in _____.
   - **a.** arteries
   - **b.** capillaries
   - **c.** veins
   - **d.** all of these

5. Blood functions to _____.
   - **a.** remove CO_2
   - **b.** carry nutrients
   - **c.** carry oxygen
   - **d.** all of these

6. Infection is fought off by _____.
   - **a.** red blood cells
   - **b.** platelets
   - **c.** white blood cells
   - **d.** all of these

7. The cells that carry oxygen are _____.
   - **a.** red blood cells
   - **b.** platelets
   - **c.** white blood cells
   - **d.** none of these

8. Clotting of blood requires _____.
   - **a.** plasma
   - **b.** oxygen
   - **c.** platelets
   - **d.** all of these

9. Type O blood has antigen(s) _____.
   - **a.** A
   - **b.** B
   - **c.** both A and B
   - **d.** neither A nor B

10. The largest filtering lymph organ is the _____.
    - **a.** spleen
    - **b.** thymus
    - **c.** tonsils
    - **d.** none of these

UNDERSTANDING CONCEPTS

Complete each sentence.

11. The _____ are the two lower heart chambers.
12. The _____ is the largest artery of the body.
13. _____ keeps blood moving in one direction.
14. _____ is the liquid portion of the blood.
15. Fluid from body tissue spaces is called _____.

THINK AND WRITE CRITICALLY

16. Compare the blood pressure in arteries, veins, and capillaries.
17. What would happen if blood pressure in veins were as high as it is in arteries?
18. A mature human red blood cell has no nucleus. How may this be an advantage?
19. What is the purpose of valves in veins and lymphatic capillaries?
20. Why would a person with anemia be tired?

21. Identify the following as having oxygen-rich or carbon-dioxide full blood: aorta, coronary arteries, coronary veins, inferior vena cava, left atrium, left ventricle, right atrium, right ventricle, superior vena cava.
22. Discuss some benefits of autologous blood transfer.
23. Explain how the lymphatic system works with the cardiovascular system.
24. Why is cancer of the blood or lymph hard to control?
25. Pulse is usually taken at the neck or wrist. Why do you think this is so even though there are many arteries?

MORE SKILL BUILDERS

If you need help, refer to the Skill Handbook.

1. **Sequencing:** Put the path of blood in sequence from the heart, to the lungs, and out to the body.
2. **Comparing and Contrasting:** Compare the life span of the different types of blood cells.
3. **Interpreting Data:** Interpret the data obtained in a lab. Find the average heartbeat rate of four males and four females and compare the two averages.
   Males: 72, 64, 65, 72
   Females: 67, 84, 74, 67

4. **Designing an Experiment:** Design an experiment to compare the heartbeat rate at rest and after exercising.
5. **Hypothesizing:** Make a hypothesis to suggest the effects of smoking on heartbeat rate.

PROJECTS

1. With supervision, prepare a heart healthy recipe. Check for recipes through the American Heart Association cookbooks. Bring a sample in to share with the class.
2. Write a report on heart transplants, their success, and what a heart-transplant patient has to do to remain healthy.

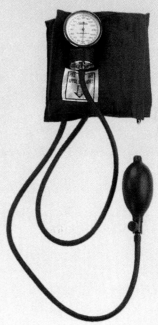

21 Respiration and Excretion

Have you ever run so fast that it felt like your lungs would burst? What did you do to ease your pain and get more air to your lungs? How long did it take your breathing rate to return to normal?

FIND OUT!

Do this activity to find out about your breathing rate.

Put your hand on your chest. Notice your breathing. You can feel your chest move up and down slightly. Take a deep breath. Notice how your rib cage moves out and upward when you inhale. Count your breathing rate for 15 seconds. Multiply by four to figure your breathing rate for one minute. Jog in place for one minute and count your breathing rate again. How long does it take for your breathing rate to return to normal? Compare your answers with your classmates'.

Gearing Up

Previewing the Chapter

Use this outline to help you focus on important ideas in this chapter.

Section 21-1   Your Respiratory System
► Functions of Your Respiratory System
► Organs of Your Respiratory System
► How You Breathe
► Diseases and Disorders of the Respiratory System

Section 21-2   Science and Society
Dangerous Breathing
► Watch Where You Exercise

Section 21-3   Your Urinary System
► Functions of Your Urinary System
► Organs of Your Urinary System
► Other Excretory Organs
► Diseases and Disorders of the Urinary System

Previewing Science Skills

► In the Skill Builders, you will sequence, outline and make a concept map.
► In the Activities, you will observe, analyze, and collect data.
► In the MINI-Labs, you will observe, interpret, diagram, and describe.

What's next?

Now that you know that exercise increases your breathing rate, find out how your body uses the air you breathe. Also learn how your body gets rid of liquid wastes through your lungs, skin, and kidneys.

21-1 Your Respiratory System

New Science Words

pharynx
larynx
trachea
bronchi
alveoli
diaphragm
emphysema
chronic bronchitis
asthma

Objectives

▶ State three functions of the respiratory system.
▶ Explain how oxygen and carbon dioxide are exchanged in the lungs and in tissues.
▶ Trace the pathway of air in and out of the lungs.
▶ Name three effects of smoking on the respiratory system.

Functions of Your Respiratory System

People have always known that air and food are needed for life. However, no one knew what it was about air that made it so vital. In 1771, a British chemist, Joseph Priestley, published the results of some experiments with air. He discovered that a mouse couldn't live in a container in which a candle had previously been burned. He reasoned that a gas in the air had been destroyed when the candle burned. He also discovered that if he put a sprig of mint into the container, the gas necessary for life returned in eight or nine days. Then a mouse again could live in this container. Think about photosynthesis. What do you think went on when the mint plant was in the container? The gas for life was later named oxygen.

Respiration is the process in which energy is released from glucose in cells. People often get the terms *breathing* and *respiration* mixed up. Breathing is the process whereby air moves into and out of lungs. Air contains oxygen, which is carried to cells by your circulatory system. At the same time, your digestive system has prepared a supply of glucose in your cells. Now oxygen, which has made this long journey, goes to work and plays a key role in releasing energy from glucose. At the end of this process, carbon dioxide wastes get carried back to your lungs in your blood. There, it is expelled from your body. Now think about why the first mouse was not able to stay alive in the container.

Organs of Your Respiratory System

Your respiratory system is made of body parts that help you breathe by taking oxygen into your body and removing carbon dioxide. The major organs of your respiratory system are shown in Figure 21-1. These organs include your nasal cavity, pharynx (FER ingks), larynx, trachea, bronchi, and lungs. Air enters your body through two openings in your nose called nostrils. Hair inside your nostrils traps dust from the air. Your nostrils lead to your nasal cavity, where air gets moistened and warmed. Glands that produce sticky mucus line the nasal cavity. The mucus traps dust, pollen, and other materials. This helps filter the air you breathe. Tiny hairlike structures, called cilia, move mucus and trapped material to the back of the throat where it can be swallowed.

Warm, moist air now moves to the **pharynx,** a tubelike passageway for both food and air. The pharynx is located between your nasal cavity and your esophagus. At the lower end of the pharynx is a flap of tissue called the epiglottis (ep uh GLAHT us). When you swallow, the epiglottis closes over your larynx. By doing this, food or liquid is prevented from entering your larynx by accident. The food goes to your esophagus instead. What do you think could happen if you talk or laugh while eating?

Between the pharynx and the trachea is a structure called the **larynx,** to which your vocal cords are attached. When you speak, muscles tighten or loosen your vocal cords. Sound is produced when air moves past, causing them to vibrate. The vocal cords of males are longer than those of females.

Below the larynx is the **trachea,** a tube about 12 cm in length. C-shaped rings of cartilage keep the trachea open and prevent it from collapsing. Why is it necessary for the trachea to stay open all the time? The trachea is lined with mucous membranes and cilia to trap dust, bacteria, and pollen.

How do cilia in your respiratory system help you?

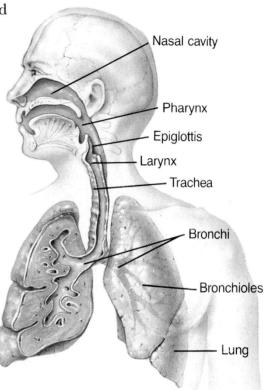

Figure 21-1. The Structures of the Human Repiratory System

How is sound produced?

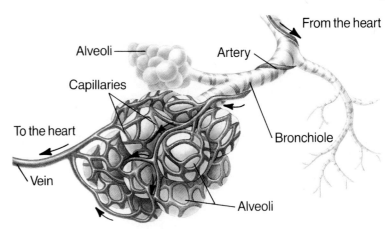

From the heart

Alveoli

Artery

Capillaries

To the heart

Bronchiole

Vein

Alveoli

Figure 21-2. In the lungs, alveoli are surrounded by capillaries.

At the lower end of the trachea are two short branches, called **bronchi,** that carry air into the lungs (*singular:* bronchus). Your lungs take up most of the space in your chest cavity. Within the lungs, the bronchi branch into smaller and smaller tubes. The smallest tubes are the bronchioles (BRAHN kee ohlz). At the end of each bronchiole are clusters of tiny thin-walled sacs called **alveoli** (al VE uh li). Your lungs are masses of alveoli arranged in grape-like clusters. Capillaries surround the alveoli. The exchange of oxygen and carbon dioxide takes place between the alveoli and capillaries. This happens easily as the walls of the alveoli and capillaries are only one cell thick. Oxygen diffuses through the walls of the alveoli and then through the walls of the capillaries into the blood. Oxygen is picked up by the hemoglobin in red blood cells and is carried to all body cells. As this happens, carbon dioxide coming back from body cells diffuses through the walls of the capillaries and through the walls of the alveoli. Carbon dioxide leaves your body when you breathe out, or exhale.

How You Breathe

Breathing is partly the result of changes in air pressure. Under normal conditions, a gas moves from an area of high pressure to an area of low pressure. When you squeeze an empty plastic bottle, air rushes out. This happens because pressure outside the bottle is less than inside the bottle. As you release your grip on the bottle, the pressure inside the bottle is less than outside the bottle. Air rushes back in.

Your lungs work in a similar way to the squeezed bottle. Your **diaphragm** (DI uh fram) is a muscle beneath

Figure 21-3. Air under pressure moves out of a squeezed bottle.

your lungs that helps move air in and out of your body. Your diaphragm contracts and relaxes when you breathe. Like your hands on the plastic bottle, the diaphragm exerts pressure or relieves pressure on your lungs. Remember earlier when you felt your chest move up and down? When you inhale, your diaphragm contracts and moves down. The upward movement of your rib cage and the downward movement of your diaphragm cause the volume of your chest cavity to increase. Air pressure is reduced in your chest cavity, and your lungs fill with air. Air pressure outside the body pushes into your air passageways and into your lungs. Your lungs are somewhat elastic and expand as the air rushes into them.

When you exhale, your diaphragm relaxes and returns to its dome shape. Your rib cage moves downward. These two actions reduce the size of your chest cavity. Your lungs also return to their original position. Pressure on your lungs is increased. The gases inside your lungs are pushed out through air passages.

Even when you exhale forcefully, a little air called residual air is always left in your lungs. During times of quiet activity, such as reading or doing homework, your lungs inhale about 500 mL of air with every breath. When you exercise vigorously, you may inhale and exhale as much as 2000 mL of air per breath.

What causes the movement of your diaphragm?

Science and MATH

At the beginning of this chapter you figured out your breathing rate for one minute. Take this number and find out how many breaths you take in a day. If every two breaths filled a liter bottle, how many bottles would you fill in a day?

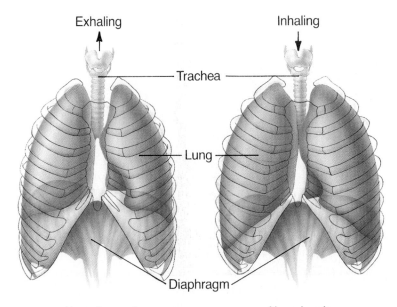

Exhaling | Inhaling

— Trachea —

— Lung —

Diaphragm

Air rushes out
Diaphragm relaxes
Chest cavity decreases

Air rushes in
Diaphragm contracts
Chest cavity increases

Figure 21-4. When you exhale, your diaphragm relaxes and pushes up on your lungs. When you inhale, your diaphragm contracts and lowers.

Diseases and Disorders of the Respiratory System

If you were asked to list some of the things that can harm your respiratory system, you would probably put smoking at the top. Many serious diseases are related to smoking. Being around others who smoke also can harm your respiratory system. Smoking, polluted air, and coal dust have been related to respiratory problems such as emphysema, bronchitis, asthma, and cancer.

Emphysema (em fuh SEE muh) is a disease in which the alveoli in the lungs lose their ability to expand and contract. Most cases of emphysema result from smoking. When a person has emphysema, smoke becomes trapped in the alveoli in the lungs. This eventually causes the alveoli to stretch and rupture. As a result, the surface area of the alveoli is decreased. Lungs become scarred. Less oxygen moves into the bloodstream from the alveoli. Blood becomes low in oxygen and high in carbon dioxide. This condition results in shortness of breath. Some people affected with emphysema can't blow out a match or walk up a flight of stairs. Because the heart works harder to supply oxygen to body cells, people who have emphysema often develop heart problems as well.

What happens when a person has emphysema?

Figure 21-5. A diseased lung (a) cuts down on the amount of oxygen that can be delivered to body cells. A normal, healthy lung (b) can exchange oxygen and carbon dioxide effectively.

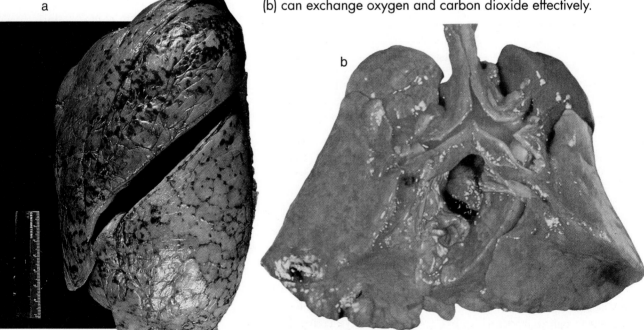

a

b

Figure 21-6. Coughing is a reflex that moves unwanted matter from respiratory passages. Cilia help trap and move this foreign matter. When cilia are damaged, the lungs lose a defense against disease. The photograph to the right shows hair-like cilia around cancer cells in the respiratory passage.

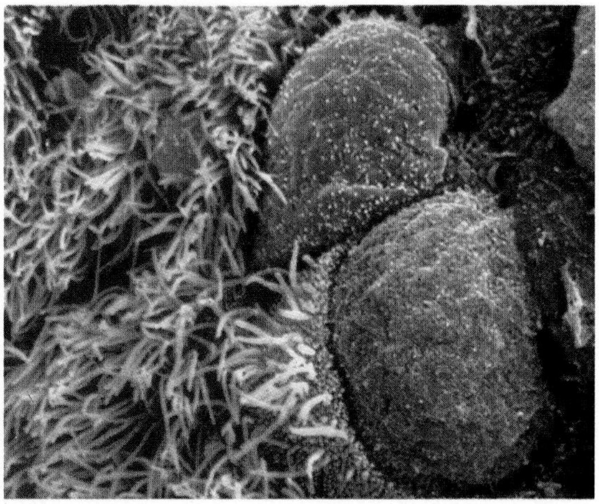

LOAN OFFICER

Chronic bronchitis is a disease in which too much mucus is produced in the bronchial tubes. Most cases of this disease result from smoking. People who have chronic bronchitis cough often to try to help clear the mucus from the airway. However, the more a person coughs, the more the cilia and bronchial tubes can be harmed. When cilia are damaged, their ability to move mucus, bacteria, and dirt out of the lungs is impaired. When this happens, harmful substances, such as sticky tar from burning tobacco, build up in the airways.

Asthma is a disorder of the lungs in which there may be shortness of breath, wheezing, or coughing. When a person has an asthma attack, the bronchial tubes contract quickly. Asthma is often an allergic reaction. An asthma attack can result from a reaction to breathing certain substances, such as plant pollen. Eating certain foods or stress have also been related to the onset of asthma attacks.

Science and WRITING

Write a letter to the local office of the American Lung Association. Find out more about a respiratory disease. Write a report on the causes of the disease, its symptoms, and treatment. Include information on how many people have the disease.

Figure 21-7. Everyone should be aware of the effects of smoking on lungs.

SMOKING
POLLUTES
YOU AND
EVERYTHING
ELSE

American Cancer Society

Lung cancer is the leading cause of cancer deaths in men and women in the United States. Inhaling the tar in cigarette smoke is the greatest contributing factor to lung cancer. Smoking also is believed to be a factor in the development of cancer of the mouth, esophagus, larynx, and pancreas.

Except for certain bacteria, all living things would die without oxygen. Your respiratory system helps you take in oxygen and get rid of carbon dioxide. This system also helps you get rid of some pathogens. You can help keep your respiratory system healthy. Avoid smoking and polluted air. Regular exercise helps you increase your body's ability to use oxygen. This makes your breathing more efficient.

SECTION REVIEW

1. What is the main function of the respiratory system?
2. What happens when oxygen and carbon dioxide are exchanged in the lungs?
3. What causes air to move in and out of the lungs?
4. How does emphysema affect a person's alveoli?
5. **Apply:** How is the work of the digestive and circulatory systems related to the respiratory system?

Skill Builder

☑ Sequencing

Sequence the pathway of air through the respiratory organs from the atmosphere to the blood and back to the atmosphere. If you need help, refer to Sequencing in the **Skill Handbook** on page 680.

ACTIVITY 21-1
The Effects of Respiration

Problem: *How does exercise affect the amount of carbon dioxide exhaled by the lungs?*

Materials
- clock or watch with second hand
- drinking straw
- 200 mL bromothymol blue solution
- 400-mL beakers (2)
- graduated cylinder

Procedure
1. Make a table like the one shown.
2. Predict how exercise will affect the amount of carbon dioxide exhaled by the lungs.
3. Label beaker A and beaker B. Pour 100 mL bromothymol blue solution into each of the beakers. Bromothymol blue will turn yellow when carbon dioxide is added to it.
4. Look at the clock and begin timing. Exhale through the straw into the bromothymol blue solution in beaker A. **CAUTION:** *Do not inhale through the straw.* Continue exhaling for 15 seconds or until the bromothymol blue solution changes color. Record the time it takes for the color change to occur. Set beaker A aside.
5. Now run in place for three minutes.
6. Exhale into the bromothymol blue solution in beaker B. Exhale using the same force as before.
7. Record the time it takes for the bromothymol blue to change color in beaker B.
8. Compare your data with the class data.

Data and Observations

Beaker A	
Beaker B	

Analyze
1. What caused the bromothymol blue in the beaker to change color?
2. Compare the time it took the bromothymol blue solution to change color before exercise and after exercise. Explain any difference.
3. What was the control in this experiment?

Conclude and Apply
4. How does exercise affect the amount of carbon dioxide exhaled?
5. Why are waste products of the body tissues exhaled through the lungs?
6. Why does exercising strenuously cause you to breathe faster than usual?

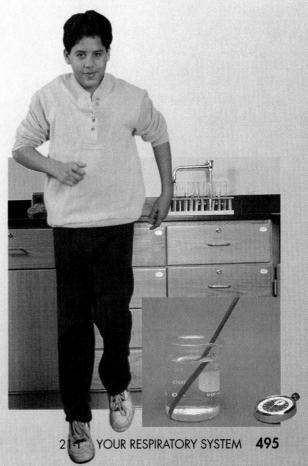

Dangerous Breathing

New Science Words

nitrogen dioxide

Objectives

▶ State two reasons why exercise is important to good health.
▶ Become aware of the dangers of exercising in environments that are polluted.

Watch Where You Exercise

You probably realize that exercise is important for good health. When you participate in regular exercise, you feel good, your muscle tone improves, and fat is lost. With regular exercise, lungs become capable of holding greater amounts of air.

Many people participate in aerobics or go jogging during lunch or after school or work. Unfortunately, busy city streets and parks where people exercise can be polluted with exhaust fumes. Although most people realize that it is not healthful to breathe polluted air, it actually may be more dangerous to do so while exercising.

Recently, two scientists at the Los Alamos National Laboratory in New Mexico discovered that exercising in polluted environments can be dangerous to your health. **Nitrogen dioxide,** found in cigarette smoke and automobile exhaust, is a chemical that is harmful if inhaled. In a research project involving rats exposed to nitrogen dioxide, researchers found that rats that exercised after being exposed to nitrogen dioxide suffered five times more lung damage than those rats that did not exercise after being exposed to the toxins. The rats were exposed to only half of the nitrogen dioxide that a typical smoker breathes in during one puff of a cigarette! This means that exercising in a polluted environment is more harmful than not exercising at all. What does this mean for our society when so many people now exercise by running? Persons who smoke while doing strenuous work or exercises should reconsider their need to smoke. Joggers should avoid areas of heavy traffic.

Nitrogen dioxide also is found in coal mines and in farm silos, where it is given off by decaying plant matter.

What happens to your lungs with regular exercise?

EcoTip

Many office buildings are constructed with no way to open windows. In addition, synthetic materials are used in building products. Air is easily contaminated with materials that are harmful to health. Hanging plants have been found to process many pollutants in these situations.

Miners and farmers should avoid strenuous labor after being exposed to high levels of nitrogen dioxide. Firefighters have also been found to be at high risk due to their exposure to heavy fumes while working hard to extinguish fires.

Although research in this area is just beginning, there appears to be a great deal of danger associated with exercising after and during exposure to nitrogen dioxide. It is hoped that there will be more information about this subject in the future. Until then, be careful about the air you breathe, during exercise. Remember, you only have one set of lungs!

SECTION REVIEW

1. Name two benefits of regular exercise.
2. Name three places where nitrogen dioxide is found.

You Decide!

Most restaurants and other public places have designated smoking areas. Some people say smoking should be banned from all public places. How do you feel about this statement? Where do you think people should have the right to smoke?

SCIENCE & SOCIETY

21-3 Your Urinary System

New Science Words

urinary system
kidneys
nephrons
urine
ureters
bladder
urethra

Objectives

▶ List three functions of the urinary system.
▶ Describe how your kidneys work.
▶ Describe the excretory functions of the skin and lungs.
▶ Explain what happens when urinary organs don't work.

Functions of Your Urinary System

Drinking water in your community is purified before it comes out of a faucet in your kitchen. Filters strain out large materials. Settling basins remove materials that float, and chemicals kill bacteria and other organisms that might cause disease.

Your excretory system works in a similar way to the equipment that purifies water. Your excretory organs are your kidneys, lungs, and skin. These organs help your body get rid of wastes. If they didn't do this, you could become very sick from a buildup of toxic substances in cells. Organs could be damaged.

The organs of your urinary system are excretory organs. Your **urinary system** is made up of organs that rid your blood of wastes and control blood volume by removing excess water produced by cells. The amount of water in blood is important to maintain normal blood pressure, the movement of gases, and excretion of solid wastes. Your urinary system also balances certain salts and water that must be present in specific concentrations for cell activities to take place.

Organs of Your Urinary System

The major organs of your urinary system are two bean-shaped organs known as the kidneys. Kidneys are located on the back wall of the abdomen at about waist level. The **kidneys** filter blood that has collected wastes from cells. All of your blood passes through your kidneys many times a day. Figures 21-8 and 21-9 show the structures of the kidneys. Here you can see that blood enters the kidneys through the aorta and leaves through a large vein.

Why is the amount of water in blood important?

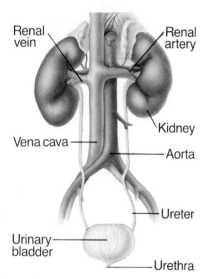

Renal vein
Renal artery
Kidney
Vena cava
Aorta
Ureter
Urinary bladder
Urethra

Figure 21-8. Organs of the Urinary System

Each kidney is made up of about one million **nephrons** (NEF rahnz), the tiny filtering units of the kidney. Each nephron is made up of a cuplike structure and a duct. Water, sugar, salt, and wastes from your blood pass into the cuplike structure. There, liquid is squeezed into a narrow tubule. Capillaries that surround the tubule reabsorb most of the water, sugar, and salt and return it to the blood. These capillaries merge to form small veins. The small veins merge to form the renal veins, which return purified blood to be circulated throughout your body. The liquid left behind flows into collecting tubules in each kidney. This waste liquid, **urine,** contains excess water, salts, and other wastes. The average adult produces about 1 L of urine per day.

The urine in each collecting tubule drains into a funnel-shaped area of each kidney that leads to the ureters (YOOR ut urz). **Ureters** are tubes that lead from each kidney to the bladder. The **bladder** is a muscular organ that holds urine until it leaves the body. A tube called the **urethra** (yoo REE thruh) carries urine from the bladder to the outside of the body. The amount you lose depends on the amount of fluid you drink.

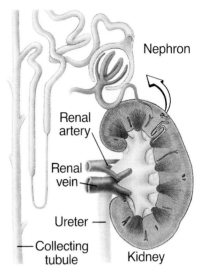

Figure 21-9. Structures of a Nephron

PROBLEM SOLVING

Frederick's First Baseball Game

Last summer, Frederick played baseball for the first time in his life. Frederick said, "I had a great time, but it was hard for me to play at times."

Frederick was born without sweat glands. He finds it difficult to stay outdoors for any length of time, especially in the summer. Frederick is not usually able to enjoy a day at the beach or to participate in sports.

However, a local restaurant raised money to develop a "cool suit" for Frederick. The suit resembles a space suit. It includes a helmet and vest that fits under clothing. Frederick will use a thermostat to control the pumping of a cool solution through the suit. The suit will enable him to play soccer and football and spend more time outside. **Think Critically:** How will the "cool suit" help Frederick live a more active life?

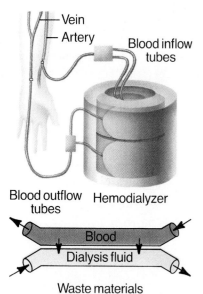
Other Excretory Organs

Your urinary system helps your body maintain homeostasis with the help of other excretory organs. In Chapter 18, you read that skin releases perspiration to cool your body. Perspiration contains water and small amounts of salt. An adult normally loses up to 0.5 L of water in a day.

Your lungs are excretory organs, too. They remove carbon dioxide produced by cell activity in your body. You also lose water each time you breathe out. The air you exhale has some moisture in it. This is evident when you see your breath on a cold day or breathe on a cold window pane and notice a cloud or fog. Each day about 350 mL of water is removed from your body through your respiratory system.

Diseases and Disorders of the Urinary System

What happens when someone's urinary organs don't work properly? Waste products that are not removed build up and act as poisons in body cells. Water that would normally be removed from body tissues accumulates and causes swelling of the ankles and feet. Fluids can also build up around the heart. The heart works harder to move less to the lungs. Without elimination, there also could be an imbalance of salts. The body responds by trying to restore this balance. If the balance is not restored, the kidneys and other organs can be damaged.

Persons who have extremely defective kidneys may have to have their blood filtered by an artificial kidney machine in a process called dialysis. During dialysis, blood from the person's artery is pumped through tubing that is bathed in a salt solution similar to blood plasma. Waste materials diffuse from the tube containing blood and are washed away by the salt solution. The cleaned blood left behind is returned to a vein. A person who has only one kidney can still function normally. One healthy kidney can do the job of two.

The urinary system is a purifying unit for the circulatory system. Wastes are filtered from blood as it passes through the kidneys. Some water and salts are reabsorbed to maintain homeostasis. Waste materials, dissolved in water, are eliminated from the body. This system helps to maintain the health of cells and, therefore, the entire body.

Figure 21-10. During dialysis, blood is cleansed with a salt solution and returned to the body.

Kidney Transplants

A person can have just one kidney and still function normally. However, when both kidneys are lost, due to an accident or disease, a kidney transplant is needed. Kidneys from close relatives are preferred for transplants. This is because the relative may have a genetically similar immune system. If this is the case, the patient will be less likely to reject the new kidney.

The donor's kidney is removed and flushed with a sterile solution so that no trace of the donor's blood remains. An incision is made in the patient's abdomen, and the diseased kidney is removed. Then, the new kidney's vessels are stitched to the patient's blood vessels, and the urethra is inserted into the bladder. The operation is simple, but the patient's body will mobilize its immune system against the donor kidney just as it would against an infection. The patient must be given drugs to stop this immune system response.

Thinking Critically: Why would many transplant patients first suffer more from infection than from organ rejection?

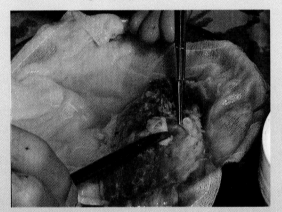

SECTION REVIEW

1. Describe three functions of the urinary system.
2. Explain how the kidneys remove wastes and keep fluids and salts in balance.
3. Why are the skin and lungs classified as excretory organs?
4. What happens when urinary organs don't work?
5. **Apply:** Explain why reabsorption of certain materials in the kidneys is important.

☑ Concept Mapping

Using a network tree concept map, compare the excretory functions of the kidneys and the lungs. If you need help, refer to Concept Mapping in the **Skill Handbook** on pages 688 and 689.

ACTIVITY 21-2
Sweat Glands in the Skin

Problem: *How are sweat glands distributed on the body?*

Materials

- iodine solution
- bond typing paper
- magnifying lens

Procedure

1. Paint a 1 × 1 cm square on the skin of the palm of one hand with two percent tincture of iodine. **CAUTION:** *Iodine is a poison; do not get it in your mouth or eyes. Iodine can stain clothing.*
2. Allow the iodine solution to dry on your skin for three to four minutes.
3. Using the thumb from the other hand, hold a 2 × 2 cm square piece of bond typing paper on the iodine spot for one minute.
4. Lift up the paper and examine it with a magnifying lens. You should see some purple/black dots. Each dot represents a sweat gland. Count the number of dots in 1 square centimeter of the paper.
5. Select another spot, such as the back of the hand or your forearm, to test for sweat gland distribution. Repeat Steps 1 to 4.

Analyze

1. How many dots per centimeter did you observe on the palm of your hand?
2. How many dots per centimeter did you observe on the second spot tested?

Conclude and Apply

3. Bond paper has starch in it. What caused the purple/black dots to appear on the paper?
4. From your observations, compare the distribution of sweat glands in different body areas.
5. If this test were done on the palm of your hand after exercising, what would you expect to see?

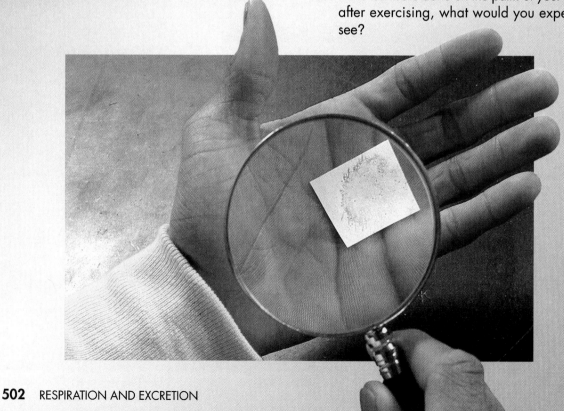

SUMMARY

21-1: Your Respiratory System

1. Your respiratory system helps you take oxygen into your lungs and body cells and helps you remove carbon dioxide.

2. Inhaled air passes through the nasal cavity, pharynx, larynx, trachea, bronchi, and into the alveoli of the lungs.

3. Breathing results in part from the diaphragm's movement, which changes the pressure within the lungs.

4. Smoking causes many problems throughout the respiratory system.

21-2: Science and Society: Dangerous Breathing

1. Regular exercise helps your body feel and work well.

2. Exercising in polluted environments can be dangerous to your health.

21-3: Your Urinary System

1. Kidneys filter blood to remove wastes and keep sodium and other chemicals in balance.

2. The kidneys are the major organs of the urinary system; they filter wastes from all of the blood in your body.

3. The skin and lungs are also excretory organs.

4. When kidneys fail to work, dialysis may be used.

KEY SCIENCE WORDS

a. **alveoli**
b. **asthma**
c. **bladder**
d. **bronchi**
e. **chronic bronchitis**
f. **diaphragm**
g. **emphysema**
h. **kidneys**
i. **larynx**
j. **nephrons**
k. **nitrogen dioxide**
l. **pharynx**
m. **trachea**
n. **ureters**
o. **urethra**
p. **urinary system**
q. **urine**

UNDERSTANDING VOCABULARY

Match each phrase with the correct term from the list of Key Science Words.

1. harmful chemical in auto exhaust
2. clusters of air sacs
3. where vocal cords are attached
4. branches of the trachea
5. muscle involved in breathing
6. disease of broken alveoli
7. a cartilage-reinforced tube through which air moves to the bronchi
8. major urinary organs
9. tubes from kidney to bladder
10. fluid waste

CHAPTER REVIEW

CHECKING CONCEPTS

Choose the word or phrase that completes the sentence.

1. When you inhale, your _____ contract(s) and move(s) down.
   - **a.** bronchioles
   - **c.** nephrons
   - **b.** diaphragm
   - **d.** kidneys

2. Air is moistened, filtered, and warmed in the _____.
   - **a.** larynx
   - **c.** nasal cavity
   - **b.** pharynx
   - **d.** trachea

3. Exchange of gases occurs between the _____ and capillaries.
   - **a.** alveoli
   - **c.** bronchioles
   - **b.** bronchi
   - **d.** none of these

4. The rib cage _____ when you exhale.
   - **a.** moves up
   - **c.** moves out
   - **b.** moves down
   - **d.** none of these

5. _____ is a lung disorder that may occur as an allergic reaction.
   - **a.** Asthma
   - **c.** Emphysema
   - **b.** Chronic bronchitis
   - **d.** All of these

6. A condition worsened by smoking is _____.
   - **a.** asthma
   - **c.** emphysema
   - **b.** lung cancer
   - **d.** any of these

7. _____ are filtering units of the kidney.
   - **a.** Nephrons
   - **c.** Neurons
   - **b.** Ureters
   - **d.** Alveoli

8. Urine is temporarily held in the _____.
   - **a.** kidneys
   - **c.** ureter
   - **b.** bladder
   - **d.** urethra

9. About 1 liter of water is lost per day through _____.
   - **a.** sweat
   - **c.** urine
   - **b.** lungs
   - **d.** none of these

10. All except _____ is(are) reabsorbed by blood after passing through the kidneys.
    - **a.** salt
    - **c.** wastes
    - **b.** sugar
    - **d.** water

UNDERSTANDING CONCEPTS

Complete each sentence.

11. The _____ blocks food from entering the larynx.

12. _____ is an exhaled gas.

13. When you inhale, your diaphragm moves _____.

14. Urine leaves the body through the _____.

15. Purified blood leaves the kidneys through the _____ veins.

THINK AND WRITE CRITICALLY

16. Why is it better to breathe through your nose?

17. Why does the trachea have cartilage but the esophagus does not?

18. What happens if the epiglottis fails to function while a person is eating?

19. Explain how the kidneys work to maintain homeostasis.

20. Describe how the respiratory and excretory systems work to maintain homeostasis.

21. Compare air pressure in the lungs during inhalation and exhalation.
22. What is the advantage of the lungs having many air sacs instead of being just two large sacs, like balloons?
23. Explain the damage smoking does to cilia, alveoli, and lungs.
24. What would happen to the blood if the kidneys stopped working?
25. Describe the action of the kidneys if you were in the desert.

MORE SKILL BUILDERS

If you need help, refer to the Skill Handbook.

1. **Making and Using Graphs:** Make a pie graph of total lung capacity.
   - Tidal volume (inhaled or exhaled during a normal breath) = 500 mL
   - Inspiratory reserve volume (air that can be forcefully inhaled after a normal inhalation) = 3000 mL
   - Expiratory reserve volume (air that can be forcefully exhaled after a normal expiration) = 1100 mL
   - Residual volume (air left in the lungs after forceful exhalation) = 1200 mL
2. **Interpreting Data:** Interpret the data below. How much of each substance is reabsorbed into the blood in the kidneys? What substance is totally excreted in the urine?

Substance	Amount moving through kidney to be filtered	Amount excreted in urine
water	125 liters	1 liter
salt	350 grams	10 grams
urea	1 gram	1 gram
glucose	50 grams	0 grams

3. **Recognizing Cause and Effect:** Discuss how lack of oxygen is related to lack of energy.
4. **Hypothesizing:** Hypothesize the number of breaths you would expect a a person would take per minute in each situation and give a reason for each hypothesis.
   - while sleeping
   - while exercising
   - while on top of Mount Everest
5. **Concept Mapping:** Make an events chain concept map showing what happens when urine forms in the kidneys. Begin with the phrase, *In the nephron...*

PROJECTS

1. Find out what the Heimlich maneuver is and how it is important in saving lives. How is its success based on the presence of residual air? Make poster showing the correct procedure and demonstrate the procedure for the class.
2. Contact your local Kidney Foundation for information on dialysis machines and kidney transplants. Ask your teacher if a guest speaker can talk to the class.

22 Body Regulation

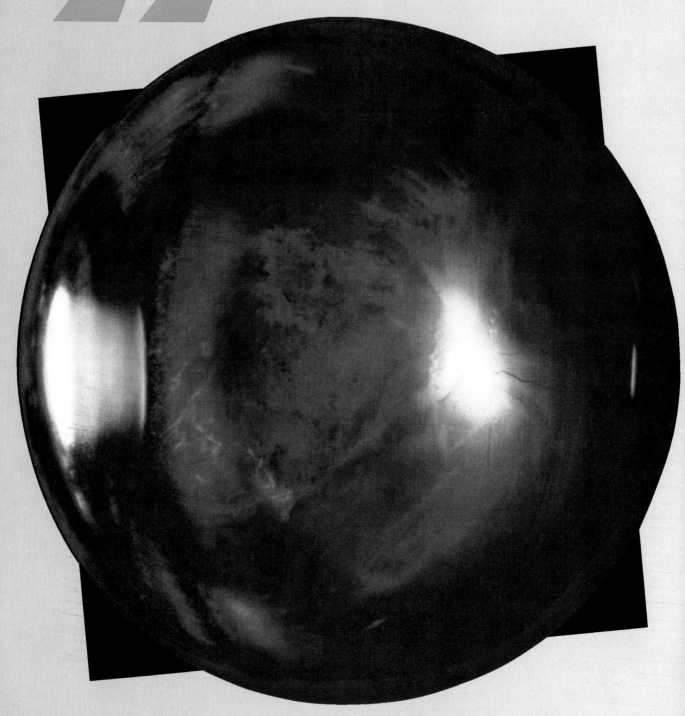

The eye on the page to your left is a complex organ that is your key to the world of vision. Sight is one of the senses that helps you keep in touch with what is going on around you. Do your eyes ever play tricks on you? Have your senses ever fooled you?

FIND OUT!

Do this activity to find out if your senses ever mislead you.

Look at the figure at the bottom of the page. Estimate the size difference between the left outer circle and the right inner circle. Now use a metric ruler and measure the sizes of the two circles to determine if their diameters differ. What did you find out?

Gearing Up
Previewing the Chapter
Use this outline to help you focus on important ideas in this chapter.

Section 22-1   Your Nervous System
▶ The Nervous System at Work
▶ Divisions of the Nervous System
▶ Reflexes
Section 22-2   The Senses
▶ In Touch with Your Environment
Section 22-3   Science and Society Alzheimer's Disease
▶ What Is Alzheimer's Disease?
▶ The Cost of Disease
Section 22-4   Your Endocrine System
▶ Endocrine System
▶ A Negative Feedback System

Previewing Science Skills
▶ In the **Skill Builders,** you will make a concept map, make and use tables, and compare and contrast.
▶ In the **Activities,** you will experiment, predict, measure, and collect data.
▶ In the **MINI-Labs,** you will experiment and collect and interpret data.

What's next?
Your senses may have misled you in the Find Out activity, but your nervous system generally works to keep you aware and responsive to your environment. In this chapter, you will also learn about chemical control systems that maintain the homeostasis of all other body systems.

Your Nervous System

New Science Words

neuron
dendrites
axon
sensory neurons
interneurons
motor neurons
synapse
central nervous system
peripheral nervous system
cerebrum
cerebellum
brainstem
reflex

Objectives

▶ Describe the basic structure of a neuron and how an impulse moves from one neuron to the next.
▶ Compare the central and peripheral nervous systems and identify their parts and functions.
▶ Interpret the pathway of a reflex.

The Nervous System at Work

It's your night to do the dishes. To make the job easier, you decide to plug in a favorite tape. About halfway through the chore, you turn to put a plate in the dish drainer and come face to face with your brother wearing an ugly rubber Halloween mask. You scream, and the dish clatters into the sink. Instantly you are out of breath and your hands begin to shake. Your knees feel wobbly, and your heartbeat speeds up. But then, after a few minutes, your breathing returns to normal and your heartbeat is back to its regular rate. What's going on here?

The scene just pictured is an example of how your body responds to changes in its environment and adjusts itself. Your body makes these adjustments with the help of your nervous system. Any change inside or outside your body that brings about a response is called a stimulus. On an average day, you're bombarded by thousands of stimuli. Noise, light, the smell of food in the cafeteria, and the feel of a cold metal doorknob in your hand are all stimuli from outside your body. A growling stomach is an example of an internal stimulus.

How can your body handle all these stimuli at the same time and yet appear so calm? How is it possible for all your systems to work in a coordinated way? Your body has hundreds of internal control systems that maintain homeostasis. Breathing rate, heartbeat rate, and digestion are just a few of the activities in your body that are constantly checked and regulated. Your nervous system and the endocrine system, a chemical control described later in this chapter, are the main mechanisms by which homeostasis is maintained in your body.

MINI-Lab

Who has a better sense of smell?
Devise an experiment testing classmates' ability to smell different foods, colognes, and household products. Record their responses in a data table according to sex. Are there differences between males and females in the ability to detect odor?

Neurons

The working unit of the nervous system is the nerve cell, or **neuron.** The neuron in Figure 22-2 is made up of a cell body and branches called dendrites and axons. **Dendrites** receive messages and send them to the cell body. An **axon** carries messages away from the neuron cell body. Any message carried by a neuron is called an impulse.

There are three types of neurons in your body: sensory neurons, motor neurons, and interneurons. **Sensory neurons** receive information and send impulses *to* the spinal cord or brain. Your skin and other sense organs are equipped with structures called receptors that respond to stimuli. These stimuli may be changes in temperature, pain, pressure, odor, sound waves, and chemicals around you. This information is picked up by nearby sensory neurons and sent in the form of impulses to your brain or spinal cord. There, a second type of neuron, an interneuron, passes the impulses to motor neurons. *Inter* means "between." **Interneurons** are nerve cells throughout the brain and spinal cord that relay impulses from sensory neurons to motor neurons. There are more interneurons in your body than the other two types. **Motor neurons** conduct impulses *from* the brain or spinal cord to muscles or glands throughout the body. For instance, when you saw the Halloween mask, sensory receptors in your eyes were stimulated. A message was sent to your brain by way of sensory neurons. Your brain responded by sending back impulses along motor neurons to your muscles. Your heart immediately started to pound and your breathing rate increased. Together, these three types of neurons act like a relay team, moving impulses through your body from stimulus to response.

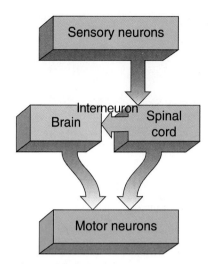

Figure 22-1. In your nervous system, impulses travel a pathway that takes them from sensory neurons to interneurons in your brain and spinal cord to motor neurons.

In what direction do sensory neurons move impulses?

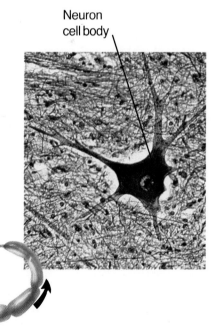

Neuron cell body

Figure 22-2. A neuron is made up of a cell body, dendrites, and an axon.

Dendrites

Nucleus

Cell body

Axon

Direction of impulse

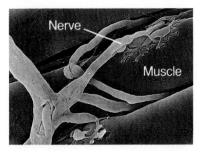

Figure 22-3. Impulses move from neurons to muscle as seen above, or to other neurons as in the illustration to the right.

Synapse

Neurons don't touch each other. How does an impulse move from one neuron to another? To get from one neuron to the next, an impulse jumps across a small space called a **synapse.** In Figure 22-3, you can see that when an impulse reaches the end of an axon, a nerve transmitting chemical is released by the axon. This chemical diffuses across the synapse and starts up an impulse in the next neuron. In this way, an impulse is passed along from one neuron to another.

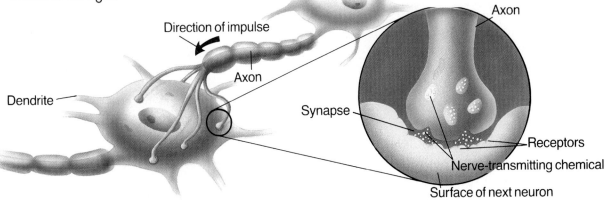

Figure 22-4. The brain and spinal cord make up the central nervous system. Spinal nerves are part of the peripheral nervous system.

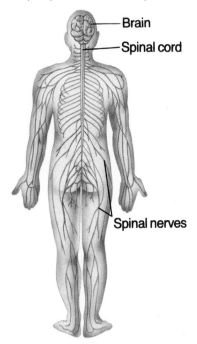

Divisions of the Nervous System

Organs of the nervous system are grouped into two major divisions: the central nervous system (CNS) and the peripheral nervous system (PNS). The **central nervous system** is made up of the brain and spinal cord. The **peripheral nervous system** is made up of cranial nerves and spinal nerves. These nerves connect the brain and spinal cord to other body parts.

The Central Nervous System

Because you have a central nervous system with a brain, your body activities are coordinated. If someone pokes you in the ribs, your whole body is aware of what's going on. Your neurons are adapted in such a way that impulses move in only one direction. Impulses in sensory neurons move only from a receptor to the brain or spinal cord, not in the other direction.

The brain is made up of approximately 100 billion neurons. Figure 22-5 shows that the brain is divided into three major parts: cerebrum, cerebellum, and brainstem. The largest part of the brain, the **cerebrum,** is divided into two large sections called hemispheres. Here, impulses from the senses are interpreted, memory is stored, and the work of voluntary muscles is controlled. The outer layer of the cerebrum, the cortex, is marked by many ridges and grooves. The diagram also shows some of the tasks that sections of the cortex control.

A second part of the brain, the **cerebellum,** is behind and under the cerebrum. It coordinates voluntary muscle movements and maintains balance and muscle tone.

The **brainstem** extends from the cerebrum and connects the brain to the spinal cord. It is made up of the midbrain, the pons, and the medulla. The brainstem controls homeostasis of heartbeat, breathing, and blood pressure. It also coordinates involuntary muscle movements.

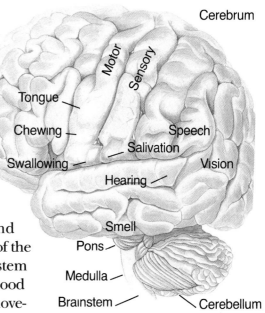

Figure 22-5. Different areas of the brain control specific body activities.

T E C H N O L O G Y

Watching the Brain at Work

Many medical centers in the United States are now using positron emission tomography (PET) for research and diagnosis of the brain. The simple sugar, glucose, is tagged with a radioactive tracer and fed to the patient. The tracer moves through the circulatory system of the brain and gives off particles called positrons. Positrons collide with electrons from the body and release a form of energy. The path of the energy appears as an image on a color monitor. The image shows where energy is used in different areas of the brain as these areas become stimulated.

Scientists can use PET to go beyond looking at just the physical makeup of the brain. By comparing PET images formed when people perform different tasks, researchers have pin-pointed the areas of the brain used for seeing, reading, hearing, speaking, and thinking.

Think Critically: How can PET help scientists understand what happens when someone has an epileptic seizure or when the brain processes language?

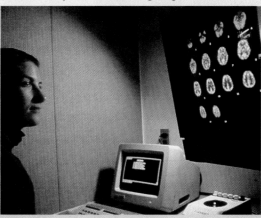

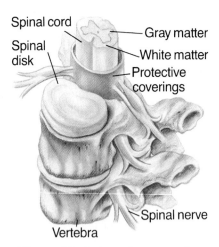

Figure 22-6. Impulses travel to and from the brain by way of the spinal cord.

Figure 22-7. The Divisions of the Peripheral Nervous System.

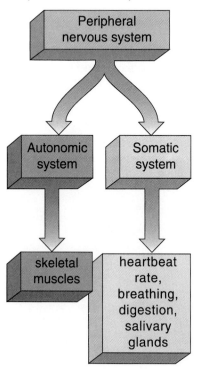

Your spinal cord is an extension of the brainstem. It is made up of bundles of neurons that carry impulses from all parts of the body to the brain and from the brain to all parts of your body. The spinal cord is about as big around as an adult thumb and 43 cm long. The CNS is protected by a bony cap called the skull, by vertebrae, and by three layers of membranes. Between some of these membranes is a fluid called cerebrospinal fluid. What purpose might this fluid serve?

The Peripheral Nervous System

Your brain and spinal cord are connected to the rest of your body by the peripheral nervous system. The PNS is made up of 12 pairs of cranial nerves from your brain and 31 pairs of spinal nerves from your spinal cord. These nerves link your central nervous system with all parts of your body. Spinal nerves are made up of bundles of sensory and motor neurons. For this reason, a single spinal nerve may have impulses going to and from the brain at the same time.

There are two divisions of the peripheral nervous system. The *somatic system* consists of the cranial and spinal nerves that go from the central nervous system to your skeletal muscles. The second division, the *autonomic system*, controls your heartbeat rate, breathing, digestion, and gland functions. When your salivary glands release saliva, your autonomic system is at work. Use Figure 22-7 to help you remember these two divisions.

Reflexes

Have you ever jumped back from something hot or sharp? Then you've experienced a reflex. A **reflex** is an involuntary and automatic response to a stimulus. You can't control reflexes, but many times they have saved lives. A reflex involves a simple nerve pathway called a reflex arc. Figure 22-8 shows a reflex arc. As someone hands you a piece of pizza, some very hot cheese falls on your finger. Sensory receptors in your finger respond to the hot cheese, and an impulse is sent to the spinal cord. The impulse passes to an interneuron in the spinal cord that immediately relays the impulse to motor neurons. Motor neurons transmit the impulse to muscles in your arm. Instantly, without thinking, you pull your arm back in response to the burning food. This is a withdrawal

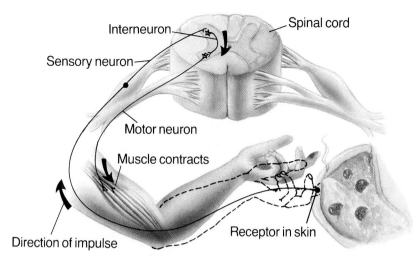

Interneuron

Sensory neuron

Spinal cord

Motor neuron

Muscle contracts

Receptor in skin

Direction of impulse

Figure 22-8. Your response in a reflex is controlled in your spinal cord, not in your brain.

reflex. A reflex allows the body to respond without having to think about what action to take. Reflex responses are controlled in your spinal cord, not in your brain. Your brain acts after the reflex to help you figure out what to do to make the pain stop.

Remember the rubber mask scare? What would have happened if your breathing and heartbeat rate didn't calm down within a few minutes? Your body system can't be kept in a state of continual excitement. The organs of your nervous system control and coordinate responses to maintain homeostasis within your body.

Where are reflexes controlled?

SECTION REVIEW

1. Draw and label the parts of a neuron and give a function for each part.
2. Compare the central and peripheral nervous systems.
3. Explain what happens to an impulse at a synapse.
4. What is the difference between sensory and motor neurons?
5. **Apply:** Describe the reflex pathway of nerve impulses when you step accidentally on a sharp object.

☑ Concept Mapping

Prepare a chain of events concept map of the different kinds of neurons an impulse moves along from the stimulus to a response. If you need help, refer to Concept Mapping in the **Skill Handbook** on pages 688 and 689.

Skill Builder

ACTIVITY 22-1
Reaction Time

Problem: *How can reaction time be measured?*

Materials
- penny
- meterstick

Procedure

Part A
1. Hold your right arm out with the palm down. Put a penny on the center of the back of your hand.
2. Tilt your hand so that the penny slides off. Try to catch the penny with your right hand.
3. Repeat Step 2 nine more times. In a table like the one shown, record how many times you catch the penny and how many times you drop the penny.
4. Repeat Steps 2 and 3 with your left hand. Record your observations.

Part B
1. Have a partner hold a penny about 0.5 m above the palm of your hand.
2. When your partner drops the penny, move your hand before the penny hits it.
3. Repeat Step 2 for different distances. Record your results in the table.
4. Repeat Steps 2 and 3 with your other hand. Record your results.

Part C
1. Have a partner hold a metric ruler at one end so that the other end of the ruler is between your thumb and index finger.
2. Keep your eyes on the bottom of the ruler as your partner releases the ruler. Try to catch the ruler.
3. Repeat Step 2 nine more times.
4. Record the distance the ruler has fallen each time you catch it.
5. Repeat Steps 2 and 3 with your other hand. Record your results.

Data and Observations

Part A				
	Right Hand		**Left Hand**	
Trial	**Caught**	**Not caught**	**Caught**	**Not caught**
1				
2				

Part B			
Trial	**Distance above hand**	**Hit**	**Not hit**
1			
2			

Part C		
	Distance fallen	
Trial	**Right hand**	**Left hand**
1		
2		

Analyze
1. What was the stimulus in each activity?
2. What was the response in each activity?
3. What was the variable in each activity?

Conclude and Apply
4. Did you catch the penny, avoid the penny, and catch the ruler faster with your writing hand?
5. How did your response time improve?
6. How can reaction time be measured?
7. Draw a conclusion about practice with regard to stimulus-response time.

The Senses

Objectives

▶ List the sensory receptors in each sense organ.
▶ Explain what type of stimulus each sense organ responds to and how.
▶ Explain the need for healthy senses.

New Science Words

retina
cochlea
olfactory cells
taste buds

In Touch with Your Environment

Many stories by science fiction writers talk about energy force fields around spaceships. When some form of energy tries to enter the ship's force field, the ship is put on alert. Your body has an alerting system as well, in the form of sense organs. Your senses enable you to see, hear, smell, taste, touch, and feel whatever comes into your personal territory. The energy that stimulates your sense organs may be in the form of light rays, heat, sound waves, chemicals, or pressure. Sense organs are adapted for capturing and transmitting these different forms of energy.

Vision

Think about the different kinds of things you look at every day. It's amazing that, all in one view, you can see words on a page, photographs in color, and a cat as it walks across the floor.

Light travels in a straight line unless something bends it. Your eyes are equipped with structures that bend and focus light. Light rays are first bent by the cornea and then a lens. The lens focuses the rays onto the retina (RET nuh). The **retina** is a tissue at the back of the eye that is sensitive to light energy. Rods and cones are cells in the retina. Cones respond to bright light and color. Rods respond to dim light. Light energy stimulates impulses in these cells. The impulses pass to the optic nerve, which carries them to the brain, where the impulses are interpreted and you "see" what you are looking at.

EcoTip

Sunglasses should protect your eyes from the sun's rays and give you an undistorted image. Before buying a pair, check to see that lines do not appear distorted.

Figure 22-9. The Parts of the Human Eye

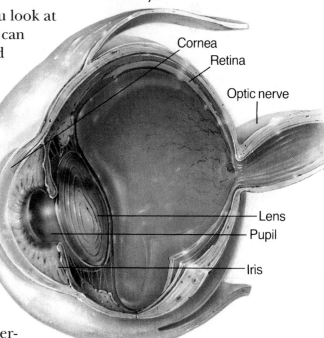

Cornea
Retina
Optic nerve
Lens
Pupil
Iris

Hearing

Sound energy is to hearing as light energy is to vision. When an object vibrates, it causes the air around it to also vibrate, thus producing energy in the form of sound waves. When sound waves reach your ears, they stimulate nerve cells deep in your ear. Impulses are sent to the brain. The brain responds, and you hear a sound.

Figure 22-10 shows that your ear is divided into three sections: the outer, middle, and inner ear. Your outer ear traps sound waves and funnels them down the ear canal to the middle ear. Once there, the sound waves cause the eardrum to vibrate much like the membrane on a drum. These vibrations then move through three little bones in your middle ear called the hammer, anvil, and stirrup. The stirrup bone rests against a second membrane on an opening to the inner ear.

Figure 22-10. Your ear responds to sound waves and to changes in the position of your head.

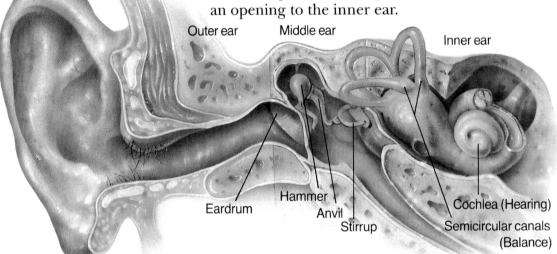

Outer ear   Middle ear   Inner ear

Eardrum   Hammer   Anvil   Stirrup   Cochlea (Hearing)   Semicircular canals (Balance)

The **cochlea** (KOH klee uh) is a fluid-filled structure shaped like a snail's shell in the inner ear. When the stirrup vibrates, fluids in the cochlea also begin to vibrate. These vibrations stimulate nerve endings in the cochlea, and impulses are sent to the brain by the auditory nerve. Depending on how the nerve endings are stimulated, you hear a different type of sound. High-pitched sounds make the endings move differently from lower, deeper sounds. Sound produced by jet engines or rock instruments are as much as ten billion times greater than your ear is adapted to handle.

Balance is also controlled in the inner ear. Special structures and fluids in the inner ear constantly adjust to the position of your head. This stimulates impulses to the brain, which interprets the impulses and helps you make the necessary adjustments to maintain your balance.

MINI-Lab

How is balance maintained?
Draw two parallel vertical lines on the chalkboard and have a student stand between them, as still and straight as possible for three minutes. Observe and watch how well balance is maintained. Next, have the student close his/her eyes and repeat standing within the lines for three more minutes. When was balance more difficult to be maintained? Explain.

Smell

A bloodhound is able to track a particular scent through fields and forest. Our ability to detect odors is not as sharp, but our sense of smell is important for survival and enjoyment.

You can smell food because it gives off molecules into the air. Nasal passages contain sensitive nerve cells called **olfactory cells** that are stimulated by gas molecules. The cells are kept moist by mucous glands. When gas molecules in the air dissolve in this moisture, the cells become stimulated. If enough gas molecules are present, an impulse starts in these cells and travels to the brain.

The brain interprets the stimulus. If it is recognized from previous experience, you can identify the odor. If you can't recognize a particular odor, it is remembered and can be identified the next time, especially if it's a bad one. Certain odors even let you recall events from your childhood.

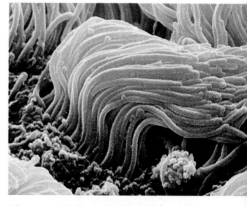

Figure 22-11. Your nasal passages contain hairlike structures called cilia that trap and filter particles from the air you breathe.

Taste

Have you ever tasted a new food or medicine with the tip of your tongue and found that it tasted sweet? Then you may have been unpleasantly surprised to find that when you swallowed it, it tasted bitter. **Taste buds** on your tongue are the major sensory receptors for taste. About ten thousand taste buds are found all over your tongue, enabling you to tell one taste from another.

Taste buds respond to chemical stimuli. When you think of food, your mouth begins to water with saliva. This adaptation is helpful because in order to taste something, it has to be dissolved in water. Saliva in your mouth dissolves food. The solution washes over the taste buds, and an impulse is started that is sent to your brain. The brain interprets the impulse and enables you to tell what you are tasting.

Taste buds respond to more than one taste sensation. However, there are areas of the tongue that seem to respond to one taste more easily than another. There are four basic taste sensations: sweet, salty, sour, and bitter. Figure 22-12 shows where these tastes are commonly stimulated on your tongue.

Figure 22-12. Taste buds contain nerve endings that react to chemicals in food.

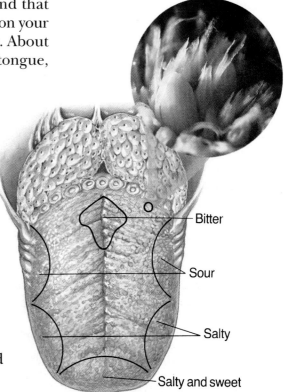

Bitter

Sour

Salty

Salty and sweet

Odor is also involved in your ability to taste. You may have noticed that when you have a head cold with a stuffy nose, your food seems tasteless. Hot food in your mouth is often smelled when the molecules you eat come in contact with the moist membranes in your nasal passages, which connect with your mouth.

Touch, Pressure, Pain, and Temperature

How important is it to be able to feel pain inside your body? Sensory receptors in your internal organs, as well as throughout your skin, respond to touch, pressure, pain, and temperature. These receptors pick up changes in touch, pressure, and temperature and transmit impulses to the brain or spinal cord. The body responds in such a way to protect itself or maintain homeostasis.

Your fingertips have many different types of receptors for touch. As a result, you can tell whether an object is rough or smooth, hot or cold, light or heavy. Your lips are sensitive to heat and prevent you from drinking something so hot that it would burn you. Pressure sensitive cells in the dermis give warning of danger to a body part and enable you to move to avoid injury.

Your senses are adaptations that help you enjoy food, sound, and color, and help you to avoid things that can be harmful. Through your senses you constantly make small and large adjustments to your environment.

SECTION REVIEW

1. What is the retina and how is it stimulated?
2. How do sound waves affect different parts of the ear?
3. How are smell and taste related?
4. Why is it important to have receptors for pain and pressure in your internal organs as well as in your skin?
5. **Apply:** What sensory receptors are involved when you accidentally close your hand in a door?

Skill Builder

☒ Making and Using Tables

Organize the information on senses in a table that names the sense organs and gives the type of energy to which they respond. If you need help, refer to Making and Using Tables in the **Skill Handbook** on page 690.

ACTIVITY 22-2
Predicting and Experimenting

Problem: *Which areas of skin are more sensitive to touch?*

Materials

- index cards
- 8 toothpicks
- glue
- metric ruler

Procedure

1. Predict which areas of the skin are more sensitive to touch. Rank the areas from 5 (the most sensitive) to 1 (the least sensitive) in column 1 of a table like the one shown.
2. Glue toothpicks onto the card as shown in the figure to the right so they are 1 mm, 3 mm, 5 mm, and 10 mm apart. Label the card.
3. With your partner's eyes closed, use the part of the card with toothpicks 1 mm apart and carefully touch the skin surface. Touch the fingertip, palm of the hand, back of the hand, forearm, and back of the neck. **CAUTION:** *Do not apply heavy pressure.*
4. If your partner feels two points, record a plus (+) in the table. If your partner cannot feel both points, record a minus (−).
5. Again, with your partner's eyes closed, use the toothpicks 3 mm apart to touch each area listed in the table.
6. Record whether your partner can feel one or two points.
7. Repeat Steps 5 and 6 with 5 mm and 10 mm sections of the card.

Analyze

1. Which part of the body tested can distinguish the closest stimuli?
2. Which part of the body tested seems least sensitive to close stimuli?
3. Rank the body parts tested from most sensitive to least sensitive.

Data and Observations

Distance	Predictions	1 mm	3 mm
Fingertip			
Palm			
Back of hand			
Forearm			
Back of neck			

Conclude and Apply

4. How do the results of your tests compare with your predictions?
5. What is located in the dermis that provides a sense of touch?
6. Which areas tested were more sensitive to touch?
7. What do the answers to 1, 2, and 3 indicate about the distribution of touch receptors in the skin?

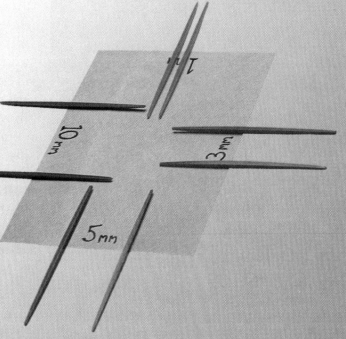

22-3 Alzheimer's Disease

New Science Words

Alzheimer's disease

Objectives

▶ Describe Alzheimer's disease.
▶ State some of the results of Alzheimer's disease on society.
▶ Explain two possible causes of Alzheimer's.

What Is Alzheimer's Disease?

Alzheimer's disease is the failure of nerve cells in the brain to communicate with each other. Researchers are attempting to determine what causes this breakdown. They have found that Alzheimer's patients have unusually low amounts of the enzyme that signals the cell to produce a nerve-transmitting chemical called acetylcholine. Without this chemical, nerve impulses aren't carried from one neuron to the next. It has also been found that the brains of Alzheimer's patients use far less oxygen than normal. Autopsies of Alzheimer's patients show that many neurons have died. The destruction of brain cells caused by Alzheimer's disease results in such severe memory loss that, over a period of years, the victim becomes a very different person. At first, patients forget simple things. Items are misplaced around the house. Later, they may not recognize family members or even know who they are. Eventually, after losing physical functioning, they die. What causes this condition?

Researchers are still working to determine the cause of Alzheimer's. One idea is that the disease may be inherited. Some researchers believe that a defect exists on chromosome 19. Children of Alzheimer's victims show a greater chance of developing the disease than others. Other evidence, however, shows that a protein called amyloid B, which helps cell growth in young brain cells, has the opposite effect in older people. There is also evidence that young people who have experimented

Figure 22-13. Support groups help people who have the responsibility for caring for people with Alzheimer's disease.

with so-called designer drugs have developed a form of Alzheimer's disease.

The Cost of Disease

It is believed that about 100 000 people die with Alzheimer's disease in the United States every year. The cost of this disease to families and society is very high. Home health care for a patient ranges from $18 000 to $20 000 a year. In a skilled care nursing home, the cost averages about $25 000 per year. In 1985, it was estimated that Alzheimer's disease and similar disorders involving loss of brain function cost the United States about $88 billion. None of these people can be cured.

There are other costs as well. The stress involved in caring for someone with Alzheimer's disease can be damaging in itself. Studies show that the extreme stress harms caregivers' immune systems and can make them more susceptible to illness.

Is a cure for Alzheimer's in sight? Because intensive research has been conducted for only about a decade, little progress has been made. Drugs that help produce more acetylcholine have been developed and tried. However, these were found to have severe side effects. Until scientists are able to find the cause of Alzheimer's disease, it will be difficult to find a cure.

Science and WRITING

Find out what Medicare is. Write a one-page description of this health plan. Include in your report how a person qualifies for Medicare benefits.

What is Alzheimer's disease?

SECTION REVIEW

1. What happens to the brain of an Alzheimer's patient that causes memory loss?
2. What is the cost of this disease for society? How might society benefit from what is learned about Alzheimer's disease?
3. What are two possible causes of Alzheimer's?

You Decide!

It can be very difficult to care for a family member who has Alzheimer's disease. Due to loss of memory, the patient needs constant care. Would you be able to help take care of such a family member in your home? What might be the advantages and disadvantages of letting the person stay in a nursing care facility instead?

Your Endocrine System

New Science Words

hormones
target tissues

Objectives

▶ Explain the function of hormones.
▶ Name three endocrine glands and explain the effects of their hormones.
▶ Explain how a feedback system works.

Endocrine System

"The tallest man in the world!" and "the shortest woman in the land!" were commonly seen entertainers in circuses of the past. These people were ordinary persons except for their extraordinary height or lack of height. In most cases, their sizes were the result of a malfunction in their endocrine (EN duh krun) systems.

The endocrine system consists of ductless glands throughout the body. Your salivary glands and your liver are glands that produce substances that flow through ducts. Endocrine glands, however, have no ducts. Their secretions move directly from the cells of the gland into your bloodstream. Endocrine secretions, called **hormones,** usually control activities in parts of the body other than right around the gland. Hormones affect specific tissues called **target tissues.** Target tissues are frequently in another part of the body at a distance from the gland that affects them. Table 22-1 shows the position of eight endocrine glands, the hormones they produce, and their target tissues.

In Chapter 19, the pancreas was described for its role in producing a digestive enzyme. However, other groups of cells in the pancreas also secrete hormones. One of these hormones, insulin (IN suh lin), enables cells to take in glucose. Glucose is the main source of energy for respiration in cells. Normally, insulin enables glucose to pass from the bloodstream through cell membranes. Persons who can't make insulin are diabetic. That means that insulin isn't there to allow glucose to get into cells.

What is a target tissue?

Figure 22-14. Some athletes are extremely tall as a result of excess growth hormone.

Table 22-1

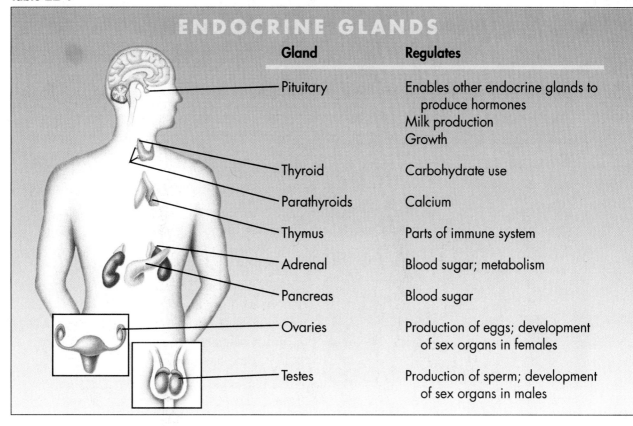

ENDOCRINE GLANDS

Gland	Regulates
Pituitary	Enables other endocrine glands to produce hormones Milk production Growth
Thyroid	Carbohydrate use
Parathyroids	Calcium
Thymus	Parts of immune system
Adrenal	Blood sugar; metabolism
Pancreas	Blood sugar
Ovaries	Production of eggs; development of sex organs in females
Testes	Production of sperm; development of sex organs in males

The reproductive glands also produce hormones. The functions of the hormones of the ovaries and testes will be discussed in Chapter 23.

A Negative Feedback System

To control the amount of hormone an endocrine gland produces, the endocrine system sends chemical information back and forth to itself. This is a negative feedback system. It works much the way a thermostat works. When the temperature in a room drops below a certain level, a thermostat signals the furnace to turn on. Once the furnace has raised the temperature to the level set on the thermostat, the furnace shuts off. It will stay off until the thermostat signals again. Once a target tissue responds to its hormone, the tissue sends a chemical signal back to the gland. This signal causes the gland to stop or slow down production. When the level of the hormone in the bloodstream drops again, the endocrine gland is signaled to start the secretion of the hormone again. In this way, the concentration of the hormone in the bloodstream is kept at the needed level, and homeostasis is maintained.

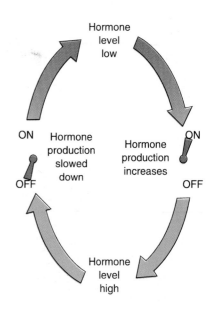

PROBLEM SOLVING

Why am I so tired?

Carrie hasn't been feeling well lately. She complains about feeling tired all the time.

"She just doesn't have any get-up-and-go," her mother told the doctor. The doctor ordered some blood tests and questioned Carrie about her diet. After school one afternoon, Carrie went to the doctor's office to hear the results of the tests. The tests showed that her blood sugar was much too high. The doctor gave her strict instructions to follow detailing what she was allowed to eat every day. He told Carrie that she showed signs of diabetes. What endocrine gland is involved in diabetes?

Think Critically: How could Carrie be tired all the time and yet have a high blood sugar reading?

Hormones secreted by endocrine glands go directly into the bloodstream and affect target tissues. The level of the hormone is controlled by a negative feedback system. In this way, many chemicals in the blood and many body functions are controlled.

SECTION REVIEW

1. How are endocrine glands different from other glands?
2. What is a hormone?
3. What is the importance of the endocrine feedback system?
4. Explain how three hormones work in the body.
5. **Apply:** How would a lack of insulin affect respiration in a person's cells?

Skill Builder

☑ Comparing and Contrasting

In what ways are the nervous system and endocrine system alike? If you need help, refer to Comparing and Contrasting in the **Skill Handbook** on page 683.

CHAPTER
REVIEW

22-1: Your Nervous System

1. A neuron is the basic unit of structure and function of the nervous system.

2. A stimulus is detected by sensory neurons. Impulses are carried to the interneurons where the proper response is determined and transmitted to the motor neurons. A response is made automatically; this is a reflex.

3. The central nervous system contains the brain and spinal cord. The peripheral nervous system is composed of cranial and spinal nerves.

22-2: The Senses

1. The eyes respond to light energy, and the ears respond to sound waves. Interpretation of the stimuli is done by the cerebrum.

2. Olfactory cells of the nose and taste buds of the tongue are stimulated by chemicals. This stimulation produces impulses that are interpreted as different tastes.

22-3: Science and Society: Alzheimer's Disease

1. Neural transmitters carry impulses across synapses between neurons.

2. In Alzheimer's disease, neural transmission is impaired, resulting in memory loss and physical disfunctioning.

3. Scientists think a virus, chemical imbalance, or heredity are possible causes of Alzheimer's disease.

22-4: Your Endocrine System

1. Endocrine glands secrete hormones directly into the bloodstream.

2. Hormones affect target tissues by increasing or decreasing their action.

3. A change in the body causes a gland to function. Once homeostasis is reached, the gland receives a signal to slow or stop its secretion.

KEY SCIENCE WORDS

a. **Alzheimer's disease**
b. **axon**
c. **brainstem**
d. **central nervous system**
e. **cerebellum**
f. **cerebrum**
g. **cochlea**
h. **dendrites**
i. **hormones**
j. **interneurons**
k. **motor neurons**
l. **neuron**
m. **olfactory cells**
n. **peripheral nervous system**
o. **reflex**
p. **retina**
q. **sensory neurons**
r. **synapse**
s. **target tissues**
t. **taste buds**

UNDERSTANDING VOCABULARY

Match each phrase with the correct term from the list of Key Science Words.

1. neurons carrying impulses from the brain
2. basic unit of nervous system
3. nerve cells between sensory and motor neurons
4. gap between neurons
5. division containing brain and spinal cord
6. an automatic response to stimuli
7. light-sensitive tissue of the eye
8. center for coordination of voluntary muscle action
9. inner ear structure containing fluid
10. nerve cells that respond to gas molecules

CHAPTER
REVIEW

CHECKING CONCEPTS

Choose the word or phrase that completes the sentence.

1. The nervous system regulates _____.
   a. heartbeat   c. digestion
   b. breathing   d. all of these

2. The neuron structures that carry impulses to the cell body are _____.
   a. axons   c. synapses
   b. dendrites   d. none of these

3. Neurons detecting stimuli in the skin and eyes are _____.
   a. interneurons   c. sensory neurons
   b. motor neurons   d. none of these

4. The _____ is the largest part of the brain.
   a. cerebellum   c. cerebrum
   b. brainstem   d. none of these

5. The _____ controls voluntary muscle.
   a. cerebellum   c. cerebrum
   b. brainstem   d. all of these

6. The _____ is the part of the brain that is divided into two hemispheres.
   a. cerebellum   c. cerebrum
   b. brainstem   d. none of these

7. The _____ is (are) controlled by the somatic division of the PNS.
   a. skeletal muscles c. glands
   b. heart   d. all of these

8. The middle ear contains the _____.
   a. anvil   c. eardrum
   b. hammer   d. all of these

9. The _____ gland controls many other endocrine glands throughout the body.
   a. adrenal   c. pituitary
   b. thyroid   d. pancreas

10. Ductless glands produce _____.
    a. neurotransmitters c. hormones
    b. target tissues   d. saliva

UNDERSTANDING CONCEPTS

Complete each sentence.

11. The _____ nervous system is made up of cranial and spinal nerves.

12. _____ are chemicals made by glands.

13. Special tissues affected by hormones are called _____.

14. The _____ gland regulates energy use in cells.

15. Failure of acetylcholine to transfer impulses occurs in _____ disease.

THINK AND WRITE CRITICALLY

16. Discuss why taste and smell are protective.

17. What would happen if a chemical was blocking many synapses?

18. Compare the way light energy and sound energy travel in human sense organs.

19. Explain how Alzheimer's disease is related to the nervous system.

20. List the effects adrenal gland hormones would have on your body as you prepare to run a race.

APPLY

21. Why is it helpful to have impulses move in only one direction in a neuron?
22. How are reflexes protective?
23. How is your endocrine system like the thermostat in a house?
24. Describe an example of a problem that results from improper gland functioning.
25. If a fly were to land on your face and on your back, which might you feel first? Explain how you would test your choice.

MORE SKILL BUILDERS

If you need help, refer to the Skill Handbook.

1. **Classifying:** Classify the types of neurons as to their location and direction of impulse.
2. **Comparing and Contrasting:** Compare and contrast the structures and functions of the cerebrum, cerebellum, and brainstem. Include in your discussion the following functions: balance, homeostasis, involuntary muscles, muscle tone, memory, voluntary muscles, thinking, senses.
3. **Sequencing:** Sequence the structures through which light passes in the eye.
4. **Interpreting Scientific Illustrations:** Using the diagram of the synapse on page 510, explain how an impulse moves from one neuron to another.
5. **Observing and Inferring:** If an impulse traveled down one neuron, but failed to move on to the next neuron, what might you infer about the first neuron?

PROJECTS

1. Find out what paralysis is. Explain why many nerves don't repair themselves. Report on efforts being made to correct certain forms of paralysis.
2. Find out how hearing aids work. Explain why not all hearing-impaired persons can use hearing aids.

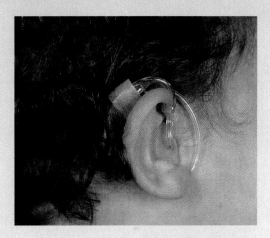

You may have heard a newspaper or television story about a large family that has all girls or all boys. What do you think are the odds of a family having all boys or all girls? What do you think is the proportion of boys to girls among children born in the general population?

FIND OUT!

Do this simple activity to find out what proportion of newborns are boys and what proportion are girls.

Take a penny and toss it in the air. There is an equal chance that it will land heads or tails. Toss the penny a hundred times and keep a record of the times it falls heads up and the number of times it falls tails up. Keep a record of the order in which the penny landed. What did your record show? Did you sometimes have five or more heads before a tails fell? What application can you make to families who have five girls or five boys? What are the chances that a girl would be born if there were a sixth child?

Gearing Up

Previewing the Chapter

Use this outline to help you focus on important ideas in this chapter.

Section 23-1   Human Reproduction
▶ The Reproductive System
▶ The Menstrual Cycle
Section 23-2   Fertilization to Birth
▶ Fertilization
▶ The Stages of the Embryo and Fetus
▶ Multiple Births
Section 23-3   Development after Birth
▶ Childbirth
▶ Infancy and Childhood
▶ Adolescence
▶ Adulthood
Section 23-4   Science and Society Aging
▶ Prolonging Life

Previewing Science Skills

▶ In the **Skill Builders,** you will sequence, graph, and outline data.
▶ In the **Activities,** you will interpret and graph data.
▶ In the **MINI-Labs,** you will interpret data and do research.

What's next?

In this chapter, you will find out that the chances of a boy or girl being born are equal. You will learn about the structures and function of the male and female reproductive systems. You will also learn about the development of a human from fertilization to old age.

Human Reproduction

New Science Words

testes
sperm
semen
ovaries
ovulation
uterus
vagina
menstrual cycle
menstruation
menopause

Objectives

▶ Explain the function of the reproductive system.
▶ Identify the major structures of the male reproductive system.
▶ Describe the functions of the major female reproductive organs.
▶ Explain the stages of the menstrual cycle.

The Reproductive System

Reproduction is the process that continues life on Earth. Human and all other sexually reproducing organisms form eggs and sperm to carry genetic information from one generation to the next. If you have ever babysat, you know that babies and young children require nearly constant attention. Mammals, including humans, produce few offspring at one time compared to invertebrate animals. Some tropical termite queens can lay 80 000 eggs a day for nearly 30 years! Can you imagine babysitting for that many offspring? Unlike many other animals, mammals must provide care for their offspring to ensure their survival.

In previous chapters, you have read that most human body systems are alike in males and females. This is not the case for the reproductive system. Males and females each have structures specialized for their role in reproduction.

The Male Reproductive System

Figure 23-1 shows the structures of the male reproductive system. The external organs of the male reproductive system are the penis and scrotum (SKROH tum). The penis is the male organ for reproduction and urination. Behind the penis is a saclike pouch called the scrotum that holds the testes. During puberty, the two **testes** begin to produce **sperm,** the male reproductive cells. Sperm are single cells with a head and tail. The tail moves the sperm, and the head contains genetic information. The scrotum helps regulate temperature for sperm production. It holds the testes outside the male's body. As a result, the testes have a lower temperature. This cooler temperature is necessary to produce sperm.

Did You Know?

An egg is much larger than a sperm. If the egg were enlarged to the size of a dime, the sperm would be the size of a period.

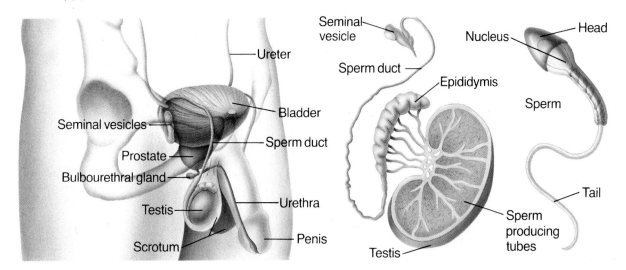

Figure 23-1. The structures of the male reproductive system are shown with a close-up of a testis and sperm.

Many organs help in the production, transport, and storage of sperm inside the male body. After sperm are produced, they travel from the testes through tubes that circle the bladder. Behind the bladder, a gland called the seminal vesicle provides sperm with a fluid that gives them energy and helps them move. This mixture of sperm and fluid is called **semen.** Semen leaves the body through the urethra, the same tube that carries urine from the body. Semen and urine never mix. A muscle at the back of the bladder contracts to prevent urine from entering the urethra as sperm are ejected from the body.

The Female Reproductive System

When a female begin puberty, the female sex organs called **ovaries** begin producing eggs. Unlike the male, most of the reproductive organs of the female are internal. The ovaries are located in the lower part of the body cavity. Each of the two ovaries is about the size and shape of an almond. About once a month an egg is released from an ovary. This process is called **ovulation** (ahv yuh LAY shun). The two ovaries take turns releasing the eggs. One month, the first ovary releases an egg; next month, the other ovary releases an egg and so on. When the egg is released, it enters the oviduct. If the egg is fertilized by a sperm, it will occur in an oviduct. Cilia help sweep the egg through the oviduct to the uterus. The **uterus** is a hollow, pear-shaped, muscular organ with thick walls in which a fertilized egg develops. The lower end of the uterus is connected to the outside of the body by a muscular tube called the **vagina.** The vagina is also called the birth canal because a baby passes through this passage-

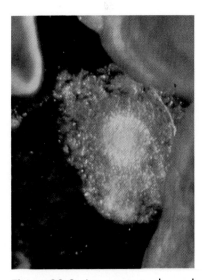

Figure 23-2. An egg just released from an ovary will begin its journey down the oviduct.

way when being born. Figure 23-3 shows the structures of the female reproductive system.

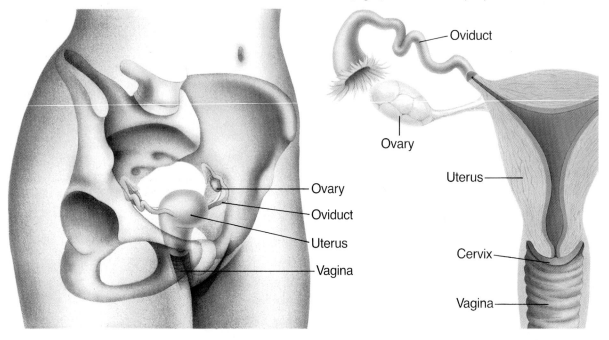

Figure 23-3. The structures of the female reproductive system are shown from the front (right) and the side (left).

Oviduct

Ovary

Ovary

Oviduct

Uterus

Vagina

Uterus

Cervix

Vagina

The Menstrual Cycle

Before and after an egg is released from an ovary, the uterus undergoes certain changes. The **menstrual cycle** is the monthly cycle of changes in the female reproductive system. This cycle of a human female averages 28 days. However, the cycle can vary from 20 to 40 days. The changes include the maturing of an egg and the preparation of the uterus to receive a fertilized egg. Figure 23-4 shows the changes in the uterus during each menstrual cycle. When an egg inside an ovary matures, the lining of the uterus thickens as it prepares for a fertilized egg.

On approximately day 14 of a 28-day menstrual cycle, an egg is released from an ovary. It remains alive for about 24 to 48 hours. During this time, it travels along the oviduct. A female can become pregnant at this time in her menstrual cycle. The egg can be fertilized if live sperm are present in the oviduct 48 hours before or after ovulation. If it is not fertilized by a sperm in the oviduct, it disintegrates. The thickened lining of the uterus is shed and bleeding occurs. This monthly discharge of the lining of the uterus and blood through the vagina is called

When does the menstrual cycle begin?

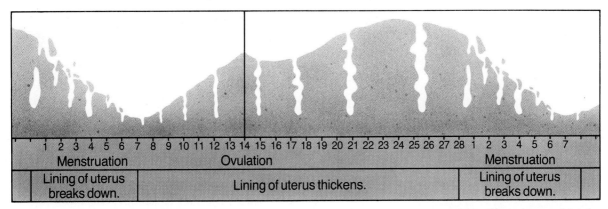

1 2 3 4 5 6 7 8 9 10 11 12 13 14	15 16 17 18 19 20 21 22 23 24 25 26 27 28 1	2 3 4 5 6 7
Menstruation	Ovulation	Menstruation
Lining of uterus breaks down.	Lining of uterus thickens.	Lining of uterus breaks down.

Figure 23-4. The menstrual cycle. The menstrual cycle begins on day one of menstruation. Ovulation occurs near day 14 of a regular 28-day cycle.

menstruation (men STRAY shun). The menstrual period usually lasts from four to six days and is a normal function of the female reproductive system.

When menstruation begins, another egg begins maturing. The uterus again prepares for the egg. Hormones from the pituitary gland and the ovaries control the events of the menstrual cycle.

Menstruation begins when a girl's reproductive organs have matured. For most females, the first menstrual period happens between ages 8 and 13. The menstrual cycle continues until age 45 to 55. Then, there is a gradual reduction of ovulation and menstruation. **Menopause** occurs when the menstrual cycle becomes irregular and eventually stops.

When the reproductive systems of males and females become mature, sperm and eggs are produced. The reproductive process allows for the species to continue.

SECTION REVIEW

1. What is the major function of a reproductive system?
2. Trace and label the route of sperm movement through the male reproductive system.
3. List the organs of the female reproductive system and describe their functions.
4. Explain the cause of menstrual flow.
5. **Apply:** What happens to the lining of the uterus after a women goes through menopause?

☑ Sequencing

Sequence the movement of an egg through the female reproductive system. If you need help, refer to Sequencing in the **Skill Handbook** on page 680.

Skill Builder

ACTIVITY 23-1
Interpreting Diagrams

Problem: *What happens to the uterus during a female's monthly cycle?*

Materials
• paper and pencil

Procedure

1. The diagrams below show what is explained in the previous section on the menstrual cycle.
2. Study the diagrams and their labels.
3. Use the information in Section 23-1 and the diagrams to complete a table like the one shown.

Data and Observations

Days	Condition of uterus	What happens
1 – 6		
7 – 12		
13 – 14		
15 – 28		

Analyze

1. What do the diagrams represent?
2. What do the pink- or red-colored parts of the diagrams represent?
3. How does the figure caption relate to the diagram in Figure 23-4?
4. At what stage in the menstrual cycle is the uterine lining the most thickened?

Conclude and Apply

5. How long is the average menstrual cycle?
6. How many days does menstruation usually last?
7. How are the diagrams different?
8. On approximately what day in a 28-day cycle is the egg released from the ovary?
9. On what days does the lining of the uterus build up?
10. Why is this process called a cycle?
11. How many days before menstruation does ovulation usually occur?
12. How does a diagram help explain the menstrual cycle?

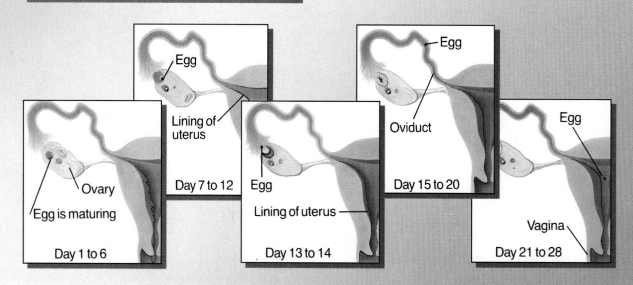

Egg
Lining of uterus
Ovary
Egg is maturing
Day 1 to 6

Egg
Lining of uterus
Day 13 to 14

Egg
Oviduct
Day 15 to 20

Egg
Vagina
Day 21 to 28

Day 7 to 12

Fertilization to Birth

Objectives

▶ Describe how an egg becomes fertilized.
▶ Identify the major events in the stages of development of an embryo and fetus.
▶ Differentiate between fraternal and identical twins.

New Science Words

pregnancy
embryo
amniotic sac
fetus

Fertilization

Before the invention of powerful microscopes, some people imagined a sperm to be a miniature person that grew in the uterus of a female. Others thought the egg contained a miniature individual that started to grow when stimulated by semen. In the latter part of the 1700s an Italian naturalist, Lazzaro Spallanzani, showed with experiments using amphibians that contact between an egg and sperm is necessary for life to begin development. With the formulation of the cell theory in 1839, scientists recognized that a human develops from a single egg that has been fertilized by a sperm. The uniting of a sperm with an egg is known as fertilization.

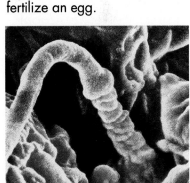
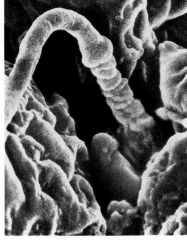

Figure 23-5. Only one sperm will fertilize an egg.

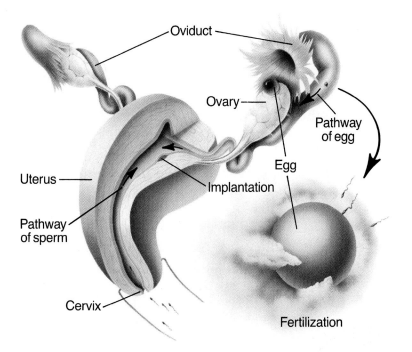

Oviduct

Ovary

Pathway of egg

Egg

Uterus

Implantation

Pathway of sperm

Cervix

Fertilization

Figure 23-6. An egg is usually fertilized in an oviduct and is implanted in the uterus.

When Is the Baby Due?

One of the first questions expectant mothers ask is "When is the baby due?" The due date is important to the family of the baby. What does a family do to prepare for a baby? The date also is important for the obstetrician, a doctor who specializes in childbirth. This doctor keeps track of the growth of the fetus. The obstetrician is concerned about the health of the baby and the mother.

Doctors generally estimate the period of human gestation at nine and one-half menstrual cycles, or about 266 days from conception. This date is estimated from the beginning of the mother's last menstrual period. Conception is thought to have occurred two weeks later.

Researchers have recently measured the periods of gestation among a small group of women with normal pregnancies. They found that the median gestation period was longer than 266 days and think that the normal period of gestation might be longer. Why are doctors interested in the duration of gestation?

Think Critically: What should the researchers do to determine a normal period of gestation?

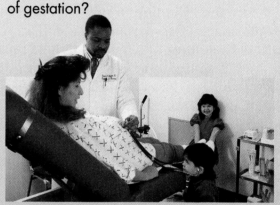

Sperm deposited into the vagina move through the uterus into the oviducts. Whereas only one egg is usually present, nearly 200 to 300 million sperm are deposited. Only one sperm will fertilize the egg. Once the sperm penetrates the outer surface of the egg, the egg sets up a chemical barrier to keep out the other millions of sperm. The nucleus of the sperm and the nucleus of the egg have 23 chromosomes each. When the egg and sperm unite, a zygote with 46 chromosomes is formed. Most fertilization occurs in an oviduct.

The zygote moves along the oviduct to the uterus. During this time, the zygote is dividing. After about seven days, the ball of cells is implanted in the wall of the uterus. The uterine wall has been thickening in preparation to receive a fertilized egg. Here the egg will develop for nine months until the birth of the baby. This period of time is known as **pregnancy.**

The Stages of the Embryo and Fetus

The outer cells of a fertilized egg attach to the wall of the uterus. During the first two months of pregnancy, the unborn child is known as an **embryo.** Nutrients from the wall of the uterus are received by the embryo through villi. Blood vessels develop from the villi and form the placenta (pluh SENT uh). The umbilical (um BIHL ih kul) cord attaches at the embryo's navel with the placenta. The umbilical cord transports nutrients and oxygen from the mother to the baby through arteries. Carbon dioxide and other wastes are carried through veins in the umbilical cord back to the mother's blood. Other substances in the mother's blood can pass to the embryo. These include drugs, toxins, and disease organisms. These substances can cause great harm to the embryo. For this reason, a mother should avoid harmful drugs, alcohol, and tobacco during pregnancy.

During the third week of pregnancy, a thin membrane begins to form around the embryo. This is called the amniotic sac and is filled with a clear liquid called amnion. The amnion in the **amniotic sac** helps cushion the embryo against blows and can store nutrients and wastes. This sac attaches to the placenta.

During the first three months of development, all of an embryo's major organs form. A heart structure begins to beat and move blood through the embryo's blood vessels. At five weeks, the embryo is only as large as a single

MINI-Lab

How long is an embryo?
Use the data from More Skill Builders, number 4, on page 549 and the data below. On a piece of paper, draw the size of the embryo at each date using a ruler. Use books available to find one event or structure at that time of development.

End of month	Length
3	7.5 cm
4	15 cm
5	25 cm
6	30 cm
7	35 cm
8	40 cm
9	51 cm

How is the embryo cushioned against blows?

Figure 23-7. The developing embryo is surrounded by protective membranes.

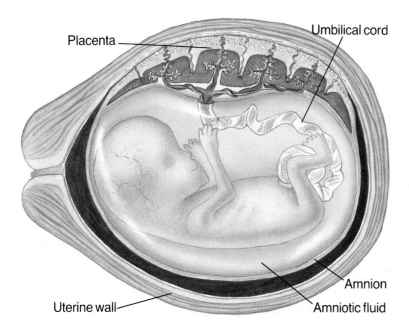

Placenta — Umbilical cord — Uterine wall — Amnion — Amniotic fluid

TECHNOLOGY

Operating in the Womb

Doctors performing fetal surgery may have patients that are only 24 weeks beyond conception and only inches in size.

Using ultrasound, doctors can see an image of the developing fetus in the womb and can detect fetal defects that frequently mean death soon after birth. One of these involves a hole in the diaphragm that allows the intestines, stomach, spleen, and liver to move into the chest cavity. When this happens, the growth of the fetus' lungs is stunted, and the baby is unable to breathe when born. The only hope has been to operate on the baby immediately following birth, but this is successful only 25 percent of the time. Now, doctors are able to operate on such a fetus while it is still in the uterus. To do this, a small incision is made in the mother's uterus. The fetus's chest is opened and abdominal organs are returned to their

proper place. Finally, a patch is placed over the hole in the diaphragm. The baby now has a good chance to survive after birth. **Think Critically:** What other prenatal conditions might be corrected using this method?

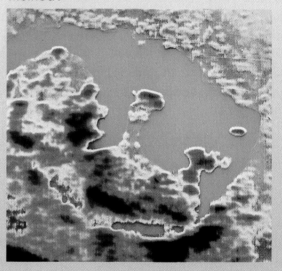

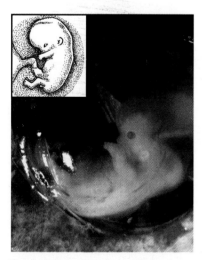

Figure 23-8. A two-month embryo shown enlarged in the photo and actual size in the drawing.

grain of rice, but there is a head with recognizable eye, nose, and mouth features. During the sixth and seventh weeks, tiny arms and legs develop fingers and toes.

After the first two months of pregnancy, the developing baby is called a **fetus** (FEE tus). At this time, body organs are present. Around the fifth month, the fetus weighs about 500 mg, the heart can be heard beating, and the mother may feel the baby's movements within her uterus. The fetus sucks its thumb. By the end of the seventh month of pregnancy, the fetus is 30 to 38 cm in length. Fatty tissue builds up under the skin, and the fetus appears less wrinkled. By the ninth month, the fetus usually has shifted to a head-down position within the uterus. The head usually is in contact with the opening of the uterus to the vagina. The fetus is about 50 cm in length and weighs from 2.5 to 3.5 kg. The baby is ready for birth.

Multiple Births

In some cases, two eggs leave the ovary at the same time. If both eggs are fertilized and both develop, twins are born. When two different eggs were fertilized by two different sperm, the two babies are called fraternal twins. Fraternal twins may be two girls, two boys, or a boy and a girl. Fraternal twins do not always look alike. In other cases of twins, a single egg may split apart shortly after it is fertilized. Each part of the egg then develops and forms an embryo. Because both children developed from the same egg and sperm, they are identical twins. Each has the same set of genes. Identical twins must be either two girls or two boys. These twins look exactly alike.

You may know some twins. In what ways are they alike or different? Are they fraternal or identical twins? Triplets and other multiple births may occur when either three or more eggs are produced at one time or an egg splits into three or more parts.

A remarkable series of events changes a single fertilized egg into a baby with billions of cells. The mother's body prepares for the baby. Special tissues nourish and protect the developing embryo and fetus. After a nine-month period, the fetus is ready to live outside the mother's body.

Figure 23-9. Pick out the fraternal and identical twins.

SECTION REVIEW

1. What happens when an egg is fertilized?
2. What is one major event that occurs during the embryo and fetal stages?
3. Explain how twins are fraternal or identical.
4. **Apply:** Why can't identical twins be a girl and boy?

☑ Making and Using Graphs

Make a graph of the embryo and fetus sizes and the months of development using this data: 1 month = 0.5 cm, 2 months = 3 cm, 3 months = 7.5 cm, 4 months = 15 cm, 5 months = 25 cm, 6 months = 30 cm, 7 months = 35 cm, 8 months = 40 cm, 9 months = 50 cm. If you need help, refer to Making and Using Graphs in the **Skill Handbook** on page 691.

23-3 Development after Birth

New Science Words

infancy
childhood
adolescence
adulthood

Objectives

▶ State the sequence of events of childbirth.
▶ Compare the stages of infancy and childhood.
▶ Relate adolescence to preparation for adulthood.

Science and READING

The Lamaze method of childbirth has become the most popular technique. What is it and why is it so popular?

What is cesarean section?

Childbirth

After nine months of developing within the mother, the baby is ready to be born. Like all newborn living things, the baby will find itself suddenly pushed out into the world. Within the uterus and amniotic sac the baby was in a warm, watery, dark, and protected environment. In contrast, the new environment is cooler, drier, brighter, and not as well protected.

The process of childbirth begins with labor, the muscular contractions of the uterus. As the contractions increase in strength and frequency, the amniotic sac usually breaks and releases its fluid. This is known as "breaking water." Usually, over a period of hours, the contractions cause the opening of the uterus to widen to allow the baby to pass through. More powerful and frequent contractions push the baby out through the vagina into its new environment. Sometimes, the mother's pelvis is too small for the baby to fit through or the baby is in the wrong position for birth. In cases like this, the baby is delivered through an incision in the mother's uterus and abdomen. This surgery is called cesarean section.

At birth, the baby is still attached to the umbilical cord and placenta. The person assisting with the birth of the baby ties the cord and then cuts it. The scar that later forms where the cord was attached is the navel. Soon after the baby's delivery, contractions expel the placenta from the mother's body. The baby takes its first breath of oxygen without the umbilical cord. The baby may cry. Crying forces air into its lungs.

Infancy and Childhood

The first four weeks after birth are known as the neonatal (ne o NA tal) period. *Neonatal* means "new born." During this time, the baby adjusts to life outside of the uterus. Body functions such as respiration, digestion, and excretion are now performed by the baby rather than through the placenta. Unlike some other living things, the human baby must depend on others to survive. A newborn colt begins walking a few hours after its birth. The human baby is fed and has its diaper changed. It is not able to take care of itself.

The next stage of development is **infancy,** the period from neonatal to one year. It is a period of rapid growth and development for both mental and physical skills. An early skill is the ability to smile that usually begins around six weeks of age. At four months, most babies can laugh, sit up when propped, and recognize their mothers' faces. At eight months, the infant is usually able to say a few simple words, such as "mama" and "kitty." One of the major events within the first year is the ability to stand unsupported for a few seconds.

After infancy is the **childhood** stage, which lasts until age 12. The physical growth rate for height and weight is not as rapid as in infancy. However, there is development of muscular coordination and mental abilities. By 18 months, the child is able to walk without help. Between two and three years, the child controls his or her bladder and bowel. At age three, the child can speak in simple sentences. By age five, many children can read a limited number of words. Throughout this stage, children develop their ability to speak, read, write, and reason. At the same time, children also mature emotionally and learn how to get along with other people. Find out how old you were when you began to talk. What were your first words?

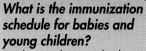

MINI-Lab

What is the immunization schedule for babies and young children?
Find out when and what vaccines are given to protect babies and young children. Check your own immunization record. What boosters were you given? What immunizations does your school require?

Figure 23-10. Compare the different abilities of an infant (a) and a six-year old (b).

a

b

Adolescence

The next stage of development is adolescence; you are in this stage. **Adolescence** begins from ages 12 to 14. A part of adolescence is puberty. As you read earlier, puberty is the time of development when a person becomes physically able to reproduce. For girls, puberty occurs between ages 8 and 13. For boys, puberty occurs between ages 13 and 15.

During puberty, hormones are produced by the pituitary gland that cause changes in the body. The hormone FSH helps produce reproductive cells. LH helps with the production of other hormones. As a result, secondary sex characteristics result. In females, the breasts develop, pubic and underarm hair appears, and fatty tissue is added to the buttocks and thighs. In males, the hormones cause the growth of facial, pubic, and underarm hair; a deepened voice; and an increase in muscle size. Each sex experiences sexual attraction to the other sex.

Adolescence also is a time of a growth spurt. Are you shorter or taller than your classmates? Because of differences in the time hormones begin functioning among individuals and between males and females, there are differences in boys' and girls' growth rates. Girls often begin their increase in growth between the ages of 11 and 13 and end at ages 15 to 16. Boys usually start their growth spurt at ages 13 to 15 and end at 17 to 18 years of age. Hormonal changes also cause underarm sweating and acne, requiring extra cleanliness and care. All of these physical changes can cause you to feel different or uncomfortable. This is normal. As you move through the period of adolescence, you will find that you will become more coordinated, be better able to handle problems, and gain improved reasoning abilities. You'll find that you enjoy spending more time with your friends.

Figure 23-11. Adolescence is a time for many changes.

Adulthood

The final stage of development is that of **adulthood.** It begins with the end of adolescence and extends to old age. There are several stages of adulthood. The early years of adulthood occur when people are in their 20s. Many of these adults are completing an education, finding employment, and possibly marrying and beginning a family. The growth of the muscular and skeletal system stops.

People in their 30s to 50s make up the stage of middle adulthood. During these years, physical strength begins to decline. As a person ages, blood circulation and respiration are less efficient. Bones become more brittle, and the skin's elastic tissues are lost, causing the skin to become wrinkled. This group is busy with family and work commitments. People in this group often care for aging parents as well as children.

Think about someone you know over age 65. How is that person alike or different from you? The young-old age group includes people from 65 to 74 years old. Around this age, many people retire. To fill their time, they may take up hobbies, travel, or volunteer at hospitals, schools, and community organizations. Many older people are an active part of society. The old-old age group is made up of people 75 years and older. Many people in this group are frail and need assistance in meeting their needs.

After birth, the stages of development of the human body begin with a baby making adjustments to a new environment. From infancy to adolescence, the body's systems mature, enabling the person to be physically and mentally ready for adulthood. During the next 50 years or longer, people live their lives making contributions to family, community, and society. Throughout the life cycle, people who care for their health enjoy a higher quality of life.

Figure 23-12. Many people in the 65 to 74 year age group continue to work.

Science and WRITING

Interview someone who's over 60 years of age. Find out what his or her life was like when he or she was your age. What does the person like to do now? Write a report to share with the class.

SECTION REVIEW

1. What are major events during childbirth?
2. Compare infancy with childhood.
3. How does the period of adolescence prepare you for the stage of adulthood?
4. Define the stages of adulthood.
5. **Apply:** Why is it hard to compare the growth and development of different teenagers?

☑ Outlining

Prepare an outline of the various life stages of human development from neonatal to adulthood. If you need help, refer to Outlining in the **Skill Handbook** on page 681.

Skill Builder

23-4 Aging

New Science Words

catalase

Objectives

▶ Discuss concerns in society for the elderly.
▶ Explain the chemical process of aging.

Prolonging Life

Take a look in a mirror and try to picture yourself at 65 years of age. Most junior high school students probably don't give too much thought to aging. In fact, you are probably eager to be older than you are. You may view people older than yourself as having freedom, money, and many privileges. However, if you think about some elderly persons that you know, you may be reminded of some disadvantages of growing older. There are many chronic diseases associated with people who are in their 60s, 70s, and 80s. Conditions associated with aging include Alzheimer's disease, arthritis, osteoporosis, diabetes, cancer, and heart disease. An older person also may have less energy than when he or she was younger and have memory loss. Hearing and sight may decline.

You might be aware of the rising costs of health care. This especially affects the elderly. Many older persons cannot afford adequate health care. This problem contributes to a general decline in health maintenance. It is estimated that within 60 years, almost a fourth of the population will be age 65 and older. With a growing older population, adequate health care for older persons is a real concern in our country.

Congress has set aside millions of dollars for research and programs on aging. Many persons are concerned that living longer does not mean living healthfully. No one wants to live 20 years longer if its means enduring a painful, chronic disease. However, the goal of many researchers is to increase years of health, not just lengthen life. In the past several years, researchers and medical professionals have found that a person can do much to promote his or her health. This includes eating right, exercising regularly, monitoring stress, and not smoking.

By choosing healthful habits, some people will have much healthier lives than others. However, everyone does age. The body breaks down as nerves degenerate, the immune system deteriorates, hormones change, and death approaches.

Researchers believe that certain genes are responsible for the aging process. Dr. Glenn Bewley at North Carolina State University is using fruit flies in his search for these genes. It is believed that the chemical destruction of cells by hydrogen peroxide plays a large role in the aging process. Hydrogen peroxide is produced by many cellular reactions. Bewley found that he could isolate in fruit flies the gene that produces **catalase,** the enzyme that breaks down hydrogen peroxide. When he did this, less catalase was produced. As a result, the life span of the fruit flies was shortened. If the gene for catalase production can be overexpressed, meaning producing more catalase, a greater amount of hydrogen peroxide would be broken down. Fewer body cells would be damaged. If researchers developed a way to overexpress the gene for catalase, would it even be useful?

SECTION REVIEW

1. What can you do now to increase your years of health?
2. What role is catalase believed to play in the aging process?

You Decide!

The life spans of many people are increasing due to the many new treatments for illness and disease doctors and scientists are discovering. In 1960, the average life expectancy for women was 73 years and 67 years for men. In 1988, it increased to 78 years for women and 72 years for men. Although people are living longer, many can't live on their own. They must depend on relatives and friends to help them with basic needs. Many also spend the rest of their lives dependent on medicine and medical technology. Do you think life should be extended when the person can no longer maintain the quality of life they once had?

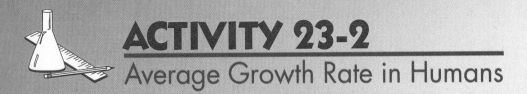

ACTIVITY 23-2
Average Growth Rate in Humans

Problem: *Is average growth rate the same in males and females?*

Materials
- graph paper
- red and blue pencils

Procedure
1. Construct a graph similar to graph A below. Plot mass on the vertical axis and age on the horizontal axis.
2. Plot the data given under Data and Observations for the average female growth in mass from ages 8 to 18. Connect the points with a red line.
3. On the same graph, plot the data for the average male growth in mass from ages 8 to 18. Connect the points with a blue line.
4. Construct a separate graph similar to graph B below. Plot height on the vertical axis and age on the horizontal axis.
5. Plot the data for the average female growth in height from ages 8 to 18. Connect the points with a red line. Plot the data for the average male growth in height from ages 8 to 18. Connect the points with a blue line.

Data and Observations

Age	Mass (kg)		Height (cm)	
	Female	Male	Female	Male
8	25	25	123	124
9	28	28	129	130
10	31	31	135	135
11	35	37	140	140
12	40	38	147	145
13	47	43	155	152
14	50	50	159	161
15	54	57	160	167
16	57	62	163	172
17	58	65	163	174
18	58	68	163	178

Averages for Growth in Humans

Analyze
1. Up to what age is average growth in mass similar in males and females?
2. Up to what age is average growth in height similar in males and females?

Conclude and Apply
3. Between what ages do females increase most in height?
4. During what ages do males increase most in height?
5. When does the mass of females change most?
6. How can you explain the differences in growth between males and females?
7. Is average growth rate the same in males and females? Explain your answer.

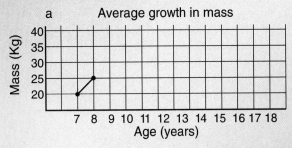

a — Average growth in mass

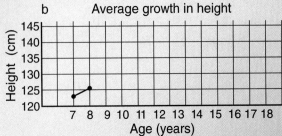

b — Average growth in height

CHAPTER
REVIEW

23-1: Human Reproduction

1. The reproductive system allows new organisms to be formed.

2. The testes produce sperm which exit the male through the penis.

3. The female ovary produces an egg that can be fertilized to produce a zygote that develops within the uterus.

4. When an egg is not fertilized, it disintegrates; the lining of the uterus is shed.

23-2: Fertilization to Birth

1. After fertilization, the zygote undergoes developmental changes to become an embryo surrounded by amniotic fluid, then a fetus.

2. The uterine muscles contract to push the baby out of the mother's uterus and vagina.

3. Twins occur when two eggs are fertilized or when a single egg splits after fertilization.

23-3: Development after Birth

1. Birth begins with labor, muscular contractions of the uterus. The amniotic sac breaks, then usu-ally after several hours, the contractions force the baby out of the body.

2. Infancy is the stage of development from neonatal to one year. It is a period of rapid growth of mental and physical skills. Childhood, which lasts to age 12 is marked by development of muscular coordination and mental abilities.

3. Adolescence is the stage of development when a person becomes physically able to reproduce. The final stage of development, adulthood, consists of many stages. All physical growth is complete.

23-4: Science and Society: Aging

1. Many conditions are associated with aging, including cancer, heart disease, and diabetes. Due to rising health care costs, many elderly are unable to get proper medical care.

2. Researchers believe the chemical hydrogen peroxide produced in cells plays a large role in the aging process.

KEY SCIENCE WORDS

a. **adolescence**
b. **adulthood**
c. **amniotic sac**
d. **catalase**
e. **childhood**
f. **embryo**
g. **fetus**
h. **infancy**
i. **menopause**
j. **menstrual cycle**
k. **menstruation**
l. **ovaries**
m. **ovulation**
n. **pregnancy**
o. **semen**
p. **sperm**
q. **testes**
r. **uterus**
s. **vagina**

UNDERSTANDING VOCABULARY

Match each phrase with the correct term from the list of Key Science Words.

1. birth canal
2. male sex cells
3. egg-producing organs
4. release of egg from the ovary
5. nourishing fluid for sperm
6. ending of the menstrual cycle with age
7. produce sperm
8. place where a fertilized egg develops into a baby
9. stores nutrients for the unborn baby
10. name for the unborn child the first two months

CHAPTER
REVIEW

Choose the word or phrase that completes the sentence.

1. The embryo develops in the _____.
   a. oviduct   c. uterus
   b. ovary   d. vagina

2. The monthly process of egg release is called _____.
   a. fertilization   c. menstruation
   b. ovulation   d. puberty

3. The union of an egg and sperm is _____.
   a. fertilization   c. menstruation
   b. ovulation   d. puberty

4. The egg is fertilized in the _____.
   a. oviduct   c. vagina
   b. uterus   d. ovary

5. Mental and physical skills rapidly develop during _____.
   a. neonatal period c. childhood
   b. infancy   d. adolescence

6. Puberty occurs during _____.
   a. childhood   c. adolescence
   b. adulthood   d. all of these

7. Sex characteristics common to males and females include _____.
   a. breasts   c. increased fat
   b. increased muscles d. pubic hair

8. Growth of the skeleton and muscles stops during _____.
   a. childhood   c. adulthood
   b. adolescence   d. none of these

9. The period of development with three stages is _____.
   a. infancy   c. adolescence
   b. adulthood   d. all of these

10. The ability to reproduce begins at _____.
    a. adolescence   c. childhood
    b. adulthood   d. all of these

UNDERSTANDING CONCEPTS

Complete each sentence.

11. The _____ is attached to the wall of the uterus.

12. The _____ contains fluid to cushion the embryo.

13. The unborn child after two months in the mother is the _____.

14. _____ begins with muscular contractions that move the baby out of the uterus.

15. _____ is the period of development following the neonatal period until one year.

THINK AND WRITE CRITICALLY

16. Why are so many sperm released if only one is needed to fertilize an egg?

17. Why is semen necessary for sperm survival?

18. What is the purpose of the thickened uterine lining?

19. Explain the difference between identical and fraternal twins.

20. What features of a pregnant woman protect the developing child?

21. Explain the similar functions of the ovaries and testes.

22. Identify the structure in which each process occurs: meiosis, ovulation, fertilization, and implantation.

23. Describe the structural differences between embryo and fetus.

24. What kind of cell division occurs as the zygote develops?

25. Describe one major change in each stage of human development.

MORE SKILL BUILDERS

If you need help, refer to the Skill Handbook.

1. Classifying: Classify each structure as female or male and internal or external: ovary, penis, scrotum, testes, uterus, vagina.

2. Concept Mapping: Fill in the concept map of egg release.

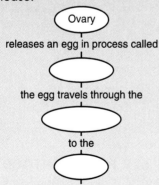

Ovary

releases an egg in process called

the egg travels through the

to the

if the egg has NOT been fertilized, the discharge of uterine lining and release of blood occurs in the process called

if the egg is fertilized it is called a

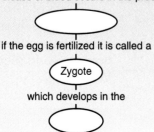

Zygote

which develops in the

3. Hypothesizing: Make a hypothesis about the effects of raising identical twins apart from each other.

4. Graphing and Interpreting Data: Use the data to make a graph showing the day of development versus size of the embryo. When is the fastest period of growth?

Week after Fertilization	Size
3	3 mm
4	6 mm
6	12 mm
7	2 cm
8	4 cm
9	5 cm

5. Sequencing: Sequence the steps involved in the birth process.

PROJECTS

1. Find newspaper articles on the effects of smoking on the health of the developing embryo and newborns. Discuss this with your class.

2. What special health care must a pregnant woman seek to help her developing child?

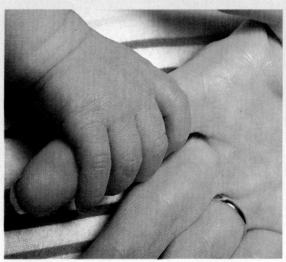

UNIT 6
GLOBAL CONNECTIONS

The Human Body

In this unit, you have studied the human body. Find out how humans influence and have been influenced by their world.

120°   60°

60°

SOCIAL STUDIES

WRITTEN IN BONE
University of Pennsylvania
Bones can tell anthropologists much about an individual. For instance, bones reveal the age, sex, race, and medical history of a person. How is it possible for anthropologists to detect this information from bones?

60°

HISTORY

FORGOTTEN FOOD CROPS
Colorado Springs, Colorado
Natural grains that native Americans once ate are being rediscovered. These food plants offer science some exciting solutions to world food problems. Why could these "new" old plants be important?

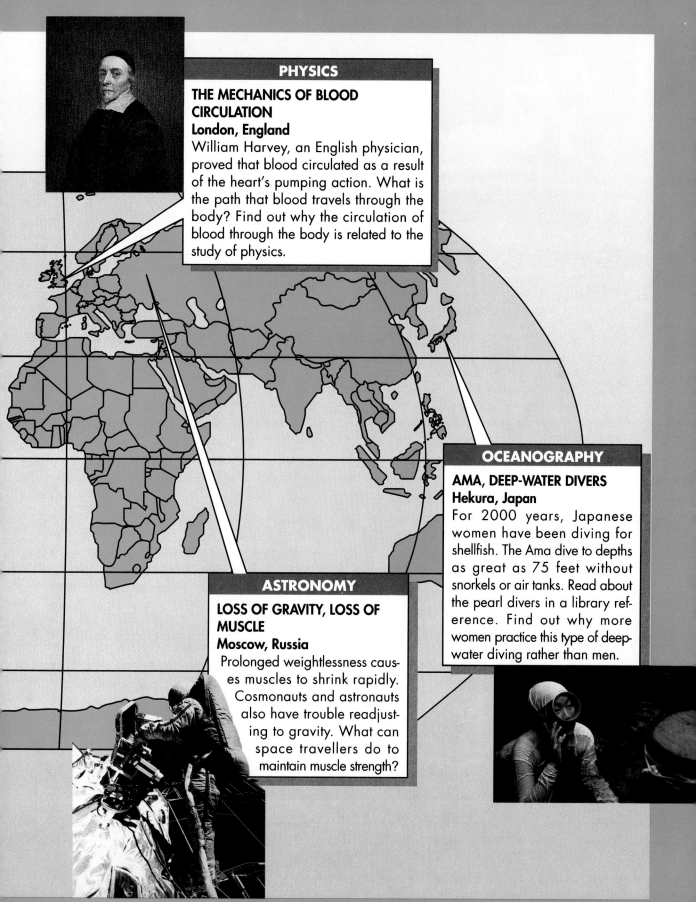

PHYSICS

THE MECHANICS OF BLOOD CIRCULATION
London, England
William Harvey, an English physician, proved that blood circulated as a result of the heart's pumping action. What is the path that blood travels through the body? Find out why the circulation of blood through the body is related to the study of physics.

OCEANOGRAPHY

AMA, DEEP-WATER DIVERS
Hekura, Japan
For 2000 years, Japanese women have been diving for shellfish. The Ama dive to depths as great as 75 feet without snorkels or air tanks. Read about the pearl divers in a library reference. Find out why more women practice this type of deepwater diving rather than men.

ASTRONOMY

LOSS OF GRAVITY, LOSS OF MUSCLE
Moscow, Russia
Prolonged weightlessness causes muscles to shrink rapidly. Cosmonauts and astronauts also have trouble readjusting to gravity. What can space travellers do to maintain muscle strength?

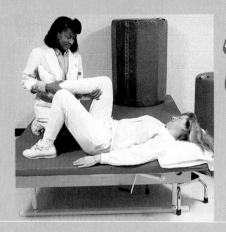

PHYSICAL THERAPIST

A *physical therapist* works with people who have had accidents, handicaps, arthritis, and heart disease. The patients range from newborn to elderly. Some physical therapists work with a wide range of problems. Others specialize, working in pediatrics, sports therapy, or neurology, as well as other specialties. Physical therapists need to be supportive of their patients, flexible, and physically strong. The work of the physical therapist is emotionally demanding but also rewarding. A physical therapist must have at least a bachelor of science degree. He or she will need to have courses in basic science, anatomy and physiology, as well as kinesiology, and a background in psychology.

For Additional Information

Contact the American Physical Therapy Association, 1111 N. Fairfax St., Alexandria, VA 22314.

UNIT READINGS

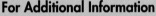Golden, Frederic. "Clever Kanzi." *Discover*, March 1991, p. 20.

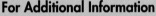Minsky, Marvin. "The Intelligence Transplant." *Discover*, Oct. 1989, p. 52.

HOME HEALTHCARE AIDE

Home healthcare aides work with the elderly, disabled, or ill. The job of the healthcare aide varies from patient to patient. Schedules also vary so that a healthcare aide needs to be very adaptable. Many people need help with personal care, such as bathing and shampooing, either for a short time after a hospital stay, or for longer periods in the case of chronic illnesses. Aides check a patient's pulse and respiration, help with prescribed exercises, assist with medicines, and even prepare meals.

Home healthcare aides should be able to read and write and have a high school diploma, plus a deep interest in helping people. New laws require 75 hours of training with a combination of 16 hours of classroom study and 16 hours of supervised practical training. Training programs may be offered by the employing agency, the Red Cross, or a community college.

For Additional Information

Contact The National Association for Homecare, 519 C St. NE, Washington, DC 20002.

Sula

by Toni Morrison

The following passage tells of two girlhood friends, Nel and Sula, who have been reunited after many years.

Nel alone noticed the peculiar quality of the May that followed the leaving of the birds. It had a sheen, a glimmering as of green, rain-soaked Saturday nights (lit by the excitement of newly installed street lights); of lemon-yellow afternoons bright with iced drinks and splashes of daffodils. It showed in the damp faces of her children and the river-smoothness of their voices. Even her own body was not immune to the magic. She would sit on the floor to sew as she had done as a girl, fold her legs up under her or do a little dance that fitted some tune in her head. There were easy sun-washed days and purple dusks in which Tar Baby sang "Abide With Me" at prayer meetings, his lashes darkened by tears, his silhouette limp with regret against the whitewashed walls of Greater Saint Matthew's. Nel listened and was moved to smile. To smile at the sheer loveliness that pressed in from the windows and touched his grief, making it a pleasure to behold.

Although it was she alone who saw this magic, she did not wonder at it. She knew it was all due to Sula's return to the Bottom. It was like getting the use of an eye back, having a cataract removed. Her old friend

Author Toni Morrison

had come home. Sula. Who made her laugh, who made her see old things with new eyes, in whose presence she felt clever, gentle and a little raunchy. Sula, whose past she had lived through and with whom the present was a constant sharing of perceptions. Talking to Sula had always been a conversation with herself. Was there anyone else before whom she could never be foolish? In whose view inadequacy was a mere idiosyncrasy, a character trait rather than a deficiency? Sula never competed; she simply helped others define themselves. Other people seemed to turn their volume on and up when Sula was in the room. More than any other thing, humor returned. She could listen to the crunch of sugar underfoot that the children had spilled without reaching for the switch; and she forgot the tear in the living-room window shade.

In Your Own Words

▶Scientists and doctors often notice the effect of mental attitude on the human body. In this passage, you can see the effect Sula's return had on her friend, Nel. Think of an event in your own life that has changed your outlook either for better or worse. How did you feel after it? What physical changes did you feel? Write a short story telling of this event and how it affected you.

UNIT
7 STAYING HEALTHY

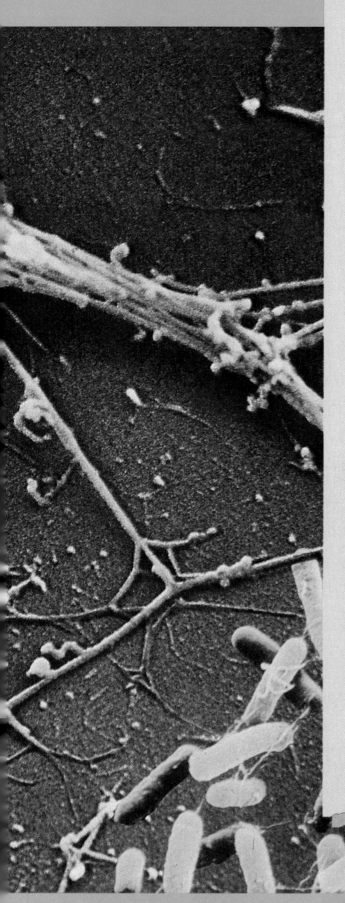

What's Happening Here?

The mighty macrophage puts forth tendril-like extensions as it reaches out to snag bacterial cells that daily attack the fortress of your body. Constantly on guard, these large white blood cells patrol the body, slipping between cells in capillary walls to sweep up invaders that threaten your health. Your body is equipped with a variety of defenses that maintain your health even though you remain unconscious of their activity. The child in the smaller photograph is very conscious of his defense system. Lacking a natural defense system, he depends on the walls of his artificial environment to protect him from assault by disease-causing agents.

UNIT CONTENTS

Chapter 24   Immunity
Chapter 25   Facts about Drugs

Aaahhh-choooo! Does pollen make you sneeze? Have you noticed that when one person in your class gets a cold, others soon have it too? Allergies and colds are examples of your body's response to substances and organisms in the environment.

FIND OUT!

Do this activity to see how disease-causing organisms can be spread.

Work with a partner. Place a drop of peppermint or lemon food flavoring on a cotton ball. Pretend that the flavoring is a mass of cold viruses. Next, rub the cotton ball in the shape of an X over the palm of your right hand and let it dry. Can you smell the flavoring? Now, shake hands with your classmate. Has the flavoring been passed to your classmate's hand? What does this exercise tell you about how some diseases can be spread?

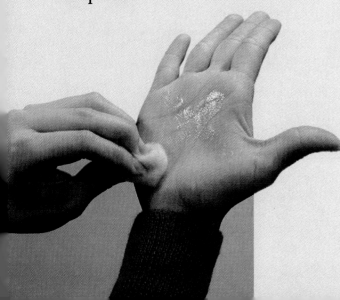

Gearing Up

Previewing the Chapter

Use this outline to help you focus on important ideas in this chapter.

Section 24-1   The Nature of Disease
▶ Discovering Disease
▶ Keeping Clean
▶ Communicable Diseases
▶ Sexually Transmitted Diseases

Section 24-2   Your Immune System
▶ Natural Defenses
▶ Specific Defenses
▶ AIDS and Your Immune System

Section 24-3   Science & Society
Preventing Disease
▶ Guarding Against Disease

Section 24-4   Noncommunicable Disease
▶ Chronic Disease
▶ Cancer
▶ Allergies

Previewing Science Skills

▶ In the **Skill Builders**, you will recognize cause and effect, compare and contrast, and make and use tables.
▶ In the **Activities**, you will experiment, hypothesize, and analyze data.
▶ In the **MINI-Labs**, you will test and observe and calculate.

What's next?

You have just seen how disease can be spread from person to person. Discover ways that disease can be spread by bacteria and viruses and what steps you and your body take to prevent this from happening. You will also learn about diseases and disorders that are caused by genetic, metabolic, and life-style factors.

The Nature of Disease

New Science Words

pasteurization
disinfectant
antiseptic
communicable disease
sexually transmitted diseases
(STDs)

Objectives

▶ Describe the work of Pasteur, Koch, and Lister in the discovery and prevention of disease.
▶ List diseases caused by viruses and bacteria.
▶ Discuss sexually transmitted diseases (STDs), their causes and treatment.

Discovering Disease

What causes disease?

"Ring around the rosie, A pocket full of posies,
Ashes, Ashes, We all fall down."

Do you know that this rhyme is more than 600 years old? The rhyme is thought to be about a disease called the Black Death or the Plague. In the thirteenth century, the Plague killed one-fourth of the people in Europe. "Ring around the rosie" was a symptom of the disease—a ring around a red spot on the skin. People carried a pocket full of flower petals ("posies") and spices to keep away the stench of dead bodies. But still, 25,000,000 people "all fell down," dead from this terrible disease.

Today we know that diseases are caused by viruses and by harmful bacteria known as pathogens, and not by some fault in a person's behavior as was once believed.

Louis Pasteur, a French chemist, was the first to discover that harmful bacteria could cause disease. He

Figure 24-1. Plague is caused by a bacterium that reproduces in fleas that live on rats.

developed a method of using heat to kill pathogens. **Pasteurization,** named for him, is the process of heating food to a temperature that kills most bacteria. Pasteur's work began the science of bacteriology.

Being able to tell *which* organism caused a disease was a problem. It was a German doctor, Robert Koch, who first developed a way to isolate and grow, or culture, just one type of bacteria at a time. Koch developed a set of rules to be used for figuring out which organism caused a particular disease. These rules are:

1. In every case of a particular disease, the organism thought to cause the disease must be present.
2. The organism has to be separated from all other organisms and grown in a pure culture.
3. When the organism from the pure culture is injected into a test animal, it must cause the original disease.
4. Finally, when the suspect organism is removed from the test animal and cultured again, it must be compared with the original organism to see if they are the same. Only when they match can you say that that organism is the pathogen that causes that disease.

Keeping Clean

Do you make it a habit to wash your hands and clean your fingernails? Into the late 1800s, doctors regularly operated in their street clothes and with their bare hands. More patients died than survived as a result of surgery. Joseph Lister, an English surgeon, was horrified. He recognized the relationship between the infection rate and cleanliness in surgery. Lister dramatically reduced deaths among his surgical patients by washing their skin and his hands before surgery. Lister used a disinfectant, but today antiseptics are used on people. A **disinfectant** kills pathogens on objects such as instruments, floors, toilets, and bathtubs. An **antiseptic** kills pathogens on skin and prevents them from growing there for sometime after. Today doctors wash their hands often with antiseptic soaps to keep from spreading pathogens from person to person. However, even with the use of disinfectants, some diseases could not be controlled. In the late 1800s and early 1900s, viruses were discovered.

Because of the work of these early scientists, and many others who followed, more is understood about the cause and control of disease.

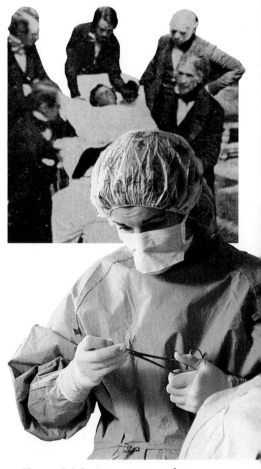

Figure 24-2. Antiseptics and strict surgical methods have made operations safer than they once were.

Figure 24-3. Many diseases are spread by contact.

Communicable Diseases

Have you ever shared a soft drink with a friend? Did you both use the same straw? Sharing eating or drinking implements is one way that many diseases are spread from person to person. A disease that is spread, or transmitted, from one organism to another is a **communicable disease.**

What causes a communicable disease? Communicable diseases are caused by agents such as viruses and pathogenic bacteria, protists, fungi. Some diseases caused by these agents are given in Table 24-1.

Table 24-1

DISEASES AND THEIR AGENTS			
Bacteria	**Protists**	**Fungi**	**Viruses**
Tetanus	Malaria	Athlete's foot	Colds
Tuberculosis	Sleeping sickness	Ringworm	Influenza
Typhoid fever			AIDS
Strep throat			Measles
Pink eye			Mumps
Bacterial pneumonia			Yellow fever
Plague			Polio
			Smallpox
	Mosquito	Virus	Viral pneumonia

Communicable diseases are spread through water and air, on food, by contact with contaminated objects, and by vectors. City water systems and swimming pools add chlorine to prevent disease. Many diseases are spread through air. When you have a cold and sneeze, you hurl thousands of virus particles through the air. Each time you turn a doorknob, or press the button on a water fountain at school, your skin comes in contact with bacteria and viruses. Finally, some of the most dangerous diseases are transmitted by sexual contact.

Examples of vectors that spread disease are rats, mice, flies, fleas, mosquitoes, birds, and cats and dogs. Six hundred years ago, the bacterium that causes Plague was spread by fleas that lived on rats.

The spread of communicable diseases is closely watched by agencies in every country. In the United States, the Centers for Disease Control (CDC) monitors the spread of diseases throughout the country. The CDC also watches for diseases brought into the country.

Sexually Transmitted Diseases

Diseases transmitted from person to person during sexual contact are called **sexually transmitted diseases (STDs).** You can become infected with an STD by having sex with an infected person. STDs are caused by both viruses and bacteria.

In Chapter 8, you learned that the AIDS virus (HIV) is a latent virus that can exist in blood and body fluids. You can get AIDS by having sex with an infected person, or by sharing an AIDS-contaminated needle used to inject drugs. AIDS is also transmitted by contaminated blood transfusions, and a pregnant female with AIDS may infect her child when the virus passes through the placenta or when nursing after birth. There is no vaccine to prevent AIDS and no medication to cure it. In the next section, more information will be given on how AIDS breaks down the immune system.

Genital herpes causes painful blisters on the sex organs. Herpes can be transmitted by an infected mother to her child during birth. The herpes virus, also a latent virus, hides in the body for long periods and then reappears suddenly. There is no cure for herpes, and there is no vaccine to prevent it.

Gonorrhea and chlamydia are STDs caused by bacteria that may not produce any symptoms. When symptoms do appear, they may include painful urination, genital discharge, and sores. Penicillin and other antibiotics are used to treat these diseases. If left untreated, either disease can cause sterility, the inability to reproduce.

Table 24-2

STDs	
Agent	**Disease**
Bacteria	Gonorrhea
	Chlamydia
	Syphilis
Viruses	Genital Herpes
	AIDS
	Genital warts

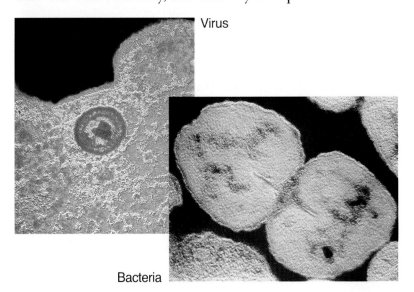

Virus

Bacteria

Figure 24-4. Sexually transmitted diseases are caused by certain viruses and bacteria.

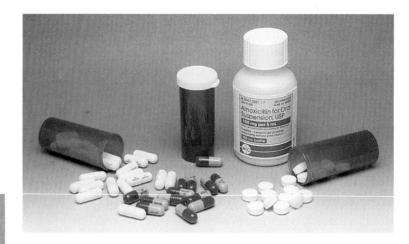

Figure 24-5. Penicillin is used to treat many diseases including some STDs.

MINI-Lab

How fast do bacteria reproduce?
Bacteria divide every 20 minutes. If your body did not defend itself, it would be invaded by thousands of bacteria in just a few hours. You can't believe that? Then make a chart like the one below. Complete it to the fifth hour. How many bacteria will there be after five hours? Graph your data. Can you see why it is important to take antibiotics promptly if you have an infection?

Time	Number of Bacteria
0 hours 0 minutes	1
20 minutes	2
40 minutes	4
1 hour 0 minutes	8
20 minutes	
40 minutes	

Syphilis has several stages. In stage 1, a sore apears on the mouth or genitals that lasts 10 to 14 days. Stage 2 may involve a rash, a fever, and swollen lymph glands. During stage 3, these symptoms then may also disappear. The victim often believes that the disease has gone away, but it hasn't. In Stage 4, syphilis may infect the cardiovascular and nervous systems. At this point, it is too late to treat syphilis. Nerve damage and death may result. Syphilis can be treated and cured with antibiotics only in the early stages.

Sexually transmitted diseases are difficult to treat. For years, penicillin was used to treat syphilis. However, the organism that causes syphilis has become resistant to the antibiotic in some persons. In 1989, an artificial form of penicillin was made in the laboratory that may be effective against the disease.

SECTION REVIEW

1. How did the discoveries of Pasteur, Koch, and Lister help in the battle against disease?
2. List a communicable disease caused by a virus, a bacterium, a protist, and a fungus.
3. What are the four stages of syphilis?
4. **Apply:** In what ways does Koch's procedure follow the scientific method?

Skill Builder

☒ Recognizing Cause and Effect

How is not washing your hands related to the spread of disease? If you need help, refer to Recognizing Cause and Effect in the Skill Handbook on page 683.

Your Immune System

Objectives

▶ Explain the natural defenses your body has against disease.
▶ Describe differences between active and passive immunity.
▶ Explain how the AIDS virus affects the immune system.

New Science Words

immune system
antigens
antibody
active immunity
passive immunity
lymphocytes

Natural Defenses

A healthy body is like a well-equipped fortress. Your **immune system** is a complex group of defenses that your body has to fight disease. It is made up of cells, tissues, organs, and body systems that fight bacteria, viruses, harmful chemicals, and cancer cells.

In Section 24-1, harmful bacteria were discussed for their disease-causing properties. However, most bacteria do not cause disease. Millions of helpful bacteria live on your skin and give you your first line of defense by killing many harmful types of bacteria. Disease-causing bacteria enter your body through breaks in your skin. Even then, your body is not defenseless. It mobilizes a series of defenses against disease-causing intruders.

Several other body systems maintain health. Your circulatory system contains white blood cells that engulf and digest foreign organisms and chemicals. These white blood cells constantly patrol the body, sweeping up and digesting bacteria that manage to get into the body. They slip between cells in the walls of capillaries to destroy bacteria around cells. When the white cells cannot destroy the bacteria fast enough, a fever may develop. But fever generally also helps to fight the pathogen.

Your respiratory system contains cilia and mucus to trap pathogens. When you cough, you expel trapped bacteria. In the digestive system, enzymes in the stomach, pancreas, and liver destroy pathogens. Hydrochloric acid in your stomach kills bacteria that enter your body on food that you eat.

All of these processes are general defenses that work to keep you disease-free. But if you do get sick, your body has another line of defense in the form of active and passive immunity.

Figure 24-6. White blood cells leave capillaries and engulf harmful bacteria in surrounding tissues.

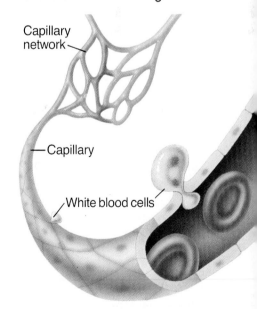

Capillary network

Capillary

White blood cells

Specific Defenses

When your body fights disease, it is really battling proteins or chemicals that don't belong there. Proteins and chemicals that are foreign to your body are called **antigens.** When your immune system recognizes a foreign protein or chemical, it forms specific antibodies. An **antibody** is a substance made by an animal in response to a specific antigen. The antibody binds up the antigen, making it harmless. Antibodies help your body build defenses in two ways, actively and passively. **Active immunity** occurs when your body makes its own antibodies in response to an antigen. **Passive immunity** occurs when antibodies, which have been produced in another animal, are introduced into the body.

Active Immunity

If your body is invaded by a pathogen, it immediately starts to make antibodies to inactivate the antigen. Once enough antibodies form, you get better. These antibodies stay in your blood on duty, becoming active when you again encounter the disease. Under these conditions, your body has active immunity to a particular disease.

Another way to develop active immunity to a particular disease is to be inoculated with a vaccine. A vaccine gives you active immunity against a disease without you having to get the disease first. For example, suppose a vaccine for measles is injected into your body. Your body to forms antibodies against the measle antigen. If you later encounter the virus, antibodies necessary to fight that virus are already in your bloodstream ready to destroy the pathogen. Antibodies that immunize you against one virus may not guard against a different virus. As you grow older, you will be exposed to many more types of viruses and will build a separate immunity to each one.

What is an antigen?

EcoTip

Reduce the use of pesticides in your home and around your garden. Many cause harmful effects on the immune systems of people.

Figure 24-7. Vaccines containing weakened antigens cause the body to make antibodies.

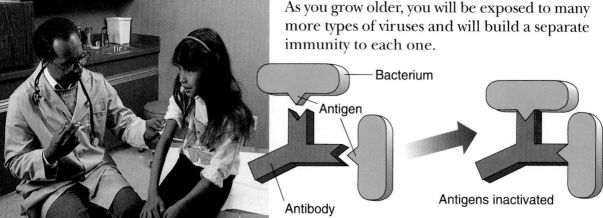

Bacterium

Antigen

Antibody

Antigens inactivated

Passive Immunity

How is passive immunity different from active immunity? Passive immunity comes from several sources. As a newborn, you were a bundle of passive immunity. You were born with all the antibodies that your mother had in her blood. However, these antibodies stayed with you only a few months. Passive immunity does not last as long as active immunity. Newborn babies loose their passive immunity in a few months. Then they are vaccinated to develop their own immunity.

Tetanus is an example. Tetanus toxin is produced by a bacterium in soil. The toxin paralyzes muscles. Death can occur by suffocation when the muscles that control breathing become paralyzed. Tetanus antitoxin is produced in horses when they respond to injections of the tetanus antigen. Samples of antibodies made by horses are injected into humans. These antibodies provide limited immunity. Booster shots are needed throughout life, especially in the case of puncture wounds.

Science and WRITING

Select a disease from this list: diphtheria, pertussis, tetanus. Use library references to write about what causes the disease; what its symptoms are; and how it is treated or prevented.

TECHNOLOGY

Super Sleuth!

Doctors have several tools for diagnosing diseases. One of the newest tools is magnetic resonance imaging (MRI).

Here's how it works. A person with a condition that needs to be diagnosed is placed in an MRI machine. The machine generates a powerful magnetic field in the body. In the body, the nuclei inside the atoms line up parallel to the magnetic field. Then, the nuclei are jolted with very fast radio waves. The nuclei resonate, or vibrate, like tiny tuning forks, producing a faint radio signal. This signal creates a picture of the body in great detail.

Using MRI, scientists have discovered changes in the brain that may be used to diagnose Alzheimer's disease. Doctors hope that MRI can be used to evaluate medicines for heart problems and cancer.

Think Critically: What advantages does MRI have over other methods that are used to diagnose disease?

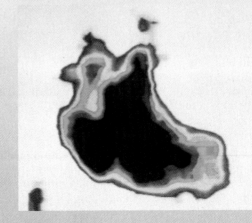

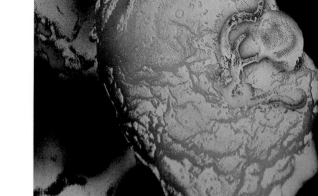

Figure 24-8. The AIDS virus destroys lymphocytes, cells in the body that are vital to fighting disease.

What are the functions of lymphocytes?

AIDS and Your Immune System

The AIDS virus is different from other viruses. It attacks cells in your immune system called lymphocytes. **Lymphocytes** are white blood cells throughout the lymphatic system that recognize antigens, produce antibodies, and destroy invading antigens.

Because the AIDS virus destroys lymphocytes, the body is left with no way to fight invading antigens. The whole immune system breaks down. The body is unable to fight the AIDS virus, or any other pathogen. For this reason, people with AIDS have died from other diseases such as pneumonia, cancer, or tuberculosis. The victim's body has become defenseless.

When a microbe attacks your body, it must get past all of your natural defenses. If it gets past your skin or other defenses, it encounters your immune system—your last line of defense. But if the AIDS virus has destroyed the immune system, there is no defense left.

SECTION REVIEW

1. List natural defenses your body has against disease.
2. Why does passive immunity need to be renewed throughout life?
3. What cells does the AIDS virus attack?
4. **Apply:** Why might someone have to receive booster injections of antibodies?

Skill Builder

☑ Comparing and Contrasting

Compare and contrast active and passive immunity. If you need help, refer to Comparing and Contrasting in the **Skill Handbook** on page 683.

ACTIVITY 24-1
Microorganisms and Disease

Problem: *How do microorganisms cause infection?*

Materials

- fresh apples (6)
- rotting apple
- alcohol
- self-sealing plastic bags (6)
- labels and pencil
- paper towels
- sandpaper
- cotton ball
- soap and water

Procedure

1. Label the plastic bags 1 through 6.
2. Put a fresh apple in bag 1 and seal the bag.
3. Rub the rotting apple over the entire surface of the remaining 5 apples. The rotting apple is your source of microorganisms. **CAUTION:** *Always wash your hands after handling microorganisms.* Take one of the apples and put it in bag number 2.
4. Drop one apple to the floor from a height of about two meters. Put this apple into bag number 3.
5. Rub one of the remaining apples with sandpaper. Place this apple in bag number 4.
6. Wash one of the last two apples with soap and water. Dry the apple well with a paper towel. Put this apple in bag number 5.
7. Use a cotton ball to spread alcohol over the last apple. Let the apple air-dry for a short time. Watch it and as soon as it is dry place the apple in bag number 6.
8. Place all of the apples in a dark place for one week. Then wash your hands.
9. Write a hypothesis to explain what you think will happen to each apple.
10. At the end of the week, compare all the apples. Record your observations. **CAUTION:** *Give all apples to your teacher for proper disposal.*

Data and Observations

Apple	Observations
1	
2	
3	
4	
5	
6	

Analyze

1. What was the purpose of apple number 1?
2. Did you observe any changes in apple number 2? Explain.
3. What happened to the bruises on apple number 3?
4. How did the sandpaper affect apple number 4?
5. What effect did the soap and water have?

Conclude and Apply

6. Did you observe any changes in apple number 6?
7. Why is it important to wash your hands before eating?
8. Why is it important to clean a wound?
9. Explain why alcohol is used to clean your skin before an injection.
10. How do microorganisms cause an infection?

SCIENCE & SOCIETY

24-3 Preventing Disease

New Science Words

vaccination

Objectives

▶ Explain how vaccination prevents certain diseases.
▶ Explain how disease can be prevented from spreading.

Figure 24-9. Edward Jenner, Originator of Smallpox Vaccine

Guarding Against Disease

Vaccination is the process of giving a vaccine by injection or by mouth. In Chapter 8, you learned that the first vaccine was invented by an English doctor, Edward Jenner. An epidemic of smallpox was killing many people in Europe. In 1980, the World Health Organization promoted a successful vaccination program to eliminate smallpox from the world.

In the 1950s, polio vaccines were developed by Jonas Salk and Albert Sabin. Because children are vaccinated against polio, your chances of getting this disease are near zero. Other diseases that you can be vaccinated against include measles, mumps, and diphtheria. Early in life, most of you received vaccines to protect you from these diseases.

Some of these diseases have begun to reappear. In the United States, more cases of measles were reported in 1989 than in 1988. College campuses are reporting cases of mumps in young adults. About 20 000 new cases of tuberculosis (TB) are reported each year.

CASES OF TUBERCULOSIS IN LARGE CITIES OF THE UNITED STATES

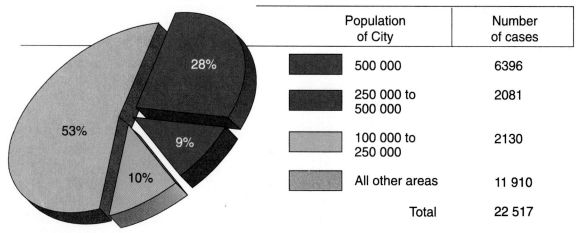

	Population of City	Number of cases
	500 000	6396
	250 000 to 500 000	2081
	100 000 to 250 000	2130
	All other areas	11 910
	Total	22 517

According to the Centers for Disease Control, there are two reasons for the return of these diseases. First, many babies are not being vaccinated against mumps, measles, tetanus, whooping cough, and polio. While some children have shown reactions to the whooping cough vaccine, most children receive vaccines for these diseases by the age of 15 months. Second, just one dose of vaccine does not always provide enough protection. Many adults forget that they need booster shots for tetanus and possibly measles.

Tuberculosis is returning due in part to the damaged immune systems of AIDS victims. Unable to fight off the tuberculosis bacterium, AIDS patients often develop that disease. Those who work or live with such individuals are then exposed to tuberculosis and have a greater chance of developing the disease.

What can you do to prevent becoming infected with these diseases? Make sure you have been vaccinated. Check your medical records to be sure you are vaccinated against all of these diseases. Also, doctors recommend a second vaccination for measles, especially among college students, to rebuild their immunity to the virus. Keeping clean, eating a balanced diet, getting rest and exercise, and getting medical care when you need it are ways to maintain health.

Table 24-3

VACCINATION SCHEDULE	
Vaccine	**Age**
Oral polio	2 months 4 months 18 months 5-6 years
Diphtheria pertussis, tetanus (DPT)	2 months 4 months 6 months 18 months 5-6 years
Tetanus-diphtheria (Td)	14-16 years, every 10 years
Measles, Mumps, Rubella (MMR)	15 months
Measles	17 years
Tuberculosis (TB)	Test in U.S.
	Some countries give a vaccine

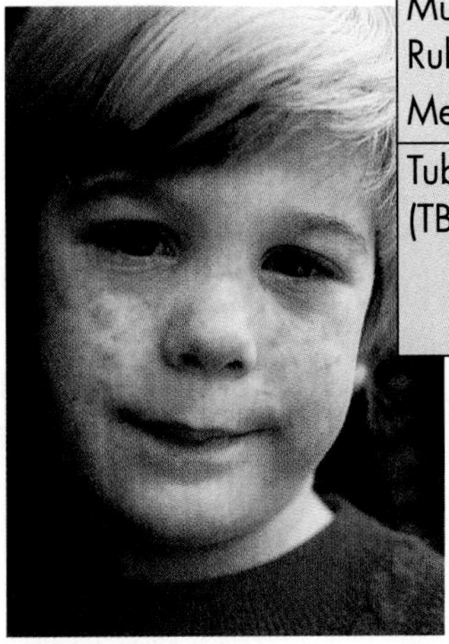

Figure 24-10. The Measles Virus

SECTION REVIEW

1. How does vaccination help prevent disease?
2. Why is vaccination important for the population of a country?

You Decide!

The last case of smallpox was in 1980 in Somalia in Africa. Now the only places where the smallpox virus exists is in the Centers for Disease Control in Atlanta, GA, and in a similar facility in the Soviet Union. Should these countries destroy the remaining virus samples? Should they keep them? What benefit might there be in keeping the virus samples?

24-4 Noncommunicable Disease

New Science Words

noncommunicable diseases
chronic diseases
cancer
tumor
chemotherapy
allergy
allergens

Objectives

▶ List two noncommunicable diseases.
▶ Describe the basic characteristics of cancer.
▶ Name two chronic diseases of the immune system.

Chronic Disease

Diseases and disorders such as diabetes, allergies, asthma, cancer, and heart disease are not caused by pathogens. These diseases are called **noncommunicable diseases** because they are not spread from one person to another. You can't "catch" them. Allergies, genetic disorders, life-style diseases, or chemical imbalances such as diabetes, are not spread by sneezes or handshakes.

Some noncommunicable diseases are called **chronic diseases** because they last a long time. Some chronic diseases can be cured. Others cannot. Chronic diseases may result from improperly functioning organs, contact with harmful chemicals, or an unhealthy life-style. For example, your pancreas produces the hormone insulin. Diabetes is a chronic disease in which the pancreas cannot produce the amount of insulin the body needs.

Arthritis is a chronic disease that results from a faulty immune system. The immune system begins to treat the body's normal proteins as if they were antigens. The faulty immune system forms antibodies against the normal proteins in joints. Movement becomes difficult and painful.

Some chronic diseases are caused by chemicals. Household cleaners, car exhaust, and cigarette smoke are examples. Cigarette smoke has been linked with lung cancer, other lung diseases, and heart disease.

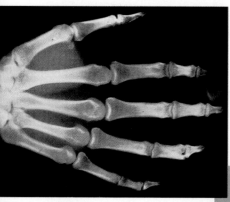

Figure 24-11. Arthritis turns the body's immune system against itself. Joints may be severely deformed.

Normal hand

Arthritic hand

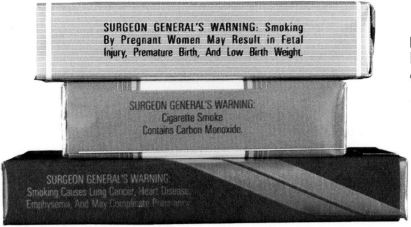

SURGEON GENERAL'S WARNING: Smoking By Pregnant Women May Result in Fetal Injury, Premature Birth, And Low Birth Weight.

SURGEON GENERAL'S WARNING: Cigarette Smoke Contains Carbon Monoxide.

SURGEON GENERAL'S WARNING: Smoking Causes Lung Cancer, Heart Disease, Emphysema, And May Complicate Pregnancy.

Figure 24-12. Tobacco products have been directly linked to lung cancer.

Cancer

Cancer is a major chronic disease. **Cancer** results from uncontrolled cell growth. There are many different types of cancer, but most of them have these characteristics:

1. Uncontrolled cell growth results in large numbers of cells.
2. The large number of cells do not function as a part of the body.
3. The cells take up space and interfere with normal bodily functions.
4. The cells do not remain in one place, but travel throughout the body. In this way, cancer spreads and grows in many areas of the body.

A **tumor** is an abnormal growth anywhere in the body. If a tumor is near the surface of the body, you may feel it as a lump. But if it is deep inside the body, it may go undetected for years. There are two kinds of tumors, benign and malignant (muh LIHG nuhnt). Benign tumors are not cancerous. Malignant tumors are cancerous and can spread.

Treatment for cancer includes surgery to remove cancer tissue, radiation with X rays to kill cancer cells, and chemotherapy. **Chemotherapy** is the use of chemicals to destroy cancer cells.

Cancers are complicated, and no one fully understands how they form. Some scientists hypothesize that cancer cells form regularly in the body. However, the immune system destroys them. Only if the immune system fails or becomes overwhelmed, does the cancer begin to expand. Smoking, poor diet, and exposure to harmful chemicals encourage some cancers to form.

Science and MATH

Aside from the health reasons for not smoking, look at an economic one. Calculate the amount of money a person will save in a week and in a year by not smoking. Assume that the person smokes a pack a day and the cost is $1.50 per pack.

Table 24-4

CAUSES OF CANCER
Carcinogens
Substances that cause cancer:
smoking · air pollution
asbestos dust · high fat diet
ultraviolet light · aflatoxins
radiation
Oncogenes
Genes that cause a normal cell to become cancerous

Allergies

Have you ever broken out in an itchy rash after eating a favorite food? An **allergy** is an overly strong reaction of the immune system to a foreign substance. Many people have allergic reactions to cosmetics, shrimp, strawberries, and bee stings. Allergic reactions to some things such as antibiotics can even be fatal.

Substances that cause the allergic response are called **allergens.** These are substances that the body would normally respond to as a mild antigen. Chemicals, dust, grass, food, pollen, molds, and some antibiotics are allergens for some sensitive people. When you come in contact with an allergen, your immune system forms antibodies, and your body may react in many ways. When the body responds to an allergen, chemicals called histamines are released. Histamines promote red, swollen tissues. Allergic reactions are sometimes treated with antihistamines. Pollen is an allergen that causes a stuffy nose, breathing difficulties, watery eyes, and a tired feeling in some people. Some foods cause blotchy rashes such as hives or, stomach cramps and diarrhea. Most allergic reactions are minor. But severe allergic reactions can occur, causing shock and even death if not treated promptly. Some severe allergies are treated with repeated injections of small doses of the allergen, which allows the body to become less sensitive to the allergen.

Noncommunicable diseases aren't spread from person to person. So, you don't have to worry about catching

What are allergens?

Figure 24-13. Some common substances such as cosmetics, foods, and wool from sheep stimulate allergic responses in people.

PROBLEM SOLVING

Allergic to What?

One hundred twenty-one Chins came from all over the United States to attend the annual family picnic.

An hour after everyone had eaten, the first round of the annual nonstop volleyball game had begun. As Cynthia Chin was about to serve, she slumped to the ground. Her father saw that Cynthia was having trouble breathing. A bee sting was on her cheek. "Call the squad," yelled her father. What happened to Cynthia?

When the paramedics came, her father handed them a card that described how Cynthia reacts to bee venom.

Think Critically: Why is it helpful for someone with a severe allergy to carry identification describing his or her condition?

diabetes, cancer, or allergies from someone else. But, left untreated, noncommunicable diseases can be as deadly as AIDS or untreated syphilis. After all, most people die from chronic heart disease and cancer, and not from a virus or bacterium.

SECTION REVIEW

1. What are two noncommunicable diseases?
2. What are the basic characteristics of cancer?
3. What are two chronic diseases of the immune system?
4. **Apply:** Joel has an ear infection. The doctor prescribes an antibiotic. After taking the antibiotic, Joel breaks out in a rash and has difficulty breathing. What is happening to him? What should he do immediately?

☑ Making and Using Tables

Make a table that lists some chronic diseases and their treatments. Use the information you have read in this section. If you need help, refer to Making and Using Tables in the **Skill Handbook** on page 690.

Skill Builder

ACTIVITY 24-2
Preventing Microorganism Growth

Problem: *What prevents the growth of microorganisms?*

Materials

- transparent tape
- sterile nutrient agar plates (4)
- filter paper
- disinfectant
- hydrogen peroxide
- pencil and labels

- scissors
- mouthwash
- metric ruler
- forceps
- alcohol
- small jars (4)

Procedure

1. Label four nutrient agar petri plates 1-4.
2. Remove the covers from the four petri dishes and rub your finger over the agar in each plate. Put the covers back on and seal dishes 2 and 4 with tape.
3. Label four jars and four 2-cm squares of filter paper: D, H, M, and A.
4. Pour 50 mL of each of the following solutions into the jars: disinfectant, 3% hydrogen peroxide, mouthwash, alcohol.
5. Drop each square into its corresponding solution: D = disinfectant, H = hydrogen peroxide, M = mouthwash, A = alcohol.
6. Using forceps, remove each piece of paper and place on the agar in petri dish 1. Cover the dish and seal with tape. **CAUTION:** *Handle forceps carefully.*
7. Place petri dishes 1 and 2 in a warm, dark place for 48 hours.
8. Remove the cover from dish 3. Place dishes 3 and 4 in a sunny place for 20 minutes.
9. Replace the lid on dish 3 and seal with tape. Store dishes 3 and 4 in a warm, dark place for 48 hours.
10. Hypothesize what will happen in each dish.
11. After 2 days, examine the dishes.
12. In dish 1, compare the growth beneath each square with the area around each square.

13. Compare the bacterial growth of all the petri plates. **CAUTION:** *Give your plates to your teacher for proper disposal.*
14. Record your observations in a table.

Data and Observations

Dish	Square	Observations
1	D	
	A	
	H	
	M	
2	none	
3	none	
4	none	

Analyze

1. Where in plate 1 was the most growth?
2. Where in plate 1 was the least growth?
3. Dish 2 and Dish 4 served what purpose?
4. Which dish had the most bacterial growth?

Conclude and Apply

5. How do antiseptics and disinfectants affect bacterial growth?
6. How does sunlight affect bacterial growth?
7. How did your results match your hypothesis about each plate?
8. What prevents bacterial growth?

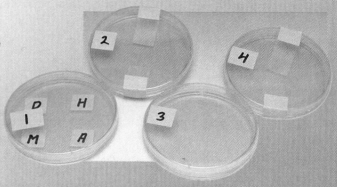

CHAPTER
REVIEW

24-1: The Nature of Disease

1. Pasteur and Koch discovered that diseases are caused by microbes. Lister used disinfectants to help control microbes.

2. Communicable diseases caused by pathogenic bacteria, viruses, fungi, and protists can be passed from one person to another by air, water, food, and animal contact.

3. Sexually transmitted diseases (STDs) are passed between persons during sexual contact. They include genital herpes, gonorrhea, chlamydia, and syphilis. AIDS is classified as a communicable disease and as an STD.

24-2: Your Immune System

1. The body is protected against pathogens by skin, cilia and mucus in the respiratory system, white blood cells in the circulatory system, and digestive enzymes. The purpose of the immune system is to fight disease.

2. Active immunity is long-lasting; passive immunity does not last.

3. AIDS is a communicable disease that may be transmitted by sexual contact, by using a needle contaminated by someone who already has the disease, by transfusion with contaminated blood, and through the placenta to a developing fetus. AIDS damages the body's immune system so that it cannot fight any disease.

24-3: Science and Society: Preventing Disease

1. A vaccine is a weakened virus delivered by injection or swallowed to develop immune protection against a disease.

2. Disease can be prevented by vaccination and good health habits.

24-4: Noncommunicable Disease

1. Causes of noncommunicable disease include genetics, chemicals, poor diet, and uncontrolled cell growth.

2. Chronic noncommunicable diseases include diabetes, cancer, arthritis, and allergies.

3. Most noncommunicable diseases can be medically treated.

a. **active immunity**
b. **allergens**
c. **allergy**
d. **antibody**
e. **antigens**
f. **antiseptic**
g. **cancer**
h. **chemotherapy**
i. **chronic diseases**
j. **communicable disease**
k. **disinfectant**
l. **immune system**
m. **lymphocytes**
n. **noncommunicable diseases**
o. **passive immunity**
p. **pasteurization**
q. **sexually transmitted diseases (STDs)**
r. **tumor**
s. **vaccination**

Match each phrase with the correct term from the list of Key Science Words.

1. cause allergic reactions
2. disease spread through air, water, or contact
3. chemical that prevents pathogen growth on the skin
4. foreign proteins attacked by the body
5. introduces antibodies for short-term immunity
6. white blood cells that fight pathogen
7. long-lasting, noncommunicable diseases
8. uncontrolled cell division
9. use of chemicals to destroy cancer cells
10. introduces antigens for long-term immunity

CHAPTER
REVIEW

Choose the word or phrase that completes the sentence.

1. A pathogen causes a specific disease if it is
   _____.
   a. present in all cases of the disease
   b. does not infect other animals
   c. causes other diseases
   d. none of these

2. Communicable diseases can be caused by
   _____.
   a. bacteria   c. protists
   b. fungi   d. all of these

3. _____ is an example of an STD.
   a. Anthrax   c. AIDS
   b. Malaria   d. Pneumonia

4. All of these diseases are caused by bacteria
   except _____.
   a. AIDS   c. chlamydia
   b. gonorrhea   d. syphilis

5. Your body's defenses against pathogens
   include _____.
   a. stomach enzymes c. white blood cells
   b. skin   d. all of these

6. All of these are noncommunicable diseases
   except _____.
   a. allergies   c. asthma
   b. syphilis   d. diabetes

7. Lymphocytes are attacked by the virus that
   causes _____.
   a. AIDS   c. flu
   b. chlamydia   d. all of these

8. _____ is a chronic joint disease.
   a. Asthma   c. Muscular dystrophy
   b. Arthritis   d. Diabetes

9. Cancer cells are destroyed by _____.
   a. chemotherapy   c. vaccines
   b. antigens   d. none of these

10. You can help prevent diseases with _____.
    a. medical care   c. cleanliness
    b. vaccinations   d. all of these

UNDERSTANDING CONCEPTS

Complete each sentence.

11. _____ is the means by which antigens or
    antibodies are introduced to the body.

12. The scientist who first studied bacteria and
    their relation to disease was _____.

13. Your blood forms _____ to fight invading
    antigens.

14. Diabetes is the result of too little _____ pro-
    duced or released from the pancreas.

15. A strong reaction to a foreign substance such
    as pollen is called a(n) _____.

THINK AND WRITE CRITICALLY

16. How did Pasteur's experiments help society?

17. What makes arthritis different from other
    immune disorders?

18. Why is it very important to wash your hands
    after using a restroom, petting a dog, han-
    dling a pet gerbil or parakeet, and before
    eating?

19. If a person gets a bacterial STD, why must it
    be treated promptly with antibiotics?

20. What's the difference between active and pas-
    sive immunity?

21. Which is better—to vaccinate people or to wait until they build their own immunity?
22. What advantage might a breast-fed baby have compared to a bottle-fed baby?
23. How does your body protect itself from antigens?
24. How do lymphocytes eliminate antigens?
25. Describe the differences among antibodies, antigens, and antibiotics.

MORE SKILL BUILDERS

If you need help, refer to the Skill Handbook.

1. **Making and Using Tables:** Make a chart comparing the following diseases and their prevention: cancer, diabetes, tetanus, measles.
2. **Concept Mapping:** Make network tree concept map, comparing the defenses your body has against disease. Compare general defenses, active immunity, and passive immunity.
3. **Classifying:** Classify the following diseases as communicable or noncommunicable: diabetes, gonorrhea, herpes, strep throat, syphilis, cancer, flu.
4. **Cause and Effect:** Use a library reference to identify the cause of each disease as bacteria, virus, fungus, or protist: athlete's foot, AIDS, cold, dysentery, flu, pinkeye, pneumonia, strep throat, ringworm.

5. **Making and Using Graphs:** Interpret the graph below showing the rate of polio cases. Explain the rate of cases between 1950 and 1965. What conclusions can you draw about the effectiveness of the polio vaccines?

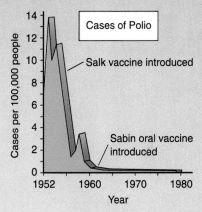

PROJECTS

1. Write a report on Lyme disease, its cause, symptoms, and treatment.
2. Collect newspaper and magazine articles about AIDS. Read them and discuss with the class how AIDS can be prevented.

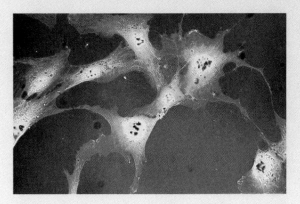

25 Facts about Drugs

Drugs are chemical substances that are used to help lessen pain, to cure disease, or control a chemical imbalance in the body. Drugs have important roles in overcoming illness and maintaining a healthy life.

FIND OUT!

Do this activity to find out which foods and drinks contain caffeine.

Read the labels of food and medicine products to see if the stimulant drug caffeine is listed as an ingredient. Design a chart to show the amount of caffeine per serving or dose in ten of these items. Rank the products from those containing the most caffeine to those containing the least. What products surprised you because of the large amount of caffeine they contain?

Gearing Up

Previewing the Chapter

Use this outline to help you focus on important ideas in this chapter.

Section 25-1 Drugs and Health
- ▶ How Drugs Affect the Body
- ▶ Tobacco
- ▶ Alcohol
- ▶ Caffeine

Section 25-2 Science and Society
Drugs in Society
- ▶ Costs of Drug Abuse

Section 25-3 Problems with Illegal Drugs
- ▶ Marijuana
- ▶ Stimulants
- ▶ Depressants
- ▶ Hallucinogens
- ▶ Opiates

Previewing Science Skills

- ▶ In the **Skill Builders,** you will make a concept map and outline.
- ▶ In the **Activities,** you will analyze, observe, and collect data.
- ▶ In the **MINI-Labs,** you will make a model and classify.

What's next?

Now you know that many foods, medicines, and drinks contain the drug caffeine. In this chapter, you will find out what effects caffeine and other drugs have on the body.

25-1 Drugs and Health

New Science Words

drug
drug misuse
drug abuse
psychological dependence
physical dependence
tolerance
withdrawal
stimulant
fermentation
depressant

Objectives

▶ Explain how drug misuse differs from drug abuse.
▶ Describe the effects of nicotine and alcohol on the body.
▶ Explain the effects of caffeine.

How Drugs Affect the Body

Make a list of five drugs that you know. What did you include? Did your list include foods, drinks, tobacco, medicines, and illegal drugs? A **drug** is any chemical substance that changes the way a person thinks, feels, or acts. Drugs provide no nutrition for the body. Different drugs can act to slow down or speed up the nervous system or to change the functions of some cells. Most drugs are derived from plants, fungi, and bacteria.

When used properly, drugs benefit health. When used improperly, they can harm the user. For example, taking too much of some kinds of blood pressure medicine can lower blood pressure so much that a person feels faint. Improper use also can cause behavior that harms the health and safety of others. Driving after drinking can result in injury to the driver and others. Because of these concerns, federal laws were passed to control the manufacture, distribution, and possession of all drugs.

Have you ever been really sick with a cold and cough? Your doctor may have prescribed medicine with a cough suppressant to keep you from coughing so hard and to let you rest. Suppose you decided to take an extra spoonful before bedtime to make sure you were able to sleep all night. This behavior is a form of drug misuse. **Drug misuse** is use of a drug for the purpose for which it was made, but taking it improperly. Taking too much or too little medicine according to directions is drug misuse. Using someone else's medicine is also drug misuse. Drug misuse is harmful to health. **Drug abuse** is the deliberate use of a drug for other than its intended purpose. Using illegal drugs is drug abuse. Drug abuse damages a person's health.

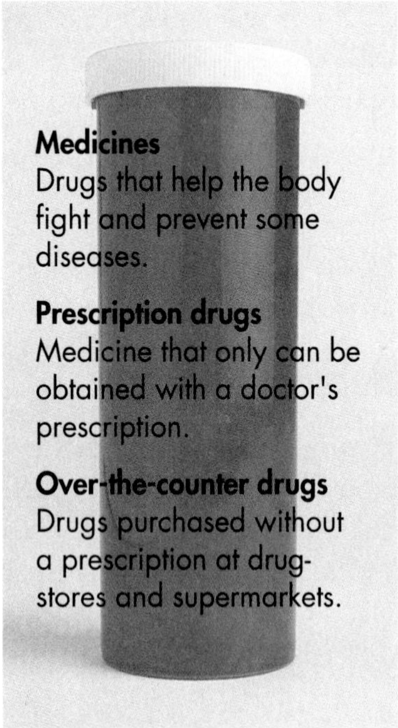

Medicines
Drugs that help the body fight and prevent some diseases.

Prescription drugs
Medicine that only can be obtained with a doctor's prescription.

Over-the-counter drugs
Drugs purchased without a prescription at drugstores and supermarkets.

Figure 25-1. Many kinds of drugs are made for helping people regain health.

When drugs are misused or abused, serious health problems can result. A person can develop chemical dependence. With this condition, a person has a psychological and/or physical need for a drug. A person who has **psychological dependence** really believes that he or she needs the drug. The person may believe that use of the drug can be controlled. A person who has **physical dependence** has a chemical need for a drug. This also is called addiction. The person becomes so used to the effects of the drug that he or she needs it to function. There are two parts to physical dependence—tolerance and withdrawal. **Tolerance** occurs when the body adjusts to a drug and needs increasingly larger doses to produce the desired effect. **Withdrawal** is an illness that occurs when the drug a person is physically dependent on is removed. Withdrawal symptoms are real and can be very painful. They include nausea, vomiting, headaches, and chills.

EcoTip

Dispose of old medicine properly. Call the local EPA to find out ways to dispose of it.

What are the two parts to physical dependence?

 # T E C H N O L O G Y

Taking Your Medicine

Some people need medicine or pain killers regularly. People with diabetes or cancer seem to respond best to frequent, low doses of medication. Taking medication by mouth can cause high blood levels of medicine as the medicine takes effect, followed by low blood concentrations as it wears off. This takes the patient on a roller coaster ride of pain or problems. Various techniques are being explored that allow a steady release medication system, flexible enough to allow a higher dosage on demand.

A drug pump may be implanted under skin and deliver medication as directed by a desktop programmer. A syringe-type pump is frequently used for newborns and for cancer patients. Other systems use biodegradable implants that slowly release

medication as the implant breaks down. Ultrasound waves, magnetism, heat, and enzyme triggers are all being studied as ways of allowing patients to increase the dosage released by an implant.
Think Critically:
What kinds of illness might this system be most useful for?

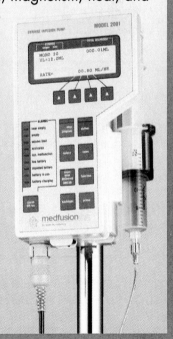

ACTIVITY 25-1
Interpreting Drug Label Information

Problem: *What information is on the label of an over-the-counter drug?*

Materials
- paper
- pencil

Procedure
1. The photograph below shows a label from an over-the-counter drug. Read it carefully.
2. Make a data table like the one shown. Use the information on the label to complete the data table.

Data and Observations

Information	Drug Label
Product	
Number of pills	
Ingredients in the medicine	
Directions for use	
Warnings	
Possible side effects	
Expiration date	
Storage of drug	

Analyze
1. What is an over-the-counter drug?
2. What is a side effect? What side effects are caused by this drug?
3. What information is given on the label of this over-the-counter drug?
4. For whom does the label specify the drug is intended?
5. Who should not take this drug without consulting a physician?
6. What is the maximum number of doses that should be taken in 24 hours?

Conclude and Apply
7. How are over-the-counter drugs different from prescription drugs?
8. Why should a person never take any kind of drug without reading the label?
9. Why would the age of a person determine drug dose?
10. Why should a person never take more than the recommended amount of an over-the-counter drug?

Arthritis Strength

PROVIDE FAST PAIN RELIEF AND HELP PROTECT AGAINST ASPIRIN STOMACH UPSET.
- Provides effective temporary relief of the minor aches and pains, stiffness, swelling and inflammation of arthritis.
* Buffered formulation which helps prevent the stomach upset that plain aspirin can cause.
- Coated caplets for easy swallowing.
DOSAGE: Adults — 2 caplets with water every 4 hours as needed. Do not exceed 8 caplets in 24 hours, or give to children under 12 unless directed by physician. CAUTION: If pain persists for more than 10 days or redness is present, or in arthritic or rheumatic conditions affecting children under 12, consult a physician immediately. Do not take without consulting a physician if under medical care. WARNING: Children and teenagers should not use this medicine for chicken pox or flu symptoms before a doctor is consulted about Reye syndrome, a rare but serious illness reported to be associated with aspirin. KEEP THIS AND ALL MEDICINES OUT OF CHILDREN'S REACH. IN CASE OF ACCIDENTAL OVERDOSE, CONTACT A PHYSICIAN OR POISON CONTROL CENTER IMMEDIATELY. If dizziness, impaired hearing or ringing in the ears occurs, discontinue use. As with any drug, if you are pregnant or nursing a baby, seek the advice of a health professional before using this product. ACTIVE INGREDIENT (PER CAPLET): Aspirin (500 mg) in a formulation buffered with Calcium Carbonate, Magnesium Oxide and Magnesium Carbonate. **Other Ingredients:** Benzoic Acid, Carnauba Wax, Citric Acid, Corn Starch, FD&C Blue No. 1, Hydroxypropyl Methylcellulose, Mineral Oil, Polysorbate 20, Povidone, Propylene Glycol, Simethicone Emulsion, Sodium Phosphate, Sorbitan Monolaurate, Titanium Dioxide. May also contain: Glyceryl Behenate, Magnesium Stearate, Sodium Lauryl Sulfate, Sodium Stearyl Fumarate, Stearic Acid, Zinc Stearate. Remove cotton and recap bottle. Store at room temperature.

Tobacco

When a person first begins to smoke, he or she may feel sick. It takes time for the body to get used to nicotine, the drug in tobacco. Many people do not think of the nicotine in tobacco as a drug. However, it is a **stimulant,** a drug that speeds up the nervous system. Nicotine speeds up the heartbeat rate and raises blood pressure. It constricts blood vessels, reducing blood flow. Nicotine also contributes to the buildup of fatty substances in blood vessels. The chance of developing blood clots that cause heart attacks and strokes increases. Nicotine causes physical and psychological dependence.

Tobacco smoke brings other substances into the body. Carbon monoxide is a harmful gas found in tobacco smoke. Carbon monoxide becomes attached to hemoglobin in red blood cells more easily than does oxygen. The hemoglobin cannot carry oxygen. As a result, cells do not get enough oxygen. The respiratory and cardiovascular systems have to work harder.

In Chapter 21, you read that tar is a thick, sticky fluid produced when tobacco burns. Tar sticks to the respiratory tract. It damages cilia and contains cancer-causing chemicals.

PROBLEM SOLVING

Passive Smoke

Tim and his family were eating in the nonsmoking section of a restaurant. However, when Tim began to eat, smoke from a burning cigarette in the smoking section wafted under his nose. It affected the taste of Tim's food. He was upset that his dinner was being disturbed by this smoke. Tim knows that nonsmokers who are exposed to tobacco smoke from cigarettes or smoke exhaled by a smoker have an increased risk of developing the same diseases as those who smoke. What would you have done if you were Tim's family?

Think Critically: Tim thinks smoking shouldn't be allowed in public places. What do you think about smoking in public places?

Unfortunately, you cannot escape the danger of tobacco smoke by just not smoking. There are real health risks from just being in a room with tobacco smoke. If you are in a room with someone who is smoking, harmful substances from smoke will enter your respiratory system. The smoke from a burning cigarette, cigar, or pipe is known as passive smoke. Passive smoke contains more tar, nicotine, carbon monoxide, and other chemicals than that inhaled by the smoker.

Alcohol

Alcohol is also a drug. Alcoholic drinks have been made and used since ancient times. The sugar in fruits and grains reacts with yeast to produce alcohol and carbon dioxide in a process known as **fermentation.**

Unlike many drugs, alcohol does not affect the nervous system directly. Most of it is absorbed through the walls of the stomach and small intestine. It enters the circulatory system undigested. Therefore, all body tissues are exposed to it directly. Alcohol is a **depressant,** slowing down the central nervous system. It affects the functions of the brain. Judgment, reasoning, memory, and concentration are impaired. Even though alcohol is a depressant, it slightly increases heartbeat and pulse rate. It causes blood vessels to enlarge. As a result, a feeling of warmth passes through the body. In reality, however, the body is losing heat from the capillaries near the surface of the skin. Alcohol is changed to carbon dioxide and water in the liver before being excreted. Heavy use of alcohol results in destruction of brain and liver cells.

Large amounts of alcohol in the bloodstream dull the senses and cause the drinker to have a slower reaction time, lose coordination, and have slurred speech. Excessive amounts of alcohol can result in unconsciousness and death.

Most states have laws that define the legal limit of the amount of alcohol allowed in the blood for a driver. Because a small amount of alcohol can cause abnormal behavior and loss of judgment, just a few drinks can cause a driver to be legally "under the influence." For example, two 2-ounce drinks of whiskey or five bottles of beer may be enough for a person to be arrested as a drunk driver.

Sometimes, people become physically dependent on alcohol. Alcoholism is a disease characterized by the abuse of alcohol. The person with this disease cannot control his

MINI-Lab

A Childproof Package?

Survey different types of packaging used in over-the-counter drugs to make them tamperproof and childproof. Design a childproof package for a product. Could your package be opened easily by a person with arthritis?

Did You Know?

About 28 million American children have at least one alcoholic parent.

or her drinking. The constant use of alcohol causes permanent damage to blood vessels and the liver. It also causes blackouts. There are many approaches used to treat alcoholism, including drugs, therapy, and self-help programs.

Caffeine

What do coffee, tea, and cola soft drinks have in common? You probably know that it is the drug caffeine. Caffeine is a stimulant, a type of drug that stimulates your central nervous system and speeds up other body systems. You may hear people say they need a cup of coffee to get started in the morning or a cola soft drink for energy in the afternoon. They may be dependent on the caffeine in the drink to feel more energetic. Caffeine also is found in chocolate and cocoa. It is probably the most used stimulant in the world because it is so readily available.

Too much caffeine can increase heartbeat rate and cause a person to be restless, have tremors, and be unable to sleep. It can also stimulate the kidneys to produce more urine. Caffeine can cause physical dependence. When people who take in a lot of caffeine stop, they can have headaches and nausea. In spite of these known effects, a study released in 1990 showed that no damage could be found from the use of caffeine products. The study followed the caffeine habits of more than 10 000 people for a period of more than five years.

Science and WRITING

Find out about the programs of Alcoholics Anonymous, Al-Anon, and Alateen. Describe the work of these groups in a report to share with the class.

SECTION REVIEW

1. How does drug misuse differ from drug abuse?
2. How does nicotine affect the body?
3. How does alcohol affect the brain?
4. What happens when a person consumes too much caffeine?
5. **Apply:** Why does constant alcohol use cause permanent damage to blood vessels?

⊠ Concept Mapping

Using a network tree concept map, show some differences between depressants and stimulants discussed in this section and give examples. If you need help, refer to Concept Mapping in the **Skill Handbook** on pages 688 and 689.

Skill Builder

25-2 Drugs in Society

New Science Words

methamphetamine

Objectives

▶ Explain the cost of drug abuse to society.
▶ List two attempts that have been made to solve the problem of drug abuse.

Costs of Drug Abuse

For some time, drug abuse has been America's greatest concern. Many people suffer because of the effects of illegal drugs. In 1989, 2500 people in the United States died as a result of drug overdoses, drug-related crimes, or drug-related accidents. Babies born to mothers that abuse drugs may be addicted and suffer effects of the drugs. In the business world, of 1000 corporate executives surveyed, 67 percent agreed that drug abuse is the nation's number one labor problem. Loss of productivity, industrial accidents, higher health care cost, absenteeism, and lateness due to employee drug abuse results in $160 billion in business loss each year. The General Motors Corporation reports that it loses $1 billion each year to employee drug abuse. Indirectly, this loss is then added to the price of new cars.

Figure 25-2. Campaigns to stop drug abuse are visible in many places.

How can these problems be solved? In 1982, a war on drugs was declared in the United States. It was designed to attack the problem of drug abuse by educating the general public about the effects of drugs. Law enforcement was strengthened through increased crackdowns on dealers, expanded courts and prisons, and even military forces to keep drugs out of the country. The program appears to have had some impact on the problem. But despite attempts to prevent illegal drugs from entering the United States, drugs continue to arrive. The 60 to 75 percent drop in the prices of some drug on the streets shows how easily available drugs are. What is the real source of the drug problem? Is it lack of education?

In South America, it is estimated that millions of hectares of land are used to grow the coca plant from which cocaine is produced. Even if this crop were destroyed, experts predict that addicts would produce a synthetic cocaine to satisfy their needs. This has already happened in the United States. A very powerful drug called **methamphetamine** (meth am FET uh men), crank, or ice speeds up body functions. Its effects last up to eight hours. Do drug suppliers provide their product because they know they will always have customers?

Some people argue that there is no solution to controlling the drug abuse problem in the United States. Drug education programs and increased law enforcement have proven effective for some, but not for all. It may be a while before the positive effects of drug education can be seen. Some experts suggest that drugs should be legalized. They suggest that the war on drugs is not practical because millions of Americans are paying for failed attempts to capture and reform hard-core drug producers. After all, alcohol and caffeine are legal. As law enforcement gets tougher, dealers may only make the drugs stronger, easier to hide, and more dangerous. What would happen if these drugs were made legal? How do you think the rate of abuse would change?

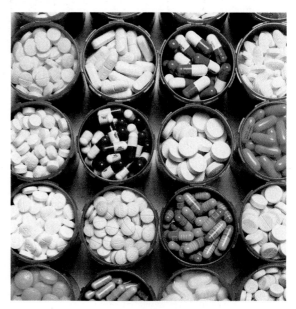

Figure 25-3. Drugs exist to help, not to be abused.

SECTION REVIEW

1. Why does drug abuse cause such a great loss to businesses each year?
2. List ways in which the government attempted to declare war on drugs to help solve the problem of drug abuse.

You Decide!

How much publicity do drugs receive? Many magazines, movies, and television programs still make drug use appear glamorous. Even tobacco and alcohol ads make it appear that people who use these products are young, well-dressed, and always having a great time. Does advertising give the wrong impression? What can be done to make people understand the truth about drugs?

Problems with Illegal Drugs

New Science Words

marijuana
hashish
cocaine
crack
hallucinogens
heroin

Figure 25-4. Marijuana is made from the parts of the hemp plant.

Objectives

▶ Compare the effects of marijuana and tobacco use.
▶ Describe the effects of stimulants and depressants.
▶ Describe the effects of hallucinogens.
▶ Explain problems of using opiates.

Marijuana

Indian hemp is a weed plant found worldwide. An illegal drug called **marijuana** or pot is made from the stems, leaves, flowers, and seeds of this hemp plant. These plant parts are crushed up and made into a cigarette (joint) for smoking. The sticky tarlike substance from the flowering top of the marijuana plant is known as **hashish.** This is more concentrated and powerful than marijuana. Hashish is smoked, chewed, or put in a drink to get its effect.

Marijuana is considered to be more dangerous than cigarettes. Many harmful chemicals have been identified in marijuana. The most powerful is THC, which produces a mind-altering effect. The effects of marijuana use depend a lot on the user's surroundings and feelings at the time it is smoked. It can both stimulate and depress. The person who uses marijuana may feel calm, relaxed, and have a feeling of well-being. Then the user may become sensitive to sights and sounds. Marijuana use impairs reaction time and coordination. It harms a person's ability to think, learn, and remember. The effects of smoking marijuana last from two to four hours. Regular users can suffer long-term effects, including losing interest in life. They substitute marijuana for other goals. They also experience feelings of anxiety, panic, and periods of depression.

Marijuana use has physical effects as well. Smoking the drug increases heartbeat rate and therefore is dangerous for persons with heart conditions. Its effects on the lungs are similar to those of tobacco use. Lung tissue can be damaged. The risks of bronchitis, emphysema, and lung cancer increase.

Even though marijuana does not cause physical dependence, users want the good feeling to continue. They develop a psychological dependence on the drug.

Stimulants

As you read earlier, nicotine and caffeine are stimulants. However, there are much stronger stimulants than those. One group of stimulants is amphetamines (am FET uh meenz). In the past, amphetamines were prescribed to increase a person's energy and decrease appetite to control weight. This is rarely done now.

Illegal amphetamines are known as pep pills and uppers. Another form of illegal amphetamines is known as speed or crank. Crank is also called ice. These drugs suppress hunger and cause the user to experience increased energy. Their use increases heartbeat rate, blood pressure, and breathing. Used over a long period of time, these drugs can lead to anxiety and feelings that someone will cause the person harm. Physical and psychological dependence can result. Withdrawal from use of these drugs can cause depression.

Another illegal stimulant is **cocaine,** a white powder made from the leaves of the South American coca plant. It is thought that the leaves of the coca plant are chewed by workers in the Andes Mountains to stimulate their bodies in this low-oxygen environment. Cocaine was an ingredient in many nonprescription drugs in the 1800s. A popular cola soft drink originally had cocaine in it and was advertised as a stimulant.

Cocaine is inhaled through the nose, swallowed, or injected. It is absorbed by membranes and enters the bloodstream quickly. Cocaine is a drug that users can become dependent on in a matter of days. The drug has a short-lived "high," or feeling of well-being. Anxiety soon replaces the good feeling. To get the same feeling, a user must take increasingly larger doses of the drug. Cocaine increases heartbeat rate and blood pressure and has been associated with sudden death due to a heart attack.

What effect do stimulants have on the body?

a

b

c

Figure 25-5. Coca leaves (a), tobacco (b), and coffee (c) contain substances that stimulate the body to different degrees. The stimulants produced from coca leaves are controlled, illegal substances.

A stronger form of cocaine is called **crack.** Crack is a smokable form of cocaine. Since the introduction of crack around 1986, it has rapidly become a much abused drug. Unfortunately, many people did not realize the rapid addictive powers of cocaine or its dangerous effects on the body. The effects of crack are more intense and short-lived than cocaine. As with all stimulants, the drug affects the central nervous system. Crack use causes constricted blood vessels, causing the heart to work harder to move blood throughout the body. As a result, blood pressure increases and irregular heartbeat can develop. Heart failure can occur. The initial high of the drug is followed by a period of depression in which the user may feel anxious and irritable and have a strong craving for more of the drug. Pregnant females using the drug pass the effects of the drug through the placenta to the developing fetus. These babies can develop physical dependence. After birth, these babies go through withdrawal.

How does crack affect the body?

Depressants

You read earlier about depressants, drugs that slow down the central nervous system. Alcohol, sleeping pills, tranquilizers, and a class of drugs called barbiturates (bar BIH chuh ruts) are all depressants. A slang word for depressant pills is "downers." Depressants slow down or prevent impulses from moving across a synapse from one neuron to another. How would this affect your heart and your respiratory system? Blood vessels dilate and blood pressure lowers. Breathing rates slow. A person under the influence of depressants may be confused, lack coordination, appear to be intoxicated, and have slow reflexes. This person is prone to accidents.

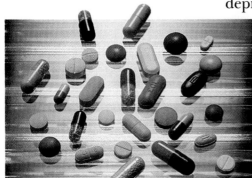

Figure 25-6. Taking combinations of depressants can be deadly.

An overdose of depressants can cause coma, depressed breathing, uncontrolled muscle spasms, and eventually death. Depressants taken in combination with other depressants, such as sleeping pills or alcohol, increase the dangerous effects. Withdrawal from depressants is difficult.

Some persons take a combination of stimulants and depressants to try to keep in a constant state of drug enjoyment. The physical and psychological damage to the body is severe and can lead to death.

Hallucinogens

Hallucinogens (huh LEWS un uh junz) are a group of drugs that affect users' perceptions and consciousness of the world around them. Under the influence of hallucinogens, the user often experiences an extreme sensitivity to light, sound, taste, and odor. This causes confusion, and the person cannot tell the difference between reality and fantasy.

In addition to psychological dependence, the use of hallucinogens can cause a person to have unpredictable, violent behavior. Coma, convulsions, and death can occur with the use of these drugs.

Two of the more powerful hallucinogens are LSD and PCP, also called angel dust. These drugs can produce dramatic effects from taking even small amounts. The senses become highly stimulated, and users talk about "seeing" sounds, "tasting" odors, and "hearing" colors. The effects may last for several hours. The hallucinations of a bad experience with these drugs can cause anxiety and panic and lead to suicide. LSD is also known to cause flashbacks to hallucinations that occurred years before.

The use of hallucinogens can bring about dramatic changes in personality. Persons who use these drugs find they can't control themselves after using even a small amount. Users may react violently toward themselves or others. In some cases, they may slip into a long, semiconscious state. The results of using these drugs are unpredictable.

What can happen to a person who used hallucinogens?

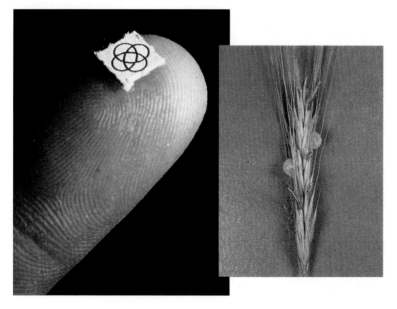

Figure 25-7. The source of LSD is a fungal infection of rye flowers. Even small amounts of LSD, such as are found in the small patch to the left, can cause hallucinogenic responses.

Opiates

Using plant substances to relieve pain has occurred often throughout history. During the third century B.C., the Greeks used a substance from the white poppy to relieve suffering from pain. This same substance was introduced to the Orient in the 1800s. However, the drug soon was used less for medical purposes than for putting oneself into a dreamlike state. Physical dependence on the drug became widespread. This drug was opium, made from the juices of the seed capsule of the white poppy. Opium and its active chemical, morphine, were used as pain killers during the Civil War. Many wounded soldiers became dependent on morphine. Because there were no laws regulating nonprescription drugs, many of them also contained opium or morphine. People became physically dependent on these medicines. There was such a protest against the use of these drugs, that Congress passed the Pure Food and Drug Act in 1906. This law required that labels on medicine show whether they contain alcohol, opium, or morphine.

Because morphine was a good pain killer but could cause physical dependence, researchers tried to make other pain-relieving drugs from opium. The powerful drug **heroin** was made from morphine. It was not supposed to cause physical dependence. However, this was not true. A much stronger drug than morphine, heroin is one of the most addictive drugs and is widely abused in the United States.

What does the Pure Food and Drug Act require?

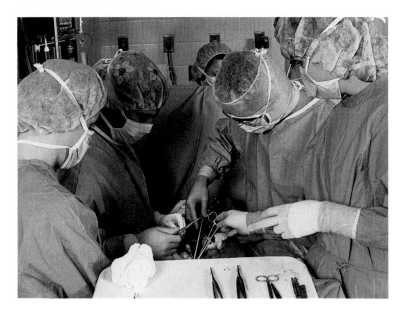

Figure 25-8. Morphine is used medically as a pain reliever after some surgeries and for some terminal cancer patients. Its use is strictly regulated.

Figure 25-9. Opium is made from the juices of the seed capsule of the white poppy.

Opiates, also called narcotics, cause a brief, dreamlike state, drowsiness, constricted pupils, and nausea. Because these drugs are often injected and the needles shared, users can develop infections from dirty needles. Tetanus; hepatitis (hep uh TITE us), a disease of the liver; and the AIDS virus are spread among heroin users when sharing needles to use the drug.

Drug abuse has become one of the greatest problems in our country today. The waste of human resources and lives due to drug abuse has affected every community. Sometimes, people feel the only way to escape their problems is to use drugs. Unfortunately, by doing this they exchange one set of problems for another. Problems of drug dependence lead to mental and physical illness and sometimes death. There is no future in drug abuse.

MINI-Lab
How are drugs classified?
Make flash cards for the following drugs. Classify them into categories of stimulants, depressants, hallucinogens, and opiates. Drugs: alcohol, amphetamines, barbiturates, crank/ice, caffeine, cocaine, crack, LSD, heroin, morphine, PCP, sleeping pills, speed, tranquilizers.

SECTION REVIEW

1. How is marijuana use similar to tobacco use?
2. Why are stimulants and depressants dangerous?
3. What are the dangers to a person's health if hallucinogens are used?
4. What are additional risks of using narcotics besides the effect of the drugs?
5. **Apply:** Why is it dangerous for a person who has been using marijuana to drive?

☑ Outlining

Outline the effects of two drugs discussed in Section 25-3. Title your outline, Problems with Illegal Drugs. If you need help, refer to Outlining in the **Skill Handbook** on page 681.

Skill Builder

ACTIVITY 25-2
The Effect of Drugs on Heartbeat Rate

Problem: *How do drugs affect the heartbeat rate of an animal?*

Materials

- dilute solutions of coffee, cola, ethyl alcohol, tobacco, and cough medicine (dextromethorphen hydrobromide)
- *Daphnia* culture
- microscope
- dropper
- aged tap water

Procedure

1. Use a dropper to place a single *Daphnia* crustacean on a culture slide.
2. Place the slide under the microscope. Use low power and count the number of times the heart of the *Daphnia* beats in one minute. (See photo for location of the animal's heart.) Record your observations in a table like the one shown.
3. Record your predictions of whether the drugs are stimulants or depressants.
4. Add two drops of one of the drug solutions to the *Daphnia* in the culture dish.
5. Count the heartbeat rate again. Record your observations.
6. Use a dropper to remove the solution. Flush the slide and *Daphnia* carefully with aged tap water. **CAUTION:** *Flush the used Daphnia into a beaker of aged tap water provided by your teacher.*
7. Repeat Steps 1 through 6 for each of the drug solutions provided. **CAUTION:** *Use a new Daphnia for each step.*
8. Record the effects of each drug on heartbeat rate.

Analyze

1. What was the control in the experiment? What were the variables?

Data and Observations   Sample Data

Drug solution	Heart rate per minute	Stimulant or depressant
No drug		
Coffee		
Cola		
Ethyl alcohol		
Tobacco		
Cough medicine		

2. How did the drugs affect *Daphnia*?
3. Which drugs caused the greatest change in the number of heartbeats per minute?

Conclude and Apply

4. Which drugs are stimulants?
5. Which drugs are depressants?
6. Compare your predicted results with the experimental results.
7. How do drugs affect the rate of heartbeat of an animal?
8. How do you think the drugs used in this activity affect people who use them?

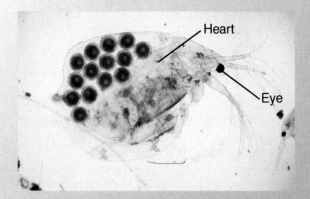

Heart

Eye

CHAPTER
REVIEW

25-1: Drugs and Health

1. Drug misuse is using a drug for the purpose it was made, but taking it improperly. Drug abuse is use of a drug for other than its intended purpose. Both are harmful to health and can cause chemical dependence.

2. Nicotine in tobacco speeds up the heartbeat rate; alcohol slows down body processes.

3. Caffeine is a stimulant.

25-2: Science and Society: Drugs in Society

1. Drug abuse costs can be measured in increased health care costs, on-the-job losses, and the cost of educating people on why they should avoid usage.

2. Education, increased law enforcement, and cooperation of countries from which drugs come are attempts to solve the drug problem.

25-3: Problems with Illegal Drugs

1. Marijuana is more dangerous than cigarettes; marijuana produces a mind-altering effect.

2. Stimulants, including amphetamines, cocaine, and crack speed up body functions; depressants, including alcohol, tranquilizers, and barbiturates slow down body functions.

3. Hallucinogens affect perception and consciousness; users can react violently.

4. Opiates, such as morphine and heroin are narcotics and are very addictive.

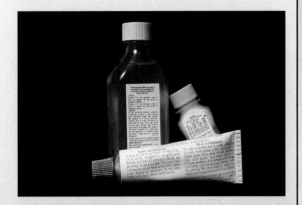

KEY SCIENCE WORDS

a. **cocaine**
b. **crack**
c. **depressant**
d. **drug**
e. **drug abuse**
f. **drug misuse**
g. **fermentation**
h. **hallucinogens**
i. **hashish**
j. **heroin**
k. **marijuana**
l. **methamphetamine**
m. **physical dependence**
n. **psychological dependence**
o. **stimulant**
p. **tolerance**
q. **withdrawal**

UNDERSTANDING VOCABULARY

Match each phrase with the correct term from the list of Key Science Words.

1. larger doses are needed to produce the effects of the drug

2. stronger form of cocaine

3. taking too much medicine

4. made from sticky residue of marijuana plants

5. using illegal drugs

6. process of making alcohol

7. drug that slows the body down

8. affect perception and consciousness

9. narcotic made from morphine

10. drug that increases heartbeat rate and breathing

CHAPTER
REVIEW

Choose the word or phrase that completes the sentence.

1. Methamphetamine is also called _____.
   a. marijuana
   c. ice
   b. heroin
   d. all of these

2. Alcohol is absorbed directly into the _____.
   a. heart
   c. large intestine
   b. stomach
   d. liver

3. The drug _____ is found in tobacco.
   a. tar
   c. carbon monoxide
   b. nicotine
   d. all of these

4. Smoking affects a person's _____
   a. heart
   c. lungs
   b. blood vessels
   d. all of these

5. _____ is an example of a depressant.
   a. Alcohol
   c. Caffeine
   b. Nicotine
   d. Amphetamine

6. An example of a stimulant is _____.
   a. amphetamines
   c. crank
   b. cocaine
   d. all of these

7. Symptoms of depressants include _____.
   a. slow reflexes
   b. lowered blood pressure
   c. dilated blood vessels
   d. all of these

8. _____ is obtained from the white poppy.
   a. Caffeine
   c. Opium
   b. Marijuana
   d. LSD

9. An example of a narcotic is _____.
   a. alcohol
   c. PCP
   b. morphine
   d. none of these

10. A majority of drugs are obtained from
    _____.
    a. plants
    c. soil
    b. animals
    d. none of these

UNDERSTANDING CONCEPTS

Complete each sentence.

11. A person who believes he or she has a need for a drug has _____ dependence.

12. _____ is the thick fluid from cigarettes that harms cilia.

13. _____ is found in coffee, tea, and chocolate.

14. The mind-altering chemical _____ is found in marijuana.

15. Cocaine comes from the leaves of the _____ plant.

THINK AND WRITE CRITICALLY

16. What is the difference between psychological and physical dependence?

17. List three plants and the drugs that are obtained from them.

18. Describe the effects of hallucinogens on the body.

19. What can happen to her baby if a pregnant female uses crack?

20. Explain why drug use is strictly controlled by the government.

APPLY

21. What are some effects on the body that are common to all stimulants?
22. What are some effects on the body that are common to all depressants?
23. Explain how industry is affected by drug abuse.
24. What differences would the way a drug is taken have on its effects?
25. Explain the physical effects of one drug discussed in this chapter.

MORE SKILL BUILDERS

If you need help, refer to the Skill Handbook.

1. **Comparing and Contrasting:** In a chart, compare and contrast the effects of stimulants and depressants.
2. **Making and Using Graphs:** Use the data from Activity 25-2 (page 594) to make a bar graph of substances and their effect on heartbeat rate in *Daphnia*.
3. **Hypothesizing:** Make a hypothesis as to what effects might be felt by a person who is smoking a cigarette and drinking coffee at the same time.
4. **Interpreting Scientific Illustrations:** Compare adult's dosage with child's on the label in Activity 25-1 (page 582). Why do you think a child's dose is different from an adult's?
5. **Concept Mapping:** Choose a brand name headache remedy and a generic brand. Compare the ingredients, cost, and amount of medication in each container. Make a network tree concept map showing your results.

PROJECTS

1. For one week, collect newspaper articles that have drug-related information in them. Bring these articles to school to share and discuss with your class.
2. Find out the pattern of smoking habits among people in the United States over the past ten years. Who smokes more, men or women; what age group; how much do people smoke?

GLOBAL CONNECTIONS

Staying Healthy

In this unit, you have studied health, disease, and drugs. Why is health important to all people? What influence does health have worldwide?

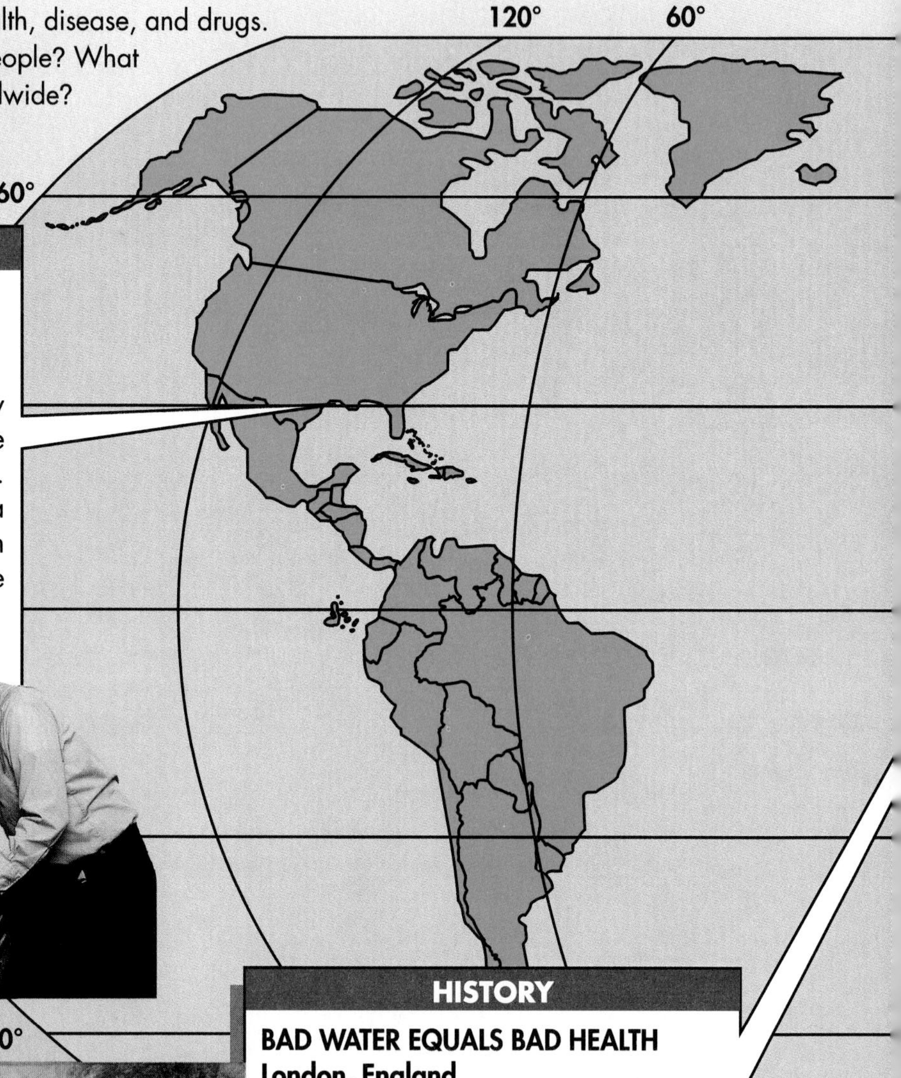

120°   60°

60°

HEALTH

ZAPPING GERMS MAY HELP CURE DISEASE
Houston, Texas

A positive mental attitude may help cure diseases of the immune system. Patients at the M.D. Anderson Hospital can use a video game to zap germs. Fun may be an important part of the cure. How can mental health influence physical health?

60°

HISTORY

BAD WATER EQUALS BAD HEALTH
London, England

In 1854, more than 500 people from the same neighborhood died of cholera in less than a week. Why? Dr. John Snow found that they all got their water from the same well. When the well was closed, the epidemic stopped. Why is it important to have a source of clean water?

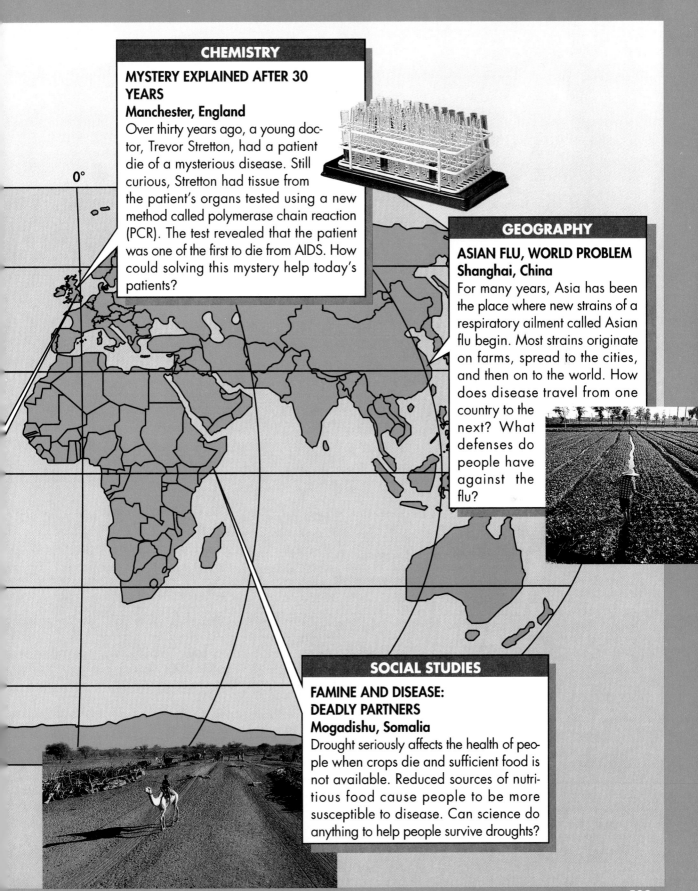

CHEMISTRY

MYSTERY EXPLAINED AFTER 30 YEARS
Manchester, England

Over thirty years ago, a young doctor, Trevor Stretton, had a patient die of a mysterious disease. Still curious, Stretton had tissue from the patient's organs tested using a new method called polymerase chain reaction (PCR). The test revealed that the patient was one of the first to die from AIDS. How could solving this mystery help today's patients?

GEOGRAPHY

ASIAN FLU, WORLD PROBLEM
Shanghai, China

For many years, Asia has been the place where new strains of a respiratory ailment called Asian flu begin. Most strains originate on farms, spread to the cities, and then on to the world. How does disease travel from one country to the next? What defenses do people have against the flu?

SOCIAL STUDIES

FAMINE AND DISEASE: DEADLY PARTNERS
Mogadishu, Somalia

Drought seriously affects the health of people when crops die and sufficient food is not available. Reduced sources of nutritious food cause people to be more susceptible to disease. Can science do anything to help people survive droughts?

0°

CAREERS

MICROBIOLOGIST

Microbiologists study the growth and characteristics of tiny living things such as bacteria, viruses, fungi, and protists. Medical microbiologists study how microorganisms cause disease and produce cures.

Microbiologists study science, math, and social studies and go on to college and graduate school before they can work.

The food industry uses microbiologists in the development of new products and in quality control. Hospitals may also employ microbiologists to track and prevent the spread of diseases within hospitals.

For Additional Information

Contact the American Society for Microbiology, Office of Educational and Professional Recognition, 1913 I Street, Washington, DC 20006.

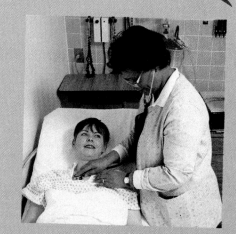

LICENSED PRACTICAL NURSE

Licensed practical nurses care for patients under the direction of doctors and registered nurses. They provide basic bedside care such as taking temperatures, pulse, and blood pressure. L.P.N.s work in nursing homes where, in addition to bedside care, they may also help develop care plans and supervise nursing aides.

A future L.P.N. should get as much science as possible in high school. Then he or she will go on to a state-approved training program at a trade school, community college, or hospital. Traditionally, a program for Licensed Practical Nurse can be completed in one year of full-time study.

For Additional Information

Contact the National Federation of Licensed Practical Nurses, P. O. Box 1088, Raleigh, NC 27619.

UNIT READINGS

▶Jaret, Peter. "The Disease Detectives." *National Geographic*, January 1991.
▶Jordon, Robert Paul. "Somalia's Hour of Need." *National Geographic*, June 1981.
▶Oliwenstein, Lori. "Medicine 1990," *Discover*, January 1991, pp. 80-83.

The Hippocratic Oath

Doctors traditionally take the Hippocratic Oath when graduating from medical school.

The Hippocratic Oath is so named for Hippocrates, a Greek physician who lived about 400 B.C. Notice how carefully it spells out the obligation of a doctor to guard the dignity and health of their patients no matter what their race, creed, or color.

I solemnly pledge myself to consecrate my life to the service of humanity;

I will give my teachers the respect and gratitude which is their due;

I will practice my profession with conscience and with dignity;

The health of my patient will be my first consideration;

I will respect the secrets which are confided in me;

I will maintain by all the means in my power, the honor and the noble traditions of the medical profession;

My colleagues will be my brothers;

I will not let considerations of religion, nationality or race, party politics or social standing to intervene between my duty and my patient;

I will maintain the utmost respect for human life from time of conception; even under threat I will not use my medical knowledge contrary to the laws of humanity;

I make these promises solemnly, freely, and upon my honor.

In Your Own Words

▶Write an essay on the lessons in the Hippocratic Oath for everyone, not just doctors.

UNIT

8 ECOLOGY

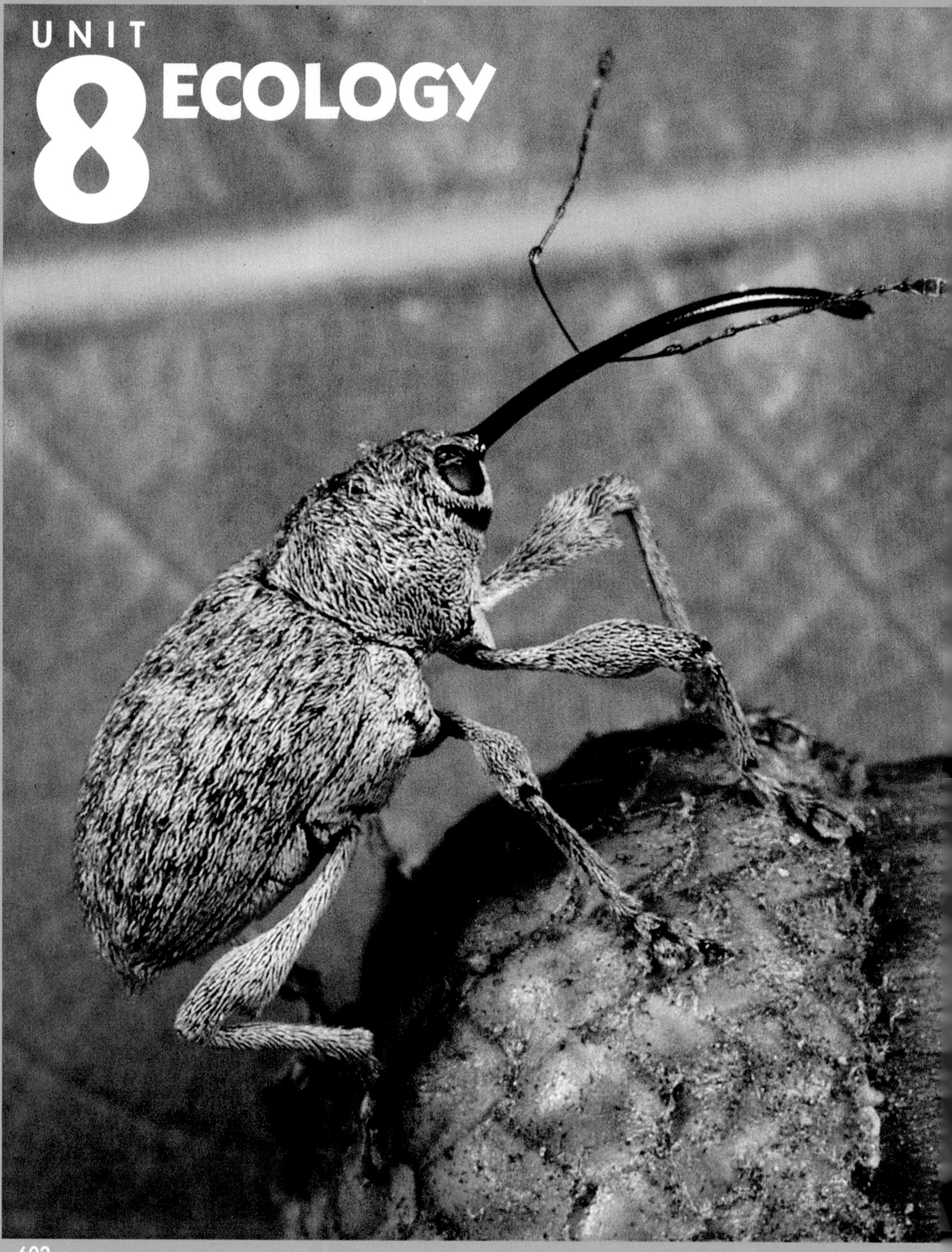

What's Happening Here?

Mighty oak trees grow from acorns like these, but not all acorns become trees. As acorns ripen and fall off the tree, many become food for bears, deer, and mice. Squirrels, magpies, and jays bury acorns as winter approaches. Some acorns are attacked by acorn weevils that drill holes through the hulls to feed and lay their eggs. Once the acorn is damaged, other organisms move in. Filbert worm moths use the holes made by the weevils to lay their own eggs. When their larvae hatch, they eat their way out. Green fungi invade and decay accelerates. Maggots and springtails arrive to eat the fungi. What's in a nutshell? Life!

UNIT CONTENTS

Chapter 26   Organisms and Their
              Environments
Chapter 27   Biomes
Chapter 28   Resources and the Environment

CHAPTER 26 Organisms and Their Environments

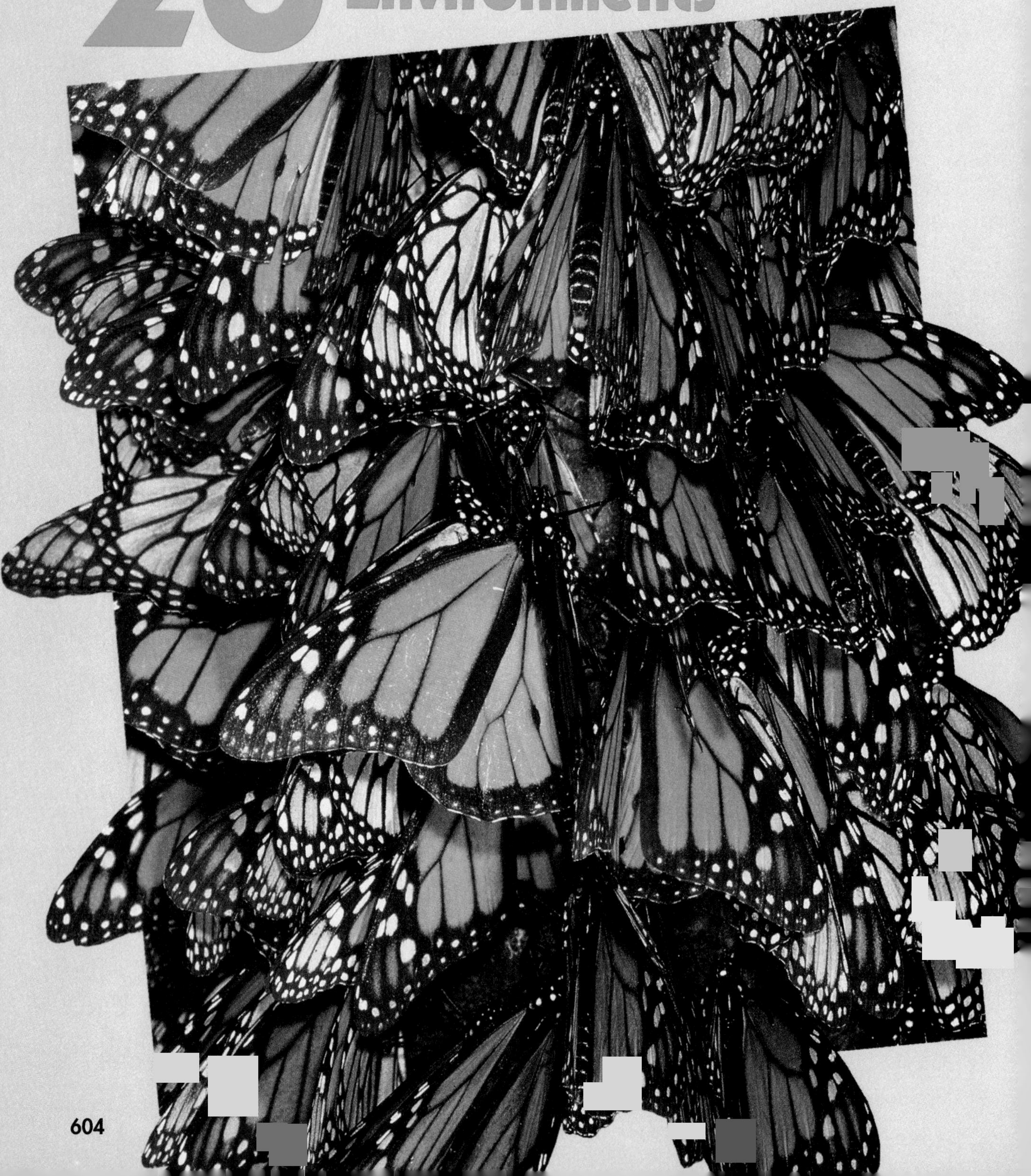

Animals such as butterflies and ladybird beetles often live in large groups. They share space, food, and nesting sites. How does the number of individuals in a group affect each organism? You share your science classroom with other individuals. How much space does each person have in your science classroom?

FIND OUT!

Do this simple activity to find out how much space each person has in your classroom.

Use a meterstick to measure the length and width of the classroom. Multiply the length times the width to find the area in square meters. Count the number of individuals in your class. Divide the number of square meters in the classroom by the number of individuals. How much space does each person have? Suppose your class size doubled. How much space would each person have then?

Gearing Up

Previewing the Chapter

Use this outline to help you focus on important ideas in this chapter.

Section 26-1   Organisms and Their Environments
▶ What Is the Biosphere?
▶ Populations
▶ Communities
▶ Ecosystems

Section 26-2   Biotic Relationships
▶ Feeding Relationships
▶ Symbiotic Relationships in a Community
▶ The Transfer of Energy in a Community

Section 26-3   Abiotic Factors in the Biosphere
▶ Cycles of Matter
▶ The Water Cycle
▶ The Carbon-Oxygen Cycle
▶ The Nitrogen Cycle

Section 26-4   Science and Society Friendly Fires
▶ Are Forest Fires Always Bad?

Previewing Science Skills

▶ In the **Skill Builders,** you will observe and infer, interpret scientific illustrations, and sequence.
▶ In the **Activities,** you will predict, count, sample, observe, record, and use field guides.
▶ In the **MINI-Labs,** you will list, identify, use scientific illustrations and classify.

What's next?

Now you know that the number of individuals in a population determines the amount of space each has. In this chapter you'll learn about populations and how organisms and environments interact.

Organisms and Their Environments

New Science Words

biosphere
ecology
biotic factors
abiotic factors
population
population density
community
habitat
niche
ecosystem

Objectives

▶ Identify the biotic and abiotic factors in the biosphere.
▶ Describe the characteristics of populations.
▶ Compare a species' habitat and its niche within a community.

What Is the Biosphere?

Deep in the Pacific Ocean is a region where the continental plates are moving apart. As these plates pull apart, volcanic rocks and lava seep into the resulting cracks, or rifts, from beneath Earth's crust. Water near this rift zone heats up, rises, cools, and falls, creating small areas of nutrient-rich warmth in the pitch black, freezing cold waters. Few organisms are found in such waters 2.5 kilometers below the sea's surface. But in these waters the crew of a tiny submarine called *ALVIN* made a discovery that astounded scientists worldwide. An entire community of organisms was found living in darkness near the rift. The community included clams, crabs, mussels, and bacteria. With no sunlight available for photosynthesis, these bacteria produce food by chemical synthesis. About 20 of these deep ocean rift communities have now been identified in this newly discovered part of the living world.

Figure 26-1. *ALVIN'S* crew photographed organisms living without light in the rift zone deep in the Pacific Ocean.

Deep ocean rift communities and all the parts of Earth where life is found make up the **biosphere** (BI uh sfihr). The biosphere extends from the deepest oceans to the upper atmosphere and includes all the air, land, and water where life exists. Within the biosphere, all living things depend upon and interact with each other and with the nonliving things in their environment. The study of interactions between organisms and their environments is called **ecology** (ih KAHL uh jee). Living things such as plants and animals in the environment are called **biotic** (bi AHT ihk) **factors.** Nonliving things in the envi-

Science and READING

In Arizona, there is a new ecological project called Biosphere II. Report to the class on what Biosphere II is.

ronment, such as soil, water, temperature, air, light, wind, and minerals, are **abiotic** (ay bi AHT ihk) **factors.**

Look at the pond in Figure 26-2. The abiotic factors include the pond's water, the soil at the pond bottom, and the temperatures of the air and water. The amount of light available for photosynthesis and the minerals dissolved in the water also are abiotic factors. What organisms make up the biotic factors in the pond? Monerans, protists, fungi, plants, and animals are the biotic factors.

Each species in the pond makes up a population. All of the populations in the pond make up the pond community. Together, the pond community and the abiotic factors make up an ecological system, or ecosystem. You'll learn more about populations, communities, and ecosystems in the following sections.

Figure 26-2. Biotic and abiotic factors work together in ecological systems like this pond.

PROBLEM SOLVING

The Milk Carton Garden

Paulo was disappointed. He was eager to start his spring vegetable garden, but the weather forecaster predicted cold temperatures for at least another week.

Because he couldn't plant outside due to the cold temperatures, he decided to plant some bean seeds inside and transplant the seedlings when the weather warmed up.

Paulo cut the top off a 0.5-liter milk carton and filled it with nutrient-rich soil. He planted 25 seeds in the carton, placed it on a window ledge in a sunny area, and kept the soil moistened. After ten days, the bean plants had sprouted and seemed to be growing well. But, after three weeks, the plants had tall, thin stems and yellowish leaves. Several plants had withered and

died. What should Paulo have done to take care of the plants?

Think Critically: Explain why the plants were healthy when they sprouted but were unhealthy after three weeks.

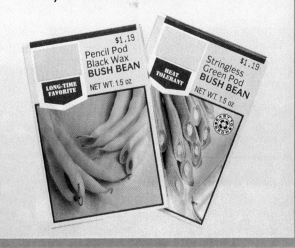

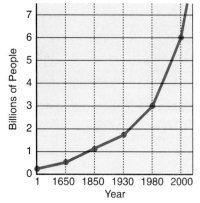

Figure 26-3. The world's population size changes over time.

Populations

Have you ever gone for a walk at dusk and noticed birds lined up on a telephone wire as shown in Figure 26-4? These birds all live together in the same place at the same time; they make up a population. All the people living in your town, the flocks of geese on a pond, and the worms in the soil under a baseball diamond each represent a population. A **population** consists of organisms of one species living together in the same place at the same time.

Populations are described according to certain characteristics. The number of individuals in a given area is called **population density.** In the chapter opening activity, you found how much space each student had in your classroom. To find the population density, you must divide the area by the number of individuals in the area (density = individuals/unit area).

Another characteristic of populations is spacing. Spacing is how individuals are arranged in an area. They may be arranged evenly, like the birds on the wire, unevenly, or in random clumps. Figure 26-4 shows the types of spacing found in populations.

Size is an important characteristic of populations. The size of a population is constantly changing as individuals move into and out of a community. Populations also change when new individuals are born and when older individuals die. The total size of a population can be determined by studying these changes over time. The United States Census Bureau uses information such as this to determine the size of the human population in the United States every ten years. Figure 26-3 shows how population size changes over time.

a

b

c

Figure 26-4. Spacing in populations varies from even (a), to uneven (b), to random clumps (c).

ACTIVITY 26-1
Counting Populations

Problem: *How can you determine the size of a population?*

Materials
- permanent marker
- clear plastic sheet

Procedure
1. Predict the number of ladybird beetles below and record the number in a table like the one shown.
2. Place a clear plastic sheet over the diagram. Make a population count by placing a check mark next to each ladybird beetle. Record the actual number of beetles in the table. Next to this number, record the amount of time it took to make the count.
3. Count the ladybird beetle population a second time by sampling. A sample is made by selecting and counting only a portion of the population. Count the number of ladybird beetles in the top left square and record this number in the table.
4. Enter the total number of squares in the table. Multiply the number of ladybird beetles in the top left square by the total number of squares. Record this estimated total number in the table.
5. At the top of the table, record the amount of time it took to make the sample count.

Data and Observations

Predicted number	Time	

Number in top left square	×	Total number of squares	=	Estimated total number
	×		=	

Actual number	Time	

Analyze
1. What was the difference between predicted and actual numbers of ladybird beetles?
2. How many ladybird beetles did you estimate were shown?
3. Which was was faster—making an actual count or sampling?
4. Were the results about the same?

Conclude and Apply
5. What is the advantage of sampling a population for counting?
6. What is an easy way to determine the size of a population?

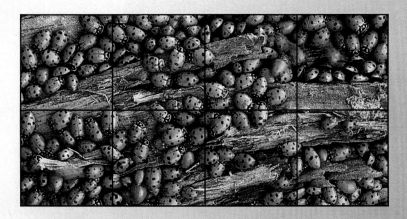

Communities

Hundreds of populations of organisms make up the oak-hickory forest community shown in Figure 26-6. A **community** is made up of all the populations of different species that live in the same place at the same time. In a community, a few species are usually more abundant than others. These species are called dominant species.

The oak and hickory trees are the dominant species in the community shown in Figure 26-6. When their leaves open in the spring, they create so much shade that plants underneath the trees cannot grow. In the autumn, their leaves fall and provide food for bacteria, fungi, and worms on the forest floor. Many other organisms eat the acorns and nuts produced by the trees. The tree trunks and branches are homes for insects, birds, squirrels, lichens, and other organisms. All the populations in this forest community depend on one another for survival.

The place where an organism lives in a community is its **habitat.** Squirrels live in the trees in the forest. You would probably find crayfish, minnows, and other organisms living in the streams in the forest. Water is the habitat of these organisms. What is your habitat?

No two species have exactly the same needs or role in a community. The role of a species within a community is its **niche** (NIHCH). What a species eats, how it gets its food, and how it interacts with other organisms are all part of its niche. You may have seen many birds at a bird feeder in the park. Sparrows, doves, and cardinals all feed on birdseed—but not necessarily the same kinds of seeds. Two different species can occupy the same habitat, but they usually cannot occupy the same niche. Figure 26-5 shows how three bird species can live in one tree and still occupy very different niches.

To compare a community, a habitat, and a niche, we can look at the floor of the oak-hickory forest community. When a termite lives on and eats the wood of a fallen tree, the tree is the termite's habitat. Breaking down the parts of the dead tree is the termite's niche within the community.

What is a community?

Figure 26-5. Although all three warblers feed in the same spruce tree, they occupy very different niches.

Bay-breasted warbler

Cape May warbler

Myrtle warbler

What is a niche?

Figure 26-6. In an oak-hickory forest, oaks and hickories are the dominant species.

Ecosystems

An oak-hickory forest community is one type of ecosystem. A coral reef such as the one shown in Figure 26-7 is another type of ecosystem. A coral reef is composed of corals, sponges, sea stars, sea anemones, clown fish, trigger fish, groupers, algae, clams, mussels, oysters, and many other organisms. The ocean water, with its currents, temperature, and salinity, affects all of the organisms living on or near the coral reef. The amount of sunlight reaching the reef helps determine how much food the plantlike protists produce, and it affects those organisms that eat the protists. Together, these biotic and abiotic factors interact and function as an ecosystem. An **ecosystem** is a community interacting with the abiotic parts of its environment. Ecosystems may be as small as the acorn you studied in the unit opener, or as large as the Pacific Ocean. There are some very large natural ecosystems, such as forests, on Earth. You will learn about these ecosystems in Chapter 27.

Figure 26-7. All of the organisms living on or near this coral reef are part of the community that interacts with the ocean water to form this ecosystem.

What is an ecosystem?

SECTION REVIEW

1. Name five biotic and five abiotic factors in the biosphere.
2. What are three characteristics of populations?
3. Describe the difference between a population and a community.
4. How are niches and habitats different ?
5. **Apply:** Ecosystems such as coral reefs are in a delicate balance. Hypothesize what would happen to that balance if one abiotic factor such as amount of sunlight suddenly changed.

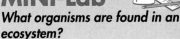

MINI-Lab

What organisms are found in an ecosystem?
Choosing an ecosystem you are familiar with, such as a stream, garden plot, or pond, identify the organisms found there. Make a list of all the populations you can see in the ecosystem. What is the niche of each species in the community?

☑ Observing and Inferring

Each person lives in a population as part of a community. Describe your population, community, habitat, and niche. (HINT: You may belong to more than one of each!) If you need help, refer to Observing and Inferring in the **Skill Handbook** on page 682.

Skill Builder

Biotic Relationships

New Science Words

competition
camouflage
mimicry
food chain
food web
energy pyramid

EcoTip

Raise praying mantises from egg cases and release them in flower beds and gardens. They control pest insects naturally.

Figure 26-8. Desert organisms compete with one another for food, water, and living space.

Objectives

▶ Identify kinds of relationships organisms have with each other.
▶ Describe food chains and food webs in a community.
▶ Explain how energy is transferred through a community.

Feeding Relationships

What are the biotic factors in a desert such as the one shown in Figure 26-8? Many desert animals burrow underground for protection from the sun, only venturing out after dark. The plants are cacti and other plants with leaves modified into needles to conserve water. In the desert ecosystem, the amounts of food, water, and nutrients are limited, yet the amounts of sunlight and living space are not. Many desert organisms have adapted to life under these conditions. Birds nest in cacti, whereas rodents burrow in the sand. Snakes and lizards, turtles, and many kinds of insects can be found in deserts. All of these organisms have relationships with one another. The relationships among living things are biotic relationships. Many biotic relationships are feeding relationships. These relationships include competition for resources and predator-prey relationships.

In the desert and in every other ecosystem, organisms compete for the same food, water, living space, and other resources. **Competition** is the contest among organisms to obtain all they need to survive. Competition determines the size and location of populations, and can occur between members of the same species. Members of one species often compete for nesting sites, mates, or feeding spots. Two robins will fight over one worm in the spring! If the competition is too strong, individuals may move into less populated areas.

Another kind of competition takes place between two different species. Both the owl and the fox catch and eat mice. Suppose half of the mouse population in a field suddenly died from a disease. What would happen to the owl and the fox? As long as there is a large mouse population, the owl and the fox can live in the same community. But they become competitors for food when the mouse population is reduced. In this case, the owl and the fox become competitors because they occupy the same niche—consumer of mice as food. Two organisms cannot occupy the same niche for long because one will eventually push the other out of that niche. In our example, the owl and the fox both feed on a wide variety of food organisms, so a smaller mouse population probably won't result in death for either. However, the owl and the fox will continue to compete for the remaining food sources in the community.

One important feeding relationship found in communities is the predator-prey relationship. In the oak-hickory forest community, owls and foxes are the predators, and mice are the prey. Animals that are prey can avoid being eaten by hiding, escaping, or defending themselves against predators. **Camouflage** is an adaptation that allows an animal to hide by blending into its surroundings. Insects such as the thorn bug in Figure 26-9 often can't be seen until they move.

Another defense against predators is mimicry. In **mimicry,** an animal copies the appearance or behavior of another organism.

Figure 26-9. Insects such as thorn bugs, leaf bugs, and stick insects resemble real thorns, leaves, and sticks.

Figure 26-10. Birds learn not to eat monarch butterflies because they contain bad-tasting chemicals. Viceroys are protected by their resemblence to monarchs. Birds avoid viceroys, too.

Symbiotic Relationships in a Community

What is symbiosis?

Figure 26-11. The oxpecker and the water buffalo have a symbiotic relationship.

In Figure 26-11, a bird called the oxpecker is eating insects that feed on the water buffalo. When two or more species live together, their relationship is called symbiosis. Symbiotic relationships provide food, shelter, support, or transportation for one or both organisms. Mutualism and parasitism are two types of symbiotic relationships.

Mutualism is a symbiotic relationship in which two organisms live together and both benefit. The water buffalo and the oxpecker both benefit from their mutualistic relationship.

Parasitism is a relationship in which one organism, the parasite, is helped while the other organism, the host, is harmed. The parasite usually lives on or in the host and absorbs nutrients from the body fluids of the host. Tapeworms live as parasites in the intestines of mammals. Mistletoe is a plant that lives as a parasite on trees.

The Transfer of Energy in a Community

Many of the interactions that you have just studied are feeding relationships. Energy in food is transferred through a community by a **food chain.** In the oak-hickory forest, the trees and other producers change the energy of sunlight into chemical energy that is stored in plant leaves, stems, roots, and seeds. Consumers living in the forest community feed on these plant parts. Other consumers, such as predators, feed on these plant consumers. Decomposers break down waste materials and dead plants and animals to get energy. Food chains are a way to describe how the energy in food moves through the biotic community.

The simple food chain in Figure 26-12 includes the plants, the rabbit, and the hawk.

There are many food chains within a community. A consumer often feeds in a variety of food chains. Hawks, foxes, and owls all are predators that eat mice and rabbits. Mice and birds eat grains and seeds, whereas rabbits and deer both eat grass. All of these organisms feed in several food chains that overlap. A series of overlapping food chains is called a **food web.** The organisms in a food web eat or are eaten by many organisms.

Figure 26-12. A simple food chain includes a producer, a herbivore, and a carnivore.

Producers are the first link in any food chain. The producers provide food for themselves and the whole community. Grass, hay, and oats are examples of producers. Producers are the organisms that convert sunlight, carbon dioxide, and water into sugar and oxygen during photosynthesis. Plant-eating consumers, the herbivores, eat green plants and change some of the food stored in plants to the energy they need for life activities. Grasshoppers are herbivores that eat grass seeds. Herbivores, in turn, are eaten by meat-eating consumers, the carnivores. Woodpeckers eat grasshoppers. Some carnivores are then eaten by other carnivores. Woodpeckers, for example, are eaten by hawks. In some food webs, consumers eat both plants and animals. Consumers that eat both plants and animals are omnivores. Humans, bears, and raccoons are omnivores.

The flow of energy from grass seeds to hawks can be shown in a diagram called an **energy pyramid,** as shown

What is a food web?

MINI-Lab

What are the requirements of ecosystems?

Using the pictures in Figure 26-13, list all of the living things pictured. Put them into categories: produers, consumers, herbivores, carnivores, omnivores. Next, list all the abiotic factors you can think of that are needed for these organisms to survive.

Figure 26-13. A Food Web

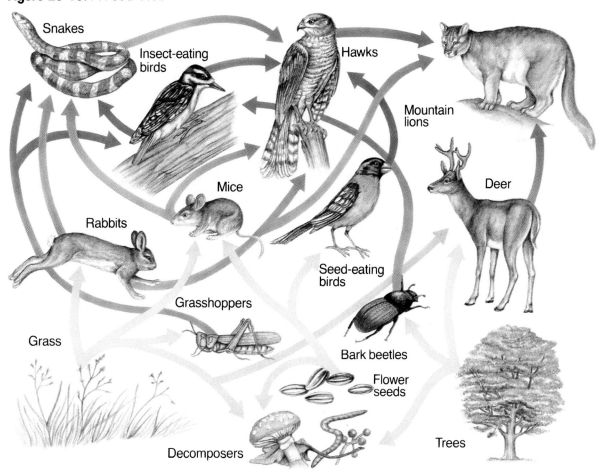

What is an energy pyramid?

in Figure 26-14. Notice that there are many more producers than herbivores, and many more herbivores than carnivores. Why do you think this is so? Less energy is available at each level of the pyramid as you move toward the top. Even though grasshoppers eat a lot of grass seed, they can't use all of the energy stored in grass seeds. In fact, only about ten percent of the energy in grass seed is available to the grasshopper. Only ten percent of the energy stored in the grasshopper is available to the woodpecker, and so on. The animals at the top of the energy pyramid depend on very large populations of producers and herbivores to stay alive.

Energy pyramids are one way to show the relationships of organisms in communities. A pyramid of numbers shows how many individuals an ecosystem can support. In the example shown in Figure 26-14, a pyramid of numbers would include 175 grass seeds, 40 grasshoppers, 5 woodpeckers, and 1 hawk. Pyramids of numbers may look different from energy pyramids. One tree may support thousands of insects. What would a pyramid of numbers look like if it included one tree and one thousand insects?

Figure 26-14. An energy pyramid usually has three or four levels. Why aren't there more levels in an energy pyramid?

SECTION REVIEW

1. Describe three relationships among organisms in a community.
2. Name and describe two examples of symbiosis.
3. Explain how a food chain is part of a food web.
4. **Apply:** Why are there more producers in an ecosystem than consumers?

Skill Builder

☑ Interpreting Scientific Illustrations

Use the energy pyramid diagram above to explain the flow of energy through a pond community. If you need help, refer to Interpreting Scientific Illustrations in the **Skill Handbook** on page 693.

Abiotic Factors in the Biosphere

Objectives

▶ Describe how materials in the biosphere are reused in a continuous cycle.

▶ Diagram the cycles of water, carbon, oxygen, and nitrogen in the biosphere.

▶ Discuss the importance of recycling these materials in the biosphere.

New Science Words

water cycle
carbon-oxygen cycle
nitrogen cycle

Cycles of Matter

Figure 26-15 shows fungi growing on a fallen tree. Fungi are decomposers. When decomposers break down waste materials and dead organisms for energy, they return carbon, oxygen, nitrogen, and other materials to the biosphere. Producers reuse these materials to make more food that is eaten by consumers. You know that energy is used as it moves through a food chain. Unlike energy, the chemical elements that make up all organisms are used over and over again. Organisms today are using the same materials that have been used since life began. Each time a substance is used, decomposed, and returned to the environment, a cycle is completed. In a cycle, the last step brings the process back to its starting point, and the cycle occurs again and again. In the biosphere, the most important materials to life on Earth are recycled. These materials are water, oxygen, carbon, and nitrogen.

Figure 26-15. Decomposers like these fungi break down dead organisms and help cycle oxygen, nitrogen, and carbon in the biosphere.

Figure 26-16. Water cycles through evaporation, condensation, and precipitation.

The Water Cycle

The continuous movement of water in the biosphere is called the **water cycle.** Trace the steps of the water cycle in Figure 26-16 as you read. The sun's energy causes some of the water in soil, oceans, lakes, rivers, and living organisms to evaporate and become water vapor in the air. As the water vapor in the air cools, it condenses and changes to water droplets and forms clouds. The water from the

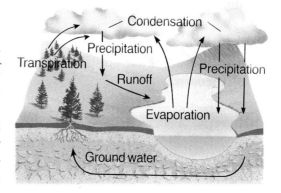

Condensation

Precipitation

Transpiration

Runoff

Precipitation

Evaporation

Ground water

Figure 26-17. In the carbon-oxygen cycle, carbon and oxen are recycled continuously during photosynthesis and respiration.

CO₂

Photosynthesis releases O₂

O₂

CO₂   CO₂   O₂

O₂

Respiration releases CO₂   CO₂

clouds returns to Earth as precipitation in the form of rain, snow, sleet, or hail. Then the cycle starts over again. You could describe the water cycle as three steps: evaporation, condensation, and precipitation.

The Carbon-Oxygen Cycle

Many other materials in the biosphere are part of cycles. The continuous movement of carbon dioxide and oxygen between the surface of Earth and the air is called the **carbon-oxygen cycle.** You can follow the carbon-oxygen cycle in Figure 26-17. During the process of photosynthesis, plants absorb carbon dioxide from the air and release oxygen. Plants, animals, and most other organisms use oxygen for respiration. Carbon dioxide is given off and returned to the cycle. Decomposers break down the carbon compounds in dead organisms and wastes and release carbon dioxide to the air. Organisms that do not decay are compressed underground. Over millions of years, they form fossil fuels such as coal, oil, and gas. When these fuels are burned, carbon dioxide again enters the air.

T E C H N O L O G Y

Monitoring Mayflies

The source of water pollution in streams is hard to detect because the pollutants are diluted by water. Pollutants concentrate in fish tissue, which makes detection easier, but fish move too much to be helpful in detecting the source of water pollution.

In a process called biomonitoring, scientists now evaluate the health of streams by looking at the organisms that live there. Macroinvertebrates, such as mayflies, caddisflies, and stoneflies, remain in one location and have differing tolerances to pollution. Scientists collect samples of organisms from the stream bed and count the

kinds and numbers of macroinvertebrates found. Mayflies are very sensitive to pollution. Large numbers of these show a healthy stream. Aquatic earthworms and midges tolerate pollution, so streams with more of these organisms may be in trouble!

Think Critically: Most macroinvertebrates live less than a year. Why is this trait useful in biomonitoring?

The Nitrogen Cycle

Nitrogen is an important material needed by living things to make proteins. Even though nitrogen gas makes up 78 percent of the atmosphere, most living organisms cannot use nitrogen in this form. Nitrogen has to be combined with other elements in a process called nitrogen fixation. You can see in Figure 26-18 that nitrogen is converted into usable nitrogen compounds by bacteria associated with plants. A small amount is changed into nitrogen compounds by lightning. The transfer of nitrogen from the atmosphere, to plants, and back to the atmosphere or directly into plants again is the **nitrogen cycle.**

Phosphorus, sulfur, and other elements needed by living organisms are also used and returned to the environment. Just as we save aluminum, glass, and paper products to be reused, the materials that organisms need to live are recycled continuously in the biosphere.

Figure 26-18. Nitrogen can be cycled from bacteria on plant roots to plants, then to animals, and directly back to plants again as a result of decomposition.

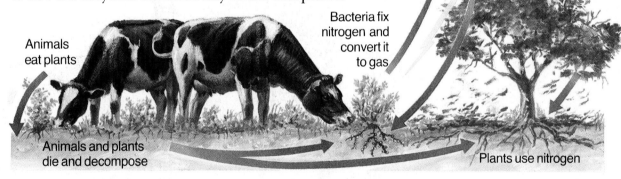

Atmospheric nitrogen converted by lightning

Bacteria fix nitrogen and convert it to gas

Animals eat plants

Animals and plants die and decompose

Plants use nitrogen

SECTION REVIEW

1. Describe how materials move through the biosphere.
2. What are the steps of the water cycle?
3. Describe the nitrogen cycle.
4. Explain the relationship between the cycling of oxygen and the cycling of carbon in the biosphere.
5. **Apply:** Do you think that fossil fuels are still being formed today? Why?

☑ Sequencing

Sequence the steps in the carbon-oxygen cycle. If you need help, refer to Sequencing in the **Skill Handbook** on page 680.

Skill Builder

26-4 Friendly Fires

New Science Words

controlled burns

Objectives

▶ Describe the role of controlled fires in forests and why the fires are controversial.
▶ Identify reasons both for and against the use of controlled burns in areas where people live.

Are Forest Fires Always Bad?

What comes to your mind first when you think of forest fires? You may think about animals such as deer running terrified through the forest, or blackened stumps of trees and scorched ground where nothing can grow. A burned forest looks so stark and damaged, it seems it will never be the same again. What most of us don't realize is that some forests actually require such fires to maintain their character. Some pine species have evolved ways to cope with periods of fire. Jack pine and lodgepole pine trees have cones that don't open to release seeds until they have been heated in a fire!

In some types of forests, biologists conduct **controlled burns,** managed forest fires that are set periodically to control the amount of vegetation underneath the dominant forest tree species. In areas where natural fires don't occur, deep piles of dead leaves, dropped needles, and dead brush build up on the forest floor. All of this dead organic matter becomes potential fuel if a fire should start. To make sure that this organic matter doesn't build up too much, biologists sometimes start small fires to burn up the material on the forest floor. This is one way biologists hope to prevent major forest fires.

What happens to the forest animals during a controlled burn? Researchers contend that wild animals are unharmed because they move away from areas on fire. Some animals, such as the rare red-cockaded woodpecker, depend upon fires to maintain their habitat. They live in open pine stands that are often invaded by hardwood trees. Fires help to keep the hardwoods from growing in the open spaces between the pines.

Controlled burns are usually less intense and produce less heat than uncontrolled forest fires. This is another reason researchers feel that it is better to have a few controlled fires periodically than a large, out-of-control fire. However, even controlled burns sometimes cause damage to areas outside of the intended area of the burn. If the wind shifts suddenly, a fire may race toward residential areas instead of staying in the forest. Homes and businesses have burned to the ground from controlled fires as well as natural forest fires. Controlled burns also result in air pollution from smoke, and newly burned areas are eyesores to those who live nearby. It may take a few years for the burned areas to begin growing again. In the meantime, local residents see damaged forest views every day.

Biologists are very careful to set fires only at times when wind conditions are right. But people who live near national forests and parks still are concerned over the need for controlled burns. They believe controlled burns are not "controlled" at all. They also aren't convinced that forest animals are unharmed as a result of these fires.

Figure 26-19. The red-cockaded woodpecker is one organism that depends on fires to maintain its habitat.

SECTION REVIEW

1. Name two reasons why biologists believe controlled forest fires are useful.
2. Why are local citizens often opposed to such fires?

You Decide!

In popular vacation spots, people often build homes in scenic areas, such as high on a ridge top. Such spots are often in forested areas that are subject to uncontrollable forest fires. Many of these vacation homes are in locations that are difficult for forest firefighters to reach. Should people be permitted to build homes in these areas?

SCIENCE & SOCIETY

ACTIVITY 26-2
Studying an Ecosystem

Problem: *How do you study an ecosystem?*

Materials

- graph paper
- notebook
- pencil
- binoculars
- field guides
- hand lens

Procedure

1. Choose a natural community near your school or home to be your ecosystem for study. You may choose to study a pond, a forest area in a park, a rotten log, or an area around your school.
2. Decide the boundaries of the ecosystem you are studying. Make the ecosystem a size you think you can study well.
3. Make a map or drawing of the ecosystem on graph paper.
4. Observe the organisms that live in the ecosystem. Use a hand lens to study small creatures. Use binoculars to study organisms you cannot get near. Look for evidence, such as tracks or feathers, of organisms you cannot see.
5. Record your observations in a table like the one shown. Make drawings. Use field guides to identify the organisms.

6. Visit the ecosystem as many times as you can and at different times of day for four weeks. Make observations and record them. Pay close attention to the relationships among organisms. Also note how the organisms interact with the nonliving environment.

Data and Observations

Date	Organisms Observed	Comments

Analyze

1. What is the ecosystem you chose?
2. Describe the nonliving environment of the ecosystem.
3. How many populations did you count?
4. Which organisms in the ecosystem are producers, consumers, or decomposers?
5. What evidence of competition did you find?

Conclude and Apply

6. Make a diagram that represents a food web for the ecosystem.
7. What might happen if a population of producers was removed from the community?
8. What might happen if either the predators or the decomposers were removed from the community?
9. What relationships can you identify among the organisms in the ecosystem, such as predator-prey, mutualism, or parasitism?
10. Explain how the nonliving environment is important in the ecosystem.
11. What might happen if the nonliving environment changed suddenly?
12. How do you study an ecosystem?

CHAPTER
REVIEW

26-1: Organisms and Their Environments

1. The biosphere is the part of Earth where all life is found, and it consists of biotic (living) factors as well as abiotic (nonliving) factors such as air, soil, water, and sunlight.

2. Populations are made up of all the members of a species living in the same place at the same time. A community includes all the populations of the area. The community and the abiotic factors make up the ecosystem.

3. An organism lives in its habitat within a community. The role or job of an organism within a community is its niche.

26-2: Biotic Relationships

1. Organisms have relationships with each other. These relationships include feeding relationships and symbiotic relationships.

2. Energy in food is transferred through a community in food chains. Overlapping food chains are food webs. Organisms are part of many food chains or webs in a community.

3. Energy stored in food moves through the community from producers to consumers to decomposers. At each level only a small amount of the energy consumed is available to the next level of organism.

26-3: Abiotic Factors in the Biosphere

1. Materials in the biosphere are cycled in order for organisms to survive.

2. Water, carbon, oxygen, and nitrogen are recycled in the environment.

3. Many of the materials needed by organisms are recycled.

26-4: Science and Society: Friendly Fires

1. Controlled forest fires are set to reduce the risk of uncontrolled fires.

2. Even controlled fires may become uncontrolled and damage areas where people live.

KEY SCIENCE WORDS

a. **abiotic factors**
b. **biosphere**
c. **biotic factors**
d. **camouflage**
e. **carbon-oxygen cycle**
f. **community**
g. **competition**
h. **controlled burns**
i. **ecology**
j. **ecosystem**
k. **energy pyramid**
l. **food chain**
m. **food web**
n. **habitat**
o. **mimicry**
p. **niche**
q. **nitrogen cycle**
r. **population**
s. **population density**
t. **water cycle**

UNDERSTANDING VOCABULARY

Match each phrase with the correct term from the list of Key Science Words.

1. living things in the environment
2. number of organisms in an area
3. all parts of Earth with life
4. job of a species in an environment
5. the cycle that includes evaporation, condensation, and precipitation
6. copying another organism's behavior or appearance
7. all the populations in an ecosystem
8. interaction of abiotic and biotic factors
9. series of overlapping food chains
10. where an organism lives in an ecosystem

CHAPTER
REVIEW

CHECKING CONCEPTS

Choose the word or phrase that completes the sentence.

1. All are abiotic factors except _____.
   a. animals   c. sunlight
   b. air   d. soil

2. Examples of ecosystems include _____.
   a. a coral reef
   b. an oak-hickory forest
   c. the Pacific Ocean
   d. all of these

3. The _____ is made up of all populations in an area.
   a. niche   c. community
   b. habitat   d. dominant species

4. Organisms can defend themselves against predators by _____.
   a. hiding   c. camouflage
   b. mimicry   d. all of these

5. An example of a consumer is _____.
   a. carnivore c. herbivore
   b. omnivore   d. all of these

6. In an ecosystem, _____ get the most energy.
   a. omnivores   c. decomposers
   b. herbivores d. producers

7. _____ is a relationship in which one organism is helped and the other harmed.
   a. Mutualism   c. Mimicry
   b. Parasitism d. None of these

8. A process directly involved in the carbon-oxygen cycle is _____.
   a. photosynthesis c. respiration
   b. burning fuel   d. all of these

9. Materials that are cycled in the biosphere include _____.
   a. nitrogen   c. phosphorus
   b. sulfur   d. all of these

10. Controlled burns of forests are needed _____.
    a. for normal growth   c. to thin out brush
    b. to improve habitats d. all of these

UNDERSTANDING CONCEPTS

Complete each sentence.

11. The _____ is the part of Earth where all life is formed.
12. _____ is food for a predator.
13. Hiding by blending into the environment is called _____.
14. _____ is a relationship beneficial to both organisms.
15. Dead organisms are broken down by _____.

THINK AND WRITE CRITICALLY

16. What would be the advantages to humans if they ate food lower on the food chain?
17. Use Figure 26-7 on page 611 and describe two food chains of the coral reef ecosystem.
18. Explain how biotic relationships help organisms survive.
19. Describe what species compete for in an ecosystem.
20. Explain the advantages of a mutualistic relationship by using an example.

APPLY

21. Explain the changes that would occur in biotic relationships if the density of a population increased dramatically.
22. A maggot grows within a gall formed on the goldenrod plant, eventually maturing and emerging as a fly while the goldenrod dies. What kind of relationship is this?

23. What would happen to an ecosystem if decomposers were removed?
24. Explain why energy flow is described as a pyramid.
25. Explain how photosynthesis and respiration are opposite reactions in the carbon-oxygen cycle.

MORE SKILL BUILDERS

If you need help, refer to the Skill Handbook.

1. **Classifying:** Classify each as producer, herbivore, carnivore, or omnivore: cow, deer, grass, shark, rabbit, bear, green algae, lion, sunflower.

2. **Graphing:** Use the following data to graph the density of a deer population over the years. Plot the number of deer on the y-axis and years on the x-axis. Explain what may have happened to change the population density.

Year	Deer (in thousands) per 400 hectares
1905	5.7
1915	35.7
1920	142.9
1925	85.7
1935	25.7

3. **Concept Mapping:** Use this information to draw a food web of organisms living in a goldenrod field.

   Goldenrod - sap is eaten by aphids
   - nectar eaten by bees
   - pollen eaten by beetles
   - leaves eaten by beetles

Stinkbugs eat beetles
Spiders eat aphids
Assassin bugs eat bees

4. **Classifying:** Classify each event in the water cycle as the result of either precipitation or evaporation:
   a. A puddle is gone after the rain.
   b. Rain falls.
   c. Snow covers the mountainside.
   d. A lake becomes shallower.

5. **Concept Mapping:** Fill in the correct terms to show the nitrogen cycle.

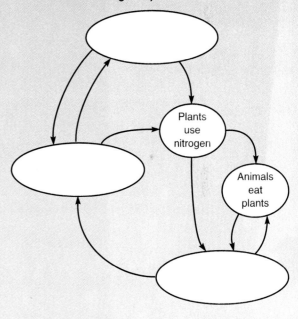

PROJECTS

1. Find out about the relationship between the cleaner wrasse and other, larger fish. Write a report about the relationship.
2. Research the phosphorus or sulfur cycle and draw a poster showing it.

CHAPTER

27 Biomes

Do you live in an area that has pine forests, mountains, and lakes? Do you live near the ocean? You know that all life exists in the biosphere. But do you know where in the biosphere you live?

FIND OUT!

Do this simple activity to find out what part of the biosphere you live in.

Look at a globe or a world map. Locate the country, state, and city where you live. What is the latitude of your state? Do you have four seasons each year? Locate the equator. Where do you live in relation to the equator? What is the climate where you live?

Gearing Up

Previewing the Chapter

Use this outline to help you focus on important ideas in this chapter.

Section 27-1   Factors That Affect Biomes
- ▶ Limiting Factors
- ▶ Succession

Section 27-2   Land Biomes
- ▶ Land Biomes
- ▶ Tundra
- ▶ Northern Coniferous Forests
- ▶ Deciduous Forests
- ▶ Grasslands
- ▶ Deserts
- ▶ Tropical Rain Forests

Section 27-3   Water Ecosystems
- ▶ Marine Ecosystems
- ▶ Freshwater Ecosystems

Section 27-4   Science and Society
Coastal Wetlands
- ▶ Wetlands or Wastelands?

Previewing Science Skills

- ▶ In the **Skill Builders**, you will hypothesize and make a concept map.
- ▶ In the **Activities**, you will study maps, observe, use a table, experiment and graph.
- ▶ In the **MINI-Labs**, you will hypothesize, compare and interpret data.

What's next?

Now that you have located where you live, learn how the climate, soil, and other abiotic factors of an area help determine what living things are found there and where they are located.

Factors That Affect Biomes

New Science Words

limiting factor
succession
primary succession
secondary succession
climax community

Objectives

▶ **Identify and describe limiting factors.**
▶ **Define *succession* and differentiate between primary and secondary succession.**
▶ **Describe climax communities.**

Limiting Factors

Have you ever seen a lobster like the one in Figure 27-1? Lobsters are found only in marine environments. The animal pictured below looks like a lobster, but it is a freshwater crayfish. What would happen to the lobster if you placed it in a freshwater stream? What would happen to the crayfish if you placed it in the ocean?

Most organisms live in a place that is, for them, the best place to live. Each species has adapted to a set of biotic and abiotic factors in its environment. Lobsters have adapted to a marine environment and cannot survive in fresh water. For lobsters, fresh water is a limiting factor. A **limiting factor** is a condition that determines the survival of an organism, population, or species in its environment. Any factor that limits the number, distribution, reproduction, or existence of organisms is a limiting factor. What are other limiting factors for the lobster?

In an oak-hickory forest, the mouse population is limited by the amount of thistle seed available for food, and the availability of mates and nesting sites. Competition among the mice for seeds, mates, or nesting sites, as well as predation by owls and hawks, are biotic factors that may limit the size of the mouse population. Abiotic factors that may become limiting include temperature, amount of sunlight, water, wind, elevation, or currents.

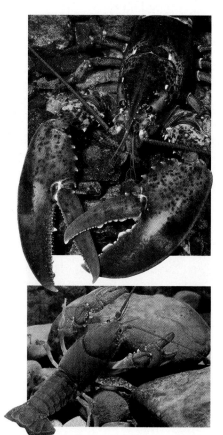

Figure 27-1. A lobster is adapted to a marine environment, whereas crayfish live in freshwater ecosystems.

Succession

Look at the field with scattered pine tree seedlings in Figure 27-2. In a few years, these seedlings will become trees, and eventually a pine forest will stand where the field is now. Birds, mice, squirrels, chipmunks, and many other animals and plants will grow in the forest. Seedlings of tree species such as oaks, hickories, and elms may begin to grow in the shade underneath the pines. As the pine trees mature and die, the forest may become an oak-hickory forest. This gradual change in a community over time is called **succession.** Succession occurs in a community in an orderly process. Ecologists have identified two types of succession: primary succession and secondary succession.

Primary Succession

On a volcanic island, lava flows out of the volcano, cools, and forms new land. Many islands were formed this way. Over time, dust and ash settle on the lava rocks. Soil particles, bacteria, pollen, spores, and plant seeds may be carried to the island by wind, birds, or water. Pioneer species such as mosses begin to grow and break down the rock. Dead plants add organic materials, and soil begins to form. Eventually plant communities develop, and animals that eat these plants move in. The volcanic island is undergoing primary succession. **Primary succession** is the development of new communities in newly created land areas. Volcanic islands, exposed coral reefs, and human-made ponds or reservoirs undergo primary succession. Primary succession may occur over hundreds or thousands of years.

Secondary Succession

The succession of a community is also disturbed by fire, floods, earthquakes, and human activities such as logging or mining. If the disturbed area is then abandoned or left alone, succession may begin again. A pasture abandoned by a farmer may be invaded by grasses, shrubs, and trees in a process called secondary succession. In **secondary succession,** a disturbed area gradually returns to its previous condition. After fires destroyed parts of Yellowstone National Park in 1988, new plants began to grow through the ashes on the forest floor. Ecologists are studying this case of secondary succession very carefully to see what organisms return to the disturbed areas, and in what order.

Figure 27-2. Succession in an open field begins with scattered pine seedlings. Years later the field is a pine forest, and eventually it becomes an oak-hickory forest.

What is secondary succession?

ACTIVITY 27-1
Interpreting a Map

Problem: *How do you use a hardiness zone map?*

Materials
- pencil and paper

Procedure
1. Study the hardiness zone map below. Hardiness zone maps show places of similar climates and vegetation type.
2. Examine the table under Data and Observations. This gives the northern limit to which some plants can live.
3. Use the map and the table to answer the questions that follow.

Data and Observations

Plant	Northern Zone Limit
White pine	2
Forsythia	2
Azalea	3
Rhododendron	2
Pyracantha	4
Chinese holly	3
Passion flower	5 and 6

Analyze
1. In which zone do you live?
2. Which zone crosses the most states?
3. Which plants grow the farthest north?
4. Which plants cannot grow in Canada?
5. What are the states in zone 6?

Conclude and Apply
6. Could people living in Ontario use azaleas in their landscapes?
7. Could Chinese holly grow in Oklahoma?
8. How would a gardener use the map?
9. How do you use a hardiness zone map?

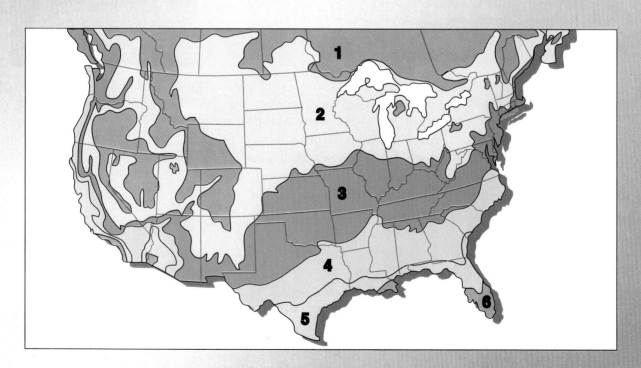

Climax Community

What do a pine forest, oak-hickory forest, and desert have in common? Any of these ecosystems may be the final stage of succession in a particular area on Earth. Succession in any one place continues until it reaches a stage where the same species continue to grow and reproduce over and over. A community that is able to maintain a balance between abiotic and biotic factors and remain stable is a **climax community.** For any area, the type of climax community that develops is determined by the limiting factors of that environment. Where rainfall is limited and daytime temperatures are very hot, a desert may be the climax community. A climax community is made up of organisms that are adapted to the climate and soil conditions. You can see why climax communities are not the same everywhere.

During each stage of succession, the members of the community change the environment, making it more or less favorable for the present populations. A sunny field favors the growth of pine seedlings, but a pine forest does not. A pine forest favors oak and hickory seedlings. Oak and hickory forests, however, favor oak and hickory seedlings. Oak and hickory forests often are climax communities. A climax community will survive as long as environmental conditions remain the same.

SECTION REVIEW

1. Describe limiting factors and give three examples.
2. What is succession?
3. Describe what steps occur in primary succession on a volcanic island.
4. What is meant by the term *climax community?*
5. **Apply:** A beaver builds a dam across a stream and creates a pond. Would succession in this pond be primary or secondary succession? Why?

MINI-Lab

How do communities change?
Use the data below to explain how tree species changed over 50 years in an area that started as an abandoned field and became a forest.

Tree Species	Age of Area (years)		
	5	20	50
Black Cherry		✓	✓
Butternut Hickory			✓
Persimmon	✓	✓	
Sassafras	✓	✓	
Shagbark Hickory			✓
Red Oak			✓
White Oak			✓
Yellow Chestnut			✓
White Ash		✓	✓
Winged Elm		✓	✓

Explain why some trees are no longer present after 50 years and why some trees did not appear until 20 or 50 years had gone by. Be sure to give the names of the trees in your answer.

☑ Hypothesizing

Make a hypothesis as to what would happen to succession in a pond if the pond owner removed all the cattails and reeds from around the pond edges every summer. If you need help, refer to Hypothesizing in the **Skill Handbook** on page 686.

Skill Builder

27-2 Land Biomes

New Science Words

climate
biomes
tundra
permafrost

Objectives

▶ Define *biomes*.
▶ Identify the location of the major land biomes.
▶ Describe the climate, dominant plant types, and characteristic animals of the major land biomes.

Land Biomes

What are biomes?

Imagine that you could get on a train at the equator and travel north or south to the poles. What changes in the environment could you see from the train's windows? Palm trees and banana trees are found at the equator, whereas magnolias, laurels, and pecan trees are found in temperate climates. Forests of pine, spruce, and firs would be seen in colder regions near the poles. At the poles, trees would disappear altogether! These changes in forest communities as you travel away from the equator are the result of gradual changes in climate. **Climate** is the average condition of the weather in an area, as determined by rainfall, temperature, and amount of sunlight—all abiotic factors. These abiotic factors as well as other limiting factors help determine what species can survive in a particular environment. These factors also help determine the structure of climax communities all over the world. Large geographic areas that have similar climates and climax communities are called **biomes** (BI ohmz). The major biomes on Earth are shown in Figure 27-3. Each major biome shares similar climate conditions, but the specific organisms found in each community will be different. Deserts in the United States and Africa look very similar, but the organisms are not the same.

Figure 27-3. The locations of the six major land biomes on Earth can be identified by using the key below.

■ Tundra
□ Northern coniferous forest
□ Deciduous forest
■ Grassland
■ Tropical rain forest
■ Desert

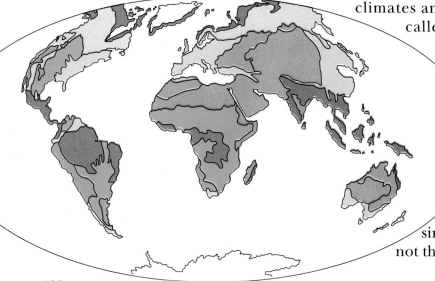

Tundra

Can you picture a region that receives little precipitation yet is covered with snow and ice for nine months each year? The **tundra** (TUN drah) is a cold, dry, treeless biome where the sun barely rises during the six to nine winter months. It is located in the far northern parts of North America, Europe, and Asia and is the most continuous of Earth's biomes. Nearly 20 percent of Earth's land area is covered by tundra.

Low temperatures and a short growing season are the major limiting factors in the tundra. Precipitation in the tundra averages less than 25 cm yearly. Temperatures drop to minus 40°C and keep the ground frozen for most of the year. In the short summer months, the snow melts and the upper layer of soil thaws. The soil underneath that remains permanently frozen is called **permafrost.** Permafrost prevents soil from absorbing water.

What kind of organisms live in such a harsh environment? Tundra plants include lichens, mosses, and flowering plants such as cranberries. Insects such as mosquitoes and blackflies grow in vast numbers. Ducks, geese, and songbirds feed on the abundant insects. Tundra mammals include caribou, reindeer, musk oxen, and arctic foxes. Many animals come for the summer, then migrate to warmer regions in the fall. Other animals remain throughout the year. Arctic hares, polar bears, and snowy owls have white fur and feathers that provide camouflage in the snow. Why is white fur an advantage for a predator like the polar bear in the tundra?

Northern Coniferous Forests

The northern *coniferous forest biome* has as its dominant plants cone-bearing evergreen trees such as pines, firs, spruces, and cedars. These forests cover large parts of northern Europe, Asia, and North America. Winters are long and cold with heavy snows. Even though summers are short, they are longer and warmer than summers in the tundra. In these forests, the ground thaws in the summer, making it possible for trees to grow. Rainfall in this biome ranges from 50 to 125 cm yearly.

Because coniferous forests are dense, little light penetrates to the soil, so there are few shrubs or grasses in this biome. These forests are very productive and play an

Figure 27-4. Land is so flat in the tundra that water does not drain away, and the permafrost prevents water absorption. This results in marshy conditions in the summer.

MINI-Lab

Is there tundra in Africa?
Using the land biome map on page 632, make a hypothesis as to whether tundra exists in Africa. Look at a globe and compare the latitude where tundra is found in the northern hemisphere with the same latitude in the southern hemisphere. How can you tell if your hypothesis is correct?

Figure 27-5. It is very dark in a coniferous forest, with deep layers of needles on the forest floor.

Figure 27-6. The crossbill is a bird that is adapted to life in coniferous forests. Its unique bill is used to dig seeds out of cones.

Figure 27-7. Deciduous forests like this once covered all of Europe and the eastern United States.

Figure 27-8. Grasslands may be very hot in the summer and very cold in the winter. Grassland species are adapted to these variations in temperatures.

important role in the timber industry. Much of the lumber used for construction comes from coniferous forests.

Coniferous forest mammals, such as moose, bears, wolves, and lynx, depend on stored body fat during the cold months. Some animals migrate to warmer climates in the fall and return in the spring. Other animals hibernate six to eight months of the year.

Deciduous Forests

Do you live in an area where the autumn leaves change color? A *deciduous forest biome* is dominated by trees that have broad thin leaves, such as beeches, maples, oaks, hickories, sycamores, and elms. This biome has four seasons with about 75 to 150 cm of rainfall distributed evenly throughout the year. Winters are cold, summers are long and warm, springs and falls are mild. The climate and rich soil support large numbers of plant and animal species. Deciduous forests are found in the eastern United States, Europe, and parts of Asia, South America, Africa, and Australia.

White-tailed deer, foxes, raccoons, opossums, and squirrels are typical mammals that live in the North American deciduous forest. Black bears are found in some regions. Mice, snakes, and other animals are found on the forest floor. Some animals hibernate during cold winters. Others, including many bird species, migrate to warmer climates for the winter.

Grasslands

About one-fourth of the land surface on Earth is covered by grassland biomes. The *grassland biome* is dominated by grasses. These biomes occur at about the same latitude as deciduous forests, but they do not receive enough precipitation to support trees. Rainfall in grasslands may be only 25 to 75 cm per year. Temperatures range from very hot in the summer to below freezing in the winter. Grasslands are called prairies in North America, pampas in South America, savannas or veldts in Africa, and steppes in Asia.

Many grasslands are subject to periodic fires. Grasses in these biomes have roots that can send out shoots to form new plants. Extensive root systems absorb water over large areas when it rains.

Some grasslands support large numbers of grazing animals. The grazing mammals in North America include bison and antelope. Zebras, wildebeasts, and giraffes are found in Africa, and kangaroos graze in Australia.

Grasslands are very important to humans. Most of the grains used for human food, such as wheat and rye, are grown in grassland areas.

Deserts

What is a desert biome?

A *desert biome* receives less than 25 cm of rainfall a year and has a high rate of evaporation. Most deserts have little cloud cover to hold the heat, so it is quickly lost once the sun goes down. The temperature may drop as much as 40°C in 12 hours. This results in hot days and cold nights. In some deserts rain may not fall for more than a year, and then a huge thunderstorm may dump more than 12 cm all at once.

Populations of organisms that live in deserts are adapted to the climate. Whenever sufficient rain falls, annual plants grow, flower, and produce seeds in a short time. Then they remain inactive during the long dry periods. Some plants store water in their thick stems and leaves. The saguaro cacti of Arizona and Mexico store water and carry out photosynthesis in thickened stems. The leaves or stems of many plants have sharp protective spines to protect them from thirsty animals.

Desert animal populations are also adapted to their environment. Kangaroo rats, pocket mice, and gerbils get water from the seeds they eat. Some kangaroo rats store seeds in their burrows to soak up the moisture found there. Blood vessels in the large ears of jackrabbits and foxes circulate blood to cool the animals.

Figure 27-9. Many desert plants have extensive root systems to collect as much water as possible when it rains. A single saguaro cactus can store as much as 900 liters of water.

Tropical Rain Forests

When you think of the tropics, do you imagine a jungle? A *tropical rain forest biome* has hot, wet weather throughout the year and the greatest variety of organisms on Earth. Rainfall averages 200 to 225 cm per year. High temperatures and abundant rainfall contribute to high humidity. Three major tropical rain forests are found in South America, Africa, and Southeast Asia.

Tropical rain forests contain more than 50 percent of all species of organisms on Earth. The soil is often not

Science and READING

The International Children's rainforest in Monteverde, Costa Rica, protects more than 5000 hectares of tropical rain forest. Find out how this rain forest was protected by children from the United States, Sweden, Canada, England, and Japan.

Life in a Glass World

Biosphere II is the name given to a unique greenhouse in Arizona that is the world's largest closed ecosystem. Eight volunteers live, work, study, and play inside Biosphere II and get all the food they need from the six biomes represented there. The biomes include an agricultural biome, a desert, a marsh, an ocean, a savanna, and a rain forest. The intensive agricultural biome has food crops, fish ponds, and domestic animals. Water in Biosphere II recycles in the rain forest, although some of the total 6.6 million liters flows into the savanna.

What can scientists learn from Biosphere II? It may help scientists better understand life on Earth, provide a model for future space colonies, and allow scientists to test some new technologies.

Think Critically: What problems do you need to solve in a closed ecosystem?

very fertile because most nutrients are taken up by plants as soon as they become available through decay.

Animal life is very diverse in the rain forest, with insects, birds, monkeys, and large cats. More than 50 percent of the mammals in rain forests live in the trees. Rain forest reptiles include chameleons, snakes, iguanas, and geckos. Many scientists are studying the remaining rain forests to learn what new organisms may be found there.

SECTION REVIEW

1. Define *biome* and list the six major biomes on Earth.
2. How do grasslands differ from coniferous forests?
3. What kinds of adaptations have desert animals made to survive without much water?
4. Why are there few shrubs in a coniferous forest?
5. **Apply:** Why don't large trees grow in the tundra?

Skill Builder

☑ Concept Mapping

Make a concept map of plant and animal species found in each land biome. If you need help, refer to Concept Mapping in the **Skill Handbook** on pages 688 and 689.

Water Ecosystems

Objectives

▶ Distinguish between marine and freshwater ecosystems.
▶ Describe the zones in the ocean.
▶ Identify the limiting factors present in marine and freshwater ecosystems.

New Science Words

littoral zone
sublittoral zone
pelagic zone
estuary

Marine Ecosystems

If you had to name the largest biome on Earth, would you answer the ocean? The major land biomes are surrounded by the oceans. The *marine ecosystem* is a continuous body of water that covers more than 70 percent of Earth's surface.

The amount of salt present is the major limiting factor in water ecosystems. Ocean water may contain as much as 3.5 percent salt, whereas fresh water contains less than 0.005 percent salt. Other limiting factors in marine ecosystems are temperature, light, the amount of dissolved oxygen, and water pressure. Light and temperature decrease as the depth of the water increases, but water pressure increases with depth.

Figure 27-10 shows the major zones of the ocean. The zone along the shore is the **littoral** (LIHT uh rul) **zone.** During high tide it is covered with water, and during low tide it is exposed to the air. Populations living in the littoral zone are adapted to the wet and dry conditions and to the force of the waves hitting the shore. Sea stars, sea anemones, and mussels cling to rocks. At low tide, mussels close their shells and crabs burrow into the moist sand to keep from drying out. The organisms that live there have to be able to withstand varying temperatures, water levels, and salt levels.

The part of the ocean floor that slopes downward is the continental shelf. The shallow water above the continental shelf is called the **sublittoral zone.** This zone has enough light and nutrients to support a wide variety of

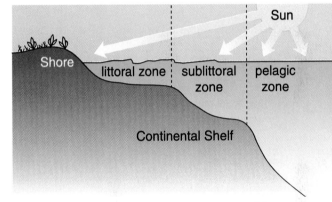

Figure 27-10. Most marine life is found in the littoral and sublittoral zones of the ocean where sunlight penetrates.

Figure 27-11. Organisms that live in the littoral zone are adapted to both wet and dry conditions.

Figure 27-12. Most marine fish caught for food or sport were hatched in estuaries like this.

EcoTip

Boat engines may leak oil into estuary waters. Make sure boat engines are in good working order before you anchor near an estuary.

What is a freshwater ecosystem?

Figure 27-13. Fast-moving water like this contains far fewer organisms than slow-moving streams.

organisms. Most life in the ocean is found in the littoral and sublittoral zones. Microscopic organisms that float or swim near the surface of the water include protozoans, algae, and invertebrates. Shrimp, oysters, and fish all feed on these organisms and are eaten in turn by other fish, squid, some whales, walruses, and seals.

The open ocean just beyond the sublittoral zone is the **pelagic zone.** Sunlight filters down to a depth of about 200 meters. Below 200 meters this zone is dark and cold. Water pressure is extremely high. Some animals living here move up to feed, and others eat dead organisms that filter down from the water above.

The area where a freshwater river or stream meets the ocean is called an **estuary.** Salt marshes, deltas, and mud flats may all be estuaries. The water is shallow in estuaries, allowing light to penetrate to the bottom. Rivers bring nutrients washed from the land to algae, marsh grasses, and other plants growing along the shore. The continuous mixing of fresh water with ocean water keeps nutrients in the estuary and removes wastes from it. Oysters, clams, mussels, and snails are abundant. Estuaries serve as breeding grounds for many marine organisms such as fish, arthropods, and mollusks. Shore birds nest and raise their young in estuaries because of abundant food resources.

Freshwater Ecosystems

Most of you probably are familiar with a freshwater ecosystem like the one in Figure 27-13. *Freshwater ecosystems* include lakes, ponds, streams, rivers, swamps, and bogs.

The types of organisms found in freshwater ecosystems depend largely on temperature, current, and the amounts of oxygen and minerals dissolved in the water.

Water temperature in freshwater ecosystems does not vary as much as the temperature of air. As a result, populations that live in water are adapted to a narrow temperature range, and many cannot survive freezing or extreme heat. The primary limiting factor in freshwater ecosystems is the amount of oxygen dissolved in the water. A fast-moving stream has more oxygen in it than a stagnant pond. Cold water can hold more oxygen, yet there may be fewer organisms in cold water because temperature is also a limiting factor.

Lakes and ponds are classified according to the amount of organic matter. Those that are rich in organic matter

PROBLEM SOLVING

What Caused the Fish to Die?

Fish breathe by allowing water to flow over the many blood vessels in their gills. As the water passes over the blood vessels, oxygen from the water is absorbed and carbon dioxide is released.

Recently, several hundred thousand fish and other marine creatures were killed along the Gulf Coast because there was not enough oxygen in the water. Unfavorable weather conditions caused the problem. After several days of high heat and calm water, the oxygen content of the water decreased to a level that could not sustain wildlife. As the water warmed up, it lost its ability to hold oxygen. The calm water also

contributed to the low oxygen levels. Turbulent water traps air bubbles, and gases from the air dissolve in the water. What caused the fish to die?

Think Critically: Why do aquariums use air pumps to bubble air through the water?

usually have cloudy or green waters. Those that contain little organic matter have water that is clearer, is blue in color, and has a sandy or rocky bottom. Which type of pond has more nutrients? Ponds with lots of organic matter have more nutrients and can support more species.

SECTION REVIEW

1. What is the main difference between marine and freshwater biomes?
2. What are the most important limiting factors in marine ecosystems? In freshwater ecosystems?
3. Name and describe the zones in the ocean.
4. Give six examples of freshwater biomes.
5. **Apply:** Developers often fill in estuaries to build homes on the shoreline. Why should this concern you?

☑ Hypothesizing

Hypothesize why some fish that live in the pelagic zone of the ocean have no eyes. If you need help, refer to Hypothesizing in the **Skill Handbook** on page 686.

Skill Builder

27-4 Coastal Wetlands

New Science Words

wetland
water table

Objectives

▶ List several important roles of wetlands in the environment.
▶ Name several different types of wetlands.

Wetlands or Wastelands?

What is a wetland?

Have you ever traveled along a coastline and noticed large wet areas? Many of us think of these areas as being useless, unattractive breeding grounds for mosquitoes. This type of area is known as a wetland. A **wetland** is an area of land that, for at least part of the year, is covered by shallow water. There are many different types of wetlands, including coastal marshes, swamps, and bogs.

Wetlands are unique systems that are home to many species of animals and plants. Snakes, fish, turtles, snails, insects, beavers, raccoons, and a wide variety of insects are often found in wetlands. They are all dependent on the many wetland plants for both food and shelter. Wetlands also provide a resting and feeding place for birds migrating during the fall and spring, and for shore birds all year.

Figure 27-14. Wetlands may include estuaries, where fresh water mixes with salt water, or freshwater ecosystems.

Wetlands that are located along the coast are very important in providing food and jobs. Ninety percent of the fish harvested each year in the United States spent at least part of their lives in coastal marshes. People who live near these wetlands rely on the fishing industry for jobs. In addition, the vast coastal marshes serve as protection against storms and floods. If not protected

from the rough open waters of the ocean, both coastal cities and rural areas might suffer great damage from high water and the powerful force of the waves.

Wetlands also serve as filters to clean surface water before it enters the water table. The **water table** is the underground water supply most humans rely upon for drinking water. When it rains, the rainwater soaks into the ground until it reaches the water table. But rain also washes pollutants into surface water such as streams. Where streams empty into the ocean, coastal wetland plants and soil absorb these pollutants, preventing them from moving into the ocean itself.

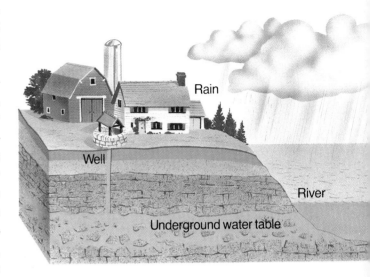

With the increasing need to build more homes, factories, schools, stores, and parking lots, land developers often choose wetland areas to develop because they appear to serve no practical use. To most people, wetlands seem useless. In the United States alone, millions of hectares of wetlands have already been drained for development. Many species of plants and animals are now endangered due to the loss of this wetland habitat.

Environmentalists are working with local governments to develop solutions. All over the country, wetland protection plans are being developed to preserve the remaining wetlands. However, as the population continues to grow, there is continuing pressure to develop wetlands. A balanced development of coastal areas may require compromise on both sides of the wetlands debate.

Did You Know?

In southern Florida, increased human population has resulted in loss of 60 percent of the original wetlands. Ninety-five percent of the wading birds in the Everglades have disappeared.

SECTION REVIEW

1. What are two important roles of wetlands?
2. List three types of wetlands.

You Decide!

In some states, developers are required to build a new wetland for any that they might destroy during development. However, recent research shows that such recreated wetlands are no replacement for the natural wetlands that required years and years for nature to build. Should developers be allowed to drain wetlands for any purpose?

ACTIVITY 27-2
Investigating a Limiting Factor

Problem: *How does water affect the germination of bean seeds?*

Materials
- one package of 50 pinto bean seeds
- water
- soil
- 2 planters

Procedure
1. Place 5 cm of soil in each of the two planters.
2. Select 25 healthy pinto bean seeds from the package.
3. Plant 25 of the bean seeds about 0.5 cm deep, evenly spaced, in one planter and the remaining 25 bean seeds in an identical planter. Label the planters A and B.
4. Place the planters near a window so they will receive the same amount of light and air.
5. Water planter A with a measured amount of water. Do not water planter B.
6. Observe the seeds daily for ten days. Record the total number of seeds that germinate and any other observations in a data table like the one shown.
7. Graph the data collected.

Data and Observations

Day	Planter A	Planter B
1		
2		
3		
4		
5		
6		
7		
8		
9		
10		

Analyze
1. How many seeds germinated in Planter A?
2. How many seeds germinated in Planter B?
3. What was the variable in the experiment?
4. Which planter was the control?
5. What factors did you try to keep the same?

Conclude and Apply
6. What do bean seeds need to germinate?
7. What was the limitng factor in this activity?

CHAPTER
REVIEW

27-1: Factors That Affect Biomes

1. Limiting factors such as water, sunlight, and temperature determine the survival of organisms, populations, and species in the environment.

2. Over time, communities change in an orderly process called succession. Succession results in a balanced ecosystem called a climax community.

3. Primary succession occurs on new land, whereas secondary succession returns disturbed areas to a more stable climax community.

27-2: Land Biomes

1. Biomes are large geographic areas with similar climates and climax communities.

2. Land biomes include tundra, coniferous and deciduous forests, grasslands, deserts, and tropical rain forests.

3. Biomes share climate conditions, but the specific organisms found in each may differ.

27-3: Water Ecosystems

1. Marine ecosystems and freshwater ecosystems differ in the organisms that live there. This is due to the amount of salt present in the water.

2. Marine organisms have adapted to a salty environment and live in different ocean zones.

3. Freshwater organisms have adapted to life in still or moving water.

27-4: Science and Society: Coastal Wetlands

1. Wetlands are home to unique organisms, serve as nesting and feeding sites for many different animal species, and filter pollutants from surface waters.

2. Wetlands include coastal marshes, swamps, and bogs.

KEY SCIENCE WORDS

a. **biomes**
b. **climate**
c. **climax community**
d. **estuary**
e. **limiting factor**
f. **littoral zone**
g. **pelagic zone**
h. **permafrost**
i. **primary succession**
j. **secondary succession**
k. **sublittoral zone**
l. **succession**
m. **tundra**
n. **water table**
o. **wetland**

UNDERSTANDING VOCABULARY

Match each phrase with the correct term from the list of Key Science Words.

1. a condition that determines the survival of an organism
2. area where fresh water and salt water mix
3. underground water supply
4. frozen soil of the tundra
5. shallow water above the continental shelf
6. gradual change in a community over time
7. a stable, balanced community
8. ocean zone along the shore
9. areas of similar climate and communities
10. an area of land covered by water

CHAPTER
REVIEW

CHECKING CONCEPTS

Choose the word or phrase that completes the sentence.

1. Limiting factors in a land biome include _____.
   a. rainfall
   b. sunlight
   c. temperature
   d. all of these

2. _____ return(s) a burned forest to its previous condition.
   a. Secondary succession
   b. Limiting factors
   c. Primary succession
   d. A climax community

3. The _____ is a treeless, cold biome.
   a. grassland
   b. desert
   c. tundra
   d. none of these

4. All are examples of grasslands except _____.
   a. pampas
   b. steppes
   c. savannas
   d. estuaries

5. Swamps, bogs, and marshes are examples of _____.
   a. grasslands
   b. deserts
   c. coniferous forests
   d. coastal wetlands

6. Oysters and clams have adapted to the mild waters of the _____.
   a. pelagic zone
   b. sublittoral zone
   c. estuary
   d. none of these

7. Limiting factors in water ecosystems include _____.
   a. current
   b. temperature
   c. dissolved oxygen
   d. all of these

8. The _____ has the most variety of organisms of any biome.
   a. desert
   b. tundra
   c. tropical rain forest
   d. deciduous forest

9. A(n) _____ is the end result of succession.
   a. wetland
   b. limiting factor
   c. climax community
   d. none of these

10. Trees are parts of the communities of each biome except _____.
    a. deciduous forest
    b. tundra
    c. tropical rain forest
    d. coniferous forest

UNDERSTANDING CONCEPTS

Complete each sentence.

11. Mouse populations in oak-hickory forests are limited by biotic factors such as competition and _____.

12. Firs, cedars, and pines are dominant plants of the _____ forest.

13. Volcanic islands develop plant communities in a process called _____ .

14. There are no trees on the grasslands due to insufficient _____ to support them.

15. Most animals of the rain forest live in _____.

THINK AND WRITE CRITICALLY

16. What are the limiting factors in a desert?
17. Compare primary and secondary succession.
18. What is the difference between coastal wetlands and the littoral zones of marine ecosystems?
19. Why are soils in rain forests not very fertile?
20. Why are grasslands important to humans?

APPLY

21. Why do mammals of the coniferous forest hibernate?
22. How does climate help determine what species live in communities?

23. What special adaptations might plants and animals that live in fast-moving water have?
24. Northern coniferous forests are climax communities. Why don't they change through succession to oak-hickory forests?
25. Make a food chain that could be found in a deciduous forest.

MORE SKILL BUILDERS

If you need help, refer to the Skill Handbook.

1. **Comparing and Contrasting:** Make a chart to compare and contrast these biomes.

Biome	Weather	Plants	Animals
Tundra			
Grasslands			
Deserts			
Tropical Rain Forests			

2. **Concept Mapping:** Make a concept map for water ecosystems. Include these terms: *marine ecosystems, freshwater ecosystems, littoral zone, pelagic zone, sublittoral zone, lake, pond, river, stream.*

3. **Graphing:** Make a bar graph of the amount of rainfall per year in each biome.

Biome	Rainfall/Year
Deciduous forests	100 cm
Tropical rain forests	225 cm
Grasslands	50 cm
Deserts	20 cm

4. **Comparing and Contrasting:** Make a chart to compare and contrast the plants and animals of the northern coniferous forests and deciduous forests.

5. **Interpreting Data:** Interpret the data given and decide which area of a stream has more varieties of living things and explain why.

Organism	Number in Pools	Number in Riffles
Midgefly larva	0	1000
Caddisfly larva	2	70
Snail	2	12
Water penny	1	7
Mayfly larva	1	250
Stonefly larva	1	61
Horsefly larva	1	8
Water strider	8	1
Dragonfly larva	2	7
Water diving beetle	3	1
Whirligig beetle	5	2

Find the total number of organisms in each area.

PROJECTS

1. Do you have relatives, friends, or a pen pal who lives in a different biome than you do? Each of you can make a list of common plants and animals in your biome and exchange the lists.
2. Research the Atacama Desert of Chile. Find out how much rainfall the desert receives in one year. Report to the class on your findings.
3. Find out where the grains that humans depend on for food originated, and in what type of biome. Include grains such as corn, wheat, rice, barley, rye, and sorghum in your answer.

28 Resources and the Environment

Water is essential for all life on Earth. You know that the water used for washing dishes will go down the drain. But then where does it go? Water may go into a sewer system and enter a water treatment plant. How does today's wastewater become tomorrow's clean water? How is water cleaned so it can be used again?

FIND OUT!

Do this simple activity to find out how water can be cleaned.

Stir some garden soil and plant material into a beaker filled with water. When the water looks muddy, pour most of it through a coffee filter into a bowl. How does the water in the beaker compare with the water in the bowl? Filters can remove some kinds of wastes from water, but do they remove all wastes? How would you remove other wastes from the filtered water?

Gearing Up

Previewing the Chapter

Use this outline to help you focus on important ideas in this chapter.

Section 28-1   Natural Resources
▶ What Are Natural Resources?
▶ Resources Are Limited

Section 28-2   Conservation and Protection
▶ What Is Conservation?
▶ Cleaning Up the Air
▶ Cleaning Up the Water
▶ Waste Disposal
▶ Protecting Soil and Forest Resources
▶ Protecting Wildlife

Section 28-3   Future Responsibility
▶ Environmental Management
▶ Individual Responsibility

Section 28-4   Science and Society Earth in 2030
▶ The Future: Grand or Grim?

Previewing Science Skills

▶ In the **Skill Builders**, you will hypothesize, make concept maps, and recognize cause and effect.
▶ In the **Activities**, you will observe, experiment, analyze, and predict.
▶ In the **MINI-Labs**, you will survey, organize information, report, compare, collect data, and record.

What's next?

Now you know that wastewater can be partially cleaned by filtering. In this chapter, you'll learn about the impact humans have on natural resources and how you can help conserve these resources.

28-1 Natural Resources

New Science Words

natural resources
renewable resources
nonrenewable resources
greenhouse effect
solid wastes
erosion

Objectives

▶ Identify natural resources and describe how they are important to living organisms.
▶ Distinguish between renewable and nonrenewable resources and give three examples of each.
▶ Describe how resources are affected by human use.

What Are Natural Resources?

Mountain gorillas live in family groups high in the mountains of Rwanda and Uganda in Africa. They eat fruits and leaves and drink water from clear mountain streams. At night, these gorillas bend branches of trees down to make nests to sleep on. How do you get ready for bed? You brush your teeth with a plastic toothbrush, take a drink of water, then slip between cotton sheets on your bed. Do you have anything in common with mountain gorillas? Both humans and gorillas rely on natural resources in their environment. **Natural resources** are the raw materials in the environment that organisms use for survival. Natural resources include biotic and abiotic materials such as water, soil, air, forests, wildlife, and minerals that organisms use in their daily lives. The food you eat, the clothes you wear, and the roof over your head all are necessary for your survival, and all came from natural resources.

The cotton used to make your sheets is a renewable resource. **Renewable resources** are those natural resources that can be replaced by nature over a period of time. Trees, wildlife, and soil are renewable resources. Cotton for sheets is a renewable resource because cotton plants can be planted every year. Air, water, and sunlight are renewable resources that all life depends upon.

Nonrenewable resources are those natural resources that are available only in limited amounts and cannot be replaced by nature. Many of the products you depend on every day are made from nonrenewable resources. Plastic toothbrushes, polystyrene cups, and gasoline all are made from petroleum, a fossil fuel. Fossil fuels are fuels made up of organisms that lived and died millions of years ago.

What are natural resources?

Figure 28-1. Nonrenewable resources such as petroleum are available only in limited amounts.

Petroleum, coal, peat, and natural gas are fossil fuels. Some minerals that are recycled very slowly, such as phosphorus, are also called nonrenewable resources.

Resources Are Limited

Have you ever rushed to the music store to buy a tape advertised in the paper, only to find the store is sold out when you arrive? If you looked at the advertisement carefully, you might see the words, "Supplies are limited." Supplies of natural resources on Earth are limited, too. Natural resources on Earth are not distributed evenly. You already know from Chapter 27 that deserts are biomes with very few natural resources. Today, many of Earth's natural resources are being damaged as a result of human activities. Air pollution, water pollution, and the problem of solid waste disposal are daily headlines. Soil, forests, and wildlife are natural resources in danger because of human actions. These problems are discussed in the following sections.

What natural resources are in danger due to human actions?

Air Pollution

Air pollution occurs when the air is polluted by gases from vehicles or power plants that burn fossil fuels. Air can be polluted by carbon monoxide, nitrogen oxide, sulfur dioxide, hydrocarbons, and by tiny particles of ash, lead, dust, or soot. Some air pollution occurs naturally, for example, when gases are released from a volcano. Most air pollution results from the burning of fossil fuels in power plants and in automobiles. The burning of coal to produce electricity releases tons of sulfur dioxide into the air each year in the United States. Sulfur dioxide and nitrogen oxide combine with water vapor in the air to produce acid rain.

Air pollution can also be caused by the burning of forests and grasslands. In Brazil, Indonesia, and India, farmers often clear land in this way. This burning also releases carbon dioxide into the atmosphere. Carbon dioxide and other gases form a layer around Earth that acts like a wall of windows in a greenhouse. The gases allow sunlight to pass through and warm Earth's surface. Heat and reflected sunlight radiate back into this gas layer and are trapped there, as shown in Figure 28-2. Scientists have found evidence that the **greenhouse effect** may be causing a rise in Earth's temperature.

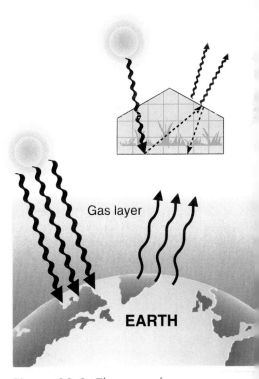

Figure 28-2. The greenhouse effect occurs when large amounts of carbon dioxide and other gases trap heat near the surface of Earth.

PROBLEM SOLVING

The Mystery of the Dirty Shirt

Frank, who lives in a large city, had plans to catch a movie and grab a burger with some friends in the evening. He decided to wash his favorite white shirt to wear with his acid-washed jeans.

Frank washed the shirt and hung it outside to dry. Later he checked to see if the shirt had dried. To his surprise, the shirt was covered with tiny black dots.

Then he remembered that the weather forecast had called for a smog alert. A layer of stagnant cool air was trapped below a layer of warm air, and the city might have problems until an air mass came through.

Think Critically: What caused the black dots on Frank's shirt?

MINI-Lab

How much garbage do you produce?

Ask your family to help you collect everything that is thrown away in your household in one week. Collect garbage in paper or plastic bags. At the end of the week, carefully weigh each bag. Add the weights to find the total amount of garbage, then divide by the number of people in your household. How much garbage did you produce in one week?

Water Pollution

In many places on Earth, water is the most scarce resource. Most of the water on Earth is in the oceans or locked in polar ice caps. Fresh water accounts for only three percent of the total amount of water on Earth. Of that three percent, only 0.003 percent is clean and safe, and available for human consumption.

Water can be polluted by oil, industrial wastes, sewage, bacteria, sediments, solid wastes, and even heat. When power plants use water from rivers for cooling purposes, the water may be returned to the river several degrees hotter than it was originally. Organisms in the river cannot adjust to such quick changes in water temperature, and they may die. Water can also be polluted by pesticides and fertilizers that are used on farms and homeowners' lawns. Rain washes these chemicals out of the soil and into nearby water sources. Even though water is a renewable resource, it is expensive to clean polluted water.

Land Pollution

Did you drink a soft drink yesterday? If you did, what did you do with the can or bottle when you were finished? If you threw it in the trash, you were contributing to land pollution. Magazines, newspapers, plastic bags, glass bottles, aluminum cans, grass clippings, and leftover foods that are thrown away end up as solid wastes. **Solid wastes** are the unwanted products that are burned, buried, and dumped each year all over the world. Every day, each person in the United States throws away 1.8 kg of solid wastes. Most of this solid waste ends up in sanitary landfills.

What happens to the garbage in sanitary landfills? Grass cuttings, animal wastes, newspapers, and dead leaves are broken down by decomposers in the soil. Wastes that can be broken down into their chemical components are called biodegradable. Waste products that cannot be broken down by natural processes, such as aluminum cans and old tires, are called nonbiodegradable. Wastes that are nonbiodegradable create pollution problems for years.

Toxic wastes are chemicals that are byproducts of industrial processes. Many are known to cause cancer, birth defects, and other health problems. These wastes are packed in steel drums. If the drums are not sealed properly, chemicals leak out and pollute both soil and water.

Soil and Forest Resources

Much of the land in Nepal lies on steep mountain slopes, where fuel for cooking is scarce. Families go higher and higher up into the mountains searching for fuel. They cut trees and bring them home, leaving the slopes bare. When the rainy season comes, there are no tree roots to absorb water and hold soil in place. Water washes soil away. **Erosion** is the loss of soil from the effects of wind, water, or ice. Rain washes away the fertile topsoil, and trees are unable to grow on the barren mountain slopes.

Poor farming and forestry practices such as those described above often result in erosion of topsoil. It takes between 500 and 1000 years for 2.5 centimeters of topsoil to form. If rain falls after a farmer plows but before crops begin to grow, erosion may occur. Erosion also occurs when the timber in a forest is harvested by a method called clear-cutting. In this method, all the trees in a section of forest are cut down and dragged out. Not only is the soil left unprotected, but the habitats of all the organisms that live in or on the trees have been disturbed.

What are nonbiodegradable wastes?

Did You Know?

It takes 6 million liters of water to produce the food the average American eats in a year.

Figure 28-3. When trees are cut for firewood on steep mountain slopes, rain washes topsoil away.

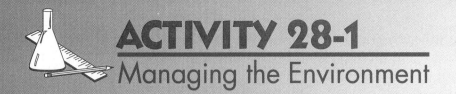

ACTIVITY 28-1
Managing the Environment

Problem: *What substances are not biodegradable?*

Materials

- water
- 2 petri dish lids
- potting soil
- a leaf
- aluminum foil
- scissors
- plastic milk container
- 2 small aluminum pie pans
- 2 clay flowerpots
- sand or gravel
- newspaper
- apple peelings
- plastic foam
- metric ruler

Procedure

1. Place layers of sand or gravel in the bottom of two clay flowerpots. Fill each pot with moistened potting soil to within 1.5 cm of the top.
2. Into one pot, place a 2-cm square of newspaper, a leaf, and a 2-cm square of apple peelings on top of the soil.
3. Into the second pot, place a 2-cm square of plastic from the milk jug, a 2-cm square of aluminum foil, and a 2-cm square of plastic foam on the soil.
4. Cover each pot with the lid of a petri dish. Make sure it fits tightly over the top of each clay flowerpot.
5. Place each pot in an aluminum pie pan. Add water to the pan. The water will rise through the holes in each pot and keep the contents moist.
6. Observe the two pots every other day for four weeks. Record your observations.

Data and Observations

Pot 1 Date	Substance	Observations
	newspaper	
	leaf	
	apple peeling	

Pot 2 Date	Substance	Observations
	plastic	
	aluminum foil	
	plastic foam	

Analyze

1. Which substances were biodegradable?
2. Which substance decomposed first?
3. What kinds of organisms were you able to observe?
4. Which substances were not biodegradable?

Conclude and Apply

5. How do substances that are not biodegradable affect our environment?
6. How can you use what you learned in this investigation?
7. How can people reduce the amount of waste they produce?

Wildlife Resources

Have you heard of the California condor? Only about 40 of these huge birds still exist, and all of them are in captivity. Condors are in danger of becoming extinct because there are so few of them left. Many species of plants and animals today also are in danger of becoming extinct because they are hunted, or because their habitats have been destroyed. Species that are in danger of becoming extinct are called endangered species.

Populations of many wild species have been decreasing, often as a result of human activities. Developers have filled in estuaries and wetlands to build housing developments, farmers have plowed grasslands to plant crops, and lumber companies have cleared forests for timber. Some wildlife species are able to survive changes like these. Raccoons often do well in housing developments, as long as they can get into garbage cans! But many times these changes in wildlife habitat are so fast that species are unable to adapt. As a result, populations decline as individual organisms die or move on to better areas.

Plant species can be important sources of food and medicines, yet many plant species are endangered also. There may be thousands of plant species in tropical rain forests that have not been studied yet, and their uses are unknown. This is one reason that scientists would like rain forest destruction to stop.

Figure 28-4. California condors are endangered as a result of habitat loss.

Why can't species adapt to changes in their habitat?

SECTION REVIEW

1. What are natural resources?
2. Differentiate between renewable and nonrenewable resources.
3. Explain the greenhouse effect.
4. Describe the difference between biodegradable and nonbiodegradable.
5. **Apply:** How have human activities increased the number of extinct plants and animals?

☑ Hypothesizing

Hypothesize why a population of raccoons is able to survive changes in its habitat. Explain. If you need help, refer to Hypothesizing in the **Skill Handbook** on page 686.

Skill Builder

28-2 Conservation and Protection

New Science Words

conservation
reforestation
wildlife preserve

Objectives

▶ **Define conservation and how it relates to natural resources.**
▶ **Describe how renewable resources can be conserved and protected.**
▶ **Identify ways to reuse nonrenewable resources.**

What Is Conservation?

For thousands of years, farmers in steep mountain regions of Nepal, Myanmar, Indonesia, and the Philippines have terraced the sides of mountains to grow rice. They learned that terraces prevent soil erosion and hold water needed for rice production. These farmers practice soil and water conservation. **Conservation** is the wise and careful use of Earth's resources.

When humans use natural resources wisely, they can live in harmony with the community and environment around them. Because the human population continues to grow, people are becoming more aware of how important it is to conserve and protect our natural resources. There are many ways to balance the human need for natural resources with the availability of those resources. How can people clean up the air and water we rely on for life? What can be done about waste disposal? In this section, you'll see some ways people can make better use of natural resources.

Cleaning Up the Air

What kind of gasoline does your family's car use? If it is a late model car, it probably uses unleaded gas. Lead was a common component of most gasoline until 1970 when the Clean Air Act was passed in the United States. Since that year, all new cars have been designed to use only unleaded gas. The Clean Air Act of 1990 requires industries to reduce their sulfur dioxide emissions by 40 percent by the year 2000.

Figure 28-5. Water wheels like this have been used for centuries to harness the force of falling water to grind grain.

Reducing acid rain is a major focus of international groups today. At least 34 countries have agreed to work on solutions to the worldwide problem of air pollution. One way to reduce sulfur dioxide emissions is to change to another, renewable source of energy. In the desert, solar panels are now used to collect solar energy during the day. At night, this stored energy is used to produce electricity. Modern windmills like those shown in Figure 28-6 generate electricity that can be stored in batteries. Hydroelectric power has been used for many years all over the world. For example, the force of falling water turns turbines to generate electricity used by the city of Niagara Falls, New York. In the future, each country or region in a country may rely on local sources of energy rather than power plants operating far away. What renewable energy sources may be found where you live?

Cleaning Up the Water

When you brush your teeth, do you leave the water running? If you do, you are wasting water! Even though water is Earth's most abundant resource, safe, clean drinking water is scarce. Many communities must spend enormous amounts of money cleaning up water or finding clean water sources. Nearly every large community has water treatment plants that kill bacteria and filter out sediments from the water supply. Some communities reuse water. For example, water used to wash clothes could be recycled and used for washing streets or cars. Some communities have programs that help people learn to conserve water at home.

Farmers conserve soil and water by changing the way they farm. Contour plowing allows farmers to plow across fields to slow down erosion. Terracing is a way to prevent erosion in hilly areas. Today, many farmers no longer plow their fields each spring. Instead, they plant new seeds right through the leftover stubble of the last crop. Farmers can also reduce water pollution by conserving soil and reducing the need for fertilizers and pesticides.

Waste Disposal

Have you ever helped clean up a park or roadside? Wastes are natural resources in different forms. Newspapers, glass bottles, aluminum cans, and even plastic milk cartons are made from natural resources. Paper

Figure 28-6. Modern windmills harness wind energy in places where the wind blows constantly and steadily.

What do water treatment plants do?

EcoTip

Always water lawns, plants, and flowers early in the morning or in the evening after the sun goes down. Watering in the heat of the day results in rapid evaporation.

Science and WRITING

The use of landfills has become an increasingly controversial issue. Write to the appropriate agency in your state and find out what the current and proposed laws are regarding the types of materials deposited and where they come from.

Did You Know?

Today, the United States has 300 million hectares of forested lands, 20 percent more trees than it had 20 years ago.

Figure 28-7. Some endangered species may recover and increase in population size once laws are made to protect them and their habitats.

products come from trees and can be recycled. Glass, aluminum, and plastic are made from nonrenewable resources. It only makes sense to recycle these resources.

Today, communities all over the world recycle to reduce wastes and reuse precious natural resources. Some cities collect grass clippings and dead leaves and take them to a community composting facility. Other cities have built trash-burning power plants that use trash to produce electricity. Industry sees the potential for recycling plastics. In Chicago, one company recycles 2 million plastic milk jugs a year into "plastic lumber."

Protecting Soil and Forest Resources

Lumber companies in the United States practice selective cutting in which the largest, shade-producing trees are removed from a forest. This provides smaller trees with more sunshine so they grow at an even faster rate. **Reforestation** is the process of replanting a cut-over area with seedling trees. Reforestation helps to reduce soil erosion because the new trees absorb rainwater, and their roots hold soil in place.

Many countries have made efforts to protect forest resources by developing national parks and forests. In Nepal and India, forestry officials are educating farmers about reforestation and helping people create their own forests to harvest for firewood. Fast-growing tree seedlings are planted in community forests so that local people learn how to care for and manage forest resources.

Protecting Wildlife

Even though extinction is a natural process, the rate of extinction of wildlife today is very high. Countries such as Kenya and Tanzania protect endangered species by creating national parks and wildlife preserves. A **wildlife preserve** is an area of land set up to protect wildlife species. Hunting and fishing are prohibited in wildlife preserves to ensure that endangered species come to no harm. Out of more than 1000 species of endangered wildlife worldwide, more than half are in the United States.

Not every endangered species becomes extinct. In fact, since 1900 several endangered species in the United States have recovered as a result of laws that protect these species and their habitats. The wild turkey, pronghorn antelope,

Test Tube Tigers

Wild Bengal tigers have been pushed into isolated areas by human encroachment into their habitat. This separates potential mates and increases the chance of inbreeding. Captive populations also have breeding problems. Nicole, a captive Siberian tigress, became the first surrogate tiger mother when she gave birth to cubs conceived through in vitro fertilization.

Nicole and two Bengal tigresses were given an injection to induce ovulation. Ripe eggs were extracted from the Bengal tigresses and mixed in a petri dish with sperm from a white tiger. Fifteen embryos were implanted in Nicole. She gave birth to three Bengal tiger cubs. The male cub and one female did not live long due to medical problems, but the second female is fine.

Think Critically: How could in vitro fertilization be used to help wild populations?

bison, bald eagle, and American alligator are five species that have gone from near extinction to large numbers of individuals today. Wildlife preserves, new conservation laws, and public education programs help to conserve wildlife and protect wildlife habitats.

SECTION REVIEW

1. Define two conservation methods used by farmers.
2. List three sources of energy that are renewable.
3. Why can recycling aluminum conserve resources?
4. How does reforestation conserve soil and forest resources?
5. **Apply:** Describe three things that you can do to conserve and protect natural resources.

☑ Concept Mapping

Skill Builder

Draw a concept map that shows events that occur when a forest is clear-cut. Include the terms: *clear-cut, soil erodes, animal species leave, rainfall, no topsoil left, land unable to support plant life.* If you need help, refer to Concept Mapping in the **Skill Handbook** on pages 688 and 689.

Future Responsibility

New Science Words

environmental management

Objectives

▶ Explain the importance of environmental management.
▶ Identify ways in which individuals can contribute to environmental management.
▶ Describe ways in which individuals can conserve and protect natural resources.

Environmental Management

If you are an architect thinking about building on a hilly site, what do you need to know? You need to know the soil type and whether there is rock underneath to support the building's weight. If there will be landscaping around the finished building, you may want to preserve the large trees that are growing there. If there is a stream at the bottom of the hill, you may have to control erosion during construction. Looking carefully at natural resources and thinking about how your actions will affect the site is one example of environmental management. **Environmental management** is the use of methods that conserve resources and protect ecosystems.

With so many people on Earth, natural resources and ecosystems are under a lot of pressure. Whenever a development is planned, its effects on the environment must be considered and weighed against the benefits. When the Alaska oil pipeline was built, many people were concerned about damage to wildlife populations and the permafrost. These environmental hazards had to be weighed against the benefits of the pipeline. In many cases, changes made at the planning stages can reduce or eliminate damage to the environment.

Figure 28-8. In planning for development, the needs of wildlife must be considered along with the potential benefits of the project.

Individual Responsibility

Have you ever bought an apple at a grocery store and bitten into it, only to find a worm? Chances are this has never happened to you because commercial apple growers spray pesticides on their trees to prevent damage from pests. Would you purchase apples with wormholes if they were grown without chemicals? What are you willing to do to help protect and conserve natural resources?

In your community the police, sanitation workers, school teachers, firefighters, and homeowners all have responsibilities. You have the responsibilities of going to school, doing homework, and helping at home. Everyone must obey laws. But in addition to these, every person in your community also has responsibilities to the environment in which he or she lives.

What can you do to help? Help your family separate household garbage and recycle glass, plastic, aluminum, and paper. Use leftover foods to make a compost pile, and use the compost to improve your garden's soil. Take your shopping bag to the grocery store, and don't buy prepackaged foods. Always turn off the lights when you leave a room. These are things you can do to save energy, use resources wisely, and improve the environment.

In your community, you can volunteer your time to a conservation or environmental organization. Many schools have begun their own recycling programs. If your school or community doesn't have a recycling program, start one! Begin a tree planting program, or ask your class to adopt a stretch of highway. Make sure that used oil, paint, and batteries are disposed of properly. Remember—there is only one Earth, and all life depends on Earth's limited resources. If each person conserves and protects these resources, life on Earth will continue to amaze and delight for years to come.

What are your responsibilities?

MINI-Lab
How many families in your school recycle?
With the help of your teacher and approval of your principal, develop a survey paper that can be sent home asking families if, what, and where they recycle. Set a deadline for the return of the papers. Organize a way to tally the information and be sure to report to the families on the results. You might want to use recycled paper for this activity!

SECTION REVIEW

1. What is environmental management?
2. Why is environmental management important?
3. Name four things you can do to help conserve and protect natural resources.
4. **Apply:** If building a house on a site will result in erosion that will affect a stream, what could the builder do to eliminate the erosion? Explain.

☑ Recognizing Cause and Effect

List as many causes and effects of pollution in your community as you can. Suggest ways each source could be reduced or eliminated. If you need help, refer to Recognizing Cause and Effect in the **Skill Handbook** on page 683.

Skill Builder

28-4 Earth in 2030

New Science Words

environmental activists

Objectives

▶ Identify three issues that concern environmental activists.
▶ Describe ways to improve environmental conditions on Earth.

The Future: Grand or Grim?

Pretend you're in a time machine heading for the year 2030. You are hoping for the best, but you know that when you left the 1990s things were looking grim. Earth's population had nearly doubled between 1960 and 1990. More than 400 hectares of forest were being destroyed each day. Pollutants in the air were causing global warming and acid rain. In the United States, people were throwing away 160 million tons of solid waste every year. They were not thinking about the environment of future generations.

As you leave the time machine in the year 2030, you are very afraid of what you might find. Will the world still exist? What if you can't return? To your surprise, Earth is beautiful. It soon becomes apparent why. Huge numbers of people became **environmental activists,** people who worked to conserve Earth's resources and protect the environment.

The plastic containers that you sent to the recycling center are still here, although you don't recognize them. They've been molded into building material that is used to make park benches. No coal, oil, or natural gas is sold. Nuclear

SPACE BIOSPHERES VENTURES

BIOSPHERE II
TEST MODULE

energy is not available either. Solar energy and wind and water power are the main sources of electricity now. Homes are super-insulated to prevent cooling or heating. People don't drive to work, but walk or bike instead. Many people work in their homes and communicate with the office by computer or telephone. Even shopping is done from the home through computers. Air quality is good because deforestation was stopped in the year 2000. Landfills are no longer used, and everything is recycled over and over again. Nearly all material used in industry is made from recycled products, including the clock that tells you it is time to head back to the 1990s!

SECTION REVIEW

1. Name three environmental crises that need our immediate attention.
2. What are three things that you can begin doing today that will affect Earth tomorrow?

You Decide!

In the United States, most energy for heat and electricity is produced by burning fossil fuels. Nuclear power generation is a much cleaner process, yet it results in radioactive wastes such as plutonium. Most used plutonium is stored in vats of water at power plants because there is no material that can be used to make containers to hold plutonium for the 240 000 years it is radioactive. Should the United States switch from fossil fuels to nuclear power for its energy needs?

ACTIVITY 28-2
Identifying Air Pollution Sites

Problem: Where can you find air polluted with particulates?

Material
- 8 strips of cardboard 5 cm × 20 cm
- 4 strips of waxed paper 5 cm × 20 cm
- scissors
- hole punch
- string
- petroleum jelly
- stapler and staples

Data and Observations

Strip	Observations
1	
2	
3	
4	

Procedure
1. Draw circles 3 cm in diameter on one strip of cardboard. Cut out the circles. **CAUTION:** *Use extreme care with scissors.*
2. Cover one side of a waxed paper strip with petroleum jelly.
3. Place the waxed paper strip behind the cut out circles on the cardboard strip. Tape the waxed paper strip in place.
4. Cover the back of the waxed paper strip with a second cardboard strip. Staple the cardboard strips together.
5. Punch a hole in one end of the double cardboard strip. Place a piece of string through the hole and make a loop in it.
6. Repeat Steps 1 through 5 with the remaining strips.
7. Hang each of the strips in a different location. Choose one location that is inside a building. Handle the strips carefully so that you do not touch the petroleum jelly in the circles. Fasten each strip to an object with the string so that it will not blow away.
8. Record the locations.
9. Predict which location you expect to have the most particulates.
10. Wait two days and then gather the strips. Use care not to smudge the petroleum-coated sides.
11. Examine the circles on each strip with a hand lens. Record your observations.

Analyze
1. What particulates did you observe on the strips hung outside?
2. What particulates did you observe on the strip hung indoors?
3. Which site had the most air particulates?
4. Which site had the least air particulates?
5. How did your results compare with your predictions?

Conclude and Apply
6. Would you expect to find more or less particulates on a windy day? Why?
7. What types of air pollution cannot be detected on the strips?

CHAPTER
REVIEW

28-1: Natural Resources
1. All living things need natural resources such as air and water to stay alive.
2. Renewable resources can be replaced by nature. Nonrenewable resources are only available in limited amounts.
3. Human use of resources causes pollution of air, water, and land.

28-2: Conservation and Protection
1. Conservation is the wise and careful use of natural resources.
2. Renewable resources are conserved through conservation and protection.
3. Nonrenewable resources are limited but can be recycled to be used again.

28-3: Future Responsibility
1. Environmental management uses methods to conserve resources and protect ecosystems.
2. Individuals can contribute to environmental management by giving consideration to the environment when development is planned.

3. Individuals can conserve and protect natural resources by recycling, using resources wisely, and becoming active members of environmental organizations.

28-4: Science and Society: Earth in 2030
1. Environmental activists work to conserve Earth's resources and protect the environment.
2. Finding renewable sources of energy and recycling nonrenewable resources lead to a better environment.

Recycled   Recyclable

KEY SCIENCE WORDS

a. **conservation**
b. **environmental activists**
c. **environmental management**
d. **erosion**
e. **greenhouse effect**
f. **natural resources**
g. **nonrenewable resources**
h. **reforestation**
i. **renewable resources**
j. **solid wastes**
k. **wildlife preserve**

UNDERSTANDING VOCABULARY

Match each phrase with the correct term from the list of Key Science Words.

1. loss of soil
2. land area for protected wildlife
3. resources that can be replaced by nature
4. raw materials in environment needed by organisms
5. unwanted waste products
6. resources that are limited
7. replanting after trees have been cut
8. retaining heat by Earth's gas layer
9. wise and careful use of Earth's resources
10. using methods to conserve resources

CHAPTER
REVIEW

Choose the word or phrase that completes the sentence.

1. Dead organisms form fossil fuels such as _____.
   a. coal   c. natural gas
   b. peat   d. all of these

2. Nonrenewable resources include _____.
   a. gold   c. wind energy
   b. solar energy d. all of these

3. Air pollution is caused by _____.
   a. carbon monoxide   c. sulfur dioxide
   b. nitrogen oxide   d. all of these

4. Trapping of _____ causes the greenhouse effect.
   a. carbon dioxide   c. sulfur dioxide
   b. carbon monoxide   d. nitrogen oxide

5. Water polluted with _____ can cause organisms to die.
   a. sewage   c. pesticides
   b. heat   d. all of these

6. _____ is (are) nonbiodegradable waste.
   a. Grass   c. Leaves
   b. Aluminum cans d. None of these

7. _____ are in danger of becoming extinct.
   a. Natural resources
   b. Solid wastes
   c. Wildlife preserves
   d. Endangered species

8. Problems with sanitary landfills include _____.
   a. leaking drums
   b. little room left
   c. containing toxic wastes
   d. all of these

9. _____ can cause erosion of soil.
   a. Heavy rains   c. Strong winds
   b. Clear-cutting d. All of these

10. An example of an extinct animal is _____.
    a. dodo bird   c. American alligator
    b. wild turkey   d. all of these

UNDERSTANDING CONCEPTS

Complete each sentence.

11. _____ wastes cause cancer, birth defects, and other health problems.

12. Wastes that cannot be broken down by natural processes are _____.

13. _____ are sprayed on crops to prevent damage from insects and worms.

14. An area set aside to protect endangered species is a _____.

15. Planting seedlings to help a forested area is called _____.

THINK AND WRITE CRITICALLY

16. Distinguish between renewable and nonrenewable resources.

17. What is the importance of decomposers in a sanitary landfill?

18. How do reforestation programs, in which villagers own the forest, prevent soil erosion?

19. How can environmental activists affect how resources are used?

20. What happens to land that has lost topsoil?

21. Why is it beneficial to grow another crop on soil after the major crop has been harvested?

22. Explain the possible problems pollutants cause to water- and land-dwelling organisms.

23. Explain how car pooling saves fossil fuel.

24. What are the advantages gained by selective cutting rather than clear-cutting a forest?

25. Why is it important to do research now on solar energy, wind power, and water power?

MORE SKILL BUILDERS

If you need help, refer to the Skill Handbook.

1. **Classifying:** Classify each of the following as renewable or nonrenewable: copper, gold, trees, iron, wildlife, fossil fuels, cotton.

2. **Hypothesizing:** Make a hypothesis predicting what the greenhouse effect might do to Earth's climate.

3. **Sequencing:** Sequence the making and use of an aluminum can. Complete the cycle by recycling it!

4. **Designing an Experiment:** Design an experiment that could show the difference in air pollutants produced by older and newer cars.

5. **Concept Mapping:** Complete an events chain concept map using these occurrences:
   - organisms died millions of years ago forming. . .
   - fossil fuels such as petroleum, which is used to make plastic bags, cups, and . . .
   - gasoline which is burned by cars releasing the gases carbon monoxide and . . .
   - nitrogen oxide, which pollutes the air and returns to Earth in . . .
   - acid rain, which pollutes rivers, lakes, and forests, causing death of many organisms.

PROJECTS

1. Write a report on the recovery of animals that were endangered. How were they saved?

2. Find out what recycled items are available in your community and how you would be able to tell they are made of recycled materials.

UNIT 8
GLOBAL CONNECTIONS

The Environment

In this unit, you have studied how living things interact with each other. Now find out how that interaction is connected to other subjects and specific places in the world.

120° 60°

60°

30°

OCEANOGRAPHY

OIL SPILL AT PRINCE WILLIAM SOUND
Valdez, Alaska

Prince William Sound in Alaska received nearly 11 million gallons of oil when the *Exxon Valdez* ripped apart on the rocks. When and how the sea life of this area restores itself is still unknown. How can oil spills be prevented?

SOCIAL STUDIES

DECLINE OF THE RAIN FOREST
Amazon Basin, Brazil

Rain forests throughout the world are endangered, especially those in Brazil. Brazil is developing some of its rain forest land for farms and mining. How might the Brazilian government protect some of the rain forest?

666

ANCIENT WEATHER BURIED IN ICE CAP
Greenland
Greenland, the world's largest island, is capped by an immense ice field two miles thick. Climatologists from all over the world study the layers of ice to learn about the weather in ancient times. Why would it be important to know about the climate hundreds of years ago?

METEOROLOGY

PERILS OF NUCLEAR FALLOUT
Chernobyl, USSR
The disaster at the nuclear reactor at Chernobyl may have long-term effects on the health of people in Northern Europe. Radioactive fallout was carried by prevailing winds and picked up by Swedish monitoring stations soon after the tragedy occurred. Should all nuclear plants be required to undergo international inspection?

CHEMISTRY

A HOLE IN THE OZONE LAYER
Antarctica
Scientists studying the ozone layer over the South Pole have noticed an expanding hole in the layer. If it continues, incidence of skin cancer could rise. Why is the ozone layer so important to life on Earth?

ENVIRONMENTAL ENGINEER

Environmental engineers apply the theories of science and mathematics to solve real environmental problems. They may design special equipment to study ocean depths or probe outer space. A bachelor's degree in engineering is needed for beginning engineering jobs. Environmental engineering is a new technology and requires a degree in engineering, with environmental concerns as a specialty.

Students interested in environmental engineering should take courses in math and science. They will also need to have a knowledge of environmental problems. They may work for a state or federal environmental agency, for a water purification plant, or for a company that cleans up environmental accidents.

For Additional Information
Contact JETS-Guidance, 1420 King St., Suite 405, Alexandria, VA 22314.

UNIT READINGS

▶Carson, Rachel. *Silent Spring.* New York: Macmillan, 1969.
▶Grove, Noel. "Air: An Atmosphere of Uncertainty." *National Geographic,* April 1987.
▶Stover, Dawn. "Inside Biosphere." *Popular Science,* November 1990.

CAREERS

MARINE ANIMAL TRAINER

As marine parks have become more popular, the need for people to train, exhibit, and care for the animal performers has increased. Dolphins, killer whales, and seals don't naturally perform tricks. These wild animals must be taught how to perform, a task that can take months.

A person who wants to become a *marine animal trainer* should have an interest in animals and their behavior. Most animal trainers learn on-the-job as apprentices. They should have at least a high school diploma with credits in biology.

For Additional Information
Contact the International Marine Animals Trainer Association, Brookfield Zoo, Brookfield, IL 60513.

Abuelitos Piscando Napolitos

(Grandparents Picking Prickly Pears)
by Carmen Lomas Garzas

The painting, *Abuelitos Piscando Napolitos*, shows the harvest of prickly pear cactus fruits, which are used in Southwestern cooking. The artist, Carmen Lomas Garza, grew up in Kingsville, Texas. The painting is one of several works that represent Garza's response to the Latino movement. The artist wanted to show the culture of Mexican-Americans "in fine art form," as well as portraying the things that are important, beautiful, and moving to the culture. In painting these pictures, she has said that she wished to portray events that are meaningful to all Mexican-American culture.

From the picture, what can you tell about the climate of this area? The prickly pear cactus is common in the American Southwest. A number of desert animals, including the pack rat, use prickly pear cactus for food and a source of water.

Spines on cactus take the place of leaves and help to discourage predators. The fleshy pads that make up the prickly pear and other cactus are actually stems whose spongy tissues hold moisture. In the brief rainy season, these stems expand quickly as the cactus' shallow, but extensive, roots absorb the rainfall.

A number of desert animals use the spiny cacti to protect themselves. The jumping cholla (choy-yuh) cactus has stems that break off at the slightest touch. Large animals find it very unpleasant. But cactus wrens prefer to nest in chollas because they use the cholla stems to protect the entrance to their burrows.

Carmen Garza inherited her talent from her grandmother who was a skilled needleworker and from her mother, a self-taught artist. As a teenager, she decided to become an artist. Choosing this career was a challenge to the traditional role most Hispanic women follow.

In Your Own Words

▶ Think of an area near where you live that you and your family enjoy. It might be picnic area, a public garden, or a park. Draw a picture of the place and write a paragraph on how it relates to the ecology of the area in which you live.

Care and Use of a Microscope

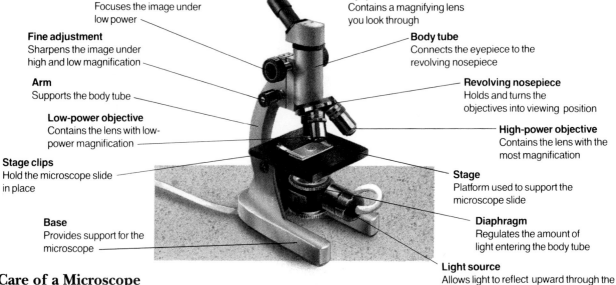

Coarse adjustment
Focuses the image under low power

Fine adjustment
Sharpens the image under high and low magnification

Arm
Supports the body tube

Low-power objective
Contains the lens with low-power magnification

Stage clips
Hold the microscope slide in place

Base
Provides support for the microscope

Eyepiece
Contains a magnifying lens you look through

Body tube
Connects the eyepiece to the revolving nosepiece

Revolving nosepiece
Holds and turns the objectives into viewing position

High-power objective
Contains the lens with the most magnification

Stage
Platform used to support the microscope slide

Diaphragm
Regulates the amount of light entering the body tube

Light source
Allows light to reflect upward through the diaphragm, the specimen, and the lenses

Care of a Microscope

1. Always carry the microscope holding the arm with one hand and supporting the base with the other hand.
2. Don't touch the lenses with your finger.
3. Never lower the coarse adjustment knob when looking through the eyepiece lens.
4. Always focus first with the low-power objective.
5. Don't use the coarse adjustment knob when the high-power objective is in place.
6. Store the microscope covered.

Using a Microscope

1. Place the microscope on a flat surface that is clear of objects. The arm should be toward you.
2. Look through the eyepiece. Adjust the diaphragm so that light comes through the opening in the stage.
3. Place a slide on the stage so that the specimen is in the field of view. Hold it firmly in place by using the stage clips.
4. Always focus first with the coarse adjustment and the low-power objective lens. Once the object is in focus on low power, turn the nosepiece until the high-power objective is in place. Use ONLY the fine adjustment to focus with this lens.

Making a Wet Mount Slide

1. Carefully place the item you want to look at in the center of a clean glass slide. Make sure the sample is thin enough for light to pass through.
2. Use a dropper to place one or two drops of water on the sample.
3. Hold a clean coverslip by the edges and place it at one edge of the drop of water. Slowly lower the coverslip onto the drop of water until it lies flat.
4. If you have too much water or a lot of air bubbles, touch the edge of a paper towel to the edge of the coverslip to draw off extra water and force air out.

Phylum Rhodophyta: most are many-celled and photosynthetic; contain red pigments; most live in deep saltwater environments; red algae

Phylum Phaeophyta: most are many-celled and photosynthetic; contain brown pigments; most live in saltwater environments; brown algae

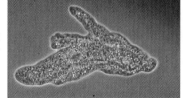

Amoeba discoides

Phylum Sarcodina: one-celled; take in food; move by means of pseudopods; free-living or parasitic; sarcodines

Phylum Mastigophora: one-celled; take in food; have two or more flagella; free living or parasitic; flagellates

Phylum Ciliophora: one-celled; take in food; have large numbers of cilia; ciliates

Phylum Sporozoa: one-celled; take in food; no means of movement; parasites in animals; sporozoans

Phylum Myxomycetes, Phylum Acrasiomycota: one- or many-celled; absorb food; change form during life cycle; cellular and plasmodial slime molds

Phylum Oomycota: live in water or on land; one- or many-celled parasites; absorb dead organic matter; cause diseases in plants and animals; water molds and mildews

Pretzel
Slime mold

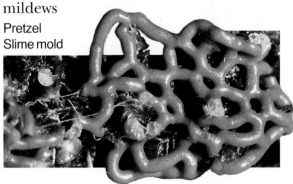

Division Zygomycota: many-celled; absorb food; spores are produced in sporangia; zygote fungi

Division Ascomycota: one- and many-celled; absorb food; spores produced in asci; sac fungi

Yeast × 7800

Division Basidiomycota: many-celled; absorb food; spores produced in basidia; club fungi

Mushroom

Division Deuteromycota: members with unknown reproductive structures; imperfect fungi

Lichens: organism formed by symbiotic relationship between an ascomycote or a basidiomycote and a green alga or a cyanobacterium; fungus provides protection and the algae or cyanobacterium provides food

Old Man's Beard lichen

Plant Kingdom

Division Bryophyta: non vascular plants that reproduce by spores produced in capsules; many-celled; green; grow in moist land environments; mosses and liverworts

Liverwort

Spore Plants

Division Lycophyta: many-celled vascular plants; spores produced in cones; live on land; are photosynthetic; club mosses

Division Sphenophyta: vascular plants with ribbed and jointed stems; scalelike leaves; spores produced in cones; horsetails

Division Pterophyta: vascular plants with feathery leaves called fronds; spores produced in clusters of sporangia called sori; live on land or in water; ferns

Club moss

Fern

Seed Plants

Division Ginkgophyta: deciduous gymnosperms; only one living species called the maiden hair tree; fan-shaped leaves with branching veins; reproduces with seeds; ginkgos

Division Cycadophyta: palmlike gymnosperms; large compound leaves; produce seeds in cones; cycads

Ginkgo biloba

Sago Palm

Division Coniferophyta: deciduous or evergreen gymnosperms; trees or shrubs; needlelike or scalelike leaves; seeds produced in cones; conifers

Slash
Pine
flower

Pine forest,
North Yukon,
Canada

Division Gnetophyta: shrubs or woody vines; seeds produced in cones; division contains only three genera; gnetum

Welwitschia mirabilis

Cranberries
and blueberries

Purple
Cornflower

Oranges
and
blossoms

Division Anthophyta: dominant group of plants; ovules protected at fertilization by an ovary; sperm carried to ovules by pollen tube; produce flowers and seeds in fruits; flowering plants

Blue
Columbine

Blind
Prickly Pear

Animal Kingdom

Phylum Porifera: aquatic organisms that lack true tissues and organs; they are asymmetrical and sessile; sponges

Phylum Cnidaria: radially symmetrical organisms with a digestive cavity with one opening; most have tentacles armed with stinging cells; live in aquatic environments singly or in colonies; includes jellyfish, corals, hydra, and sea anemonies

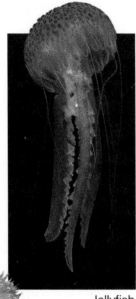

Jellyfish

Frilled Anemone

Phylum Platyhelminthes: bilaterally symmetrical worms with flattened bodies; digestive system has one opening; parasitic and free-living species; flatworms

Flatworm

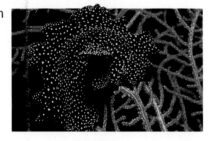

Phylum Nematoda: round bilaterally symmetrical body; digestive system with two openings; some free-living forms but mostly parasitic; roundworms

Phylum Mollusca: soft-bodied animals, many with a hard shell; a mantle covers the soft body; aquatic and terrestrial species; includes clams, snails, squid, and octopuses

Snail

Spanish Shawl Nudibranch

Phylum Annelida: bilaterally symmetrical worms with round segmented bodies; terrestrial and aquatic species; well-developed body systems; includes earthworms, leeches, and marine polychaetes

Christmas Tree worm

Phylum Arthropoda: very large phylum of organisms that have segmented bodies with pairs of jointed appendages, and a hard exoskeleton; terrestrial and aquatic species; includes insects crustaceans, spiders, and horseshoe crabs

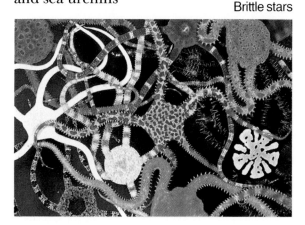

Swallowtail butterfly

Sally Light-foot crab

Jumping spider

Phylum Echinodermata: saltwater organisms with spiny or leathery skin; water-vascular system with tube feet; radial symmetry; includes starfish, sand dollars, and sea urchins

Brittle stars

Seahorse

Toucan

Phylum Chordata: organisms with internal skeletons, specialized body systems, and paired appendages; all at some time have a notochord, dorsal nerve cord, gill slits, and a tail; include fish, amphibians, reptiles, birds, and mammals

Peninsula turtles

Mare and foal

Organizing Information

Classifying

You may not realize it, but you impose order on the world around you. If your shirts hang in the closet together, your socks take up a corner of a dresser drawer, or your favorite audio cassettes are stacked together, you have used the skill of classifying.

Classifying is grouping objects or events into groups based on common features. When classifying, you first make careful observations of the group of items to be classified. Select one feature that is shared by some items in the group but not others. Place the items that share the same feature in a subgroup. Place other items in subgroups based on other shared features. After you decide on the first feature that divides the items into subgroups, examine the items for other features and further divide each subgroup into smaller and smaller groups until the items have no features in common.

How would you classify these socks?

Classify the socks based on observable features. You might classify sport socks in one subgroup and dress socks in another. The sport socks could be subdivided into a white subgroup and a striped subgroup. Note that for each feature selected, each sock only fits into one subgroup. Keep selecting features until all the socks are classified. The chart shows one classification.

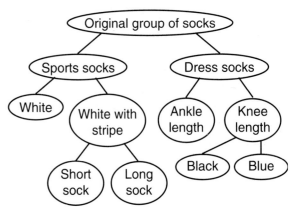

Remember, when you classify, you are grouping objects or events for a purpose.

Sequencing

A sequence is an arrangement of things or events in a particular order. A common sequence with which you are familiar is students sitting in alphabetical order. Think also about baking chocolate chip cookies. Certain steps have to be followed in order for the cookies to taste good.

When you are asked to sequence things or events, you must first identify what comes first. You then decide what should come second. Continue to choose things or events until they are all in order. Then, go back over the sequence to make sure each thing or event logically leads to the next.

Suppose you wanted to watch a movie that just came out on videotape. What sequence of events would you have to follow to watch the movie? You would first turn the television set to Channel 3 or 4. You would then turn the videotape player on and insert the tape. Once the tape has started playing, you would adjust the sound and picture. Then, when the movie is over, you would rewind the tape and return it to the store.

Outlining

Have you ever wondered why teachers ask students to outline what they read? The purpose of outlining is to show the relationships between main ideas and information about the main ideas. Outlining can help you organize, remember, and review written material.

When you are asked to outline, you must first find a group of words that summarizes the main idea. This group of words corresponds to the Roman numerals in an outline. Next, determine what is said about the main idea. Ideas of equal importance are grouped together and are given capital letters. Ideas of equal importance are further broken down and given numbers and letters.

To get an idea how to outline, compare the following outline with your textbook.

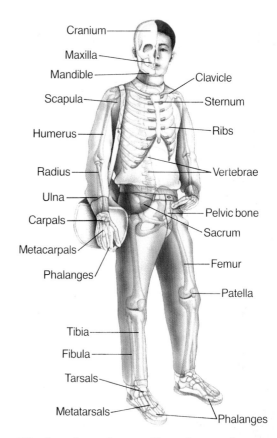

Chapter 17 Bones and Muscles

I. The Skeletal System
  A. The Human Skeleton
    1. What Is a Skeleton?
      a. made up of bones
      b. a frame work
    2. Four Main Jobs
      a. shapes and supports the body
      b. protects internal organs
        1. skull protects brain
        2. backbone protects spinal cord

Notice that the outline shows the pattern of organization of the written material. The bold face title is the main idea and corresponds with I. The letter A and numbers and letters that follow divide the rest of the text into supporting ideas.

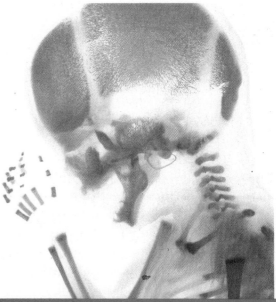

Thinking Critically

Observing and Inferring

Imagine that you have just finished a volleyball game with your friends. You hurry home to get a cold drink. Opening the refrigerator, you see a jug of orange juice at the back of the top shelf. The jug feels cold as you grasp it. "Ah, just what I need," you think. You hear the tone rise as you pour the juice into a tall glass. When you quickly down the drink, you smell the oranges and enjoy the tart taste in your mouth.

As you imagined yourself in the story, you used your senses to make observations. The basis of all scientific investigation is observation. Scientists are careful to make their observations accurate. Instruments, such as microscopes or telescopes, are used to extend their senses.

Often they use instruments to make measurements. When observations involve measurements, they are called quantitative observations. Because measurements are easy to communicate and provide a concrete means of comparing collected data, scientists use them whenever possible.

When you make observations in science, you may find it helpful first to examine the entire object or situation. Then, look carefully for details using your sense of sight. Write down everything you see before using another sense to make additional observations. Continue until you have used all five senses.

Scientists often use their observations to make inferences. An inference is an attempt to explain or interpret observations or to determine what caused what you observed. For example, if you observed a CLOSED sign in a store window around noon, you might infer the owner is taking a lunch break. But, perhaps the owner has a doctor's appointment or has taken the day off to go fishing. The only way to be sure your inference is correct is to investigate further.

When making an inference, be certain to make accurate observations and to record them carefully. Then, based on everything you know, try to explain or interpret what you observed. If possible, investigate further to determine if your inference is correct.

Comparing and Contrasting

Observations can be analyzed and then organized by noting the similarities and differences between two or more objects or situations. When you examine objects or situations to determine similarities, you are comparing. Contrasting is looking at similar objects or situations for differences.

Suppose you were asked to compare and contrast a grasshopper and a dragonfly. You would start by examining your observations. You then divide a piece of paper into two columns. List ways the insects are similar in one column and ways they are different in the other. After completing your lists, you report your findings in a table or in a graph.

Similarities you might point out are that both have three body parts, two pairs of wings, and chewing mouthparts. Differences include grasshoppers cause damage to crops but dragonflies destroy harmful insects or the grasshopper flies short distances but the dragonfly can fly long distances.

Recognizing Cause and Effect

Have you ever observed something happen and then tried to figure out why or how it came about? If so, you have observed an event and inferred a reason for the event. The event or result of action is an effect, and the reason for the event is the cause.

Suppose that every time your teacher fed fish in a classroom aquarium, she tapped the food container on the edge. Then, one day she tapped the edge of the aquarium to make a point about an ecology lesson. You observe the fish swim to the surface of the aquarium to feed.

What is the effect and what would you infer would be the cause? The effect is the fish swimming to the surface of the aquarium. You might infer the cause to be the teacher tapping on the edge of the aquarium. In determining cause and effect, you have made a logical inference based on careful observations.

Perhaps, the fish swam to the surface because they reacted to the teacher's waving hand or for some other reason. When scientists are unsure of the cause for a certain event, they often design controlled experiments to determine what caused their observations. Although you have made a sound judgment, you would have to perform an experiment to be certain that it was the tapping that caused the effect you observed.

Experimentation Skills

Measuring in SI

You are probably familiar with the metric system of measurement. The metric system is a uniform system of measurement developed in 1795 by a group of scientists. The development of the metric system helped scientists avoid problems with different units of measurement by providing an international standard of comparison for measurements. A modern form of the metric system called the International System, or SI, was adopted for worldwide use in 1960.

You will find that your text uses metric units in almost all its measurements. In the activities you will be doing, you use the metric system of measurement.

The metric system is easy to use because it has a systematic naming of units and a decimal base. For example, meter is the base unit for measuring length, gram for measuring mass, and liter for measuring volume. Unit sizes vary by multiples of ten. When changing from smaller units to larger, you divide by ten. When changing from larger units to smaller, you multiply by ten. Prefixes are used to name larger and smaller units. Look at the following table for some common metric prefixes and their meanings.

METRIC PREFIXES			
Prefix	Symbol	Meaning	
kilo-	k	1 000	thousand
hecto-	h	100	hundred
deka	da	10	ten
deci-	d	0.1	tenth
centi	c	0.01	hundredth
milli-	m	0.001	thousandth

Do you see how the prefix *kilo-* attached to the unit *gram* is *kilogram* or 1 000 grams, or the prefix *deci-* attached to the unit *meter* is *decimeter* or one tenth (0.1) of a meter?

You have probably measured distance many times. The meter is the SI unit used to measure distance. To visualize the length of a meter, think of a baseball bat. A baseball bat is about one meter long. When measuring smaller distances, the meter is divided into smaller units called centimeters and millimeters. A centimeter is one hundredth (0.01) of a meter which is about the size of the width of the fingernail on your little finger. A millimeter is one thousandth of a meter (0.001), about the thickness of a dime.

Most metersticks and metric rulers have lines indicating centimeters and millimeters. Look at the illustration. The centimeter lines are the longer numbered lines and the shorter lines between the centimeter lines are millimeter lines.

When using a metric ruler, you must first decide on a unit of measurement. You then line up the 0 centimeter mark with the end of the object being measured, and read the number of the unit where the object ends.

Units of length are also used to measure the surface area. The standard unit of area is the square meter (m^2), or a square one meter long on each side. Similarly, a square centimeter (cm^2) is a square one centimeter long on each side. Surface area is determined by multiplying the number of units in length times the number of units in width.

The volume of rectangular solids is also calculated using units of length. The cubic meter (m^3) is the standard SI unit of volume. A cubic meter is a cube one meter on a side. You can determine the volume of rectangular solids by multiplying length times width times height.

Liquid volume is measured using a unit called a liter. You are probably familiar with

a two-liter soft drink bottle. One liter is about one-half of the two-liter bottle. A liter has the volume of 1000 cubic centimeters. Since the prefix *milli-* means thousandth (0.001), a milliliter equals one cubic centimeter. One milliliter of liquid would completely fill a cube measuring one centimeter on each side.

During science activities you will measure liquids using beakers and graduated cylinders marked in milliliters. A graduated cylinder is a tall cylindrical container marked with lines from bottom to top. Each graduation represents one milliliter.

Scientists use a balance to find the mass of an object in grams. you will likely use a beam balance similar to the one illustrated. Notice that on one side of the beam balance is a pan and on the other side is a set of beams. Each beam has an object of a known mass called a rider that slides on the beam.

You must be careful when using a balance. When carrying the balance, hold the beam support with one hand and place the other hand under the balance. Also, be careful what you place on the pan. Never place a hot object or pour chemicals directly on the pan. Determine the mass of a suitable container and place dry or liquid chemicals into the container. Then determine the mass of the container and the chemicals. Finally, calculate the mass of the chemicals by subtracting the mass of the empty container.

Before you find the mass of an object, you must set the balance to zero by sliding all the riders back to the zero point. Check the pointer to make sure it swings an equal distance above and below the zero point on the scale. If the swing is unequal, find and turn the adjusting screw until you have an equal swing.

You are now ready to use the balance to find the mass of the object. Place the object on the pan. Slide the rider with the largest mass along the beams until the pointer drops below the zero point. Then move it back one notch. Repeat the process on each beam until the pointer swings an equal distance above and below the zero point. Read the masses indicated on the beams. The sum of the masses is the mass of the object.

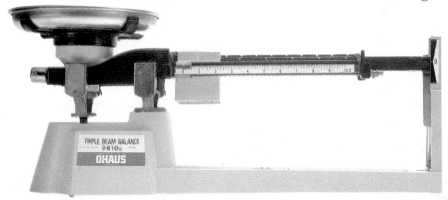

Hypothesizing

What would you do if the combination lock on your locker didn't work? Would you try the combination again? Would you check to make sure you had the right locker? You would probably try several possible solutions until you managed to open the locker.

Scientists generally use experiments to solve problems and answer questions. An experiment is a method of solving a problem in which scientists use an organized process to attempt to answer a question.

Experimentation involves defining a problem and formulating and testing hypotheses, or proposed solutions to the problem. Each proposed solution is tested during an experiment which includes making careful observations and collecting data. After analysis of the collected data, a conclusion is formed and compared to the hypothesis.

Imagine it's after school, and you are changing clothes. You notice a brownish-black spot on a favorite shirt. Your problem is how to remove the stain from the shirt without damaging the shirt. You think that soap and water will remove the stain. You have made a hypothesis, or proposed a solution to the problem. But, making a hypothesis is not enough. A hypothesis has to be something you can test. You try soap and water, but the stain doesn't budge.

Then you decide that you need to use a stronger solvent than water. You have revised your hypothesis based on your observations. The new hypothesis is still only a proposed solution until you test it and examine the results. If the test removes the stain, the hypothesis is accepted. But, if the test doesn't remove the stain, you will have to revise and refine your hypothesis again.

Using Variables, Constants, and Controls

When scientists perform experiments, they are careful to manipulate or change only one condition and keep all other conditions in the experiment the same. The condition that is manipulated is called the independent variable. The conditions that are kept the same during an experiment are called constants. The dependent variable is any change that results from manipulating the independent variable.

Scientists can only know that the independent variable caused the change in the dependent variable if they keep all other factors the same in an experiment. Scientists also use controls to be certain that the observed changes were a result of manipulation of the independent variable. A control is a sample that is treated exactly like the experimental group except that the independent variable is not applied to the control. After the experiment, the change in the dependent variable of the control sample is compared with any change in the experimental group. This allows you to see the effect of the independent variable.

Suppose you watch your guppies one morning and they don't seem as active as usual. You check the aquarium and notice that the aquarium heater is not working. You wonder how water temperature affects the activity level of guppies and decide to design an experiment. What would be your independent and dependent variables, constants, and control in your experiment? What would your hypothesis be?

This is how you might set up your experiment. Obtain several identical clear glass containers, and fill them with the same amount of water. Let the containers set.

On the day of your experiment, you fill a container with an amount of aquarium water equal to that in the test containers. After measuring and recording the water temperature, you heat and cool the other containers adjusting the water temperatures in the test containers so that two have higher temperatures and two have lower temperatures than the aquarium water temperature.

You place a guppy in each container. You count the number of horizontal and vertical movements each guppy makes during five minutes and record your data in a table. Your data table might look like this:

Number of Guppy Movements		
Container	Temperature (°C)	Number of movements
Aquarium Water	38	56
A	40	61
B	42	70
C	36	46
D	34	42

What are the independent and dependent variables in the experiment? Because you are changing the temperatures of the water, the independent variable is the water temperature. Since the dependent variable is any change that results from the independent variable, the dependent variable is the number of movements the guppy makes during five minutes.

What factors are constants in the experiment? The constants are using the same size and shape containers, filling them with equal amounts of water, and counting the number of movements during the same amount of time. What was the purpose of counting the number of movements of a guppy in an identical container filled with aquarium water? The container of aquarium water is the control. The number of movements of the guppy in the aquarium water will be used to compare the movements of the guppies in water of different temperatures.

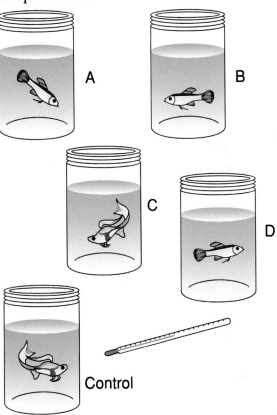

Interpreting Data

After doing a controlled experiment, you must analyze and interpret the collected data, form a conclusion, and compare the conclusion to your hypothesis. Analyze and interpret the data in the table. What conclusion did you form? The data indicate that the higher the temperature the greater the number of movements of the guppy. How does the conclusion compare with your hypothesis? Was it supported by the experiment or not?

Graphic Organizers

Concept Mapping

If you were taking an automobile trip, you would probably take along a road map. The road map shows your location, your destination, and other places along the way. By examining the map, you can understand where you are in relation to other locations on the map.

A concept map is similar to a road map. But, a concept map shows the relationship among ideas (or concepts) rather than places. A concept map is a diagram that visually shows how concepts are related. Because the concept map shows the relationships among ideas, it can clarify the meaning of ideas and terms and help you to understand what you are studying.

Look at the construction of a concept map called a **network tree.** Notice how some words are circled while others are written on connecting lines. The circled words are science concepts. The lines in the map show related concepts, and the words written on them describe relationships between the concepts. A network tree can also show more complex relationships between the concepts. For example, a line labeled "affected by" could be drawn from plants and animals to chemistry, because chemical processes occur in plants and animals. Another example of a relationship that crosses branches would be a line connecting Earth changes and matter and energy labeled "caused by interactions of." Earth changes are caused by interactions of matter and energy.

When you are asked to construct a network tree, state the topic and select the major concepts. Find related concepts and put them in order from general to specific. Branch the related concepts from the major concept and describe the relationships on the lines. Continue to write the more specific concepts. Write the relationships between the concepts on the lines until all concepts are mapped. Examine the concept map for relationships that cross branches, and add them to the concept map.

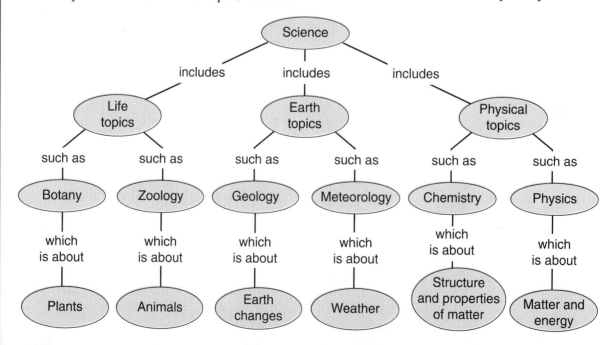

An **events chain** is another type of concept map. An events chain map is used to describe ideas in order. In science, an events chain can be used to describe a sequence of events, the steps in a procedure, or the stages of a process.

When making an events chain, you first must find the one event that starts the chain. This event is called the initiating event. You then find the next event in the chain and continue until you reach an outcome. Suppose your mother asked you to wash the dinner dishes. An events chain map might look like the one below. Notice that connecting words may not be necessary.

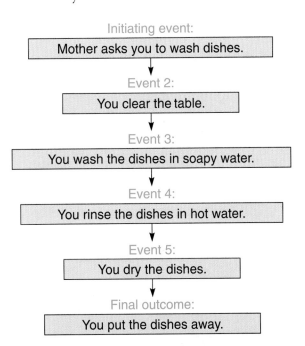

Initiating event:
| Mother asks you to wash dishes. |

↓

Event 2:
| You clear the table. |

↓

Event 3:
| You wash the dishes in soapy water. |

↓

Event 4:
| You rinse the dishes in hot water. |

↓

Event 5:
| You dry the dishes. |

↓

Final outcome:
| You put the dishes away. |

A **cycle concept map** is a special type of events chain map. In a cycle concept map, the series of events do not produce an final outcome. The last event in the chain relates back to the initiating event.

As in the events chain map, you first decide on an initiating event and then list each important event in order. Since there is no outcome and the last event relates back to the initiating event, the cycle repeats itself. Look at the cycle map of physical changes of water:

Complete Insect Metamorphosis

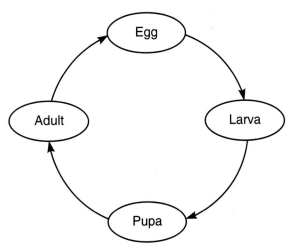

There is usually not one correct way to create a concept map. As you are constructing a map, you may discover other ways to construct the map that show the relationships between concepts better. If you do discover what you think is a better way to create a concept map, do not hesitate to change it.

Concept maps are useful in understanding the ideas you have read about. As you construct a map, you are constructing knowledge and learning. Once concept maps are constructed, you can use them again to review and study and to test your knowledge.

Making and Using Tables

Browse through your textbook, and you will notice many tables both in the text and in the activities. The tables in the text arrange information in such a way that it is easier for you to understand. Also, many activities in your text have tables to complete as you do the activity. Activity tables will help you organize the data you collect during the activity so that it can be interpreted easily.

Most tables have a title telling you what is being presented. The table itself is divided into columns and rows. The column titles list items to be compared. The rows headings list the specific characteristics being compared. Within the grid of the table the collected data is recorded. Look at the following table:

EFFECT OF EXERCISE ON HEARTBEAT RATE

Pulse taken	Heartbeat rate	
	individual	class average
at rest	73	72
after exercise	110	112
1 minute rest after exercise	94	90
5 minute rest after exercise	76	75

What is the title of this table? The title is "Effect of Exercise on Heart Rate." What items are being compared? The heart rates for an individual and the class average are being compared at rest and for several durations after exercise.

What is the average heart rate of the class 1 minute after exercise? To find the answer you must locate the column labeled "class average" and the row "1-minute rest after exercise." The data contained in the box where the column and row intersect is the answer. Did you answer 90? Whose heart rate was 110 after exercise? If you answered the individual, you have an understanding of how to use a table.

RECYCLED MATERIALS

Day of Week	Paper (kg)	Aluminum (kg)	Plastic (kg)
Mon.	4	2	0.5
Wed.	3.5	1.5	0.5
Fri.	3	1	1.5

To make a table, you simply list the items compared in columns and the characteristics compared in rows. Make a table and record the data comparing the mass of recycled materials collected by a class. On Monday, students turned in 4 kg of paper, 2 kg of aluminum, and 0.5 kg of plastic. Wednesday, they turned in 3.5 kg of paper, 1.5 kg of aluminum, and 0.5 kg of plastic. On Friday, the totals were 3 kg of paper, 1 kg of aluminum, and 1.5 kg of plastic. If your table looks like the one shown, you should be able to make tables to organize data.

Making and Using Graphs

After scientists organize data in tables, they often display the data in graphs. A graph is a diagram that shows a comparison between variables. Since graphs show a picture of collected data, they make interpretation and analysis of the data easier. The three basic types of graphs used in science are the line graph, bar graph, and pie graph.

A line graph is used to show the relationship between two variables. The variables being compared go on two axes of the graph. The independent variable always goes on the horizontal axis, called the x-axis. The dependent variable always goes on the vertical axis or y-axis.

Suppose a school started a peer study program with a class of students to see how it affected their science grades.

AVERAGE GRADES OF STUDENTS IN STUDY PROGRAM	
Grading Period	Average Science Grade
First	81
Second	85
Third	86
Fourth	89

You could make a graph of the grades of students in the program over a period of time. The grading period is the independent variable and should be placed on the x-axis of your graph. The average grade of the students in the program is the dependent variable and would go on the y-axis.

After drawing your axes, you would label each axis with a scale. The x-axis simply lists the grading periods. To make a scale of grades on the y-axis, you must look at the data values. Since the lowest grade was 81 and the highest was 89, you know that you will have to start numbering at least at 81 and go through 89. You decide to start numbering at 80 and number by twos through 90.

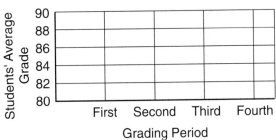

You next must plot the data points. The first pair of data you want to plot is the first grading period and 81. Locate "First" on the x-axis and 81 on the y-axis. Where an imaginary vertical line from the x-axis and an imaginary horizontal line from the y-axis would meet, place the first data point. Place the other data points the same way. After all the points are plotted, connect them with a smooth line.

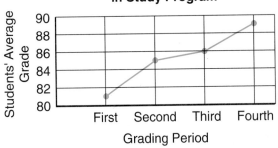

What if you wanted to compare the average grades of the class in the study group with the grades of another class? The data of the other class can be plotted on the same graph to make the comparison. You must include a key with two different lines each indicating a different set of data.

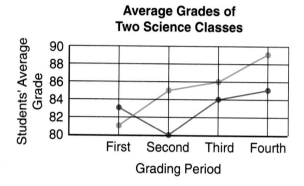

Average Grades of Two Science Classes

KEY   Class or study students ————
          Regular class ————

Bar graphs are similar to line graphs, except they are used to show comparisons between data or to display data that does not continuously change. In a bar graph, thick bars show the relationships between data rather than data points.

To make a bar graph, set up the *x*-axis and *y*-axis as you did for the line graph. The data is plotted by drawing thick bars from the *x*-axis up to an imaginary point where the *y*-axis would intersect the bar if it was extended.

Look at the bar graph comparing the wing vibration rates for different insects. The independent variable is the type of insect, and the dependent variable is the number of wing vibrations per second. The number of wing vibrations for different insects is being compared.

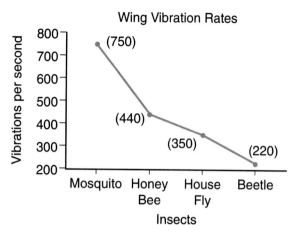

Wing Vibration Rates

A pie graph uses a circle divided into sections to display data. Each section represents part of the whole. When all the sections are placed together, they equal 100 percent of the whole.

Suppose you wanted to make a pie graph to show the number of seeds that germinated in a package. You would have to determine the total number of seeds and the number of seeds that germinated out of the total. You count the seeds and find that there are 143 seeds in the package. Therefore, the whole pie will represent this amount.

You plant the seeds and determine that 129 seeds germinate. The group of seeds that germinated will make up one section of the pie graph, and the group of seeds that did not germinate will make up another section.

To find out how much of the pie each section should take, you must divide the number of seeds in each section by the total number of seeds. You then multiply your answer by 360, the number of degrees in a circle. Round your answer to the nearest whole number. The number of seeds that germinated would be determined as follows:

$$\frac{143}{129} \times 360 = 324.75 \text{ or } 325 \text{ degrees}$$

To plot this group on the pie graph, you need a compass and a protractor. Use the compass to draw a circle. Then, draw a straight line from the center to the edge of the circle. Place your protractor on this line and use it to mark a point on the edge of the circle at 325 degrees. Connect this point with a straight line to the center of the circle. This is the section for the group of seeds that germinated. The other section represents the group of seeds that did not germinate. Complete the graph by labeling the sections of your graph and giving the graph a title.

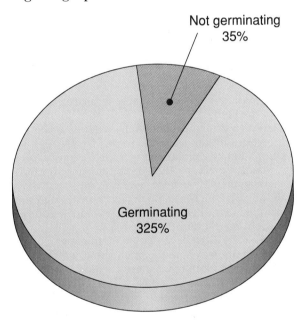

Not germinating
35%

Germinating
325%

Interpreting Scientific Illustrations

Illustrations are included in your science textbook to help you understand, interpret, and remember what you read. Whenever you encounter an illustration, examine it carefully and read the caption. The caption is a brief comment that explains or identifies the illustrations.

Some illustrations are designed to show you how the internal parts of a structure are arranged. Look at the illustrations of the stem in Figure 11-3 on page 256. The stems have been cut so that they show sections that are at right angles to the length of each stem. This type of illustration is called a cross section. If the stems were cut lengthwise in half, the sections would be called longitudinal sections.

Symmetry refers to a similarity or likeness of parts. Many organisms and objects have symmetry. When something can be divided into two similar parts lengthwise, it has bilateral symmetry. Look at the illustrations in Figure 13-3 on page 304. The right side of the butterfly looks very similar to the left side. It has bilateral symmetry.

Other organisms and objects have radial symmetry. Radial symmetry is the arrangement of similar parts around a central point. The sand dollar in Figure 13-3 has radial symmetry. See how it can be divided anywhere through the center into similar parts.

Some organisms and objects can not be divided into two similar parts. If an organism or object can not be divided, it is asymmetrical. Think about an amoeba. Regardless of how you try to divide an amoeba, you can not divide it into two parts that look alike.

Now look at the section of the dicot stem on page 256 again. Can you see that it has radial symmetry in cross section? If you were to make a longitudinal section through the dicot stem, you would see that it would have bilateral symmetry as well.

In your reading and examination of the illustrations, you will sometimes see terms that refer to the orientation of an organism. The word dorsal refers to the upper side or back of an animal. Ventral refers to the lower side or belly of the animal. The illustration of the planarian in Figure 13-12 on page 315 has both dorsal and ventral sides.

GLOSSARY

This glossary defines each key term that appears in **bold type** in the text. It also shows the page number where you can find the word used. Some other terms that you may need to look up are included, too. We also show how to pronounce some of the words. A key to pronunciation is in the table below.

PRONUNCIATION KEY

a . . . **ba**ck (bak)	oh . . . **go** (goh)	sh . . . **sh**elf (shelf)
ay . . . **day** (day)	aw . . . **so**ft (sawft)	ch . . . nature (nay chur)
ah . . . **fa**ther (fahth ur)	or . . . **or**bit (or but)	g . . . **g**ift (gihft)
ow . . . **flow**er (flow ur)	oy . . . **coin** (coyn)	j . . . **g**em (jem)
ar . . . **car** (car)	oo . . . **foo**t (foot)	ing . . . **sing** (sing)
e . . . **le**ss (les)	ew . . . **foo**d (fewd)	zh . . . vi**si**on (vihzh un)
ee . . . **lea**f (leef)	yoo . . . **pu**re (pyoor)	k . . . **c**ake (kayk)
ih . . . **tri**p (trihp)	yew . . . **few** (fyew)	s . . . **s**eed, **c**ent (seed, sent)
i (i + con + e) . . . **i**dea	uh . . . comm**a** (cahm uh)	z . . . **z**one, rai**s**e (zohn, rayz)
(i dee uh), **li**fe (life)	u (+ con) . . . flow**er** (flow ur)	

A

abiotic (ay bi AHT ihk) **factors:** nonliving things in the environment, including soil, water, temperature, air, light, wind, and minerals. (607)

acid rain: rain that combines with sulfur dioxide and nitrogen oxide in the air to form sulfuric acid and nitric acid and then falls to Earth. (268)

active immunity: immunity caused by the body making its own antibodies. (564)

active transport: movement of material through a cell membrane with the use of energy. (58)

adaptation: any characteristic of an organism that helps it to survive in its environment. (8)

adolescence: the period in human growth that begins around ages 12 to 14 and lasts until age 20. (542)

adulthood: the period in human growth that begins with the end of adolescence (age 20) and extends to old age. (542)

aerobic: requiring oxygen for respiration. (190)

aggression: a forceful act used to dominate or control another animal. (401)

AIDS: acquired immune deficiency syndrome, a fatal communicable disease caused by an RNA virus; spread by sexual contact, by use of contaminated needles, through the placenta or by nursing by an AIDS - infected mother. (186)

algae: plantlike protists that contain chlorophyll and make their own food; they have no roots, stems, or leaves and live in or near water. (203)

alleles (uh LEE LZ): the different forms a gene may have for a trait. (106)

allergens: substances that cause an allergic response in the body. (572)

allergy: a strong reaction of the immune system to a foreign substance. (572)

alternation of generations: in some protists and in plants, a cycle that alternates between sporophyte and gametophyte generations. (238)

alveoli (al VE uh li): in the lungs, clusters of tiny thin-walled sacs where oxygen and carbon dioxide are exchanged. (490)

Alzheimer's disease: a disease of unknown cause in which nerve cells in the brain fail to communicate with each other, causing memory loss. (520)

amino (uh MEE noh) **acids:** the building blocks of proteins. (443)

amniote egg: a type of egg that provides a complete environment for the developing embryo. (364)

amniotic sac: a thin membrane surrounding an embryo, filled with amnion (a clear liquid). (536)

amphibian: a cold-blooded vertebrate whose permeable skin, strong skeleton, and hibernation or estivation abilities adapt it to life in water and on land; examples are frogs, toads, salamanders. (356)

anaerobic: describes organisms that can't live in environments with oxygen. (190)

angiosperm: a vascular plant in which the seed is enclosed in a fruit, such as an apple. (256)

anorexia nervosa: an eating disorder in which a person eats very little to avoid gaining weight; it causes extreme weight loss that can damage organs and cause death. (456)

antibiotic: a drug used to kill bacteria. (194)

antibody: a substance made by the body in response to an antigen. (564)

antigens: proteins and chemicals that are foreign to the body. (564)

antiseptic: a substance that kills bacteria on living tissue. (559)

anus: an opening at the end of the digestive tract through which solid wastes leave the body. (317)

appendages: structures growing from the body, such as arms and legs. (332)

arteries: vessels that move blood from the heart. (465)

Arthropoda (AR thruh pahd uh): largest animal phylum; includes insects, shrimp, spiders, and centipedes. (332)

asci: the spore-producing sacs of sac fungi. (213)

asexual reproduction: reproduction in which a new organism is produced from a single parent. (80)

asthma: a disorder in which the bronchial tubes contract rapidly, causing shortness of breath or coughing; caused by smoking, allergy, or stress. (493)

atherosclerosis (ath uh roh skluh ROH sus): a circulatory system disorder in which fatty deposits form on artery walls and restrict blood flow. (468)

atria (AY tree uh): the two upper chambers of the human heart (*singular:* atrium). (464)

auxin (AHKS ihn): a plant hormone that causes plants to grow or bend toward light. (283)

axon: the part of a neuron that carries messages away from the cell body. (509)

B

basidium: the club-shaped spore-producing structure of club fungi. (214)

behavior: the way an organism acts toward its environment. (394)

bilateral symmetry: describes animals that have body parts arranged in the same way on both sides of their body. (304)

binomial nomenclature: the system of naming all organisms with two words; *Homo sapiens.* (157)

biodegradable: a substance that easily decomposes in the environment, usually by bacteria or fungi breaking it down into its basic elements. (66)

biogenesis: the theory that living things can be produced only from other living things. (11)

biological indicators: organisms that reflect the condition of the environment. (360)

biome (BI ohm): a large geographic area that has similar climates and climax communities. (632)

biosphere: all areas of Earth where life exists, including air, land, and water. (606)

biotic (bi AHT ihk) **factors:** living things in the environment, such as plants and animals. (606)

bladder: a bag-shaped muscular organ that stores urine until it leaves the body. (499)

blood pressure: pressure of blood in arteries. (467)

bog: low-lying, spongy, wet ground composed mainly of dead and decaying plants. (246)

brainstem: the part of the brain extending from the cerebrum to the spinal cord; controls involuntary muscle movements. (511)

bronchi: two tubes off the trachea that carry air into the lungs (*singular:* bronchus). (490)

budding: a type of asexual reproduction in which a new organism grows from the body of its parent; for example, yeast reproduces this way. (213)

bulimia (buh LEE mee yuh): an eating disorder in which a person eats huge amounts of food and then vomits to prevent weight gain. (456)

C

cambium (KAM bee um): tissue in vascular plants that grows to produce new xylem and phloem cells. (260)

camouflage: an adaptation that allows an animal to hide by blending into its surroundings. (613)

cancer: a major chronic disease resulting from uncontrolled cell growth. (571)

capillaries: microscopic blood vessels that connect arteries and veins; nutrients, oxygen, and wastes are exchanged through their one-cell-thick walls. (465)

carbohydrates: organic compounds that provide most of the body's energy; made up of carbon, hydrogen, and oxygen. (56, 443)

carbon-oxygen cycle: the continuous movement of carbon dioxide and oxygen between Earth's surface and the air. (618)

cardiac muscle: involuntary muscle tissue found only in the heart. (427)

carnivore: an animal that eats only other animals, such as a cat. (380)

carotenoids (kuh ROT uh noydz): red, yellow, or orange pigments found in plant-cell chloroplasts and in all cyanobacteria. (231)

carrying capacity: the number of animals that can obtain food and shelter from the environment in a given area; the ability of an environment to support its animal population. (407)

cartilage: a thick, tough, smooth, flexible tissue that is harder than flesh but softer than bone (like your ears); it covers the ends of bones to allow movement and cushion shock. (352, 422)

catalase: enzyme that breaks down hydrogen peroxide. (545)

cell: the smallest unit of an organism that can perform life functions. (6)

cell membrane: the selectively permeable outer boundary of a cell that allows food and oxygen to move into the cell and wastes to leave it. (37)

cell theory: a major theory of life science: all organisms consist of cells; cells are basic units of structure and function in organisms; and all cells come from other cells. (34)

cellulose: the organic compound that forms plant cell walls; made up of long chains of sugar molecules. (233)

cell wall: a rigid structure made of cellulose that surrounds a plant cell membrane to support and protect it. (41)

central nervous system: part of the body's control system, including the brain and spinal cord. (510)

centromere: a knotlike region that holds double-stranded chromosomes together. (76)

cerebellum: the part of the brain that coordinates muscle movements. (511)

cerebrum: the largest of the three parts of the brain; interprets impulses from the senses, stores memory, and controls voluntary muscles. (511)

chemical digestion: processing of food by fluids in the mouth, stomach, and small intestine, to break down large molecules into smaller ones that can be absorbed by cells. (451)

chemotherapy: the use of chemicals to destroy cancer cells. (571)

childhood: the period in human growth from age one to age 12. (541)

chitin: a strong, flexible carbohydrate forming the cell walls of hyphae and found in the body-covering and wings of insects. (211)

chloroplast: a plant cell organelle in which light energy is changed into chemical energy in the form of sugar during the process of photosynthesis. (41)

chordate: a member of the animal phylum Chordata that has a notochord, a hollow dorsal nerve cord, and gill slits at some time in its life cycle. (350)

chromatin: long strands of DNA in a cell's nucleus; chromatin coils into the form of chromosomes when a cell divides. (38)

chromosomes: threadlike strands of DNA and protein in a cell nucleus that carry the code for the inherited characteristics of an organism. (76)

chronic bronchitis: a disease in which too much mucus is produced in the bronchial tubes. (493)

chronic disease: a noncommunicable disease that lasts a long time. (570)

chyme (KIME): the thin, watery liquid in the digestive tract; partially digested food. (453)

cilia: short, hairlike structures that extend from the cell membrane and help tiny organisms move; found in respiratory passages. (207)

circadian rhythm: behavior that recurs on a 24-hour cycle. (404)

class: the third-highest taxonomical category, below a phylum (animals) or division (plants). (163)

classify: to group ideas, information, or objects, based on their similarities. (156)

clear-cut: the removal of all trees from an area of land. (360) **climate:** the average weather in an area, determined by rainfall, temperature, and sunlight. (632)

climax community: a stable community with a balance of abiotic and biotic factors. (631)

closed circulatory system: a blood-circulation system using vessels to transport blood to the internal organs, as in humans. (326)

cnidarians (ni DAIR ee uhnz): a phylum of animals having stinging cells. (311)

cocaine: a highly addictive stimulant drug made from the leaves of the South American coca plant. (589)

cochlea (KOH klee uh): a sound-sensitive structure in the inner ear; shaped like a snail's shell. (516)

coevolution: occurs when two species evolve structures and behaviors in response to changes in each other over a long period of time. (286)

cold-blooded: describes an animal whose body temperature varies with the temperature of its surroundings. (351)

collar cells: cells that line the inside of a sponge and help water move through the sponge. (309)

communicable disease: a disease that is transmitted from one organism to another. (560)

communication: an exchange of information among animals, by means of cries, movements, touch, speech, pheromones, and so on. (403)

community: all the populations of different species that live in the same place at the same time. (610)

competition: the striving among organisms for the existing food, water, and living space available in an ecosystem; competition determines the size and location of populations. (612)

compound light microscope: an instrument that uses lenses to magnify objects. (31)

conditioning: modifying behavior so that a response previously associated with one stimulus becomes associated with another stimulus. (398)

conservation: the wise and careful use of Earth's resources. (654)

consumers: organisms that can't make their own food. (63)

contour feathers: on birds, the strong feathers that give birds their coloring and sleek shape. (372)

control: in an experiment, the standard for comparison. (15)

controlled burns: managed forest fires set periodically to control vegetation and plant debris underneath the dominant forest tree species. (620)

coronary circulation: the flow of blood to heart tissues. (467)

courtship behavior: behaviors that help males and females of a species prepare for mating. (402)

crack: a strong form of cocaine. (590)

crop: in an earthworm, a sac in the digestive system that stores soil eaten by the worm. (328)

cuticle: a waxy protective layer on stems and leaves of a plant that helps the plant conserve water. (233)

cyanobacteria (si AN oh bak TEER ee uh): bacteria that make their own food from sunlight; often a blue-green color. (191)

cyclic behaviors: innate behaviors that occur in a repeating pattern. (404)

cyst: a young, parasitic worm with a protective covering. (318)

cytoplasm (SI toh plaz uhm): the fluid material inside the cell membrane that contains structures that carry out life processes. (38)

D

day-neutral plant: a plant that isn't very sensitive to the length of darkness and thus can flower over a wide range of days. (284)

deforestation: destruction of Earth's forests. (164)

dendrite: the portion of a neuron that receives messages and sends them to the cell body. (509)

depressant: a substance that slows the central nervous system, affecting judgment, reasoning, memory, and motor control. (584)

dermis: the inner layer of skin; it contains blood vessels, nerves, and sweat glands. (433)

development: the changes living things undergo. (8)

diaphragm (DI uh fram): a muscle beneath the lungs that helps move air in and out of the body. (490)

dichotomous key: a step-by-step guide to identifying an organism, requiring the choice of one of two descriptions at each step. (168)

dicots (DI kahts): angiosperms having two seed leaves inside their seeds; for example, maple trees. (256)

diffusion: the movement of molecules move where they are concentrated to where they are less concentrated; a type of passive transport in cells. (58)

digestion: the process that breaks down food into small molecules that can be absorbed. (451)

diploid chromosome number: in organisms that reproduce sexually, the total number of paired chromosomes in a body cell of the organism. (83)

disinfectant: a substance that kills bacteria on nonliving objects. (559)

division: the second-highest of the taxonomical categories in the plant kingdom (in the animal kingdom, the word *phylum* replaces division.) (163)

DNA: *de*oxyribo*nucleic a*cid; an acid in the nuclei of cells that codes and stores genetic information; consists of strands of molecules that control cell activities using coded instructions. (86)

dominant: the form of a trait that appears to dominate or mask another form of the same trait. (108)

dorsal nerve cord: a bundle of nerves that lies above the notochord in a chordate animal; the spinal cord in most vertebrates. (350)

down feathers: on birds, the soft, fluffy insulating feathers that cover their skin. (373)

drug: any chemical substance that changes the way a person thinks, feels, or acts. (580)

drug abuse: deliberate use of a drug for other than its intended purpose. (580)

drug misuse: use of a drug for the purpose it was made, but taking it improperly. (580)

E

echinoderms (ih KI nuh durmz): spiny-skinned invertebrate animals that live on the seafloor, including sea stars and sand dollars. (342)

ecology: the study of relationships between organisms and their environments. (23)

ecosystem: a community interacting with the nonliving (abiotic) parts of its environment. (611)

egg: in organisms that reproduce sexually, the gamete from the female parent. (82)

electron microscope: an instrument using beams of electrons that magnifies objects too small to be seen with a light microscope. (32)

embryo: a fertilized egg during early growth; in humans, a fertilized egg during the first two months of pregnancy. (537)

embryology: the study of embryos, which are the earliest stages of an organism's development. (142)

emphysema (em fuh SEE muh): a disease in which the alveoli in the lungs lose their ability to expand and contract, mostly caused by smoking. (492)

endangered species: one whose population is so small that it is in danger of extinction. (144)

endocytosis: a process by which cells transport a large body, such as a large protein molecule, through the cell membrane into the cytoplasm. (60)

endoplasmic reticulum (end oh PLAZ mihk re TIK yew luhm): a cell organelle consisting of folded membranes that move materials around within the cell. (39)

endoskeleton: the internal skeleton of an organism that supports and protects the internal organs and provides a frame for muscles. (351)

endospore (EN doh spor): a thick-walled cell that some bacteria produce around themselves, especially for protection from heat and drought. (194)

energy pyramid: a model of the flow of energy in a food chain; less energy is available at each level of the pyramid as you move toward the top. (616)

environmental activists: people who work to conserve Earth's resources and protect the environment. (660)

environmental management: conserving resources and protecting ecosystems by carefully managing their use. (658)

enzyme (EN zimz): a protein that speeds chemical reactions in cells without being changed itself. (57)

epidermis: the surface or outer layer of the two layers of skin. (432)

epiphyte: a plant that grows on other plants for physical support. (242)

equilibrium: condition in which the number of molecules of a substance is maintained at the same amount throughout a space. (59)

erosion: the wearing away of soil by wind, water, and ice. (651)

estivation: an adaptation for survival in hot, dry weather during which an animal becomes inactive and all body processes slow down. (356)

estuary: the area where a freshwater river or stream meets the ocean; examples are salt marshes, deltas, and mud flats. (638)

ethnobotany (eth noh BAH tuhn ee): the study of tribal people and their use of plants. (288)

eukaryote: an organism or cells with a formed nucleus and organelles surrounded by membranes. (161)

evolution: changes that occur over time in the hereditary features of organisms. (130)

exocytosis: a process by which a cell moves large molecules out through the cell membrane. (60)

exoskeleton: on all arthropods, the hard, lightweight external covering that shields, supports, and protects their bodies. (333)

extinction: the dying out of an entire species. (144)

F

family: the fifth-highest taxonomical category, below an order. (163)

fats: nutrients that release energy; also help the body store some vitamins. (444)

fermentation: a process by which yeast and some bacteria release energy needed for life processes by breaking down glucose into alcohol and carbon dioxide, without the use of oxygen. (65, 584)

fertilization: in organisms that reproduce sexually, the fusion of two gametes. (83)

fetus (FEE tus): a developing embryo; in humans, after the first two months of pregnancy. (538)

filter feeder: an organism that obtains food by filtering it from the water in which it lives. (309)

fins: fanlike structures on fish; adapted for steering, balancing, and moving through the water. (351)

fish: a cold-blooded vertebrate whose gills, fins, and scales adapt it to living in water. (351)

fission: a reproduction method used by bacteria in which one divides to form two bacteria having identical genetic material. (189)

flagellum (fluh JELL uhm): a whiplike tail on bacteria and some protists that helps them move through a moist environment. (189)

food chain: the feeding relationships that transfer energy through a community; starts with producers and moves through herbivores to carnivores. (614)

food group: a group of foods containing the same nutrients; for example, the meat group. (448)

food web: a series of overlapping food chains. (615)

fossils: remains of life from an earlier time. (137)

fracture: a break in a bone. (422)

free-living: organisms that find their own food and place to live without depending on other organisms; the opposite of a parasite. (315)

frond: the leaf of a fern. (244)

G

gametes: in organisms that reproduce sexually, the sex cells or haploid cells that join to form a zygote. (82)

gametophyte: the form of a plant that produces male and/or female gametes. (237)

gene: the region of DNA that directs the making of a specific protein, thus controlling traits that are passed to offspring. (89)

genetic engineering: experimental methods for altering genes in offspring, to produce desirable traits or eliminate undesirable traits. (121)

genetics: the study of how a gene affects the traits of an offspring. (106)

genome: a map of the location of individual genes on every chromosome of an individual. (122)

genotype: the combination of dominant and/or recessive genes (alleles) present in the cells of an organism. (110)

genus: the second-largest taxonomic category. (157)

gestation period: the time between fertilization and the birth of an offspring. (381)

gill: in water-dwelling creatures, a breathing organ that extracts oxygen from the water. (324)

gill slits: paired openings in the throat; in fish, they develop into gills for breathing under water. (351)

gizzard: in an earthworm, a muscular structure in the digestive system that grinds up soil. (328)

Golgi (GAWL jee) **bodies:** cell organelles consisting of stacks of membrane-covered sacs that pinch off and move proteins to the outside of the cell. (39)

gradualism: a model that describes evolution as working steadily, gradually, and continuously to slowly change species into new species. (135)

greenhouse effect: the process by which heat radiated from Earth's surface is trapped and reflected back to Earth by gases in the atmosphere, causing worldwide temperatures to increase. (649)

guard cells: in a plant leaf, cells that surround the stomata to open and close them. (261)

gymnosperm: a vascular plant that produces seeds on the scales of cones, such as pine cones. (255)

H

habitat: the place where an organism lives within a community. (610)

hallucinogens (huh LEWS un uh junz): drugs that affect the user's perception of the world, causing reality to be confused with fantasy. (591)

haploid chromosome number: in organisms that reproduce sexually, the number of chromosomes in a gamete. (83)

hashish: a drug that is more concentrated and powerful than marijuana. (588)

hemoglobin: a chemical in red blood cells that carries oxygen to tissues and gives blood its red color. (472)

herbivore: an animal that eats only plants. (380)

heredity: passing traits from parent to offspring. (106)

hermaphrodite: an animal that produces both sperm and eggs. (310)

heroin: a powerful pain-relieving drug made from morphine; it is highly addictive. (592)

heterozygous (het uh roh ZI gus): an organism that has two different alleles for a trait. (110)

hibernation: an adaptation for winter survival during which an animal becomes inactive and all body processes slow down. (356)

homeostasis: an organism's or cell's constant adjustment to maintain stable conditions in itself, despite changes in its environment. (7)

hominids: earliest humanlike primates; eat both meat and vegetables and walk upright on two feet. (147)

homologous: body parts in different species but which are similar in origin and structure, such as limbs on different animals. (141)

Homo sapiens: our own species, a hominid primate mammal. (148)

homozygous (ho muh ZI gus): an organism that has two identical alleles for a trait. (110)

hormones: secretions from endocrine glands that control certain body activities. (522)

hypertension (hi pur TEN chun): a circulatory disorder in which blood pressure is too high. (468)

hyphae (HI fee): masses of threadlike structures that form the body of a fungus. (211)

hypothesis: a prediction that can be tested. (14)

immovable joint: a juncture of two or more bones, made so that no movement occurs. (423)

immune system: a complex group of defenses that the body uses to fight disease. (563)

imprinting: a type of learning in which an animal forms a social attachment to another organism during a specific period after birth or hatching. (397)

incomplete dominance: a condition that exists when both alleles for a trait are expressed. (114)

incubate: to keep an egg or newborn animal warm; the heat helps eggs develop until they hatch and helps young to survive. (372)

infancy: the period in human growth from four weeks after birth to one year. (541)

innate behavior: behavior that an organism has when it is born and does not have to learn. (394)

insight: a form of reasoning that enables animals to use past experiences to solve new problems. (399)

instinct: a complex pattern of innate behavior involving multiple actions. (395)

interferon (ihn tuhr FEER ahn): a protein produced in animal cells that blocks viruses from reproducing in other cells. (184)

interneurons: nerve cells throughout the brain and spinal cord that transmit impulses from sensory neurons to motor neurons. (509)

invertebrate: an animal without a backbone. (303)

involuntary muscle: a muscle that can't be consciously controlled, such as heart and digestive muscles. (426)

joint: any place where two or more bones meet. (423)

kidneys: two organs that filter blood to produce the waste liquid called urine. (498)

kingdom: the highest of the taxonomic categories, having the largest number of species; kingdoms include all other categories. (156)

L

larva: a stage in development between egg and adult. (310)

larynx: the structure between the pharynx and trachea to which the vocal cords are attached. (489)

latent virus: a virus that becomes part of a cell's DNA and lies dormant until something causes it to become active, whereupon it destroys the cell and makes new viruses. (183)

law: a rule that describes a pattern in nature and what will happen under specific conditions. (18)

learning: the process of developing a behavior through experience; an organism repeats behaviors that fulfill a need and avoids those that achieve nothing or cause pain. (396)

lichen: a fungus living in a mutualistic relationship with green algae. (215)

life span: the length of time an organism lives. (8)

ligament: a tough band of tissue that holds bones together. (423)

limiting factor: a condition, such as the quality or amount of water or food, that determines whether an organism, population, or species survives in its environment. (628)

lipid: an organic compound that stores and releases large amounts of energy; fats or oils. (57)

littoral (LIHT uh rul) **zone:** the ocean zone along the shore that is covered with water during high tide and exposed to air during low tide. (637)

liverwort: a simple, rootless, nonvascular plant having a flattened, leaflike body. (236)

long-day plant: a plant that requires short nights (long days) to flower. (284)

lymph (LIHMF): fluid in body tissues made up of water, dissolved substances, and lymphocytes. (480)

lymphatic (lihm FAT ihk) **system:** collects fluid from body tissues and returns it to the blood through lymphatic vessels. (480)

lymph node: structures throughout the body that filter microorganisms and foreign material from lymph before it returns to blood. (481)

lymphocyte (LIHM fuh site): a white blood cell that fights disease-causing antigens by engulfing and digesting them. (481, 566)

lysosome (LI suh sohm): an organelle with chemicals that digest waste and worn-out cell parts. (40)

mammal: a warm-blooded vertebrate with insulating hair and mammary glands. (379)

mammary glands: glands in female mammals that produce milk for feeding young. (379)

manatee: a large, saltwater mammal living in warm coastal waters; commonly called a sea cow. (386)

mantle: in a mollusk, the outside covering of the soft body; it secretes chemicals that become the shell or protects the body if no shell exists. (324)

marijuana: a drug made of stems, leaves, flowers, and seeds of Indian hemp; also called pot. (588)

marrow: a red or yellow fatty tissue in certain bones that produces red and white blood cells. (422)

marsupial: a mammal with a pouch on its abdomen for carrying and nursing its young. (381)

mechanical digestion: processing of food by chewing, by churning, and by the action of bile, to break it into smaller particles. (451)

medusa: a cnidarian (stinging-celled animal) that is bell-shaped and free-swimming. (312)

meiosis: the division of the cell nucleus to produce sex cells (gametes). (82)

melanin (MEL uh nuhn): a chemical produced by the epidermis that gives skin its color. (433)

menopause: in older females, the period of years when the menstrual cycle becomes irregular and eventually stops. (533)

menstrual (MEN strul) **cycle:** in females, the cycle of egg production and menstruation. (532)

menstruation (men STRAY shun): in females, the monthly discharge through the vagina of the lining of the uterus and some blood if fertilization of an egg has not occurred. (533)

metabolism: all of the changes in an organism that enable it to live, grow, and reproduce. (63)

metamorphosis: in insects, the changes of form during the life cycle: egg, larva, pupa, adult. (337)

methamphetamine (meth am FET uh men): a very powerful stimulant. (587)

migration: the instinctive seasonal movement of animals, such as birds flying south for the winter. (405)

mimicry: a defense against predators in which an animal copies the appearance or behavior of another organism. (613)

minerals: inorganic nutrients that regulate chemical reactions in the body, such as building cells and sending nerve impulses. (446)

mitochondria (mi toh KAWN dree uh): a cell organelle that breaks down food molecules and releases energy. (40)

mitosis: the process by which a nucleus divides into two nuclei, each containing the same number of chromosomes that the parent cell had. (75)

mollusk: a soft-bodied invertebrate that usually has a shell, such as a snail. (324)

molting: in animals, the periodic shedding and replacing of the old body covering, such as skin or an exoskeleton. (333)

monocots (MAHN uh kahts): angiosperms having a single seed leaf inside their seeds. (256)

monotreme: a mammal that lays eggs having a tough, leathery shell; for example, the platypus. (382)

moss: a simple, rootless, nonvascular plant with leaflike growths that spiral around a stemlike structure. (236)

motivation: some stimulus within an animal that causes it to act. (398)

motor neurons: nerve cells that conduct impulses from the brain or spinal cord to muscles or glands throughout the body. (509)

movable joint: a place where two or more bones meet or are attached and allow movement. (423)

mRNA: *m*essenger *r*ibo*n*ucleic *a*cid, a nucleic acid produced from DNA that begins protein construction. (90)

mutation: any permanent change in the genetic material (DNA) of a cell. (91)

multiple alleles: having more than two alleles that control a trait. (115)

muscle: tissue that can relax and contract to allow movement. (426)

mutualism: a relationship in which two organisms live together; both benefit in some way. (215)

natural resources: raw materials in the environment that organisms use for survival, such as air, water, soil, and forests. (648)

natural selection: Darwin's theory that organisms best adapted with traits for an environment will survive to pass on those traits to their offspring. (132)

nephron (NEF rahn): the filtering unit of the kidney. (499)

neurons: nerve cells that carry impulses throughout the body. (509)

niche: the role of a species within a community. (610)

nitrogen cycle: the continuous movement of nitrogen from the atmosphere, to plants, and back to the atmosphere (or directly into plants) again. (619)

nitrogen dioxide: a major air-polluting chemical in cigarette smoke and automobile exhaust that is harmful when inhaled. (496)

nitrogen-fixing bacteria: bacteria that change nitrogen in the air into nitrogen compounds that are useful to plants and animals. (194)

noncommunicable disease: a disease that cannot be spread from one organism to another. (570)

nonrenewable resources: natural resources that are available only in limited amounts and are not being replaced by nature. (648)

nonvascular plant: a plant lacking tube-like vessels to transport food and water; it absorbs water directly through its cell membranes. (234)

notochord: a flexible, rodlike structure along the dorsal side (back) of a chordate animal; the backbone in vertebrates. (350)

nucleic acids: large organic molecules that store important information in cells and direct their activities; two types are DNA and RNA. (57)

nucleus: a structure inside a cell that directs the cell's activities; contains chromatin; chromosomes in a dividing cell. (38)

nutrients: the chemicals in foods that provide energy and materials for life activities. (442)

olfactory cells: nerve cells in the nasal passages that respond to chemical stimuli in air. (517)

omnivore: an animal that derives its energy from both plants and other animals. (380)

open circulatory system: a blood-circulation system that lacks vessels and instead bathes internal organs in blood, as in mollusks. (324)

order: the fourth-highest taxonomical category, below a class. (163)

organ: a structure made up of different types of tissues that work together to do a specific job; for example, the heart. (45)

organelles: membrane-bound structures within the cytoplasm of eukaryotic cells; organelles break down food, move wastes, and store materials. (38)

organism: a living thing that is made of one or more cells, uses energy, moves, responds to its environment, reproduces, adapts, and has a life span. (6)

organ system: a group of organs working together for a specific job; for example, the digestive system. (45)

osmosis: the passive transport of water through a cell membrane by diffusion. (59)

ovary: in angiosperms, the swollen base of the pistil, where ovules form (264); in female animals, the organ that produces ova, or egg cells. (531)

ovulation (ahv yuh LAY shun): in human females, the monthly release of an egg from an ovary. (531)

ovule (OHV yewl): the reproductive part of a female plant that contains the eggs. (262)

palisade (pal uh SAYD) **layer:** in a plant leaf, rows of closely packed cells that are near the surface and contain chlorophyll. (261)

parasite: usually an organism, but anything that obtains food from a host organism and at the same time harms the host organism. (183)

passive immunity: immunity caused by antibodies introduced from an outside source. (564)

passive transport: movement of material through a cell membrane without the use of energy. (58)

pasteurization: heating food to a temperature below boiling long enough to kill most bacteria. (559)

pathogen: any organism that causes disease. (194)

pedigree: a diagram that traces the history of a trait in a family. (119)

pelagic zone: the open ocean just beyond the sublittoral zone. (638)

periosteum (per ee AHS tee uhm): a tight-fitting membrane covering bone. (421)

peripheral nervous system: part of the nervous system, including cranial nerves and spinal nerves that connect the brain and spinal cord to other body parts. (510)

peristalsis (pe ruh STAHL sihs): contractions that move food through the digestive system. (452)

permafrost: in tundra areas of Earth, the deeper soil that remains permanently frozen underneath the topsoil layer. (633)

pesticide: a chemical that kills undesirable plant or animal pests. (340)

pharynx (FER ingks): a tubelike passageway for both food and air, located between the nasal cavity and the esophagus. (489)

phenotype (FEE nuh tipe): a physical trait in an organism; resulting from its genetic makeup. (110)

phloem (FLOW em): tubular cells in vascular plants that move food from leaves and stems to other parts of the plant for use or storage. (260)

photoperiodism: the flowering response of a plant to change in the length of day and night. (284)

photosynthesis (foht oh SIHN thuh sus): a chemical reaction used by producers, such as green plants, to produce food; light energy is used to produce chemical energy, converting carbon dioxide and water into sugar and oxygen. (63, 279)

phylogeny: the evolutionary history of an organism. (160)

phylum: the second-highest of the taxonomical categories in the animal kingdom. (163)

physical dependence: taking a drug because the body has a chemical need for it and can't function without it; also called addiction. (581)

pioneer species: the first plants to grow in a new or disturbed area; their decay creates material on which other plant species grow. (239)

pistil (PIHS tul): the female reproductive organ of a flower. (264)

placenta: part of the sac that surrounds an embryo in mammals; attached to the uterus; many blood vessels provide life support for an embryo. (381)

placental mammal: a mammal whose young develop inside the female in a uterus. (381)

plasma: the liquid part of blood, made mostly of water but also containing dissolved nutrients, minerals, and gases such as oxygen and carbon dioxide. (472)

platelet: a cell fragment that helps blood clot. (472)

poaching: illegal hunting of animals. (386)

pollen grain (PAHL un GRAYN): the reproductive part of a male plant that contains the sperm. (262)

pollen tube: a hollow structure that grows from a pollen grain into an ovule, through which a sperm swims into the ovule for fertilization. (262)

pollination: the transfer of pollen grains from the stamen to the ovule. (264)

polygenic (pahl ih JEHN ihk) **inheritance:** groups of gene pairs act together to produce a trait. (116)

polyp: a cnidarian (stinging-celled animal) that is tube-shaped and sessile. (312)

population: organisms of one species living in the same place at the same time. (134, 608)

population density: the number of individuals per unit of living space. (608)

Porifera: the phylum to which sponges belong; the name means "pore-bearing." (308)

predator: an organism that kills and eats prey to obtain energy. (352)

pregnancy: period between fertilization and birth. (536)

preening: a behavior of birds in which a bird uses its beak to rub oil over its feathers to condition them and make them water repellent. (373)

prey: an organism that is eaten by a predator. (352)

primary succession: the development of new communities in newly created land areas, such as new volcanic islands. (629)

primates: the group of mammals to which monkeys, apes, and humans belong. (146)

probability: a branch of science that determines the likelihood of something happening. (109)

producers: green plants that make their own food by photosynthesis. (63)

prokaryote: single-celled organism that doesn't have an organized nucleus or organelles. (161)

protein: an organic compound made up of amino acids; used throughout the body for growth and to replace and repair cells. (57, 443)

prothallus: the structure in ferns that produces gametes. (244)

protists: members of the Kingdom Protista; simple organisms having cells with a nucleus; probable ancestors of the fungi, plant, and animal. (202)

protozoa (proht uh ZOH uh): one-celled animal-like protists; many are parasites. (206)

pseudopod (SEWD uh pahd): a footlike extension of cytoplasm used by some organisms to move and to trap food. (206)

psychological dependence: taking a drug only because you think that you need it. (581)

pulmonary (PUL mo ner e) **circulation:** the flow of blood from the heart, to the lungs, and back to the heart. (466)

punctuated equilibrium: a model that describes evolution as working rapidly, changing species to new species by the mutation of a few genes. (135)

Punnett Square: a tool that shows how genes can combine; used to predict results in genetics. (110)

purebred: an organism that always produces the same traits in its offspring. (108)

R

radial symmetry: describes animals that have body parts arranged in a circle around a central point, similar to a bicycle wheel. (304)

radioactive elements: elements whose atoms give off radiation, a form of atomic energy. (138)

radula: in mollusks, a tongue-like organ with rows of teeth that scrape and tear food. (325)

recessive: the form of a trait that appears least often in offspring; for example, left-handedness is recessive compared to right-handedness. (108)

reflex: a type of innate behavior that is an automatic response to a stimulus; not involving the brain. (512, 395)

reforestation: replanting an area with seedling trees. (656)

regeneration: a type of asexual reproduction in which a whole new organism grows from just a part of the parent organism; a sea star. (309)

relative dating: estimating the age of a fossil by comparing it to younger fossils in the rock layer above and to older fossils in the rock layer below. (138)

renewable resources: natural resources that constantly are being replaced by nature. (648)

replication: the process by which DNA copies itself. (88)

reptile: a cold-blooded vertebrate that has dry, scaly skin and that lays eggs covered with a leathery shell; examples are lizards, snakes, turtles. (363)

respiration: a process by which some organisms release the energy they need for life processes by combining oxygen with glucose. (64, 280)

response: the reaction to a stimulus. (7)

retina: light-sensitive tissue at back of the eye. (515)

rhizoids: rootlike filaments containing only a few long cells; they hold moss plants in place. (236)

rhizome: the underground stem of a fern. (244)

ribosome: a cell organelle on which protein is made. (39)

S

saliva: the watery substance produced in the mouth that begins the chemical digestion of food. (452)

saprophyte (SA proh fite): any organism that uses dead material as a food and energy source. (193)

scales: hard, thin, overlapping plates that cover and protect a fish's body. (351)

scientific methods: problem-solving procedures used by scientists: define the problem, make a hypothesis, test the hypothesis, analyze the results, and draw conclusions. (14)

scrubber: a machine that blows water mist through gases in the smokestack of a fossil fuel-burning plant to remove sulfur dioxide and nitrogen oxide. (269)

secondary succession: the gradual return of a disturbed area to its former communities. (629)

sedimentary rock: a type of rock formed when fine particles like mud and sand settle out of water and become cemented together. (137)

semen: the mixture of sperm and a fluid that nourishes the sperm and helps them to move. (531)

sensory neurons: nerve cells that transmit stimuli from receptors to the brain or spinal cord. (509)

sessile: describes organisms, such as trees, that remain attached to one place during their lifetime. (308)

setae (SEE tee): in a segmented worm, bristle-like structures on the outside of the body that help it grip soil and move. (327)

sex-linked gene: an allele inherited on a sex chromosome. (119)

sexually transmitted diseases (STDs): diseases transmitted during sexual contact. (561)

sexual reproduction: a type of reproduction in which a new organism is produced by combining sex cells from two parents. (80)

short-day plant: a plant that requires long nights (short days) to flower. (284)

skeletal muscles: voluntary muscle tissue attached to bones; the muscles that makes the bones move. (427)

skeletal system: the body's network of bones, which form a rigid frame to support the body, protect internal organs, generate red blood cells, and store calcium and phosphorus. (420)

smooth muscle: involuntary muscle tissue that forms the walls of the stomach, intestines, uterus, and blood vessels. (427)

social behavior: interactions among organisms of the same species, including mating, caring for young, protection, getting food, and claiming territory. (403)

society: a group of animals of the same species living and working together in an organized way. (403)

solid wastes: solid products that can be recycled, burned, buried, or dumped. (651)

sori: structures that produce spores on the underside of fern fronds (*singular:* sorus). (244)

species: organisms whose members are alike and successfully reproduce among themselves. (130)

species diversity: the great variety of plant and animal species on Earth. (164)

sperm: the gamete or reproductive cell from the male parent, produced by the testes. (82, 530)

spiracles: in an arthropod, openings in the abdomen that allow oxygen and carbon dioxide to move into and out of the lungs. (333)

spleen: the largest organ in the lymphatic system; it filters blood and destroys old and damaged red blood cells. (481)

spongy layer: in a plant leaf, a layer of loosely arranged cells with xylem and phloem tissues; lies between the palisade layer and the lower epidermis. (261)

spontaneous generation: a belief that living things come from nonliving matter; for example, that frogs arise spontaneously from mud. (10)

sporangia: the round, spore-producing cases of zygote fungi. (212)

spore: a resistant reproductive cell that forms new organisms without fertilization; in fungi, ferns and some protists. (212)

sporophyte: a capsule in which spores are produced by meiosis in plants such as mosses. (237)

stamen (STAY mun): the male reproductive organ of a flower. (264)

steroid: a drug similar to testosterone; used to increase muscle mass; improves performance. (430)

stimulant: a substance that stimulates the central nervous system and speeds up other body systems; for example, the caffeine in coffee, tea, chocolate, and cola drinks. (583)

stimulus: anything an organism responds to, such as sound, light, heat, vibration, odor, movement, hunger, thirst, and so on. (7, 282)

stomata: in a plant leaf, small pores in the surface that allow carbon dioxide, water, and oxygen to enter and leave (*singular:* stoma). (261)

sublittoral zone: the shallow water above the continental shelf. (637)

succession: a gradual, orderly change of species in a community over time. (629)

symbiosis: a condition where two organisms live together for mutual benefit. (215)

synapse: the small space between two neurons across which impulses can travel. (510)

systemic (sihs TEM ihk) **circulation:** the flow of blood from the heart, to all body tissues (except lungs and heart), and back to the heart. (467)

T

target tissue: tissue affected by hormones. (522)

taste buds: tissue located on the tongue that responds to chemical stimuli. (517)

taxonomy (tak SAHN uh mee): the science of grouping and naming organisms.

technology: the application of scientific knowledge to improve the quality of human life. (22)

tendon: a thick band of tissue that attaches a muscle to a bone. (427)

tentacles: the armlike structures that surround the mouths of some organisms and help them to capture food. (311)

territory: an area that an animal defends from other members of the same species. (401)

testes: organs in males that produce sperm. (530)

theory: description of nature; subject to change when evidence changes. (18)

thymus: lymph organ that produces lymphocytes; behind the sternum. (481)

tissue: similar cells that do the same sort of work; for example, all muscle tissue contracts. (45)

tolerance: occurs when the body adjusts to a drug and needs increasing doses to produce the same effect. (581)

toxin: a poison produced by disease-causing organisms (pathogens). (194)

trachea: a tube that carries air to the bronchi. (489)

transgenic organisms: organisms that contain genetic information from another species. (92)

transpiration: in plants, loss of water vapor through the stomata of a leaf. (277)

trial and error: behavior that is modified by experience. (397)

tRNA: *t*ransfer *ribo*nucleic *a*cid, a nucleic acid produced from DNA that picks up amino acids in the cytoplasm and transfers them to the ribosome. (90)

tropism: the response of a plant to a stimulus. (282)

tube feet: in an echinoderm, structures attached to the water vascular system that act like suction cups and help the echinoderm to move, feed, get oxygen, and get rid of waste. (342)

tumor: an abnormal growth of tissue. (571)

tundra (TUN drah): a cold, dry, treeless biome where the sun is barely visible during the six to nine months of winter. (633)

umbilical cord: a bundle of blood vessels connecting the placenta to the embryo's navel in mammals; carries nutrients and oxygen to the embryo. (381)

ureters (YOOR ut urz): tubes that lead from each kidney to the bladder. (499)

urethra (yoo REE thruh): a tube leading from the bladder to the outside of the body. (499)

urinary system: a system of excretory organs that rids blood of wastes, excess water, and excess salts. (498)

urine: waste liquid collected by the kidneys and containing water, salts, and other wastes. (499)

uterus: in females, the pear-shaped, muscular organ in which a fertilized egg develops into a baby; also called the womb. (531)

vaccination: administration of a weakened virus to develop immunity against a disease. (568)

vaccine: a solution made from a killed or weakened virus; causes artificial immunity. (184)

vacuole: a storage area in a cell for water, food, or waste products. (41)

vagina: in females, the passageway that leads from the uterus to outside of the female's body; also called the birth canal because offspring pass through it when being born. (531)

variable: in an experiment, the factor tested. (15)

variation: the occurrence of an inherited trait that makes an individual different from other members within the same species. (133)

vascular plant: a plant having tube-like vessels that transport food and water to its cells. (234)

vascular tissue: in vascular plants, tissue made up of long cells that form tubes. (241)

veins: vessels that move blood toward the heart, carrying wastes. (465)

ventricles (VEN trih kulz): the two lower chambers of the human heart. (464)

vertebrate: animal with a backbone. (303)

vestigial structure: a body part that is reduced in size and is no longer used by the organism. (141)

villi (VIHL i): tiny, fingerlike projections on the inner surface of the small intestine. (454)

virus: a microscopic particle made of either a DNA or an RNA core and covered with a protein coat; it infects host cells in order to reproduce. (182)

vitamins: organic nutrients that promote growth, regulate body functions, and help the body use other nutrients. (445)

voluntary muscle: a muscle you can control, such as arm and leg muscles. (426)

warm-blooded: describes an animal whose body temperature stays the same, regardless of temperature changes in its environment. (351)

water cycle: the continuous movement of water in the biosphere through evaporation, condensation, and precipitation. (617)

water table: the upper surface of underground water; this underground water supplies drinking water for most humans. (641)

water vascular system: a network of water-filled canals, unique in echinoderms. (342)

wetland: an area of land covered by shallow water at least part of the year; for example, marshes, swamps, and bogs. (640)

wildlife preserve: an area of land set aside to protect wildlife species. (656)

withdrawal: an illness that occurs when a person stops taking a drug on which the person is physically dependent. (581)

X

xylem (ZI lum): tubular vessels in vascular plants that transport water and minerals from the roots up through the plant. (260)

Z

zygote: in organisms that reproduce sexually, the cell that forms in fertilization. (83)

INDEX

The Index for *Merrill Life Science* will help you locate major topics in the book quickly and easily. Each entry in the Index is followed by the numbers of the pages on which the entry is discussed. A page number given in **boldface type** indicates the page on which that entry is defined. A page number given in *italic type* indicates a page on which the entry is used in an illustration or photograph. The abbreviation *act.* indicates a page on which the entry is used in an Activity.

A

Acid rain, 268-269, **268**
  scrubbers, **269**
Active transport, **58**
AIDS virus, 186-187, **186,** 481-482, 561, 566, *566*
Air pollution, 649, 654-655, *act.* 662
  see also Natural resources
  Clean Air Act of 1990, 654
  greenhouse effect, *649,* **649**
Alcohol, 584-585
Algae, 203, *205*
  see also Protists
  brown algae, 205
  diatoms, 203-204, *203*
  dinoflagellates, 204, *204*
  euglenas, 203, *203*
  green algae, 204, *204*
  red algae, 205
Allergies. *See under* Diseases
Alternation of generations, **238**
Alzheimer's disease, 520-521, **520**
Amoeba, *206*
Amphibians, **356**
  see also Vertebrates
  as biological indicators, **361**
  frogs, 357-358, *357, 358, 361*
  origin of, 357
  population declines, 360-361

salamanders, *356,* 357-358, *361*
  toads, 356-358, *356, 357*
Anabolic steroids, 430-431
Angiosperms, **256**
  see also Plants
  cotyledons, **256**
  dicots, 256, *256*
  flowers, 263-264, *act.* 270
  importance of, 258
  monocots, 256, *256*
  reproduction, 263-264
Animals, 302
  see also Invertebrates; Vertebrates
  bilateral symmetry, **304,** *act.* 305
  classification of, 303-304
  experimentation on, 306-307
  radial symmetry, **303,** *act.* 305
  wild animal rehabilitation, 406-407
Antibiotics, **194**
Appendages, **332**
Aristotle, 156
Art, Science and, 415, 669
Arteries, **465**
Arthropoda, **332**
Arthropods, 332-333, *332*
  see also Invertebrates
  arachnids, 333-334, *333, 334*
  centipedes, 335, *335*
  crustaceans, 335-336, *335, act.* 339

exoskeleton, **333**
  insects, 336-338, *336*
  millipedes, 335, *335*
  spiracles, **333**
Audubon, John James, 415

B

Bacon, Sir Francis, 101
Bacteria, 189-190, *189, act.* 196, 562, *act.* 574
  see also Monerans
  aerobes, **190**
  endospores, **194**
  fission reproduction, **189,** *189*
  flagellum, **189**
  nitrogen-fixing bacteria, **194,** *194, 619*
  obligate anaerobes, **190**
  sexual reproduction, 189
H.M.S. Beagle, 177
Behavior, **394**
  aggression, **401**
  circadian rhythm, **404**
  communication, **403**
  conditioning, 398-399, **398,** *act.* 400
  courtship, 402-403, *402,* **402**
  cyclic behaviors, 404-405, *404*
  imprinting, **397**
  innate behavior, 394-396, **394**
  insight, **399**

instinct, **395**
learning, 396-397, **396**
migration, **405**
motivation, **398**
reflex, **395**
social behavior, **403**, *act.* 408
territorial behavior, 401-402, *401*
trial and error, 397-398, **397**
Bewley, Glenn, 545
Biodegradable substances, **66**
Biological indicators, **361**
Biomes, *632*, **632**
   see also Ecosystems; Water ecosystems
   climax community, **631**
   deciduous forests, 634, *634*
   deserts, 635, *635*
   grasslands, 634-635, *634*
   hardiness zones, *act.* 630
   limiting factors, **628**, *act.* 642
   marine ecosystem, 637-638
   northern coniferous forests, 633-634
   primary succession, **629**
   secondary succession, **629**
   succession, 628-629, *629*, **629**
   tropical rain forests, 635-636
   tundra, **633**
Biosphere, **606**
   abiotic factors, **607**, 617-619
   biotic factors, **606**
   carbon-oxygen cycle, *618*, **618**
   nitrogen cycle, *619*, **619**
   water cycle, 617-618, *617*, **617**
Biotic relationships
   competition, 612-613, **612**
   energy pyramids, 615-616, **615**, *616*
   food chains, *614*, **614**
   food relationships, 612-613
   food webs, 614-615, **614**, *615*
Birds, 372
   see also Vertebrates
   amniote egg, **364**, *364*
   bones, 374, *374*
   classification of, 376
   contour feathers, **372**, *373*, *act.* 378
   digestion, 374-375, *375*
   down feathers, *373*, **373**, *act.* 378
   egg incubation, **372**, 375
   eggs, 375
   flight adaptations, 372-374

flightless, 374, *374*
importance of, 377
origin of, 377
preening, *343*, **373**
reproduction, 375
respiration, 375
Blood, 471
   autologous blood transfer, 478-479, **478**
   blood pressure, **467**
   blood types, 115, 474-476
   cells, 472-473, *act.* 477
   clotting, 473, *473*
   diseases of, 476
   functions, 471
   hemoglobin, *472*, **472**
   homologous blood transfer, **478**
   lymphocytes, **481**, 566
   plasma, *472*, **472**
   platelets, *472*, **472**
Bog, 246
Bones, 421-422, *421*, *act.* 425
   see also Skeletal system
   of birds, 374, *374*
   development, 422, *422*
   fracture, *422*, **422**
   marrow, **422**
   periosteum, **421**
Botulism, 194
Brain, 510-511, *511*
   see also Nervous system
   brainstem, **511**
   cerebellum, **511**
   cerebrum, **510**

Caffeine, 585
Carbohydrates, 56, *443*, **443**
Cardiovascular system, 464
   see also Circulatory systems
   arteries, **466**
   blood pressure, **467**, *act.* 470
   blood vessels, 466-467, *466*
   capillaries, 466-467, **466**, *563*
   coronary circulation, **467**
   drugs and, *act.* 594
   heart, 464, *464*
   heart atria, **464**
   heart disease, 468
   heart ventricles, **464**
   pulmonary circulation, 465-466, *465*, **465**

systemic circulation, *467*, **467**
veins, **466**
Careers, 100, 176, 224, 296, 414, 552, 600, 668
Carson, Rachel, 225
Cartilage, 352, **422**
Cell structure, 36-42, *37*
   cell membrane, **37**
   cell wall, 41
   centromere, **76**
   chromatin, **38**
   chromosomes, **76**, 86, 88, *112*
   cytoplasm, **38**
   endoplasmic reticulum (ER), *39*, **39**
   Golgi bodies, *39*, **39**
   lyosomes, **40**
   mitochondria, **40**
   nucleus, **38**
   organelles, **38**, 39-41
   ribosomes, **39**
   vacuoles, **41**
Cell theory, 33-35, **34**, 535
Cells, **6**, 36, 44, *44*
   see also Organs
   active transport, **58**
   bacterial cells, *42*
   blood cells, 472-473, *act.* 477
   cell cycle, 75, *75*
   diffusion, **58**, 59
   endocytosis, **60**
   eukaryotic, 36
   exocytosis, **60**
   growth, 74
   metabolism, **63**
   mitosis, 75-78, **75**, *76-77*, *act.* 79
   passive transport, **58**
   plant, *45*
   plant cells, *41*
   plant vs. bacterial cells, 41-42, *act.* 43
   prokaryotic, 36, *36*
   tissues, **45**, *act.* 48
Chargaff, Edwin, 87
Circadian rhythm, **404**
Circulatory systems
   see also Cardiovascular system
   closed circulatory systems, **326**
   lymphatic system, 480-482, **480**, *480*, *481*
   open circulatory systems, **324**
Classification, 154-173, 156, *act.* 159, 674-679, 680
   see also Taxonomy
   of animals, 303-304

of the Arctic wolf, *163*
to classify, **156**
of plants, 234
of vertebrates, *act.* 388
Climate, **632**
Cnidarians, **311,** *act.* 314
  body plans, 312, *312*
  corals, 313, *313*
  importance of, 313
  medusa forms, *312,* **312**
  origin of, 313
  polyps, *312,* **312**
  reproduction, 312
  tentacles, **311**
Communities, **610**
  habitats, **610**
  niches, **610**
Concept mapping, 688-689, *688,*
  689
  cycle concept maps, 684
  events chains, 684
  network trees, 688
Consumers, **63**
Correns, Karl, 114
Crick, Francis, 86, *86*
Crop, **328**
Cyanobacteria, 191, *191, act.* 192
  see also Monerans
Cycles, 617-619
  carbon-oxygen, **618,** *618*
  nitrogen, **619,** *619*
  water, **617,** *617*

Dart, Raymond, 147
Darwin, Charles, 131-133, 135,
  177
Deforestation, **154**
  clear-cutting, **360**
Deoxyribonucleic acid (DNA),
  57, 86-87, *86, 87, act.* 94
  chromosomes and, **76,** 86, 88,
  112
  evolution and, 142
  genes and, 89-90, **89**
  replication, 88, *88*
  RNA compared to, 90
Diffusion, 58-59, **58**
Digestion, **451,** *act.* 458
  chemical digestion, **451**
  chyme, **453**
  enzymes and, 452, *452*
  in the large intestine, 455

mechanical digestion, **451**
in the mouth, 452
peristalsis, **452,** *453*
saliva, **452**
in the small intestine, 453-454,
  454
in the stomach, 453, *453*
Digestive system, human, *451*
Diseases, 558-559
  see also Heart disease; Immune
    system
  AIDS virus, 186-187, **186,** 481-
    482, 561, 566, *566*
  allergens, **572**
  allergies, 572-573, **572**
  Alzheimer's disease, 520-521,
    520
  antigens and, **564**
  antiseptics and, **559**
  arthritis, 570, *570*
  of the blood, 476
  cancer, **571**
  chemotherapy, **571**
  chronic diseases, **570**
  communicable diseases, **560**
  disinfectants and, **559**
  feline leukemia, 184
  microorganisms and, *act.* 567
  noncommunicable diseases,
    570
  pathogens, **194**
  of the respiratory system, 493-
    494
  sexually transmitted diseases
    (STDs), 561-562, *561,* **561**
  tumors, **571**
  vaccination against, 568-569,
    568
DNA. *See* Deoxyribonucleic acid
  (DNA)
Drugs, **580**
  abuse of, **580,** 586-587
  alcohol, 584-585
  caffeine, 585
  cocaine, *589,* **589**
  crack, *589,* 590
  depressants, **584,** 590
  from fungi, 216-217
  hallucinogens, *591,* **591**
  hashish, **588**
  heartbeat rate and, *act.* 594
  heroin, **592**
  label information, *act.* 582
  marijuana, 588-589, *588,* **588**
  methamphetamine, **587**

misuse of, **580**
opiates, 592-593
physical dependence on, **581**
psychological dependence on,
  581
stimulants, **585,** 589-590
tobacco, 583-584
tolerance for, **581**
from tropical forests, 288-289
withdrawal from, **581**

Ears, *516*
  cochlea, **516**
Eating disorders, 456-457
  anorexia nervosa, **456**
  bulimia, **456**
Echinoderms, 342, 343
  see also Invertebrates
  importance of, 344
  sea stars, *342,* 343, *344*
  tube feet, **342,** *343, 344*
  water-vascular system, *342,* **342**
Ecology, **23,** 606
Ecosystems, **611,** *act.* 622
  see also Biomes; Water ecosys-
    tems
  competition in, 612-613, **612**
Elements
  in human body, 55
  radioactive, **138**
Embryology, **142**
Endocrine system, 522-524, *523*
  hormones, **522**
  negative feedback, 523-524
  target tissues, **522**
Environment. *See* Biomes;
  Ecology; Natural resources
Environmental engineer, 668
Enzymes, **57,** 452, *452*
Epidemiologist, 224
Equilibrium, **59**
Estivation, **356**
Ethnobotany, **288**
Eukaryotes, *161,* **161**
Evolution, 130-153, **130**
  see also Species
  adaptation, **8,** 133-134
  coevolution, 286-287, **286**
  DNA and, 142
  embryology and, **142**
  fossil evidence for, 136-137
  gradualism, **135**

homologous structures, **141**
of humans, 146-149
by natural selection, 131-133, **132**
phylogeny, **160**
of plants, 231-233, 257
punctuated equilibrium, 135
variation, 133-134, **133**
vestigial structures, **141**
Excretory organs, 500
Eyes, *515*
retina, **515**

Farmer, 176
Fats, *444,* **444**
Feline leukemia, 184
Fermentation, 65, **584**
Ferns, 243
fronds, **244**
life cycle, 244, *244, act.* 248
sori, **244**
Fertilization, **83,** 535-536
Fingerprints, 115, *115*
Fish, 351-352, **351**
see also Vertebrates
bony fish, 353-354, *353*
cartilaginous, 352, *352*
fins, **351**
jawless fish, 352
lampreys, *352*
scales, **351**
water temperature and, *act.* 355
Flower, 263
see also Plants
parts of 264, *264*
Forest fires, controlled burns, 620-621, **620**
Fossil record, 138-140, *act.* 150
Fossils, **137**
of plants, 231, *231*
radioactive dating of, 138, *act.* 143
relative dating of, **138**
Franklin, Rosalind, 86
Free-living organisms, **315**
Fungi, 211-212, *211*
asci, **213**
basidium, **214**
bread mold, *212, act.* 218
chitin, **211**
club fungi, 214, *214*
drugs from, 216-217

hyphae, **211**
imperfect fungi, 214
lichens, **215**
sac fungi, 213, *213*
sporangia, **212**
spores, *212,* **212**
yeasts, 213, *213*
zygote fungi, 212, *212*

Gamete
See Reproduction
Gardener, professional, 296
Genetic counselor, 176
Genetics, 106-127, **106**
see also Heredity; Reproduction, sexual
alleles, **106,** *107*
alleles, multiple, **115**
chromosome maps, 122, *123*
dominant factors, **108**
genetic disorders, 117
genetic engineering, **121**
genotypes, **110**
heterozygous organisms, **110**
homozygous organisms, **110**
Human Genome Project, 122-123
incomplete dominance, **114**
mutations, **91,** 117, 134
pedigree, **119**
phenotypes, **110**
polygenic inheritance, **116,** *act.* 124
Punnett square, 110-111, *110,* **110,** *act.* 113
purebred, **108**
recessive factors, **108**
sex determination, 118
sex-linked disorders, 119
sex-linked genes, **119**
Geologic time scale, *139*
Gills, **324,** 351, *351*
Gizzard, **328**
Global Connections, 98-99, 174, 175, 222-223, 294-295, 412-413, 550-551, 598-599, 666-667
Graphs, 691-693, *691, 692, 693*
Gymnosperms, *255,* **255**
see also Plants
reproduction, 262-263

Habitats, **610**
Harvey, William, 466
Hearing, 516, *516*
Heart disease, 468
see also Disease
atherosclerosis, *468,* **468**
hypertension, **468**
Heredity, 104-127, **106**
see also Genetics
Hibernation, **356,** 404-405
Hippocratic Oath, 601
Home healthcare aide, 552
Homeostasis, **7,** 434, 508
Hooke, Robert, 33
Hormones, 522- 524, **522**
Human growth, *act.* 546
see also Reproduction, human
adolescence, **542**
adulthood, 542-543, **542**
aging, 544-545
amniotic sac, **537**
catalase, **545**
childbirth, 540
childhood, **541**
embryo, 537-538, *537,* **537,** *538*
fetus, **538**
infancy, **541**
twins, 539, *539*
Humans
ancestors of, 147-149
Homo sapiens, 148-149, **148**

Illustrations, scientific, 693
Immune system, **563**
see also Disease
active immunity, **564**
AIDS virus and, 566, *566*
antibodies, *564,* **564**
lymphocytes, **566**
passive immunity, **564,** 565
Information organization, 680-681
classifying, 680
outlining, 681
sequencing, 680
Insects, 336-338, *336*
Instinct, **395**

International System of Units (SI), 19-21, 673, 684-685
Invertebrates, **303**
  see also Animals; Arthropods; Cnidarians; Echinoderms; Sponges; Worms

Janssen, Zacharias, 31
Jenner, Edward, 184, 568
Johanson, Donald, 147
Johnson, Ben, 431

Koch, Robert, 559
Kohler, Wolfgang, 399

Laboratory technician, 100
Lamarck, Jean Baptiste de, 131
Landsteiner, Karl, 115, 474, 475
Laughlin, Harold, 136, 137
Leakey, Louis, 148, 175
Leakey, Mary, 148, 175
Leakey, Richard, 148, 175
Leaves, 261
  see also Plants
  guard cells, **261**
  palisade layer, **261**
  spongy layer, **261**
  stomata, **261**, 276-277, *277, act.* 281
Licensed practical nurse, 600
Life, origin of, 10-12
  biogenesis, **11**
  spontaneous generation, **10**
Linnaeus, Carolus, 157
Lipids, **56**
Lister, Joseph, 559
Literature, Science and, 101, 177, 225, 297, 553, 601
Liverworts, 236-237, **236**, *act.* 240
  see also Plants
  importance of, 239
  reproduction, 238
Lomas Garza, Carmen, 669
Lymphatic system, **480**, *481*
  lymph, 480-481, *480*, **480**
  lymph nodes, **481**

lymphocytes, **481**, 566

Madson, John, 297
Mammals, 379-380, **379**
  see also Vertebrates
  carnivores, **380**
  classification of, 382-383
  development, 381-382, *381*
  gestation period, **381**
  herbivores, **380**
  importance of, 384-385
  mammary glands, **379**
  marsupials, 381-382, *381*, **381**
  omnivores, **380**
  origin of, 384
  placenta, **381**
  placental mammals, **381**
  reproduction, 381-382
  teeth, 380
  umbilical cord, **381**
Manatees, 386-387, **386**
Marine animal trainer, 668
Marsupials, 381-382, *381*, **381**
Matter, 54-56
Meiosis, 82-85, **82**, *84-85*
Mendel, Gregor, 107-109, *107*, 112
Metamorphosis, **337**
  of frogs, *358*
  of insects, *337*
Metric system. *See* International System of Units (SI)
Microbiologist, 600
Microscopes, 30-32, *31*, 670
  compound light microscope, **31**
  electron microscope, **32**
Migration, **405**
Miller, Stanley L., 12
Minerals, **446**
Mitosis, 75-81, **75**, *76-77*
Mollusks, *324*, **324**
  bivalves, 325, *325*
  cephalopods, 325-326, *325*
  importance of, 326
  larva, *330*
  mantle, **324**
  radula, **325**
  univalves, 325, *325*
Molting, *333*, **333**
Monerans, 160-161, 188
  see also Bacteria; Cyanobacteria

saprophytes, **193**
Monotremes, *383*, **383**
Morgan, Thomas Hunt, 106
Morrison, Toni, 553
Mosquitoes, *208*
Mosses, 236, *act.* 240
  see also Plants
  alternation of generations, **238**
  club mosses, 242, *242*
  gametophytes, **237**
  importance of, 239
  life cycle, 237-238
  peat moss, 246-247
  spike mosses, 242
  sporophytes, *237*, **237**
Muscular system, 426-429, 426
  cardiac muscle, **427**
  of humans, *426*
  involuntary muscles, **426**
  muscle tissues, 427, *427*
  muscles, **426**, *act.* 436
  skeletal muscles, **427**
  smooth muscles, **427**
  tendons, **427**
  voluntary muscles, **426**
  work of muscles, 428-429, *428*
Mushroom farmer, 224
Mutualism, 215, 286

Natural resources, **648**, 649
  see also Air pollution; Water
  biodegradable substances, *act.* 652
  conservation, **654**, 658-659
  environmental activists, **660**
  environmental issues, 660-661
  environmental management, **658**
  forest resources, 651
  land pollution, 650-651
  nonrenewable resources, 648-649, **648**
  reforestation, **656**
  renewable resources, **648**
  soil erosion, **651**
  waste disposal and, 655-656
  wildlife, 653
Nervous system, 508-521, *510*
  see also Brain
  axons, *509*, **509**
  central nervous system, 510-512, **510**
  dendrites, *509*, **509**

interneurons, **509**
motor neurons, **509**
neurons, *509,* **509**
peripheral nervous system, **510,** 512, *512*
reflexes, 512-513, **512,** *513*
sensory neurons, **509**
spinal cord, 512, *512*
synapses, *510,* **510**
Nucleic acids, 57
Nutrients, *442,* **442**
   amino acids, **443**
   carbohydrates, 56, *443,* **443**
   fats, *444,* **444**
   food groups and, 448-449, *448,* **448**
   proteins, 57, 443-444, **443**
   vitamins, 445-446, **445,** *act.* 450

Oparin, Alexander I., 11-12
Organisms, 6-9, **6**
   adaptation, **8**
   development, **8**
   life span, **8**
   transgenic, 92-93, **92**
Organs, **45**
   see also Cells
   organ systems, **45**
   transplant rejection, **46**
   transplants, 46-57
Osmosis, **59,** *act.* 62

Pain, 518
Painting, 415, 669
Parasites, **183,** 208, 212, 285, 614
Pasteur, Louis, **11,** 195, 558
Pasteurization, **559**
Pathogens, **194**
Pavlov, Ivan P., 398-399
Peat bogs, 246-247
Permafrost, **633**
Pesticides, 340-341, **340**
   DDT, 340-341, **340**
Photosynthesis, 63, *act.* 68, 277-279, **278**
Physical therapist, 552
Plant pathologist, 296

Plant reproduction
   see also Reproduction
   angiosperms, 263-264
   gymnosperms, 262-263
   ovary, **264**
   ovules, **262**
   pistil, **264**
   pollen grains, **262**
   pollen tube, **262**
   pollination, **264**
   stamen, **264**
Plants, 230-231
   see also Angiosperms; Ferns; Gymnosperms; Leaves; Liverworts; Mosses; Plant reproduction; Stems
   auxins, **283**
   carotenoids, **231**
   cellulose in, **233**
   classification of, 234
   cuticle, **233**
   day-neutral plants, **284**
   dicots, **256**
   drugs from, 288-289
   epiphytes, **242**
   evolution of, 231-233, 257
   gas exchange in, 276-277
   hardiness zones for, *act.* 630
   horsetails, 242-243
   long-day plants, **284**
   monocots, **256**
   nonvascular plants, **234,** 236-239, *act.* 240
   photoperiodism, **284**
   photosynthesis, 277-279, **278**
   pioneer species, **239,** *239*
   respiration in, 279-280, **279**
   rhizomes, **244**
   roots, 259
   seed dispersal, 265-266
   seed germination, 265-266, *act.* 642
   seed parts, *264, act.* 267
   seed plants, 254-255, 257-258
   short-day plants, **284**
   transpiration, **277**
   tropisms, **282,** *act.* 290
   vascular plants, **234,** 241
   vascular tissue, **241**
Poaching, **387**
Populations, **608,** *act.* 609
   population density, **608**
Porifera, **308**
Predators, **352**
Pressure, 518

Prey, **352**
   camouflage, *613,* **613**
   mimicry, *613,* **613**
Priestley, Joseph, 488
Primates, 146-147, **146**
   hominids, **147**
Probability, **109**
Problem solving
   allergies, 573
   biotic potential, 133
   blood types, 475
   classification, 158
   climbing vines, 283
   color vision in dogs, 384
   complex carbohydrates, 449
   cool suit, 499
   diabetes, 524
   E. coli bacteria, 190
   fern sori, 245
   heartworm disease, 317
   human gestation, 536
   marsupial frogs, 359
   medicine brands comparison, 16
   mitosis, 78
   muscle work, 429
   osmosis, 61
   oxygen in water, 639
   passive smoke, 583
   seed viability, 265
   seedlings, 607
   slime molds, 209
   smog, 650
   spider webs, 334
Problem solving strategies
   cause and effect recognition, 683
   comparing and contrasting, 683
   critical thinking, 17-18, 682-683
   observing and inferring, 682
Producers, **63**
Prokaryotes, *161,* **161**
Protein, digestion of, *act.* 458
Proteins, 57, 443-444, **443**
   amino acids, **443**
Protists, *202,* **202,** *act.* 210
   see also Algae; Protozoa
   algae, 203-205, *203,* **203,** *204, 205*
   funguslike protists, 208-209
   mildew, 209
   protozoa, 206-209, *206,* **206,** *207*
   slime molds, 209

water molds, 209
Protozoa, **206**
  see also Protists
  amoeba, *206*
  cilia, **207**
  ciliates, 207, *207*
  flagellates, 207, *207*
  pseudopods, **206**
  sarcodines, 206, *206*
  sporozoans, 208

R

Reaction time, *act.* 514
Recycling, 66-67
Redi, Francesco, 10, 11
Reflexes, 395, 512-513, **512,** *513*
Regeneration, **309**
Reproduction
  see also Plant reproduction
  alternation of generations, **238**
  asexual, **80**
  of birds, 375
  by budding, **213**
  hermaphrodites, **310**
  larva, **310,** *330*
  of mammals, 381-382
  by regeneration, 81, **309**
  sexual, **80,** *83*
Reproduction, human, 530
  see also Human growth
  female reproductive system, 531-532, *532*
  fertilization, 535-536
  male reproductive system, 530-531, *531*
  menopause, **533**
  menstrual cycle, 522-523, **532,** *533, act.* 534
  menstruation, **533**
  ovaries, **531**
  ovulation, *531,* **531**
  pregnancy, **536**
  semen, **531**
  sperm, **530**
  testes, **530**
  uterus, **531**
  vagina, **531**
Reproduction, sexual, **80,** 82-85
  see also Genetics
  diploids, **83**
  eggs, **82**
  fertilization, **83**

gametes, **82,** 83-85
haploids, **83**
meiosis, **82,** 84-85, *84, 85*
sperm, **82**
zygotes, **83**
Reptiles, 363-364, *363,* **363**
  see also Vertebrates
  amniote eggs, *364,* **364**
  orders of, 365
  origins of, 364
Research biologist, 100
Respiration, **64,** *act.* 68, 279
  in plants, 279-280
Respiratory system, 488, *489*
  alveoli, *490,* **490**
  asthma, **493**
  bronchi, **490**
  chronic bronchitis, **493**
  diaphragm, 490-491, **490,** *491*
  emphysema, *492,* **492**
  exercise and, *act.* 495, 496-497
  larynx, **489**
  lung cancer, 494
  lungs, 490, *490,* 500
  nitrogen dioxide and, **496**
  pharynx, **489**
  trachea, **489**
Response, **7**
Ribonucleic acid (RNA), 57
  DNA compared to, 90
RNA. *See* Ribonucleic acid (RNA)

S

Sabin, Carl, 568
Safety, laboratory, 21, 671-672
Salk, Jonas, *306,* 568
Schleiden, Matthias, 33, 34
Schwann, Theodor, 34
Science, 13
Scientific methods, **14,** *act.* 24
  constants, 686-687
  controls, **15,** 686-687
  data interpretation, 687
  hypothesis, **14,** 686
  illustration interpretation, 693
  laws, **16**
  theories, **16**
  variables, **15,** 686-687
Scientific names. *See* Taxonomy
Sedimentary rock, **137**
Sense organs, 515, 518
  see also names of specific senses

Sessile organisms, **308**
Skeletal system, 420-425, **420**
  see also Bones
  endoskelton, **351**
  exoskelton, **351**
  of humans, *420*
  immovable joints, **423**
  joints, 423-424, *423,* **423**
  movable joints, **423**
Skin, 432-433, *432,* 500
  dermis, *432,* **433**
  epidermis, *432,* **432**
  functions, 434-435
  injury to, 433, *433*
  melanin, *433,* **433**
  robot skin, *434*
  sweat glands, *act.* 502
  touch sensitivity of, *act.* 519
Slaughter, Robert, 137
Smell, 517
  nasal passages, *517*
  olfactory cells, **517**
Society, **403**
Spallanzani, Lazzaro, 10, 11, 535
Species, **130**
  see also Evolution
  endangered, 144-145, **144**
  extinction of, 144-145, **144**
  identification, dichotomous keys, 167-168, *168,* **168,** *act.* 170
  population, **134**
  variations, 133-134, **133**
Sponges, 308
  body plan, *309*
  collar cells, **309**
  importance of, 311-312
  origin of, 310
  reproduction, 309-310
Stems, 259-261
  see also Plants
  cambium, **260**
  phloem, **260**
  xylem, **260**
Stimulus, **7,** 282
Symbiosis, **215**
  coevolution, 286-287, **286**
  in communities, 614
  mutualistic relationships, **215,** 286, 614
  parasitic relationships, 285, 614
Symmetry, 303-304
  bilateral symmetry, **304,** *304*
  radial symmetry, **303,** *304*

Tables, 690, *690*
Taste, 517-518
    taste buds, **517,** *517*
    tongue, *517*
Taxonomy, **156**
    see also Classification
    binomial nomenclature, **157,**
        166-167
    classes, **163**
    common names and, 166-167
    dichotomous keys, 167-168,
        168, **168,** *act.* 170
    division, **163**
    families, **163**
    genus, **157,** 163
    kingdoms, **156,** 160, *162*
    orders, **163**
    phylogeny and, **160**
    phylum, **163**
    species, **157,** 163
Technology, 22-23, **22**
Technology examples
    amino acid racemization, 140
    artificial skin, 434
    biodegradable plastics, 64
    biological indicators of pollu-
        tion, 618
    bioremediation, 195
    biospheres, 636
    cholesterol in eggs, 376
    diamonds in microscopes, 33
    DNA and classification, 161
    drug pumps and implants, 581
    drugs from snake venoms, 366
    fat substitutes, 445
    fetal surgery, 538
    hemopump, 469
    jojoba oil, 235
    kidney transplants, 501
    leeches in microsurgery, 329
    plant genetics, 278
    positron emission tomography,
        511
    recombinant DNA, 89
    in vitro fertilization, 657
    yeast artificial chromosomes,
        213
Temperature, 518
Territory, **401,** 407
    carrying capacity and, **407**
Tissues, **45,** *act.* 48

Tobacco, 583-584
Touch, 518, *act.* 519
Toxins, **194**
Trees. *See* Deforestation; Plants;
    Tropical forests
Tropical forests, 635-636
    deforestation of, 164-165, **164,**
        289
    drugs from, 288-289
    species diversity in, **164**

Urinary system, *498,* **498**
    bladder, **499**
    disorders of, 500
    kidneys, **498**
    nephrons, *499,* **499**
    ureters, **499**
    urethra, **499**
    urine, **499**

Vaccines, **184**
van Helmont, Jan Baptist, 10
Van Leeuwenhoek, Anton, 31
Vertebrates, **303,** 350-351
    see also Amphibians; Animals;
        Birds; Fish; Mammals;
        Reptiles
    chordates, *350,* **350**
    classification of, *act.* 388
    cold-blooded animals, **351**
    dorsal nerve cord, **350**
    endoskeleton, **351**
    gill slits, **351**
    notocords, **350**
    warm-blooded animals, **351**
Veterinarian's assistant, 414
Virchow, Rudolph, 34
Viruses, **182,** 184
    active viruses, 183, *183*
    AIDS virus, 186-187, **186,** 481-
        482, 561, 566
    disease prevention for, 184
    gene therapy and, 185
    interferon, **184**
    latent viruses, *183,* **183**
    reproduction, 183, *183*
Vision, 515
Vitamins, 445-446, **445,** *act.* 450

Wallace, Alfred Russell, 175
Water, 9, 447-448
    see also Natural resources
    conservation of, 655
    as energy source, *654,* 655
    as a limiting factor, *act.* 642
    pollution, 650
    water cycle, 617-618, *617,* **617**
    water table, **641**
Water ecosystems
    see also Biomes; Ecosystems
    estuaries, *638,* **638**
    freshwater ecosystems, 638-639
    oceans
        littoral zone, *637,* **637**
        pelagic zone, **638**
        sublittoral zone, *637,* 637
    wetlands, 640-641, *640,* **640**
Watson, James, 86, *86*
Watson, John B., 399
Wetlands, 640-641, *640,* **640**
White, Ryan, *482*
Wildlife, 653
    endangered species, 656-657
    preserves, **656**
Worms
    see also Invertebrates
    earthworms, 327-328, *328*
    flatworms, 315-316
    leeches, 329-330
    planarians, *315,* 316
    roundworms, 317-318, *317, 318*
    segmented, 327, *327, act.* 331
    setae, **327**
    tapeworms, 316, *316*

Xylem, **260**
    See under Plants

Zoologist, 414
Zygote, **83,** *83,* 536

PHOTO CREDITS